*Introduction to*
# INDUSTRIAL MANAGEMENT

# Introduction to
# INDUSTRIAL
# MANAGEMENT

*Text, Cases, and Problems*

BY

## FRANKLIN E. FOLTS, M.B.A.

PROFESSOR IN INDUSTRIAL MANAGEMENT
GRADUATE SCHOOL OF BUSINESS ADMINISTRATION
GEORGE F. BAKER FOUNDATION
HARVARD UNIVERSITY

THIRD EDITION

NEW YORK · TORONTO · LONDON
McGRAW-HILL BOOK COMPANY, INC.
1949

INTRODUCTION TO INDUSTRIAL MANAGEMENT

# PREFACE

The first edition of this book appeared in 1932. At that time it was looked upon as an experiment in the textbook field. The following paragraphs adapted from the Preface to the First Edition indicate why this was so.

This volume was prepared for use in those departments of economics, schools of business administration, and schools of engineering that offer introductory courses in industrial management. The primary object has been to deal with business and economic conditions as they exist in industry rather than to promulgate theories or generalities concerning them. This does not mean that the book contains no theories, for both text and case material embody business and economic principles in current use, and solution of the problems which students are asked to solve will necessitate an appreciation of sound theory. Theory, however, is never discussed for the sake of theory. Its goal is always the solution of a practical situation.

Centering of text material around concrete business situations necessitates a change from the conventional discussion of topics in watertight compartments. Thus, questions such as foremanship, technological unemployment, worker training, and safety are not considered as isolated abstractions but are intimately tied into the cases and problems at hand wherever they occur. For this reason, separate, detailed consideration of such topics is believed unnecessary.

While text material adequate for a background for each major management topic is included, the object of the book is to force the student to think in terms of cases and problems taken from actual business life. Thus, ability to memorize becomes distinctly secondary to ability to analyze. Each has its place in the course, but there is no question as to the predominance of ability to analyze.

An introductory course in industrial management, as is true

v

of any elementary course, is limited by definite restrictions of
time and space. Nothing is more disheartening to an instructor
or confusing to a student than the inclusion in a text of considerable material which cannot be brought into classroom discussion.
For this reason, topics have been deliberately left out or abridged
which would be included or further amplified if an exhaustive
treatment of industrial management were being attempted.

When the second edition was published in 1938, experience
with the new type of approach had made it clear that ability to
reason to sound *business* decisions on actual industrial problems
can be developed in the classroom. Students liked the case and
problem approach to an understanding of principles and fundamentals. Instructors had found that once they had worked their
way through to satisfying solutions to the problems the burden
of preparation was not excessive. Experience with the text in
varied settings indicated that the analysis and reasoning called
for by the problems was well within the scope of mental development of undergraduate students. The second edition, therefore,
differed from the first only in that the expository material included a more complete amplification of the business subjects
included in the first edition. Some additional subject areas were
included.

This, the third edition, follows the pathway pioneered by its
two predecessors. The experience of varied users of the text
during the long interval of time that has elapsed since the last
revision is reflected in the current writing. Deletions, contrac-
tions, more exposition at indicated points, and more problems
are the result of this experience.

During the past ten years American industry has been put to
the greatest test that industrial society has known. Analysis of
this critical management period seems to establish conclusively
the validity of the concepts discussed in the first section of both
earlier editions, Economics of Production. Therefore this section has been amplified to include the experience of the Second
World War years and of the reconversion period that followed.

The problems of operation and control that constitute the
balance of the book have likewise been reexamined to reflect the
changing industrial emphasis and practices that have taken

place during the past decade. An example is the new chapter, Wage Determination, covering aspects of wage administration which, though not new, have become of much greater importance since the war. In addition to the replacement of certain dated problems by entirely new ones, the total number of problems has been increased from 55 to 63. This has been done to provide users with an added measure of flexibility and greater choice of problems to be assigned. It is hoped that these measures will increase the usefulness of the present edition in the hands of teachers.

Acknowledgment is due Dean Donald K. David and Associate Dean Stanley F. Teele of the Harvard Graduate School of Business Administration for making this revision possible. Also the writer wishes to make known his appreciation for the help of Miss Molly Granger, whose interest in the preparation of the manuscript has made the project feasible.

FRANKLIN E. FOLTS

BOSTON, MASS.
*June,* 1949

# CONTENTS

*Part II*

## FACTORS OF PRODUCTION

# PART I

## ECONOMICS OF PRODUCTION

# CHAPTER I

## THE BUSINESS OF PRODUCTION

The factory is the basic element in industry. It is the common denominator of modern industrial method, the almost universal mechanism of production. The handicraft arts of colonial days and the skilled craftsmen who practiced them have largely disappeared, capitulated to the teamwork of the executive, the scientist, the technician, the machine, and the machine operative. These conquering forces have attained their full effectiveness in the factory. Today's production, whether it be highly standardized mass production or small-scale, intricate, special-order fabrication, is factory production.

The factory provides us with most of the products we consume and the services that make us comfortable. In almost equal degree, we are dependent on it for command over these consumables and services. As a people, we secure such of the necessities and luxuries of life as we possess through efforts either directly or indirectly expended in the service of industry. This is as true of the note clerk in a bank and the freight truck driver as it is of the turret lathe operator, the motion and time-study engineer, and the factory purchasing agent.

Our economic and social problems, therefore, are problems indigenous to an industrial society. Today, it is commonly recognized that the causes of much of our social strife are rooted in the industrial process. What seems to be less generally understood is the inevitability of the emergence of powerful trade and industrial union organizations as mouthpieces of labor in the political arena. Today, the factory is a pervasive and dominant institution of our society, and its concomitant problems are at the vortex of great forces that surge within what we know as Western civilization.

**1. The Factory and Its Processes.** A factory is a business establishment where raw materials are worked upon to produce

3

useful things. Industrial processes can be classified as extractive, conditioning, analytical, or synthetic. The extractive process consists of isolating a wanted substance from foreign matter with which it is associated in its natural state. Much commercial salt (NaCl) is produced by the evaporation of brine. The brine is a solution of salt in water, in which state the salt is unsatisfactory for most uses. Useful salt is produced by disassociating the salt from sea water or water from salt springs. The process of evaporating the brine by either solar or generated heat to produce salt is an extractive process.

The conditioning process is one which changes the form or nature of the material so as to make it more valuable in use. Leather production is a good example. The tanning of raw hides results in leather, a product of greater durability and usefulness than the untreated skins. Little has been taken away from or added to the raw material. Essentially, the production process consists of conditioning the raw material, the hides.

Another common conditioning process is that of the foundry. Pig iron, the raw material, is melted in a special type of furnace called the "cupola." The iron in molten form is poured into molds, where it is allowed to cool and harden. The process changes the form of the iron, the shape desired being obtained through the medium of the mold. In this process, the change sought is change in form, and the process is essentially a form conditioning process.

The analytical process is quite different from both the extractive and the conditioning types of process. Its essential characteristic is subdivision of a raw material into several different products. Much of the refining of petroleum falls into this class. In an oil-refining plant, crude oil is subjected to heat and pressure in such a way that the raw material is broken down into gasoline, lubricating oil, fuel oil, and various other products. Meat packing is a similar process. The raw material is subdivided into a number of finished products, the industry being noted for its by-products which have grown in number and diversity of character as research has developed uses for those parts of the raw material which cannot be utilized in the preparation of edible meat products.

The basic characteristic of the synthetic type of process is union of two or more raw materials to form a finished product having usefulness greater or other than that of the isolated materials. In a cement plant, limestone and clay are ground fine, mixed, heated to a high temperature, and reground. The resultant commodity is Portland cement. This product is obtained by synthesis, *i.e.*, by bringing together certain raw materials in proper quantities and under proper conditions.

The automobile manufacturing plant is a highly developed example of this type of processing. Scores of different raw materials are formed into component parts and subassemblies which are then accurately fitted together on assembly lines to make up that complicated mechanism we know as the automobile. This type of manufacture is commonly designated as assembly industry. However, it is as essentially synthetic in nature as the manufacture of cement or the compounding of paints.

Seldom do all the operations carried on in one factory fall into merely one of the four types of process just described. Usually, the operation of a factory or the production of one product involves employing more than one type of process. Companies which make textile machinery usually separate the process into three divisions. The first of these is the production of castings in a foundry department. This is a conditioning type of process. The castings from the foundry go to the machine shops, where they are re-formed on lathes, drills, grinders, and similar machine tools. This is also essentially a form conditioning process. Finished parts from the machine shops, together with other finished parts purchased outside, are brought together in the third step, the assembly division. Here they are fitted together, and complete machines are erected from them. This process is unlike the two conditioning processes which have preceded it. It is essentially a synthetic process. To whatever extent it is necessary to rework parts in the assembly rooms to secure desired fit in assembly, conditioning is carried on in the assembly department. However, modern techniques of machining give such precision that practically no such reworking is required, and the erection of complete textile machines from finished parts is characteristically a synthetic process. The combining of several types of process in one factory is common, but study of any factory process will show that it consists of one or more of the four basic types: extraction, conditioning, analysis, and synthesis.

**2. Essentials of Production.** Whatever the character of the factory process, production always requires certain common means. In addition to raw materials, there must be workmen to carry on the operations, tools and machines to aid the workmen, power to drive the equipment, buildings to house the operations, and managers to supervise the utilization of these facilities in carrying out the production process. The relative proportions in which these various means of production are employed in any one factory depend on the nature of the process. The operating statement of a manufacturing business, which shows the details of the costs of manufacture, reflects the extent of utilization of the various means of production.

We can now amplify our definition of a factory as being a place where the means (sometimes called "factors") of production, namely, plant and equipment, labor, and management, are utilized to convert the other factor, raw materials, into products which have greater value in use than the original raw materials.

**3. The Factory—Several Points of View.** Since the beginnings of the factory system, people have been variously interested in this method of production as an aspect of civilization. Economic historians have traced the mechanization of industry and have measured its progress in terms of horsepower per employee and volume of output per employee. These students of industrial history have also been much interested in such matters as industrial integration, industrial migrations, and the trends of factory industry. Much of the fruit of their labors is available to us in the voluminous literature of economic history.

The political economist looks upon factory production from a somewhat different point of view. He is more interested in the disposition of the returns industry makes to the various contributors to the production process than he is in how the process came about. He thinks and writes in terms of such concepts as capitalism, socialism, and communism.

The political observer and doer today looks upon the factory and its operations most carefully. His chief efforts have to do with legislation and public administration. He is concerned with factory production because his constituency has told him to be. A very great portion of the voters of this country support themselves through their industrial connections as owners, managers, or workers. It is only natural, then, that the politician should interest himself in industry. It follows that as the industrial activities of the nation have increased, political interest in industry has likewise become increasingly active. The most controversial and far-reaching legislation of the past decade has been concerned with the factory process and, in one sense at least, the factory itself has become the most pervasive consideration in the thoughts and acts of politicians and legislators.

**4. The Businessman's Viewpoint.** The businessman sees the factory in a light quite different from those just described. He regards it as an opportunity for proprietary profit and, more recently, an opportunity for tangible service to the social community. The dyed-in-the-wool industrialist has an inborn desire to make things, to do things, to make the wheels go around. To him the factory and its problems constitute a how-to-do-it challenge. He is interested in creating something, how to do it well, how to do it better. And all the time he works toward this goal, he is striving equally hard to find out how to do it more easily. The more easily a thing can be made, the less it will cost. The lower his cost, the greater his share of the market, or the greater the market itself. This means profit, and profit is the essence of business as the American businessman knows business. Whatever the opinion of the historian, the economist, or the politician, potential profits are the lifeblood of American business. This is as true today, 1949, as it was in 1938 and 1928. Most important of all, most businessmen of this country understand that the greatest profit accrues to him who renders the greatest service.

**5. Why Students of Industrial Management Must Know and Be Interested in Many Viewpoints.** In approaching production problems from his own point of view, the businessman finds that he is continually running into other points of view. This is not surprising. The astonishing thing is the extent to which some of the most successful businessmen have been aware of these other viewpoints and the effort they have made to understand

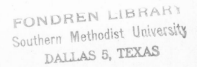

them.  It is quite probable that the outstanding successes of the few and the mediocre performances of the many have been in direct proportion to the understanding which the individual executive has had of the necessity of knowing divergent viewpoints and working in terms of them.  Today, more than ever before, the businessman as a problem solver continuously feels the impact of these varied interests in his doings.  The National Labor Relations Act, the Social Security Act, and a hundred other pieces of legislation are aimed at control of his activities.  Some businessmen seem to be spending their time berating the "interference of government."  Some are bewildered: "We don't know what we can do and what we can't do."  Some have foreseen the increasing impact of other interests on their problems, and while it is hardly accurate to say that these more farsighted men have prepared for the new days of management, at least they are keeping their attention fast on the how-to-do-it point of view that they have always held.  They are trying to teach the team new plays that will make competitive victory possible under the new rules of the game.

The greatest concern of the sincere student of business today should be the understanding of divergent viewpoints of the factory and its activities.  It is important to learn the ways and methods of the how-to-do-it businessman.  It is equally important to know and understand the other points of view which have become so influential in shaping how-to-do-it policies and methods.

This text proposes to develop a sound point of view for the business manager by analyzing industrial problems and businessmen's solutions to industrial problems.  Each chapter contains the experience of some actual manufacturing business, with explanations as to why the executives did what they did, why they did not do something else, or what the management should have done.  These experiences are presented as the basis for generalizations to serve as guides to action to be taken in other cases.  No formulas for problem solution are presented, for, so far as the writer knows, formulas that can be depended on do not exist.  Every business problem is to some extent unique, and if the platitude "Experience is the best guide" applies anywhere, it does in business-problem solution.

Accompanying each chapter are one or more business problems that have actually been faced by the managements of the companies described. The experience of seeking solutions for these problems is probably of greater value than study of the explained cases. In seeking solutions for these problems, one does well to keep in mind the viewpoint of the modern industrial executive: Production is a business carried on for profit. Profits from production will not long exceed the ability of a company to produce a better product and make it readily available in the market at a lower cost. Executive decisions are business decisions rather than technical decisions; this is so largely because of the importance of perceiving and understanding a wide variety of related viewpoints that will otherwise clash disastrously with attempts at business success.

**6. Summary.** The factory is a business establishment where materials are utilized by the other elements of the production process, plant and equipment, labor and management, in making products that have demand value. The management of the factory and its processes is a business rather than a technical problem. Many techniques are important in manufacturing, but they must be directed and coordinated by executive control if they are to contribute to profits.

The business executive is essentially a problem solver. His vestments of responsibility and authority make his days a succession of yes or no decisions. A company is offered a new machine, the installation of which would make it possible to dispense with the services of several men and by so doing would reduce costs of production. Someone must decide whether to buy or not to buy. An executive must say yes or no.

A company is offered a million-dollar order. If the order is accepted, plant capacity must be increased by 10 per cent. That will necessitate an additional long-time investment in buildings and equipment of $200,000. An executive must say yes or no.

The prices of the basic raw materials used by a company are lower than at any time in the preceding four years. Should the company borrow $450,000 from the banks and buy enough of these raw materials to take care of the company's needs for the coming 12 months?  Some executive of the company must decide and accept the responsibility for the outcome with a definite yes or no.

Five workmen go before a company's production manager and tell him that 60 per cent of the workers in the company's foundry have joined a national union.  They ask that the company enter into a wage contract with them as representing *all* the workmen in the foundry.  What should the manager do?

The daily life of an industrial executive consists of a succession of problems to which he must either supply solutions or approve solutions proposed by his assistants.  His success as an *executive* is dependent on his ability consistently to be right in his decisions.

The aim of the student of industrial management should be facility in problem solution.  The viewpoint in seeking solution of a business management problem is invariably profit.  In pursuing the profit objective, the experienced executive will never ignore the other varied viewpoints on factory production nor fail to anticipate the import of these in arriving at decisions.

### QUESTIONS

1. Classify the following production processes.  Explain for each process why you classify it as you do.

A commercial bakery
Construction of a steel bridge
Coal mining
Commercial fish packing
Papermaking
Making of alloy steel
Logging and lumber-mill operation
Manufacture of footballs
Flour milling
Highway paving
Making of cotton cloth
Manufacture of television-receiving sets
Making of phonograph records

2. What is the function of management as a factor of production?

3. It has been said that the making and keeping of delivery promises and the building and maintaining of a reputation for product reliability are sound management objectives. Do you agree? Explain.

4. What advantages would you expect the college-trained production executive to have over the man who has "risen from the ranks" without such a background? What disadvantages may the college-trained man have to overcome?

5. Read a current issue of a daily newspaper carefully, and make a list of what seem to you to be the most important *industrial management* problems suggested by the "news." Be prepared to explain the business significance of at least one of them.

# CHAPTER II

## SPECIALIZATION OF LABOR
### (DIVISION OF LABOR) [1]

### STANDARD AUTO SERVICE CORPORATION

### 1. A Typical Example of Mass Production Methods—Labor Specialization.

The Standard Auto Service Corporation owned a chain of service stations located in the larger cities of California. Each unit was modern in every respect and offered superior service at less than usual costs. Low service charges were possible because of the large volume of business transacted, a characteristic cause-and-effect concept in modern industrial policy.

The newest service station of the company was to be equipped with an automobile-washing system capable of cleaning 60 cars an hour. This speed would be obtained through an extensive use of mechanical equipment and detailed division of the washing task into 14 specialized jobs requiring from one to four workers each. As a result, the cost of washing a car would be greatly decreased, and an attractive lowering of the price to be charged for car washing would result.

### 2. The Mass Production Concept.

In any attempt to examine American economic belief of the past quarter of a century, it would seem that first attention must be given to the doctrine of economy of mass production. In the minds of the schoolboy and statesman alike, one finds the picture of a typical workman, electric wrench in hand, beside a moving belt, systematically tightening bolt #1262-A on the chassis of "Eclipse" automobiles

[1] Richart T. Ely, *Outlines of Economics* (6th ed.), p. 118, The Macmillan Company, New York, 1937.

Frank W. Taussig, *Principles of Economics,* Vol. I, pp. 30–48, The Macmillan Company, New York, 1913.

F. R. Fairchild, E. S. Furness, and N. S. Buck, *Elementary Economics,* Vol. I, pp. 75–83, The Macmillan Company, New York, 1926.

Sumner H. Slichter, *Modern Economic Society,* pp. 104–121, Henry Holt and Company, Inc., New York, 1931.

as they move past him at the rate of one every two minutes. The production schedule of the company calls for an output of 300,000 cars for the current year, and a budget of anticipated costs has been erected upon the assumption that the schedule will be maintained. If cars are produced at the scheduled rate, actual costs will closely approximate budgeted costs. If costs can be kept within the proposed budget, the sales department can sell the scheduled output of the year. Production and sales of 300,000 units for the year will mean high wages for Eclipse employees. High wages create purchasing power. Purchasing power supports demand. Demand makes possible mass production, which, in turn, makes for low costs, high wages, greater purchasing power, and increased profits. So goes the general thought.

**3. General Acceptance of the Mass Production Concept.** While it may well be said that the economy of mass production is but one of many economic beliefs of the time, in American industry of the twentieth century it is difficult to discover a goal, an aim, a practice, or a policy that is not directly a part of, or supplementary to, belief in the basic advantage of large-scale output.

A study of modern industrial management must, then, concern itself with an investigation of the validity of this belief, as well as the causes and effects of its general acceptance.

**4. Nature and Development of Mass Production.** Mass production, as we find it today, is based upon the extensive application of certain industrial concepts which have been utilized from the beginnings of the industrial revolution, a period commonly characterized as embracing the general application of power in the productive process, division of labor, and transfer of skill. Basically, modern practice adds little to this list. Division of labor has become intensified as "labor specialization." The application of the principle of specialization has been extended beyond the field of labor. Process specialization, product specialization, plant specialization, equipment specialization, management specialization (organization), all of which are common problems of modern operation, are but extensions in application of the theories of Adam Smith [2] and Charles Babbage.[3]    The concepts are the same, though the terms, the environment, and the problems resulting therefrom have changed in their implications and significance.

Essentially, mass production economy embraces problems of specialization, of simplification, of standardization, of diversification, of coordination, of integration, and of waste control.    An examination of mass production must include all these.    Specialization offers an obvious point of attack and will be dealt with by means of a study of the experiences of a considerable variety of companies, some large, some small.

**5. Importance of Location in a Mass Production Program.** The Standard Auto Service Corporation was organized to establish a chain of automobile service stations and soon had three "super-service" stations in successful operation.    At each unit complete lubrication, tire, gasoline, and battery service was offered.    Stations were carefully located for the convenience of local, commuter, and tourist traffic, usually on a main traffic artery and near a high-class apartment district.    Company managers believed that the relatively high rental costs resulting from selection of such valuable sites were justified in view of the large volume of business potentially obtainable in such locations, as also were the costs of building, equipping, and operating stations in such manner as to attract the desired volume.    The stations themselves were arranged to service the motorist's needs rapidly and in an attractive manner.    Much attention was paid to the establishment of permanent customer connections.

The operating personnel of these stations was carefully trained both in the technique of duties and in such matters as courtesy and information service to customers.    An example of the detailed nature of this training was the uniform procedure established for gasoline-pump attendants.    When a car stopped at a station pump, the attendant's first duty was to remove the cap from the gasoline tank.    With the cap plainly visible in one hand, he was then to greet the customer and ask permission to fill the tank.    Each gasoline pump was provided with a damp chamois

[2] See Adam Smith, *Wealth of Nations,* 1776.
[3] See Charles Babbage, *Economy of Manufactures,* 1832.

skin. As soon as the customer's order for gasoline was completed and the tank cap replaced, the attendant picked up the chamois and wiped the outside of the windshield of the car with it. He then requested the customer's permission to check the amount of oil in the crankcase. If permission was granted, a sale of oil frequently resulted. After attending to the oil supply, the attendant added water to the radiator if needed. If he believed the customer to be a stranger in the community or at that station, the attendant presented him with a small card which listed the various services sold at this and other stations of the company.

This attention to detail was characteristic of all employee training. It had resulted in attracting permanent customers and also in increasing the average sale to customers. The attendants were carefully selected and were well paid. They were distinctively uniformed, and each plant was a model of attractive cleanliness. An exceptional spirit of company loyalty was characteristic of all employees. The company management was constantly on the alert to improve its service and to that end was always investigating new methods and equipment.

The company was about to erect a service station larger than any other in the city in which it was to be located. It was to feature the latest developments and was to offer more complete service to the autoist than was rendered in any of the company's other stations. Brake testing, adjustment, and repair were to be added, and the management was considering the installation of car-washing equipment.

**6. Speed—An Advantage of Mass Production.** With regard to car washing, the management had been attracted by the large-scale "auto laundries" which had recently made their appearance in some of the larger cities. Company executives believed that the speed and efficiency with which these systems operated would prove attractive to customers, and the relatively large output of which such systems were capable indicated possibilities of sizable profits. The addition of car washing would practically complete the service offered to customers. In the past the company had not engaged in this activity because of the large space required and the relatively high labor cost involved. Modern auto laundries had neither of these disadvantages, and as there was no such washing system in the city where the new station was to be established, company executives believed that the inclusion of large-scale automobile washing was desirable.

**7. Hand Method of Automobile Washing Described.** When the usual methods of car washing were employed, the customer drove his car into the garage, received a claim check for it, and was told that his automobile would be ready for him in from two to six hours. Much washing was done at night. The washing process was usually performed by a crew of two men, but sometimes one man carried out the entire operation.

The first step, after the car was placed on the wash rack, was to remove all articles from the interior and then to brush out all dirt from the cushions. The floor mats were next removed and cleaned. This done, the washer flushed the car for several minutes with a stream of clear water from a hose. This softened the dirt and grime and made its removal easier. The next step was to remove dirt and grease from wheels, springs, and the under side of the fenders. This was accomplished with a hose which threw a stream of warm liquid at high pressure. On the most modern racks, this stream consisted of a mixture of soap and water or an emulsion of oil and water. This step completed, the springs, wheels, and fenders were thoroughly rinsed with cold water. The washer then took a bucket of warm soap suds and sponged the entire car, with the exception of the parts where there might be grease. Those parts received the same treatment, but another sponge was used in order to prevent the transfer of grease to the body, hood, and such surfaces. After the car was completely washed by hand with soap and water, it was rinsed with a hose and wiped off with a clean sponge to make sure that all soap had been removed. At this time, special attention was paid to the windshield and windows, both inside and out.

If the washing crew consisted of two men, the car was then turned over to the second one. This man first removed all stains and surplus water with a clean chamois. This done, he polished the body, hood, and fenders with soft cloths. Windows and exterior and interior metalwork then received his attention. When the entire automobile was polished to his satisfaction, the interior trim and cushions were cleaned with a special type of vacuum cleaner, and the floor mats were vacuumed and adjusted in the car. Any articles which had been removed from the car were replaced, and the car was ready for the customer.

The entire process required from 1½ to 2 hours when one man worked alone. When two men worked as a crew, the time could frequently be reduced to one hour.

**8. Large-scale Automobile Washing.** In the modern car-laundry method under consideration, the automobile went through practically the same process. However, by replacing the two-man crew with a force of from 34 to 40 men and girls, each specializing on a certain operation or part of an operation, the application of the principle of specialization of labor and use of specialized equipment made it possible to reduce the total time required for washing a car to 13 minutes. The process would necessitate the erection of a building of special design with equipment to correspond. Such a plant 100 by 100 feet would have an output capacity of one car a minute. The diagram, Exhibit 1 on page 18, shows the layout of such a system.

In this system, a car to be washed was driven up the entrance ramp and onto a moving circular platform at the left. This track was propelled by an electric driving mechanism which could be so adjusted that the platform made a complete revolution in from 13 to 30 minutes. The various workers were stationed at different points about the track so that upon the completion of a revolution the car had passed through the entire process and, cleaned and polished inside and out, was ready to be delivered to the customer. The track had a capacity of 13 cars. Thus, when it was operated at its maximum speed, cars were washed at the rate of one a minute. The metal track, or platform, was floored with heavy wooden planking so spaced as to allow the water to drain through into a sluiceway beneath the track. An abundance of light was provided by large windows which occupied the maximum wall space available. There were also large skylights in the roof.

Inside the moving platform on which the cars were washed was a glass-protected promenade which in other installations had proved a great attraction to the customer, who could follow the progress of his car through the complete washing operation.

Elaborate waiting rooms were to be located in a separate building. These rooms would be equipped with such features as radio and automatic phonograph. Attractive accessory and tire displays, together with effective printed matter, were to be used to bring the various services of the station to the customer's attention.

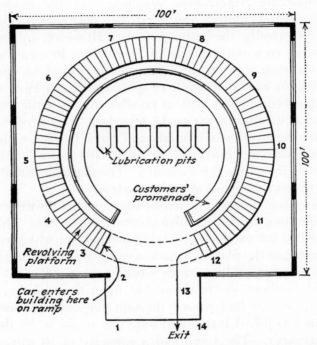

EXHIBIT 1. STANDARD AUTO SERVICE CORPORATION. DIAGRAM TO SHOW LAYOUT OF PROPOSED LARGE-SCALE WASHING SYSTEM.

**9. Labor Specialization in Automobile Washing.** The washing process itself was essentially the same as that used when two-man crews were employed. Its chief difference was in the specialization of the workers. Instead of one or two men doing the complete washing job, a large crew was employed. Each worker had a specific task to perform. Each task constituted one step in the washing process, and the cooperative efforts of the entire crew were required to complete the washing and polishing.

In the plan being considered, a car to be washed was driven by company employees to the entrance ramp, where loose articles within the car were removed and placed in a locker provided for that purpose. There was a separate locker for each car, and a locker identification tag was attached to the car when the contents were removed to the locker. Two men spent their entire time at this task, which is located in the foregoing diagram by the numeral 1.

As soon as the car had been emptied, it was driven by another employee up the ramp and onto the moving platform. One man specialized on this task. Job 3 was carried on by one man who used compressed air to blow dust from the seats and floor of the car interior. The automatically rotating platform carried the car on to job 4. At that point an overhead sprinkler flushed the entire car with water to loosen grime and dirt. The valve which controlled this sprinkler was operated by a man on a raised platform. This worker also washed the car top with a long-handled brush and then removed excess water from the top with another brush.

At point 5 the springs, chassis, and underside of the fenders were thoroughly washed. Four men worked on this job, two on each side of the track. Each man was equipped with a hose which threw a heated emulsion of oil and water at high pressure. The temperature of the mixture was 135 degrees Fahrenheit, and the pressure used was 400 pounds.

At the next point, 6 on the diagram, four men sponged the entire car, using warm soap suds. After that, the car moved on to operation 7, which consisted of a thorough rinsing. Two men performed this task, using hoses and clear water. At point 8 on the track, two men used compressed air to blow all surplus water from the car surfaces.

**10. Coordination—An Essential of Successful Labor Specialization.** The following operation, number 9, was performed by a group of four girls who, with chamois and cloths, wiped and polished the entire car, inside and out. Operation 10 was an exact duplication of operation 9. This repetition was necessary because otherwise a bottleneck [4] would develop at that point.

---

[4] When the flow of product through a process is held up at some point in the process because of slowness of the operation at that point, a bottleneck is said to

One four-girl crew could not completely wipe and polish the car in the time available. It was not practical to' use more than four girls on the task at one time for they would seriously interfere with each other's work. Thus, it was necessary to do one of two things, either slow down the speed of the revolving track or repeat the operation. Slowing down the track to enable one group of four girls to wipe and polish satisfactorily would cut the rate of output of the plant approximately one-half. It was, therefore, desirable to repeat the operation. By this means, maximum speed was maintained and a bottleneck was avoided.

From the second polishing operation, cars progressed to the eleventh station on the line, where two men equipped with specially designed vacuum cleaners thoroughly vacuumed the interior, after which the cars were ready for inspection. Two men, at point 12 on the diagram, inspected each car, rectified any minor defects in the job, and O.K.'d cars for release to customers.

**11. Importance of Inspection.** In a large-scale car-washing operation such as that being considered, inspection was a most important function. It was imperative from the standpoint of assuring the customer of a quality job. In a process so highly subdivided, no one individual was responsible for the quality of the work. A first-class washing job was dependent on each worker's doing his allotted task thoroughly and well. Quality was thus dependent on the efforts of all rather than on desire to excel or pride in workmanship of one individual. Getting each worker to do his or her best was a problem. Inspection thus became important for the protection of the company's reputation for quality and in order to maintain individual effort through fixing individual responsibility for any lack of thoroughness.

After the car had been inspected, it was driven from the wash rack. One man could do this work and just keep up with the output of the wash rack when it was being operated at capacity. This man turned the car over to the last group of workers, 14

---

exist. Bottlenecks are best prevented by careful coordination of all operations in the process in terms of the time required for each. This necessitates proper breakup of the process into component parts or operations, and proper manning of each individual operation to secure such coordination. A continuous process can never be more rapid than its slowest element.

on the diagram, which consisted of two men who replaced all articles previously removed from the car.

**12. Necessity for Replacement Workers.** In addition to the 32 men and girls required on the washing rack, from 4 to 6 workers were required to maintain and operate the mechanical equipment and to reclaim supplies such as rags and oils. These workers were trained to take the place of workers along the revolving platform in case such workers were temporarily absent or left their jobs. Such trained replacements would be important, for, while it would take a much shorter time for a worker to learn one of the specialized jobs than it would to become an expert all-round washer, it was much more essential that every specialized worker be an expert at his or her individual task. The speed of the entire process could be no greater than the speed of the slowest employee, and therefore a reserve supply of experienced workers was essential to effective operation of the entire system.

**13. Mechanical Pacing of Workers.** Another characteristic of the process which made expert workers necessary was the lack of opportunity for "warming up." Unless deliberately controlled in the matter, a worker when beginning a job normally requires a certain period of time in which to reach top working speed and efficiency. With the mechanically operated track, the speed of work was automatically set, and the worker in keeping up with the mechanical conveyor was forced to acquire top speed at the start and to maintain it. This would have the advantage of eliminating the inefficient worker as well as cutting to a minimum periods of submaximum productivity for the good worker. On the other hand, it definitely limited the occasional superior worker whose ability would have enabled him to effect greater output were it not that he could not speed up beyond the rate of the group as regulated by the machine.

**14. Importance of Uniform Raw Materials.** Executives of Standard Auto Service Corporation were attracted by the proposed method of washing largely because of the speed with which a car could be washed and the relatively low cost of doing the job. Both of these features were, in the main, the result of two things: the breaking down of the process of washing a car into a number of simple, standard parts and the extensive use of mechanical equipment. The nature of the process was such as to make this breaking down effective. The job to be done was a fairly standard one. True, cars varied as to the amount and character of dirt on them. There were large cars and small cars, closed and open ones. Wheels were occasionally of wood, sometimes of wire. These variations were not so great, however, as to make breaking down the process difficult. An occasional open car affected only the jobs of the top washer and the polishers. For all practical purposes the "material" (the cars) was similar and the process uniform.

Moreover, by varying the number of workers assigned to the task, it was possible to break down car washing into tasks which could be accomplished in the same length of time. One man could drive cars into the building in the same time as was required for four men to sponge the body and two men to vacuum the interior.

**15. Use of Mechanical Equipment.** In substantial degree the subdivision of the washing process made economical the extensive use of mechanical equipment. When automobile washing is done by a crew of one or two men, the equipment provided is usually limited to the bare necessities, such as sponges, polishing cloths, soap solution, water supply, and provision for disposal of the water used. Greater investment in mechanical devices is not economical, principally because of inability to use them intensively. When one man completely washes a car, only one part of the process is being carried on at one time, and only such equipment as is helpful in that part is in use. Any equipment provided for other parts of the process is idle. When the work is subdivided and all parts of the process are carried on simultaneously, all the mechanical equipment provided for the complete process is in constant use. Investment in mechanical equipment is profitable only in proportion as the equipment is used in the production process; idle equipment pays no dividends. Thus, the subdivision of the car-washing process and its accompanying specialization of labor, by creating a situation which makes for intensity of utilization of equipment, fosters the use of mechanical devices. The two outstanding characteristics of the proposed method of car washing, breakdown of the process into a number of simple, standard parts and the extensive use of mechanical equipment, are closely interrelated. Specialization makes the use of mechanical devices economical; the extensive use of mechanical equipment intensifies the advantages of labor specialization.

**16. Results of Labor Specialization.** The ability to break down the process into simple, standard parts made possible labor specialization and lower labor costs. Extensive use of the most efficient mechanical devices would reduce the total amount of labor expended in the washing of a car. Specialization and simplification of the work would eliminate time lost in changing from one part of the process to another, since each worker would be confined to but one step in the process. Repetition of the simple task would make the worker extremely efficient on the job and would tend to eliminate all unnecessary movements, thus reducing physical fatigue. First-class, experienced car washers were not easy to obtain. By subdividing the process, such experts were made unnecessary. Inexperienced workers could be trained to the simple tasks relatively quickly, and maximum performance on the job was ensured by the mechanical conveyor. Expert washers commanded relatively high wages; this would not be true of the type of worker required if the tasks were subdivided. All these advantages would make for a relatively low labor cost per car washed.

**17. Effects of Mass Production on Plant and Equipment Operating Costs.** In addition to the labor cost advantage, several other desirable results were likely to be obtained. A much smaller building would be required for a 600-car output per day if the proposed system was utilized than would be the case if two-man crews with individual wash racks were employed. This would make for a greater washing output per square foot of floor space with a consequent reduction of operating cost. Costs thus affected would include plant maintenance, interest on investment, ground rent, depreciation on building and equipment, and the like.

The relatively short time required to wash a car under the proposed system would likewise tend to reduce these same costs.

**18. Effect on Quality of Output.** The use of a standard washing process with highly specialized workers using the best of equipment should result in a washing job of excellent quality. This would be true, however, only if careful, regularized inspection was maintained. The proposed process provided for just such a safeguard, and work of a uniformly high quality should result.

**19. Effect on Sales Volume and Price.** The speed of the process was believed to be one of its most important characteristics. Managers of the Standard Auto Service Corporation were of the opinion that it would cause steady customers at the service station to have their cars washed more frequently. A 15-minute wait would be all that was required of the motorist, who could spend that time pleasantly either on the promenade watching the progress of his car or in the well-appointed waiting rooms. The short waiting period would make it possible to direct the customer's attention to other services of the company, and would offer opportunity for displaying for the car owner's consideration an attractive line of accessories. In the past, the company had found that the policy of providing rather complete service at one station tended to raise the average amount of the sales check. At other company stations, sales had averaged not less than $1.50, and it was believed that the addition of car washing to the services offered would raise this figure materially.

If the proposed plan was adopted, a flat charge of $1.25 was to be established for car washing. This was $0.75 to $1.25 lower than the prices charged by first-class car-washing establishments in the city.

**20. Risks of a Specialized Investment.** The total cost of the proposed service station including land, buildings, equipment, and fixtures would be approximately $200,000. Of this amount, $102,690 would be the cost of building and equipping a car-washing plant with a maximum capacity of 600 cars each 10 hours of operation. This total expenditure would have to be made at the outset, since the character of the process made it impossible to start with a smaller investment and increase capacity as volume of business grew. As a result of this condition, location of the new station would be of great importance. The large initial investment made neecssary a location such that volume could be built up rapidly to a point approximating the capacity of the washing plant. During the early months when business was being developed, the costs of operation per car washed would be relatively great. Depreciation, property taxes, interest charges, and plant maintenance would be relatively constant with little change due to fluctuation in volume of business. So far as these items were concerned, it would cost no more to wash 600 cars in a 10-hour day than it would to wash 60 in an equal period of time. Thus, the nearer to capacity the plant could be operated, the lower the cost of these items per car washed.

**21. Importance of Volume.** The use of a high degree of labor specialization likewise tended to make operating costs inflexible. It was necessary to have practically the same crew on the wash rack to turn out 20 cars per hour as it was to turn out 60 per hour. Thus, again, early operation at a figure approaching capacity was important.

Because of the relative importance of getting volume of business if the proposed type of car washing was to be included in the services offered at the new station, company executives believed that the higher priced of two locations under consideration would be desirable. The less costly location might possibly yield as high a volume as the other. However, the location with the higher rental was such as to ensure volume more certainly, and the risks incident to large initial investment and heavy developmental operation losses seemed to warrant the selection of the more costly of the two locations.

**22. Uniform Volume Desirable.** The more expensive location had one other advantage. It was larger and space was available for parking 75 cars. This was important since it might, in some degree, relieve a serious weakness in the proposed plan. In addition to the necessity for a large volume of business to make the wash rack pay, it was desirable that the rate at which cars came to the station to be washed be as nearly uniform as possible. It was obvious that business would be slack at certain hours of the day, and that some days would be busier than others. Weather conditions would greatly affect the amount of washing available. A certain amount of storage space would be valuable in smoothing out hourly peaks, since it was likely that some customers would be glad to leave their cars to be washed and return for them in an hour or two.  Parking space would make it possible to store up a certain amount of the rush-hour business for building up the dull hours of the day.

This extra space might also become of great value should business eventually be built up in excess of the one-car-per-minute capacity.  As it would be impossible in the proposed building to speed up the process beyond its set maximum rate, any future expansion would require extra space for the installation of a second complete wash rack.

**23. Minimum Volume Requirement to Cover Costs of Operation.**  However, the managers did not believe that such demand would develop.  They studied the situation carefully and concluded that at an average daily output of 200 cars, the income from the proposed plant would exactly pay all costs of operation: labor, supplies, and other burden costs, including such items as supervision, office workers' salaries, interest on borrowed money, taxes, depreciation, power, heat, light, water, and repairs.  On any volume in excess of this 200-car daily average, profits on capital invested by the proprietors would be realized.  They believed these cost estimates to be accurate.  They were convinced of the technical efficiency of the proposed washing process. Careful study indicated that, with proper management, washing jobs in excess of an average of 200 per day could be obtained. The company was financially capable of making the investment, and executives were firm in their belief that washing service would increase demand for the company's other services.  They recognized the dangers incident to a high initial investment in buildings and equipment of so specialized a nature, the problems growing out of fluctuating demand for car washing, the risks of inflexible operating costs, and the importance of selecting a location such that a large volume of business could be obtained. After carefully investigating and considering these and other aspects of the situation portrayed in the case, executives of the Standard Auto Service Corporation purchased the better of the two sites obtainable and proceeded to erect a "super-service" station including a car-washing plant which had a maximum output of 60 cars per hour.

**24. Summary and Conclusions.** The experience of the Standard Auto Service Corporation is an excellent illustration of the application of the economic principle of division of labor and its relation to mass production. It portrays many of the business considerations inherent in the utilization of the concept in profit-making endeavors.

Labor specialization was possible in this case because of the nature of the process and the character of product worked upon. These facilitated subdivision of the complete process into simple, standard operations which could be rapidly and satisfactorily performed by relatively unskilled, available labor.

Breakdown of the process into simple components made possible the extensive use of mechanical aids. This result often follows labor specialization and makes it easier to devise inexpensive mechanical equipment. The simpler the function, the less complicated, and therefore the less costly, will be the mechanical requirements of devices designed to carry out or facilitate the operation.

The tendency to mechanize specialized tasks is furthered by a business consideration, the intensification of use of such equipment when the process is highly subdivided. Idle equipment is the bane of the industrial executive. Idle equipment earns no return on the money invested in it. Often it depreciates or becomes obsolescent as rapidly when idle as when in use. Costs of maintenance are sometimes no greater for equipment in operation than for idle machines and tools. The tendency toward constant use which is characteristic of equipment employed by specialized labor often results in the installation and use of mechanical aids the existence of which is made technically practical by the simplification of the tasks performed by specialized workers.

Standard Auto Service Corporation executives expected labor specialization to result in lower labor cost for each car washed. Labor would be more efficient as a result of frequent repetition of the task and elimination of nonproductive effort. Worker idleness would be reduced by the pacing effect of the circular conveyor. Increased use of mechanical devices would make workers' tasks easier. Less skilled, more readily available workers would be used, and wage rates would therefore be lower.

These low unit labor costs would be offset in some degree by high plant and equipment costs. Low total cost per car washed would result only if high plant costs were exceeded by labor cost savings. Low total unit costs would be obtained only if the plant was operated at a relatively high rate. The nearer this rate approached capacity, the lower the cost of washing each car and the greater the profit from the venture.

The critical problem of Standard Auto Service Corporation executives, therefore, was a strictly business one. Would the proposed charge for car washing and the quick service at the proposed location attract a sufficient volume of steady business to allow the potential economies in the process to yield a satisfactory profit? Further, would the probable profits warrant the assumption of the risks inherent in such highly specialized investment? In their consideration of the economic principle of labor specialization and the technicalities of its application to auto washing, these executives had to reach decisions in terms of business concepts: cost of performing the service, volume of business obtainable, effect of volume on costs, and financial ability of the company to carry the venture through to such time as it could be reasonably expected to yield a profit.

Industrial management is much more than a matter of production technique. Production techniques are important, but the problem of the industrial executive is to employ them to the end that a business profit be obtained. The business characteristics and implications of production techniques are, therefore, the major considerations. Any attempt to understand economic principles of production and the techniques of their application involves focusing of attention upon the business aspects of production. The industrial executive is primarily a businessman. His understanding of production problems and methods enables him to produce a product or service so attractive in the market that the public will pay the requisite price in volume sufficient to yield a profit.

**25. Labor Specialization in the Second World War.** If one were to attempt to pick any one industrial principle to be officially cited for its contribution to the amazing industrial accomplishment of the Second World War, the chances are that the simple concept of labor specialization would be the recipient of the honor. There is no question but that more jobs were subdivided into more simple tasks than had ever been the case before. Three conditions inherent in the character of wartime production were responsible: The number of skilled workers available was tragically less than the number demanded by the war effort; the time element of the war demand allowed no margin for the training of skilled workers and very little for training inexperienced workers to perform semiskilled tasks; and, finally, cost of production was of secondary concern. These three—the volume required, the demand for quick delivery, and the lessened emphasis on cost—created an abnormal situation which tended to maximize the benefits of labor specialization and to minimize the evils of what would normally be considered overspecialization.

Overnight the war caused a ten-thousandfold jump in the demand for electronic crystals. There probably was not a score of skilled crystal makers with the requisite know-how in all the United States; the condition was critical, and "best minds" went to work on it. They shortly came up with a simple but highly effective answer. Careful study of the total job revealed that one small fraction of the task called for a degree of skill that could be acquired only by a few people with special aptitude by means of months (perhaps years) of training and practice. The rest of the job could be broken down into small tasks that could be learned in a few days, sometimes in a few hours, by people who had never seen the inside of a factory before. By confining the few skilled craftsmen to that small part of the work for which their skill was required and training inexperienced workers to perform the other tasks, it was possible to meet the terrific wartime demand for this essential item, and to meet it quickly. There probably was no more dramatic instance of the contribution of labor specialization to the war industry effort.

The grinding of optics, lenses, and prisms was another instance of separating a composite into its skilled and unskilled components, confining skilled workers to tasks that constantly called for the application of their skills, and breaking down the remainder of the work into tasks so simple that the inexperienced could master them quickly. Early in 1940, arsenals and Navy yards placed a call with the government employment service for 350 qualified lens grinders. When the employment service and the civil service found it impossible to locate such competent skilled craftsmen, a careful study of the trade revealed the possibility of specializing the work. The fully competent lens grinder is supposed to be able to perform successfully any or all of 20 tasks, of which the following are typical:

1. Cut optical glass
2. Grind all types of lenses
3. Grind all types of prisms
4. Grind reticles
5. Grind windows or covers
6. Correct prisms for polish
19. Cement ocular prisms
20. Roof prisms (correction)

Study of the operations required for the production of one type of military prism (task type 3 in the foregoing list of 20) showed that it could be broken down into 15 separate operations. The first of these, grinding one side individually by hand to establish a base for subsequent operations, could be taught an inexperienced worker quickly. The last two operations, beveling to a 45-degree angle and hand correction, required considerable skill and experience. None of the operations called for the over-all skill possessed by the highly versatile craftsman competent to perform all the 20 complete tasks listed above. Careful selection of workers, training to perform one specific operation, and use of people possessing skill only when skill was required made it possible to meet the tremendously expanded requirements of the armed services.

Probably no handcraft was more in the public eye during the war than welding. Hundreds of thousands of men and women became proficient at welding tasks in a few weeks. Almost none of these workers were trained as all-round, so-called "first-class," general welders. Each new welder was taught one kind of work or a very few kinds, a condition that was unknown before the war. Here again it was extreme specialization of labor that produced results—a great volume of output quickly.

It takes years to become a competent screw machine setup man. Prior to the war it was common practice for a skilled man to have a group of screw machines assigned to him. He made the setups on them; he watched their output to see that it was always up to standard; he made the necessary running adjustments (usually minor); he did the requisite maintenance work on his group of machines. Commonly the only help he had was a trucker who brought raw materials to the machines and took tote boxes of finished parts away. The war brought a tremendous increase in demand for a wide variety of screw machine products, many of them calling for very complicated setups. The answer commonly found in screw machine shops was to confine the experienced screw machine man to setup work only. By so doing a skilled man could do the skilled setup work of three or four or five times the number of machines he had handled prewar. Less skilled people could be trained relatively quickly to do the other work around the screw machine department.

Practically all metalworking shops forsook the use of skilled machinists in favor of little-skilled or unskilled machine tenders. By means of ingenious machine fixtures, jigs, and attachments, the man who ran a machine became in essence a specialist in putting pieces into a machine and taking them out when the machine had completed its work on them. Sometimes even this task was broken down into two parts: one man loaded the machine while a second man unloaded it. In this way the time during which the machine was idle while being loaded and unloaded was reduced by a fraction of a minute and its output for the day was increased. In the meantime the skilled machinists who were relieved of machine operation by this device could spend all their time and energies building the machine fixtures and attachments which made the use of unskilled machine tenders possible.

During the war there probably was no plant, large or small, directly or indirectly connected with the war effort, that did not make use of the principle of labor specialization to expand its work force and to wring the last unit of output from its machines and its skilled labor. Some of this was cost saving, but much of it was such an extreme subdivision that it tended to be costly. Handling and intraplant transportation costs increased out of proportion to volume increase. The same was true of supervision, planning, and coordinating and control costs of all kinds. But specialization of labor accomplished its purpose and was justified as a war measure.

With the ending of war contracts, much of this overspecialization has had to be undone. Oftentimes the required volume of a single item became too small to support such extreme specialization, and the costs of coordinating such multiplicity of activities made continuation competitively unwarranted. Much of postwar reconversion has been a matter of just such unscrambling of excessive job breakdown as a part of the essential process of again becoming competitive on a cost basis.

**26. Characteristics of Postwar Labor Specialization.** One lasting effect of the war and of the sellers' market that immediately followed was a substantial narrowing of the spread between wage rates of skilled and unskilled factory workers. Wages of both classes rose, but the rates of little or less skilled workers have gone up faster than the rates of the more skilled. As this differential narrows, at least one of the normal advantages of labor specialization tends to disappear because there is less potential labor dollar saving in breaking down a job into its skilled and unskilled elements.

Another result of this wage rate change is the tendency to replace labor with equipment. Automobile laundries are somewhat more mechanized than before the war. Large power-driven brushes have been installed in some units to reduce the number of workers who wash the cars with sponges and soap and water. Larger and more powerful air blowers for removing water more thoroughly from the washed vehicles have reduced the number of workers required to dry and polish. In some installations the number of hand workers has been cut by 40 to 50 per cent of prewar requirements for the same (or greater) volume of output.

Industry is one of the most highly dynamic activities of modern society. Any general economic change has its impact on the factory. And it should never be forgotten that the factory must immediately react to such impact. The effect of the wartime conditions and the postwar changes on the practice and application of labor specialization is a typical example of this cause-and-effect relationship. Yesterday was a boom period in labor specialization; today's conditions have brought about changes in application of the concept. Perhaps we may see a time when specialized labor is only a matter of history. That is doubtful, but the successful manager is one who uses this technology intelligently in terms of existing business conditions. And business conditions are always in process of change.

## QUESTIONS

1. List the arguments in favor of the inclusion of a large-scale automobile-washing plant by the Standard Auto Service Corporation at its new unit.

2. List the objections to the adoption of such a car-washing system by the company.

3. One of the advantages claimed for the system was that its adoption would materially decrease the costs of washing a car. Make a list of all the expenses which would be incurred by a company washing 480 automobiles per eight-hour day under the old hand system of two-man crews. Explain in detail how each of these items of daily expense would be affected by a change to the large-scale system.

4. If, on a stormy day, the volume of washing with a large-scale installation should decrease from the 480-car capacity output to 160 cars during an eight-hour run, how would each of the items of operating costs be affected? What would be the effect upon the cost of washing each car?

5. Would changes in the volume of daily output have the same effect on the unit cost of washing cars by the old hand method, without labor specialization and without the extensive use of mechanical equipment, as they would have on the unit cost of washing cars by the proposed system? Explain.

6. What is the meaning of the term "overhead" [5] or, as it is frequently called, "plant burden"?

7. If the case of automobile washing is typical of most enterprises, what can we say is the effect of changes in volume of output on overhead cost per unit of product turned out?

8. How does change in volume of output affect unit labor costs?

9. What is the bearing of such consideration of the costs of operation upon the question of the desirability of adopting the large-scale washing system in the case under discussion?

10. Should the Standard Auto Service Corporation have adopted the large-scale car-washing system in its new service station?

11. How did labor specialization aid in the war effort?

12. What happened to labor specialization after the war?

13. Will factory managers continue the practice of labor specialization? Explain.

[5] See *Encyclopaedia Britannica,* or any similar standard reference work, if not familiar with this term.

## Problem 1

### AMPID COMPANY

The Ampid Company manufactured automobile-washing devices and equipment. Its line varied from such small items as high-pressure nozzles to complete semiautomatic, large-scale car-washing installations.[6] It had achieved great success with the systems; and company executives believed that the principles involved, the use of unskilled, specialized labor and automatic mechanical conveying of the work throughout the process, might advantageously be applied to other types of service work.

Executives of the Ampid Company knew that some large automobile service stations did a profitable business in the cleaning of the exteriors of automobile motors. This work involved the removal of grease and hardened road dust from all parts beneath the car hood. The character of the grime was such as to require the use of inflammable solvents like gasoline or kerosene. Even then it was necessary to use wire brushes and metal scrapers to get satisfactory results on the average job. The task varied greatly as between cars. If a motor was cleaned frequently, the removal of the grime was not difficult, and it could be accomplished by one man in from one to two hours. However, motors often went without cleaning for several years, in which event it frequently took a man as long as a day to do a satisfactory job.

Certain problems were involved in the work. "Live" electric wiring with many open points of contact about the motor made caution essential to avoid fire or explosion. In some establishments it was a rule that before cleaning work was started, the battery terminals must be disconnected as a safeguard. Even then, care was required to keep washing solutions away from wiring since they were detrimental to insulation. It was also necessary to exercise every care in keeping both the washing solutions and the removed grease and tar from painted surfaces of the car.

[6] See Standard Auto Service Corporation case, p. 17, for description of a typical large-scale washing system.

Because of variation in the condition of motors it was customary to charge for cleaning by the hour, and flat rates were exceptional.

Ampid Company officials believed that if a method of motor cleaning could be devised which would greatly lessen the cost to the customer and at the same time make flat-rate charges possible, garages using such a system could develop considerable volumes of such business.

Company engineers studied the problem for several months and eventually came to the conclusion that the task of motor cleaning was not suited to the use of methods similar to those developed for large-scale automobile washing.

Wherein is the task of motor cleaning unsuited to large-scale mechanized performance using highly specialized labor?

### Problem 2

### KENWAY COMPANY

The Kenway Company was a manufacturer and jobber of stationery and office supplies. For several years the business had grown rapidly. As a result the office force had been greatly increased to a point such that costs at the central office had become unduly large. As one step in the reduction of these costs, centralization of the stenographic force was proposed.

At the central office were located the general manager, treasurer, sales manager, and factory manager. Each of these executives had a secretary to take care of his office work, including the taking of dictation and typing. The company employed three buyers. Each of these men had a secretary-stenographer who served callers, made appointments, and attended to the record files and his correspondence.

A city sales force of 10 men worked out of the central office. Originally, salesmen had been given separate offices, but lack of space had made a continuance of that policy impossible. As the business grew and the sales force expanded, the 10 salesmen occupied four offices. Each of these offices was served by a secretary who handled the salesmen's telephone calls, met customers, arranged appointments, and performed the usual office routine and stenographic work. It was necessary that these girls be conversant with the salesmen's plans and activities. Contact with customers called for tact and ability. Usually the salesmen were in the office only from 8:30 to 9:00 A.M. and for a short time prior to closing at night. Thus, for a considerable portion of the day, office contacts with customers were in the hands of the salesmen's secretaries.

There were three typist-stenographers in the accounting department. These girls typed forms and reports in addition to handling correspondence.

The proposal to centralize all this office help met with much opposition. The chief accountant stated that the typing of reports called for special ability and training. He further stated that the work of his department was such that periodic peaks of work were unavoidable and that it was necessary to maintain a force adequate to handle these peak loads even though it was difficult to keep the stenographers fully occupied at other times.

The salesmen objected to the change on the basis that their secretaries performed very important functions in the building up and maintenance of customer good will, and that their stenographic activities were secondary to these considerations. As the salesmen were in the office but a short time each day, they felt that it was necessary to have the girls available at that time to take their dictation. The buyers objected to the change on grounds similar to those advanced by the city salesmen.

Even the chief executives offered objections to the plan although they were responsible for the agitation for lower costs. They felt that their positions were such as to require special consideration in the matter of secretarial and stenographic service. Their time was valuable, and to that extent constant attendance of a secretary was, they pointed out, economical even though the secretary was not constantly busy with their work. Furthermore, the prestige of their positions would be affected if the secretaries were removed, and they felt that a certain amount of overhead cost was justified on this basis.

In the proposal to centralize the stenographic force, it was pointed out that certain definite economies would result. Daily work could be better apportioned, and therefore it would be possible to reduce the size of the force. A study of the amount of typing done in the office showed that the output was only 30 per cent of that normally attained in other offices. Centralization of the work force would make possible a better check on the individual worker, would provide a competitive incentive, and should result in greatly increasing the efficiency of each worker and in the weeding out of inefficient girls.

## QUESTIONS

1. Prepare a plan of office reorganization for the Kenway Company that should reduce costs and yet should satisfy all persons concerned.

2. In view of the general opposition to the plan, do you think that centralization of the stenographic force should have been attempted? Explain your answer.

### Problem 3

### MELLON COMPANY

The Mellon Company maintained specialized crews of "setup" men for setting up new jobs on the machines and adjusting them so that all parts of the products to be manufactured would be properly turned out. The amount of idle time resulting from this procedure, however, caused the management to consider changing the practice.

The Mellon Company operated a large machine shop. It was the practice in many departments of the plant to have under the department foreman a number of setup men, whose duties consisted of setting up new jobs on the machines and adjusting the machines to ensure proper manufacture. When this adjustment had been completed, the setup men turned the machines over to comparatively unskilled operatives, whose work was to see that the parts making up the products which the company manufactured were turned out on a quantity basis. The machines were automatic in operation, fed themselves, and discharged finished pieces into containers designed for their reception.

After a machine had been set up, the duties of the machine operative consisted of occasional inspection of the pieces turned out to see that the machine was operating properly, supplying the machine with raw materials, removing finished parts, and keeping the machine and work place clean. Most machine operatives were paid on a piecework basis. Their earnings were determined by the regularity with which their machines turned out perfect work and the care with which they kept their machines supplied with raw materials. When inspection of a part showed that a machine was doing imperfect work, the operative called the foreman, who either adjusted the machine or called one of the department setup men to make the necessary changes.

Operatives tended from 4 to 12 machines each; the work was rarely arduous, and much of the operatives' time was spent sweeping the floor and wiping and oiling the machines. The more conscientious workers kept continually occupied at the cleaning tasks, but many of the men frequently found time to talk with one another. Company executives, however, believed it inadvisable to increase the number of machines assigned to each man. Occasionally several machines in a group needed the operative's attention at one time, and an increase in the number of machines assigned to a man would tend to increase machine idleness. Whenever a new job required resetting of one or more of the machines in an operative's group, the operative would be idle at least part of the time while the setup man made the necessary adjustments. During the setting up, the operative was paid on an hourly basis. Average setup time throughout the shop had been 30 minutes for each machine changed.

A monthly report received by the superintendent showed a total of 206 hours of "waiting time" during which machine operatives were paid hourly rates. The question arose as to the advisability of continuing the practice of having the setup work done by specialized crews. When the practice had been instituted, it was believed that the company would be able to reduce costs through having low-paid, unskilled machine tenders and through the increased skill in setting up that would be developed by the setup men.  It was also expected that the employment of un-skilled labor would protect the company when skilled labor was scarce.  By using setup men, furthermore, a certain amount of preparatory work could be done in advance.

For some time the assistant superintendent had felt that the advantage of having setup men was not so great as had been expected.  A certain type of special work in small lots, for which the setup time was long in proportion to the running time, had made the use of setup men appear uneconomical.  Some of the automatic machines required frequent adjustments, and such machines were idle while awaiting the arrival of a setup man.  In other cases the setting-up operation was so simple that a skilled man was not required.

Two possible changes were proposed.  The first was to dis-continue the special setup crews and to train the operatives to perform the setup function in addition to their other tasks.  The second possibility was to make each setup man responsible for checking and keeping adjusted the machines he set up in addi-tion to his former duties, thus increasing the size of the setup crews somewhat.  All cleaning and maintenance work on ma-chines would be specialized and made the responsibility of men whose work would be limited to these functions.  One or more men in each department would be assigned only to supplying raw materials to the machines and to removing finished parts from the machines.

### QUESTIONS

1. Should the system in effect have been continued, or should a change have been made to one of the two proposed methods?

2. If a change was advisable, which of the two proposed methods should have been employed?

# CHAPTER III

## FURTHER APPLICATION OF THE SPECIALIZATION PRINCIPLE

### LEWISTON TRANSPORT COMPANY

**1. An Illustration of the General Applicability of the Specialization Principle.**

The Lewiston Transport Company which operated an extensive trucking business was experiencing a decline in volume of business with an even more rapid falling off in profits. A consideration of general business conditions, competition in the trucking field, and the character of the company's operating costs convinced company officials that drastic internal economies and reorganization were imperative. A program largely based upon extensive application of the specialization principle was devised, thoroughly tried out, and found effective in restoring to the company its former profit-making ability.

**2. Pervasiveness of Specialization in Industry.** Success in application of the principle of specialization in the field of labor has led to its extensive utilization throughout the industrial organism. Today we hear of specialized equipment, specialized plants, process specialization, product specialization, and even of management specialization. Rarely does a company embark upon a program limited to any one phase of specialization activity. Even when the original intent is specific within some one of these, or other, fields, the development of a working plan soon reveals relationships which involve many functions or activities.

**3. Interrelation of the Various Applications of the Specialization Principle.** Labor specialization is closely related to equipment specialization. The more general the purpose of a machine, the less likely is it to be operated by only one man. Even when one operative is assigned exclusively to a general-purpose machine, he rarely specializes in one type of operation on that machine. As a rule, the more flexible a machine in its actual and

41

potential capacities, the more adaptable and unspecialized its operative will be.

Product specialization and process specialization go hand in hand. The less the variety of finished product turned out in a plant, the fewer will be the processes carried on within the plant at any one time. The fewer the processes carried on, the smaller the number of types of jobs involved. The fewer the job types, the greater the amount and degree of labor specialization. Specialized equipment usually entails careful planning and control for its most effective utilization, and detailed specialization of management naturally ensues.

**4. Analyzing the Results of Specialization.** It is usually difficult in practice to differentiate in a single case between results obtained from labor specialization and from the specialization of related factors and activities. That each plays its part and produces certain results will be evident upon careful scrutiny. But to evaluate those results quantitatively is rarely possible. That this is so is of little concern to the management, whose objective is the improvement of the relationship of the parts that contribute to the whole. From the standpoint of the student of modern industry, the important things are (1) to sense the pervasive quality of the specialization principle; (2) to recognize it in its sundry applications; (3) to grasp the import of the relationships involved; and (4) to evaluate the results obtained, the weaknesses, and the dangers incident to specific applications.

**5. Experience of the Lewiston Transport Company.** The following experience, that of the Lewiston Transport Company, is set forth here in considerable detail as an illustration of what one usually finds in any specific study of specialization in modern industry.

The Lewiston Transport Company, located in a large Middle Western city, operated one of the largest trucking businesses in the United States. Within the city, the company operated a fleet of heavy trucks which delivered freight from shipping terminals and wholesalers' warehouses and which collected freight for delivery to railroad, steamship, and long-distance trucking companies for shipment. Suburban service of this type was rendered within a radius of 30 miles. The company also operated delivery-truck fleets for several large department stores. As a result of depressed business conditions, the company faced a situation of decreased volume of business and narrowed profit margin. Solution of the problem was sought in more efficient and attractive trucking equipment, control of loading to improve load factor, and specialization of labor, equipment, process, and management.

**6. Effect of Decline in Volume of Business on Equipment Utilization—Management Specialization as a Remedy.** The decline in volume of business obtained had adversely affected the efficiency with which automotive equipment was utilized. Frequently trucks were not loaded to capacity, and as a result the load factor had fallen. To remedy this situation, a foreman was detailed to give his entire attention to the loading, dispatching, and routing of trucks. Small loads were brought together at central points by light, high-speed trucks. There they were consolidated and dispatched in full-load lots. In this way trucks were kept loaded at or near capacity, and duplication of deliveries over the same route was avoided. The detailing of a foreman to give his entire time to the loading, dispatching, and routing of trucks was an excellent example of modern practice in the matter of management specialization.

**7. Management Specialization Illustrated.** It is still not unusual to find a departmental foreman in a shop rather autocratic within the confines of his department. He trains his workers, assigns them to tasks, disciplines them, promotes them, and discharges them upon occasion. He is responsible for the condition and use of machines and tools within his department. He requisitions from the storeroom his needed raw materials. He plans the work required of his department, determining by whom and when the various tasks are to be performed, in such a manner as to ensure the completion of jobs within the time limits available for the various orders. He has a score of other responsibilities to discharge: proper utilization of materials, inspection for quality, the compilation of information requisite for payroll and cost records, and many others. His responsibility and authority are fixed, in major part, in terms of the physical extent of his department.  Other foremen discharge similar functions for other areas within the plant.  Foremanship as a part of management is thus organized as specialized jobs, the basis of organization being plant operating departments.

**8. Specializing Management on the Basis of Functions Performed.**  Under certain circumstances it has been found desirable to depart from this basis of foremanship specialization.  It is common practice to specialize the *function* of part and product design and specification, thus relieving the operating department foreman of all responsibility in this respect.  His job, as regards these functions, is limited to following instructions—the execution of orders.  Not often is an operating department foreman charged with the generation of power utilized within his department, nor is he required to purchase the materials and supplies which his workers use.

In recent years, the concept of specializing management on the basis of functions rather than in terms of plant areas has been extensively applied where the relationships involved permit.  It is not at all uncommon to relieve the foreman of the task of planning what should be done at a certain time within his department.  In highly centralized scheduling departments, this task may go even to the extent of specifying not only times but also machines and operatives to be employed on particular jobs.  The problems of scheduling are thus centralized in the hands of specialists, with frequently attendant advantages similar to those resulting from the specialization of the function of truck loading, scheduling, and routing in the experience of the Lewiston Transport Company.

**9. Relation of Management Specialization to Equipment and Labor Specialization.**  The company's improvement in dispatching made possible increased use of trailers with a consequent reduction in labor costs.  Both truck drivers and their assistants were members of the local chauffeurs' union.  Both received high wage rates as skilled operatives although all the assistants' and much of the chauffeurs' time was occupied in the unskilled tasks of loading and unloading.

Twice in the past the company had attempted to replace drivers' assistants with nonunion common labor.  On both occasions the union had fought the move so vigorously that the management had been forced to abandon the plan.

The use of high-speed truck tractors and trailers improved this situation. The truck tractor and trailer combination consisted of two or more units. The tractor was a truck of short wheel base and without a body. The loads were carried in the trailer units. In operation, the tractor was coupled to a trailer unit which had been previously loaded. The tractor then hauled the trailer to its destination, where it was uncoupled. Often the tractor did not wait for the trailer to be unloaded but at once picked up an empty trailer, hauled it back to the point where it was to be loaded, uncoupled it, immediately picked up a loaded trailer, and went out again. In this way, the tractors were kept in operation a large part of the time, and only the trailers were idle during the loading and unloading periods. The major part of the chauffeur's time was utilized in driving since it was unnecessary for him to wait for trailers to be loaded and unloaded. Also it was often possible to replace the chauffeur's assistant with a loader who was hired as a common laborer and as such was paid lower wages.

The chauffeurs' union had no jurisdiction over loaders who were more or less permanently stationed at dispatching and receiving points, and thus it was no longer able to push its demands that such work be done by members of that union. As all the tractor drivers' time was now occupied in driving, there was no need for chauffeurs' assistants when tractors and trailers were used. Thus the company was able to specialize the jobs of loading and driving, to choose men best fitted for each kind of work, and to pay wages commensurate with the requirements of the tasks.

**10. Effect of Equipment Specialization on Labor Specialization.** In this case, labor specialization had become possible as a result of equipment specialization. As a unit, the truck was essentially a dual-purpose machine: it provided carrying space and furnished motive power. Basically, it was much the same as a railroad freight train with the cars permanently attached to the engine. The replacement of trucks by tractors and trailers divided the dual function of the trucks, the power function being vested in the tractor and the carrying function in the trailer. Such subdivision of the transport job by means of equipment specialization made labor specialization possible.

**11. Relationship of Specialized Equipment to Mass Production.** It should also be noted that in this instance specialization of the heavy equipment resulted in its more intensive use, a result too uncommon in equipment specialization. Frequently the replacement of general-purpose machines with specialized machines so limits the use of the equipment as to render it idle to a greater extent than was true of the general-purpose device. Conditions peculiar to the Lewiston Transport Company situation freed it from this adverse effect of the use of specialized equipment. The company did not attempt to apply the principle of specialized power and carrying equipment in other than the field of heavy hauling over established routes. The varying character and demand in store delivery service made such specialized equipment unsuited to that type of work. The company management showed excellent judgment in utilizing specialized equipment for large volume operations of repetitive, slightly varying nature, and general-purpose equipment in situations where flexibility was required to meet fluctuations in volume and nature of the work involved. Generally speaking, specialized equipment is best suited to mass production of standard parts, products, or services which are little affected by style or seasonal fluctuations in demand.

**12. Reduction of Labor Force in a Garage Made Possible through Specialization of Mechanics.** In the company's garage, 23 skilled mechanics had been employed. As jobs came in, they had been assigned to whichever men were available. Only experienced mechanics had been employed, and no attempt had been made to concentrate individual workers on specific types of work. Investigation showed that from 25 to 30 per cent of the work done by these men required little or no skill in its performance.

In the reorganization of the shop, men were assigned to concentrate on specific types of work. These specialists were selected because of aptitude displayed in the past. The following assignments were made:

One blacksmith and spring repairman
One brake repairman
One motor mechanic
One ignition, starter, lights, and battery man
One iron worker and body repairman
One machinist to do lathe work and welding
One carpenter
One tinsmith, who was also to handle radiator and fender repairs
One mechanic to do testing and assist in diagnosing causes of breakdown
Two mechanics to be used for whatever purpose variations in volume of different types of work demanded
One general mechanic to work a shift from 3 to 11 P.M.
Two mechanic's helpers
One mechanic's helper who was also to act as assistant machinist
One odd-job man for use wherever needed

The supervisory force was to consist of a superintendent, a purchasing agent and stockman, and a bookkeeper.

As a result of reorganizing the jobs in the shop, the work force was reduced somewhat. Seven mechanics, one washer, and one odd-job man were released. Also, the greaser was given the job of going after needed repair parts, thus eliminating the "picker-up" who had previously been on the payroll.

**13. Importance of Volume of Work in Determining Basis and Degree of Labor Specialization.** The division of the work had been carefully planned, as to both basis of specialization and degree of subdivision. The shop did not have enough spring-repair work to keep a man continuously employed at that task. The work was essentially a specialized type of blacksmithing. There was considerable other blacksmithing required in the shop, and study of past experience indicated that one man could normally just take care of all such work if spring repairs were included. The similarity of this last type of job to general blacksmithing tasks made it feasible to specialize on that *basis,* and the volume of work to be performed made the assignment of one man to all such tasks a sound *degree* of specialization.

**14. Spare Parts and Assemblies as an Aid to Labor Specialization in a Garage.** Past records showed that spring repairs did not occur with any great degree of regularity. This handicap to spring repair specialization was overcome through the stocking of spare springs and spring parts. When a spring broke, the blacksmith removed the broken member and replaced it with one from stock. The broken parts were placed in storage to be repaired whenever a slackened demand upon the blacksmith's time permitted. In this way the variations in volume of spring work were made ineffective as a deterrent to job specialization.

There was a further advantage in the shortening of the time during which a truck was idle for repair of springs.

**15. Additional Examples of Limitations upon Labor Specialization in a Garage.** Similar care and judgment were exercised in specializing other tasks in the shop. One mechanic was assigned to all motor repair and overhauling work other than that resulting from failure in ignition, starter, lights, or battery. These last were similar in their nature and of sufficient volume to warrant the assignment of a specialist to these tasks. The volume of valve grinding, however, was not sufficient to keep one man continuously occupied. Therefore, valve grinding was classed with other motor repairs and made a part of the work of the motor specialist. Valve grinding was not so highly skilled a task as certain other jobs of motor repair. Consequently, a semi-skilled task was performed by the skilled mechanic who was required to handle the more intricate problems of motor upkeep and repair. This resulted in a relatively high cost for valve grinding. However, considering the volume of this work available and its relationship to other types of motor repairs, the assignment of the task to the skilled motor specialist was probably wise.

Careful study of the list of job assignments shows that the two cases here discussed are typical examples of practices followed in the reorganization of the shop personnel. Fluctuations in volume of work that could not well be handled in other ways were taken care of through the use of helpers and the odd-job man. Careful attention to the extent of specialization and the basis of division in terms of related functions resulted in the realization of many of the advantages of labor specialization in a setting not completely adapted to its use, without the usual attendant disadvantages.

**16. A Skilled Worker's Reaction to Specialization on a Skilled Job—One Example.** Similar changes were made in the paint-shop personnel.  The work in that shop consisted of spray painting, rubbing down and polishing, varnishing, and decorating and lettering.  Much of this work did not require skill for its satisfactory performance, but it, as well as such highly skilled work as lettering, had always been done by the two expert painters employed in the shop.  One of the painters was discharged, and the other devoted his entire time to the highly skilled tasks of which he was capable and which he much preferred to perform.  The unskilled work was assigned to the garage watchman, who was able to do it during hours on duty in which he otherwise would have been idle.  This last is an example of economies to be derived from labor diversification in a situation where labor specialization was not warranted.  The work of the night watchman was not similar to that of spray painting.  The nature of the jobs was such, however, as to make it advisable to combine these two tasks as duties of one individual.

**17. Attempts to Increase Volume as a Means of Making Specialization More Effective.**  At the same time efforts had been made to increase the total volume of business obtained by the company.  The rolling stock of the company offered an effective advertising medium.  In the past, trucks had been repainted at intervals of three or four years, and revarnished every six or eight months.  This work was done in the company's own paint shop.  The management decided to varnish the trucks more frequently.  Varnish preserved the paint underneath and gave the truck the appearance of being freshly painted.  A trademark, designed to make the company name stand out attractively from the background of the truck bodies, was applied to every truck.  In the past, the body-building and repair shop of the company had given little consideration to designing assemblies of cab, chassis, and body which would result in attractive lines.  All emphasis had been placed on utility and durability.  This policy was changed, and as rapidly as possible truck bodies were rebuilt to designs calculated to attract attention and elicit favorable customer comment upon their new graceful lines and colorings.

**18. Effects of Specialization on Labor Costs in a Garage.**  Four months after these changes were effected, the superintendent prepared a report to show labor expenditures for a week as compared with similar expenditures for the corresponding week of the previous year. Following is a summary of that report:

### Wages Paid, One Week

| Summary After Changes Were Made | | Summary Before Changes Were Made | |
|---|---|---|---|
| Mechanics | $ 665.30 | Mechanics | $1,016.15 |
| Painter | 35.75 | Painters | 87.80 |
| Coverman | 35.75 | Coverman | 38.50 |
| Washers | 137.50 | Washers | 196.90 |
| General | 116.40 | General | 144.90 |
| Greasers | 22.00 | Greasers | 26.95 |
| | | Picker-up | 23.65 |
| Total | $1,012.70 | Total | $1,534.85 |

| | |
|---|---|
| Before Changes Were Made | $1,534.85 |
| After Changes Were Made | 1,012.70 |
| Savings, One Week | $ 522.15 |

The management checked these figures with the weekly payrolls of the past four months and found them to be representative.

**19. Other Results of Specialization in This Case.** No insurmountable difficulties had been encountered as a result of the changes. The amount of outside repairs required had been reduced materially. By shortening the time required for repairs, truck idleness had been cut down. An example of methods employed to effect such time saving was the use of spare motors. When a truck motor needed a thorough overhauling, which would necessitate the laying up of the truck for from 24 to 48 hours, the entire motor was removed from the truck, and a spare motor put in its place. This change could be made in a very short time with a corresponding lessening of truck idleness. The policy of maintaining spare assemblies was extensively used; and a considerable stock of complete ignition units, carburetor units, spare springs, fenders, fans, wheel bearings, starters, generators, etc., was carried.

The management realized that the spare parts and assemblies program entailed a considerable investment in inventory. However, in view of the benefits of the plan this was not deemed excessive, and it was expected that the gradual standardization of rolling stock, both as to make and to a certain extent as to type, would reduce the initial investment in inventory materially.

The Lewiston Transport Company found the foregoing proceedings with respect to truck appearance, load factor, labor specialization, and shop equipment satisfactorily effective in the improvement of company profits. The new methods employed in the shop had also resulted in improved quality of workmanship. This would have a cumulative effect which would eventually result in savings in addition to the cost reduction immediately effective from the plan.

**20. Summary and Conclusions.** *Nature of Specialization.* In large measure, the economies of modern methods of mass production find their beginnings in the specialization concept. Specialization as indicating concentration, direct approach, singleness of purpose, absence of variation, limitation of range, and intensive rather than extensive adaptation and development seems in large measure to be the stuff of which mass production as a program is made. Specialization of labor, specialization of process, plant specialization, machine specialization, and even specialization in management itself are the most common avenues of approach when things are wrong and the most commended devices when success rewards.

*The Worker's Reaction to Specialization.* Labor specialization is lauded as a social contribution and condemned as a social catastrophe. Not infrequently labor specialization is criticized as having bad effects upon the worker.[1] It is said that he becomes a robot, that his work is no longer interesting, and that monotony with a whole train of evil effects follows. A study of the cases on specialization which have been treated thus far shows that any such broad generalization is false. When specialization results in confining the skilled worker to skilled work, it certainly does not tend to decrease the interest of the worker in his job. The

[1] See L. C. Marshall, *Readings in Industrial Society,* pp. 397–399, University of Chicago Press, Chicago, 1918.

skilled painter in the paint department of the Lewiston Transport Company was glad to confine his time to doing only the skilled tasks of which he was capable. Similarly, in the company's repair shops the restricting of mechanics and machinists to jobs in which they were most interested and to which they were best adapted did not bring about the so-called "evils" of repetitive work. Actually, the men were proud of their selection as experts in restricted fields and worked hard to further their reputations.

*An Example of the Monotony of Repetitive Work.* It cannot be questioned that there are many occasions where a high degree of labor specialization has resulted in the creation of jobs of such simplicity as to seem to the observer monotonous in the extreme. One of the best examples of such work is that of a girl whose duty it was to make sure that cardboard containers had been filled. A machine fed rubber jar rings into small, flat boxes. The machine never made a mistake in count, but it did upon rare occasions allow a container to go past without putting anything in it. Just behind the machine sat a girl whose job it was to eliminate any such unfilled boxes. The machine ejected the filled boxes upon a mechanical conveyor which passed in front of the girl. The tops of the boxes pointed toward this worker and were open to allow inspection. Conditions were such that it was not easy to make this inspection visually; the work was best done by sense of touch. What the girl did was to insert the thumb of her right hand into each box as it passed her. If there were rings in the box, she withdrew her thumb; if there were none, she flipped the empty box from the conveyor at the time she withdrew her thumb. In performing this operation, the girl held her arm extended before her and constantly swung her thumb back and forth, in and out of the passing boxes, several times a second. This movement of the thumb was the only movement made by any part of the girl's body in performing the task. The job seemed to be a perfect example of the horror of repetitive work. No mental effort was required, and there was but a minimum of physical exertion. When questioned, the department foreman said that at one time considerable difficulty had been experienced in keeping girls on that particular job. By careful selection of workers for the task, this high turnover had been reduced until it was no higher than the average for the plant. The foreman said that he was experiencing no trouble with the job and that the girls liked the work. Physically they were at rest; mentally they were far away. Conversations with workers on that particular job were convincing in establishing the accuracy of the foreman's statements. The explanation seemed to be that girls who were fitted for the occupation had been selected for the job. Undoubtedly there were many women in that plant who could not have stayed for a day on that routine, monotonous job. Proper selection of the workers, however, had resulted in getting operatives who were efficient at the work and happy with it.

That repetitive work is not distasteful to all workers has been well established by automobile manufacturers on their assembly lines. There have been many examples of worker objection to change from what they termed a soft job, a job which was in reality a simple repetitive task requiring the minimum of responsibility and mental effort.[2]

*Effect of Specialization on Skill Required of the Worker.* One might reasonably say that a major objective of labor specialization is to fit the job to the worker. In the larger number of cases it is probable that labor specialization has reduced the skill required of the workers. The reduction of a complex task into its simple components often means that none of the more highly specialized workers need have the breadth of skill required of the worker who performed the task before it was broken down. When labor specialization has been opposed, it has usually been on the score that management was thereby seeking to replace skilled workers with unskilled labor.

A type of labor specialization commonly found is that which seeks to break down the job in such a way as to isolate the skilled from the unskilled components, or to separate different skills. When jobs are specialized in this way, it frequently becomes profitable to employ more highly skilled workers than were employed before the task was broken down. Prior to specialization, the worker was paid a wage rate commensurate with the greatest

[2] Henry Ford, in collaboration with Samuel Crowther, *My Life and Work*, Doubleday & Company, Inc., New York, 1926.

component skill required even though much of his time was spent on work that could have been performed equally well by less skilled workers commanding lower wages. Under such circumstances the employer was unlikely to make the effort to find, or pay wages that would attract, the most able workers. When the task is broken down and the skilled operations are separated from the unskilled, the employer often finds it advantageous to pay a wage sufficiently high to attract the most skillful workers to those specialized operations calling for skill.

When the unspecialized job calls for the exercise of a combination of several diverse skills, the employee chosen is likely to be a Jack-of-all-trades, not highly skilled in any of them. Specialization of such a job into tasks each of which calls for but one type of skill makes possible the employment of highly skilled workers to replace the all-round worker used on the unspecialized job.

It is a mistake to assume that labor specialization is necessarily a process of replacing skilled workers with unskilled ones. From the management standpoint it is essentially a business problem. When breakdown of a job results in tasks suited to unskilled workers, management usually finds it profitable to man these operations from this broader labor market. When the new job specifications call for continuous employment of skill by the workers, management will seek the most skillful applicants because it is profitable to do so.

Essentially it is a matter of economical use of labor and the wage dollar. Usually the greatest gain is to be had by defining tasks in terms of labor capacity and availability, the right job for the right man.

*Effects of Specialization on Wage Rates and Earnings.* Labor specialization has been criticized as a device of management for paying lower wages. Specialization of labor does not always mean lower wages. As has been pointed out, often it results in the utilization of more skillful, higher wage workers. Furthermore, even though less skilled operatives are used, the increased productivity of these workers often makes possible payment of higher wages to the individual than he would otherwise receive.

Low labor costs and high wage earnings are not incompatible with labor specialization.

*Risks of Equipment Specialization.* The risks inherent in equipment specialization are usually greater than those that must be dealt with in labor specialization. When a worker is specialized on one simple task, no long-time commitment is ordinarily made. The job may be discontinued or the task changed, and the operative can often change with it. When a single-purpose machine is purchased in preference to a more general-purpose mechanism, an irrevocable decision has been made. The highly specialized machine can do one job and do it superlatively well, but that is all it can do. It may be a beautifully engineered precision mechanism, highly efficient at its appointed task, but when that job is gone or substantially changed, the machine—though still strong, unworn, and accurate—is worthless. The employment of specialized plant and equipment in industry is accompanied by varying degrees of risk of change. Maximum use from the day of its installation is of great importance with the specialized machine.

*Losses and Gains from Plant and Process Specialization.* The advantages and disadvantages of plant and process specialization are essentially similar. Both are closely related to determination of product line. To produce one product in a single complete plant is the acme of the production expert's idea of efficiency. Such an ideal is rarely attainable or desirable from the profit viewpoint. The chief advantages are those which grow out of resulting simplicity: effectiveness of single-minded purpose, ease of control, applicability of other types of specialization, and the benefits that accrue therefrom. Among the disadvantages are the risks of change and the unwillingness of the consumer to adapt himself to the dictates of ultra efficiency in processing. From the standpoint of the market and its financial implications, putting all the eggs in one basket may place a tremendous stress on that one basket, to say nothing of the strain of eternal vigilance on the part of management. Specialization has its drawbacks.

*Two Common Types of Management Specialization.* In the field of management personnel, specialization is essentially a problem of basis and degree. Fundamentally, there are two bases upon which management may be subdivided to accomplish specialization: (1) functions to be performed or (2) areas of responsibility with little restriction as to functions. The diagram

**EXHIBIT 1**

Zones of Authority in Line and Functional Types of Management

| | Line Type | | | | | Functional Type | | | |
|---|---|---|---|---|---|---|---|---|---|
| | Foundry | Forge | Machine Shop | Assembly | | Foundry | Forge | Machine Shop | Assembly |
| Purchasing | XXXXXXX | XXXX | XXXX | XXXXXX | Purchasing | xxxxx | xxxxx | xxxxx | xxxxx |
| Planning | XXXXXXX | XXXX | XXXX | XXXXXX | Planning | xxxxx | xxxxx | xxxxx | xxxxx |
| Scheduling | XXXXXXX | XXXX | XXXX | XXXXXX | Scheduling | xxxxx | xxxxx | xxxxx | xxxxx |
| Inspection | XXXXXXX | XXXX | XXXX | XXXXXX | Inspection | xxxxx | xxxxx | xxxxx | xxxxx |
| Labor Control | XXXXXXX | XXXX | XXXX | XXXXXX | Labor Control | xxxxx | xxxxx | xxxxx | xxxxx |
| Maintenance | XXXXXXX | XXXX | XXXX | XXXXXX | Maintenance | xxxxx | xxxxx | xxxxx | xxxxx |

shown in Exhibit 1 is a simple means of demonstrating these two bases of specializing management.

In a plant consisting of a foundry, a forge shop, a machine shop, and an assembly shop, the following functions, among others, are performed: purchasing, planning, scheduling, inspection, labor control, and maintenance. The departmental subdivisions—foundry, forge, machine shop, and assembly shop— are divisions in terms of plant areas. Purchasing, planning, scheduling, inspection, labor control, and maintenance are management functions which must be discharged within each plant area.

*The Line Type of Management Specialization.* The job of managing the complete enterprise may be broken down in two ways. If the breaking down is to be in terms of plant areas, an executive, likely to be called the foundry superintendent, is placed in charge of the foundry. His job is to supervise all the functions—purchasing, planning, scheduling, inspection, and so forth—within the foundry department. He is responsible for all these activities, but only to the extent that they are carried on within his departmental area, the foundry. Another executive, the forge shop superintendent, has a like task within the confines of the forge shop and is responsible for all functions within that departmental area. A machine shop superintendent has a similar responsibility within the machine shop, and the assembly division superintendent within his area. These four superintendents are specialists: a foundry management specialist, a forge shop specialist, a machine shop specialist, and an assembly division specialist. None of them is a specialist in terms of the six functions portrayed in Exhibit 1: purchasing, planning, scheduling, inspection, labor control, maintenance. They are specialists in terms of plant areas only. The vertical $x$ lines in the diagram show the zones of authority in this type of specialization, which is commonly spoken of as *line type* of organization in business management.

Exhibit 2 shows the same division of responsibility and authority in the more common organization chart form.

*The Functional Type of Management Specialization.* A second method of specializing the job of managing this enterprise is to use the functions performed in the various departments as the basis for breaking down the task of management. An executive, called the purchasing agent, is placed in charge of purchasing activities for all four departments of the plant. He is responsible for effective purchasing for the foundry, the forge shop, the machine shop, and the assembly division. His function is purchasing, and it cuts across all plant department lines and is coextensive with the limits of the enterprise as a whole. Planning is similarly specialized. One executive is charged with the responsibility of effecting all planning for all departments: foundry, forge, machine, and assembly. Another executive is similarly in charge of all scheduling. A chief inspector is in charge of inspection in all four departments. A personnel manager is given responsibility for personnel control without limitation as to depart-

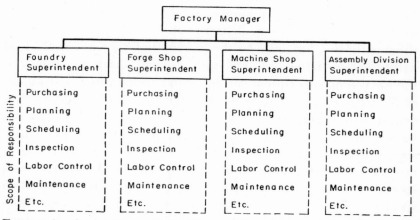

EXHIBIT 2.   ORGANIZATION CHART SHOWING LINE TYPE OF SPECIALIZATION OF MANAGEMENT.

mental lines, and similarly maintenance for the entire plant becomes the responsibility of a chief engineer. Such division is in terms of functions performed rather than in terms of plant areas, and is commonly spoken of as the functional type of organization. The horizontal $x$ lines in the right half of Exhibit 1 show the zones of authority in this type of management specialization.

Exhibit 3 is an organization chart showing management specialization on the basis of function.

*The Place of the Staff Executive in Management Specialization.* These are the two basic types of management specialization: line type, where the subdivision is essentially a matter of plant areas, and functional type, where specialization is in terms of functions to be performed. A third situation exists when in a line organization a functional specialist acts in a purely advisory capacity either to his senior executive or to junior executives, or both.  Such an advisory specialist is usually referred to as a staff officer and is one of the essential elements in the line and staff type of organization.

*Determination of Basis and Degree of Management Specialization.*  Selection of the proper basis of management specialization and the degree to which such specialization can be most advantageously carried are organization problems of utmost importance.

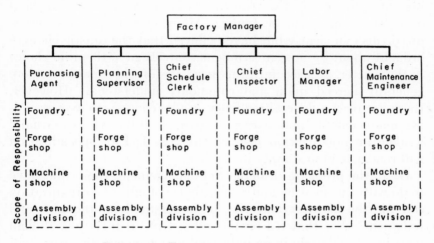

EXHIBIT 3.  FUNCTIONAL-TYPE ORGANIZATION.

There is no one best form of management organization applicable to all businesses, nor will any one form of organization continue indefinitely to be best suited to any one business.  In modern management some degree of specialization is practically always necessary.

The extensive state and Federal labor legislation of the 1930's and 1940's has practically forced an increase in specialization of labor management.  Governmental regulation in the form of new laws and their administrative interpretations (sometimes conflicting) has put the knowledge and understanding required for intelligent and safe compliance beyond the time and experience scope of most foremen and supervisors.  Thus it has become common to place the responsibility for labor management in the hands of specialists.  In some companies labor management itself has been subdivided, and not infrequently companies have specialized labor relations managers, personnel directors, employ-ment directors, and training directors.  This forced specialization has often yielded the common advantage of more expert perform-ance of each of the subdivisions.  At the same time it has too frequently been accompanied by an unfortunate isolation of parts which are essentially one whole and, what is even more serious, by the divorcing of labor relations from the line operat-ing functions where the true causes of worker satisfaction and dissatisfaction are to be found.  Many executives have recog-nized this evil clearly but have believed that the drastic changes brought about by new government controls gave them no choice in the matter, at least until the new rules of the game were more generally agreed upon and commonly understood.  However, there has been a general tendency in this country to overspecial-ize management, and excessive specialization will eventually weaken an organization just as surely as lack of specialization will render it immediately ineffective.

Of all the problems of industrial management, those that have to do with the creation and maintenance of effective organization call for the greatest maturity of understanding, thought, and judgment.  For that reason the subject of organization, though usually treated early in an industrial management discourse, will be deferred until late in this volume.  It is hoped that discussion of some of the varied problems of the industrial executive may serve as preparation to the solution of issues that have to do with the building up of effective executive organization.

*Specialization, the First Principle of Modern Industry.*  With-out prejudice, it would seem that one might say that specializa-tion pervades modern industry.  Sometimes it is in one field or function; usually in many.  Specialization produces good results and bad.  The outcome is largely the result of relationships pe-culiar to each individual case.  The creation and maintenance of relationships which bring about good results are tasks of man-agement.  And management in the fulfillment of these functions finds it expedient to call to its aid one of the very forces it seeks to control, specialization.

## QUESTIONS

1. Explain how decline in volume of business of the Lewiston Transport Company had adversely affected the company's utilization of its equipment.

2. "The detailing of a foreman to give his entire time to the loading, dispatching, and routing of trucks was an excellent example of modern practice in the matter of management specialization."

    *a.* Explain the meaning of this statement.

    *b.* How did management specialization tend to offset the adverse effect of decreasing volume of business on equipment utilization in this case?

3. What is meant by functional specialization of management? Illustrate.

4. Explain and illustrate the line type of management specialization.

5. Is a staff officer a functional specialist? Explain by means of an illustration.

6. Draw an organization chart for a company having the same major plant departments and management functions as are shown in Exhibit 1. Break down the labor control function into three parts: industrial relations, personnel management, and employment. Show these three and purchasing as if they were organized functionally. Show other activities as organized on a line basis. Use the type of organization chart shown in Exhibits 2 and 3. If correctly drawn, your chart will show the type of management organization known as *line and staff,* a combination of functional organization with line organization.

7. In the case of the Lewiston Transport Company, how did the use of specialized equipment (tractors and trailers) make labor specialization possible?

8. What are some of the advantages and disadvantages of

    *a.* Process specialization?

    *b.* Equipment specialization?

    *c.* Plant specialization?

9. Upon what basis were the jobs in this company's garage specialized?

10. Of what importance is volume of work in determining a satisfactory degree of specialization? Illustrate with reference to labor specialization in the garage of this company.

11. Explain how the use of spare parts and assemblies was of advantage in the labor specialization program. What disadvantage did this plan have?

12. Explain why motor valve grinding was relatively costly in the shop of the Lewiston Transport Company.

13. How does the worker react to specialization? Explain.

14. What is the meaning of the term "specialization"?

## TAYLOR ELECTRICAL COMPANY

The production manager of the Taylor Electrical Company was considering three methods of making 50 base plates. The first of these methods, hand production, required no investment in equipment, but did call for the employment of skilled workmen at a relatively high wage rate. The second method involved the use of dies adaptable to more than one purpose and relatively low-rate, semiskilled workers for machine operation. If this method was employed, a certain amount of skilled workmanship would be required to finish the base plates. The third method under consideration included the utilization of special-purpose dies which could be used only to execute this one design. This method required no skilled workmanship in the manufacture of the part and needed only the services of a low-wage machine operative.

The Taylor Electrical Company manufactured small electric motors. Most of its output was of standard design. Parts were manufactured and assembled, and the finished products placed in stock. Shipments were made from this finished goods inventory.

One of the most successful numbers in the company's line was a small induction motor used in electrical phonographs. During a five-year period, sales of these motors had averaged 8,000 per year, although the demand had fallen off in the last two years. Company engineers believed that a redesigning of the mechanism was necessary.

When a new product had been designed or an old one redesigned, the plans and specifications were submitted to the sales department for criticism, after which they were turned over to the production manager. He checked the plant equipment to make sure that the company had the required machines to manufacture the article, and had the tool designer design whatever tools, dies, jigs, gauges, and the like were required for production. When these designs were completed, they were submitted to the production manager, who prepared estimates of the equipment cost and the total cost to manufacture.

The redesigned phonograph motor required a new base plate. The designing department and production manager decided that 50 of these should be made. If they were found satisfactory, it was expected that 8,000 would be required the first year and that this volume would be manufactured in four lots of 2,000 each.

There were three methods of making the initial lot of 50 base plates:

1. They could be made from sheet steel by hand.

2. They could be stamped out on a press using blanking dies, and then finished by hand.

3. They could be stamped out complete on a press using permanent dies.

To make the 50 plates by hand would require 50 hours of labor at a cost of $1.50 per hour.

If blanking dies were used, the cost of the dies would be $50. It would cost $4 for labor to operate the punch press and dies, and there would be an additional labor cost of $25 for finishing the stamped blanks.

If the new design was satisfactory, these blanking dies could be reworked at a cost of from $150 to $175 to make permanent dies. The exact cost of completing the blanking dies to make permanent dies would depend on whether or not any changes were made in the proposed design after the new motors were tried out. The life of blanking dies would be the same as that of permanent dies, 100,000 pieces.

The third possibility was to make permanent dies to begin with and stamp the plates out complete in one press operation. If this was done, the cost of dies would be $200 and the labor charge for punching out 50 plates would be $4. The permanent dies would have a life of 100,000 plates.

Which of the three methods should the production manager adopt for the manufacture of the trial order of 50 base plates?

1. Hand manufacture

2. Use of blanking dies possessing a fairly wide range of usefulness

3. Use of special-purpose, permanent dies whose usefulness would be limited to the one design of base plate

## Problem 5

## A. O. SMITH CORPORATION

One of the major products of the A. O. Smith Corporation was automobile frames. These frames were automatically assembled from pressed steel side bars and cross members with malleable-iron or forged-steel fittings such as spring hangers. The assembled parts were automatically riveted in place, after which the frame was spray-painted and shipped or stored for future delivery. An example of the extent to which the company had succeeded in automatizing these operations in the face of varying demand is found in the methods used in the machining of spring hangers.

The malleables or forgings from which the A. O. Smith Corporation made spring hangers required several types of machining operations: milling, drilling, reaming, and tapping. A single job might require one or more of these operations repeated several times, a total of 10 or 12 operations being not uncommon. The number and nature varied with the size and type of frame. Variation in design was intensified by the attempts of automobile manufacturers to gain favor for their respective products through improvements and innovations in spring suspension. Ball-bearing shackles, rubber mountings, and automatic and centralized lubrication systems were examples.

In choosing equipment to turn out a spring hanger, management was confronted with two sets of influences. The basic policies of the A. O. Smith Corporation demanded automatic machining of the parts. This would necessitate the design and construction of a special machine which would include all the operations of boring, milling, reaming, tapping, and the like. The machine would be so designed that when an operator placed a forging in it, the machine would automatically convey the forging to the point where the first operation would be performed. The machine would automatically perform this first operation, transport the part to the next operation, position the part, perform the operation, and send the part on to the next operation, and so on until the part was completely finished, ready for the assembly line. Such a machine would actually be an automatically coordinated combination of several drill presses and milling machines. The machine would have to be specially designed in order to get the desired combination of operations in proper sequence with automatic conveying and positioning between the several operations. Such a machine would require but a single attendant. Properly designed, it should possess the advantages characteristic of special-purpose equipment.

An alternative to the development of such an automatic machine would be the installation of standard equipment for performing the various tasks. None of the operations was uncommon and none was of a character that would require costly equipment or labor. Simple, standard machine shop equipment would do the work.

The latter method of machining frame castings did not fit into the A. O. Smith Corporation program of automatic production. It did, however, possess certain qualities characteristic of general-purpose equipment—it was extremely flexible in its adaptability to changes in product design, and obsolescence would be a relatively unimportant cost factor.

Neither of the two alternatives satisfied the requirements of the situation. The problem was given to the company's research engineers, and a typical A. O. Smith Corporation solution was evolved. The result was an automatic, special-purpose machine possessing the flexibility characteristic of general-purpose equipment. The new device differed from the special-purpose machine already described in one respect only: the various operating units which performed the different drilling, reaming, tapping, and milling operations were built to be interchangeable with each other on the machine base. The various operating units of the machine could be assembled for whatever number and order of operations a particular part demanded. For example, if a part called for two drilling operations to be followed by two milling operations, four additional drilling operations, two reaming operations, and two tapping operations, the necessary operating units would be assembled in that sequence above the revolving circular table which carried the part automatically from operation to operation. If the next part to be machined required a different sequence of other numbers of these operations, the standard operating units would be reassembled in the new sequence to do the work called for on the new part. Tool sizes could be varied at will within the limits of the requirements of the work. Once it was set up, the machine was as fully automatic as a special-purpose machine. In fact, it was a machine especially designed to produce automatically the one part called for. Just so long as it retained that particular setup it was so specialized that it could produce nothing else; it was strictly a single-purpose machine. But its parts could be quickly disassembled, rearranged, and re-erected in such form as to do a quite different series of tasks. This would make it a highly specialized machine designed to produce a different part until such time as its interchangeable component operating parts were again reassembled.

The machine as designed by A. O. Smith Corporation engineers was capable of machining not only spring hangers but every fitting part used in the fabrication of the auto frame. It fulfilled the requirements of equipment to be used in automatic fabrication and assembly of automobile frames, a product subject to style whims of the buying public and engineering changes in product design.

## QUESTIONS

1. Explain the advantages and disadvantages of special-purpose machines.

2. Explain the advantages and disadvantages of general-purpose machines.

3. Describe production conditions which would be suitable for each type.

4. What advantages did the machine designed by A. O. Smith Corporation engineers have over the usual special-purpose and general-purpose types of machines?

5. Explain any disadvantages this machine may have.

### Problem 6

### LEHN & FINK, INC.

Lehn & Fink, Inc., undertook, in addition to its other products, the production of a line of cosmetics. For some time manufacture of these items was controlled by the stockroom needs for each article. Later this plan was changed to make for greater specialization of process at any one time. A material increase in production efficiency resulted.

The line of cosmetics manufactured by Lehn & Fink, Inc., included several hundred items. A large number of these items were always in production although the exact ones being manufactured changed from day to day. Whenever the inventory ran low on an item, a requisition was sent from the stockroom to the production superintendent, who had the desired quantity made up.

This plan resulted in frequent short runs of each article in the factory, with much confusion and inefficiency. It was necessary at all times to carry relatively large stocks of a great number of raw materials to guard against delays in filling a stockroom requisition. The same thing was true of containers and packing materials. Inability to plan production in advance made purchasing difficult and often uneconomical. The situation made prompt delivery on orders difficult. Back orders were common. The constant change from the processing of one product to the processing of another resulted in frequent transfers of workers from job to job. Many labor hours were lost in changing work and working places and in making ready for the various runs.

An analysis of production conditions was made, and as a result many changes were effected. The new plan centered around the principle of specialization of process, and resulted in greatly increased production efficiency. Production was planned in advance and put on a two-month need cycle. Whenever an item was processed, a supply sufficient for two months' sales was made up. Thus, unless some extraordinary condition obtained, no article would be in process more than once in the two-month period. A careful study of past sales was made to determine the two-month requirement figure. This figure was adjusted by taking into consideration the probable normal increase in business and market trends of the particular item under consideration. In fixing the final figure, it was so arranged that a minimum supply of three weeks' sales requirements would be on hand at the low stock point.

On the basis of this stock schedule, a manufacturing schedule was constructed. The sequence of production of the various items was determined from the stockroom records. Each month, the stockroom made up an inventory report and sent it to the production superintendent. Those items which were lowest in the inventory were put into production first. This procedure provided the flexibility necessary to obtain the essential correlation between production and sales. While the production sequence was always planned a month in advance, it varied from period to period to conform to market demands.

After the monthly production schedules were fixed, purchasing schedules were set up. These were planned so as to have the material on hand 10 days prior to the production date, and they included a minimum emergency supply sufficient to process three weeks' demand for the item. Container and packing material purchases were controlled in the same manner. The purchasing department followed up the purchase requisition to make sure that the proper amounts of the desired raw materials and supplies would be on hand when needed.

In the production of each item, the process was divided into simple operations. An operative performed but one operation at a time, with all materials being delivered to the worker. It was found possible to give each operative the type of work for which he or she showed the greatest aptitude.

As a result of the careful preplanning and specialization of the production processes, it was found possible to rearrange the layout of the plant in such a manner as to eliminate much nonproductive time and motion.

After the new methods had become well established and minor readjustments effected, a careful check was made on the efficiency of the department under the new specialized type of processing. It was found that the changes had brought about remarkable economies, and the output of the department indicated that it was at least 200 per cent more efficient than it had been prior to the establishment of the new system.

## QUESTIONS

1. Changes in processing methods outlined in this case are reported to have resulted in remarkable economies. ". . . the output of the department indicated that it was at least 200 per cent more efficient than it had been prior to the establishment of the new system." This increase in "efficiency" may have meant either that the output of the department for one month had increased without a comparable increase in costs of producing the output, or that the monthly output had remained the same but that the costs of producing that output had been less. In either case, unit cost, the cost of producing a single unit, was lowered. Analyze this situation to show specifically what caused the increase in efficiency.

2. Insofar as your knowledge of this business permits you to do so, list in detail the items of cost which would have been incurred in the cosmetics department during a period of one month.

3. Segregate these cost items under three headings: direct labor, raw materials, burden. Classify as direct labor only those labor costs which result from work done directly on the product itself; for example, wages paid to workers engaged in compounding the raw materials, in tending machines which fill containers with the cosmetics, or in labeling the containers. Do not include in this classification such wages as those paid to inspectors, to supervisors, and to people engaged in transporting the work between the various steps of the process, since these employees are not engaged in working directly on the product itself. Under the second heading, raw materials, list all the raw materials which enter into the finished product. If the amount of a raw material used in a given lot is so small that it would be difficult to determine the exact amount which would enter into that lot, do not include it in this classification. Coloring matter used in the cosmetics might be an example of such an item. Do not list supplies which do not themselves enter into the finished product. Examples of this latter type are lubricating oils used on the

machines and cleaning solutions used in washing bottles and jars. In the third classification, burden, include all items not listed as direct labor or materials.  This three-group classification of costs is commonly used in business.  It provides a useful basis for considering the effects of changes in operating methods upon unit production costs.

4. In the case of the cosmetics department of Lehn & Fink, Inc., the amount of increase in output per dollar of costs incurred on a monthly basis is not the most desirable way of measuring the results of changes in production methods.  Changes in the items manufactured during the one month as compared with the other might make such a measurement valueless.  Better procedure would be to compare the unit cost of producing each item of which a manufacturing lot was turned out with the unit cost of producing that item under the old conditions.  This comparison can be readily effected if cost sheets for the two manufacturing lots, one to show costs on the old basis of operation and one on the new, are available.  The cost sheets on page 72 illustrate the value of such a comparison as a means of judging managerial action.

What are the various advantages to Lehn & Fink, Inc., of compiling in cost sheet form as illustrated the costs of processing each lot of each product turned out in the cosmetics division?

5. What seems to be a typical effect of increasing the length of run (size of lot) of a given product upon (a) labor costs, (b) raw materials costs, and (c) burden costs?

6. What would you say are the advantages of process specialization, and what disadvantageous tendencies must be guarded against?

7. In what respects is process specialization related to labor specialization and to large-scale production?

Cosmetics Department, Cost Sheet, Item 46.   Lot 922
(Prior to process reorganization)

| Operation | Labor | Materials | Burden |
|---|---|---|---|
| Compounding.............................. | $ 40 | $140 | $ 34 |
| Filling Containers......................... | 54 | 139 | 50 |
| Labeling................................ | 12 | 32 | 11 |
| Packing................................. | 65 | 120 | 59 |
| Total............................... | $171 | $431 | $154 |
| Labor.................................. | $171 | .... | .... |
| Materials............................... | 431 | .... | .... |
| Burden................................. | 154 | .... | .... |
| Total Cost to Produce This Lot........... | $756 | .... | .... |

Number of Units Packed and O.K.'d by Inspector....................... 2,400
Cost, per Unit, to Produce............................................. $.315

Cosmetics Department, Cost Sheet, Item 46.   Lot 1141
(After process reorganization)

| Operation | Labor | Materials | Burden |
|---|---|---|---|
| Compounding.............................. | $ 360 | $1,410 | $ 308 |
| Filling Containers......................... | 490 | 1,390 | 420 |
| Labeling................................ | 110 | 320 | 94 |
| Packing................................. | 580 | 1,200 | 518 |
| Total............................... | $1,540 | $4,320 | $1,340 |
| Labor.................................. | $1,540 | ...... | ...... |
| Materials............................... | 4,320 | ...... | ...... |
| Burden................................. | 1,340 | ...... | ...... |
| Total Cost to Produce This Lot........... | $7,200 | ...... | ...... |

Number of Units Packed and O.K.'d by Inspector....................... 24,000
Cost, per Unit, to Produce............................................. $.30

# CHAPTER IV

## SIMPLIFICATION

### JANTZEN KNITTING MILLS

**1. A Company Simplifies Its Line, Thereby Lowering Production Costs, and at the Same Time Increases Its Volume of Output.**

The Jantzen Knitting Mills manufactured a variety of knit goods. At one time the company management, wishing to lower production costs in the interest of selling a greater volume of output, adopted the policy of eliminating certain items from the company's line. This simplification practice was carried to the extent of eliminating all items with the exception of swim suits, and these were produced in a few excellently styled numbers for which there was great market demand.

As a result of this program, costs of production were reduced, largely through specialization and intensive utilization of production facilities.

**2. The Ramifications of Specialization.** We have seen specialization as an essential principle of production management. Its ramifications and diverse applications, each making its separate contribution, unite to effect gains which are greater in the composite than the total of the individual contributions of component parts. Plant specialization makes for process specialization. Process specialization makes possible the use of specialized machines and equipment. All these applications tend to further the economical use of specialized labor.

**3. The Importance of Product Specialization.** There are, however, distinct limitations to specialization within the production organism. Plant and process specialization depend rather largely upon ability to market a restricted number of types, styles, and sizes of a few articles in volume sufficient to keep a production unit of economical size busily employed. In other words, specialization in production operation requires, in considerable degree, specialization of output. While not entirely essen-

73

tial to successful specialization in mass production, product specialization is highly desirable from the standpoint of production economy.

**4. Simplification to Gain Product Specialization.** In the fight for market outlets, it has been common practice for manufacturers to widen constantly the variety of output. This has frequently resulted in very undesirable production situations, and in recent years many companies have spent much effort in the simplification of their lines. Frequently it has been found possible to simplify a company's output through the elimination of items, styles, and sizes which, upon careful analysis, have been found to have little or no profit-making possibility, direct or indirect. The effect of such simplification from the standpoint of economical production of the remaining items has sometimes been amazing.

Such was the experience of the Jantzen Knitting Mills, whose management has ascribed much of the early success of the company to a carefully conceived and consistently applied policy of simplification of a line of products, "swim suits," which in the opinion of certain executives was distinctly unsuited to such a program.

**5. The Company Eliminates All Items but Swim Suits from Its Line.** The Jantzen Knitting Mills, like other knitting companies, had in the past produced a great variety of articles, such as sweaters, coats, caps, and stockings, with swim suits a minor item in the line. For a period of years, the management, with highly satisfactory results, had been eliminating various products until the line was restricted to swim suits.

**6. Expansion of Swim-suit Volume.** In the meantime, volume of swim-suit output had rapidly increased. Over a period of seven years the company had increased its share of the country's total bathing suit business from 1 to 12 per cent. Originally no merchandise was sold outside the eleven states of the Pacific Coast region. By the time the company had completely restricted its product line to swim suits, 78 per cent of the company's business was done in the territory east of these eleven states. In addition, representatives had been established in several foreign countries.

**7. Simplification within the Swim-suit Line—How Accomplished.** During the years of rapid expansion of swim-suit volume and elimination of other articles from the company's line, drastic simplification had been practiced within the swim-suit line itself. The company had adopted the policy of restyling its line every year, and by so doing had found it possible to reduce greatly the number of patterns made each year as well as the variety of colors in which each pattern was produced. The company had developed a superior stitch with which its swim-suit fabric was knit. The exceptional elasticity of the goods thus produced had made it possible to fit correctly all customers with fewer sizes in each style and color.

**8. Make-up of the Simplified Line.** The management decided that the swim-suit line would be produced in one quality only. Thirteen sizes of 17 styles in 11 combinations of 10 colors would be manufactured. The line was to be restricted to fashionable and to fast-turning numbers. New styles were to be added only when managers were convinced that large-volume sales of new numbers would result. Old numbers were to be dropped immediately when sales volume did not reach a predetermined minimum.

**9. Effect of Simplification on Labor Cost and Equipment Investment.** Simplification of the company's product had resulted in many economies. Garment production per operative had risen steadily from 1,503 garments per operative per year to 2,715 garments per operative per year. As a result of simplification, special machines were installed for certain operations. Prior to the simplification program, a worker sewing a particular seam had turned out nine seams per hour. With a special machine for this operation, the worker with no greater effort produced 45 of these seams per hour. Another example of special installation was the purchase for $1,900 of a special press designed to operate exclusively on swim suits. Yet at the same time, the reduction in the number of types of equipment required and the more intensive utilization of each piece of equipment employed had greatly decreased the machinery and equipment investment in proportion to volume of sales. An annual output of $2,544,000 was accomplished with a total of such investment of only $100,000.

**10. Effect on Supervision.** Simplification of the company's line had made supervision much simpler, with the result that foremen and superintendents found much more time for work of a constructive nature. Indirect labor costs had thus been considerably reduced, the output per indirect worker having been increased from 16,470 garments to 17,832 garments per year.

**11. Effect on Raw Materials.** The quality of raw materials had been improved greatly. Yarn was now dyed in the wool, an improvement made possible through large purchases, since wool could be dyed economically only in lots of from 5,000 to 10,000 pounds. The utilization of fewer colors and larger volume of the standard colors thus made possible the exclusive use of dyed-in-the-wool yarns. Reduction in the number of raw material items had a further advantage in that purchasing was simplified and, therefore, more efficient. Storage, issuance, and inventory control of raw materials were much easier and less costly.

**12. Effect on Production Control and Scheduling—the Seasonal Problem.** Production scheduling was greatly simplified and made more efficient. The retail market for the company's product was confined largely to the three months, June, July, and August. Reduction of the company's line to a relatively small number of items facilitated continuous production and eliminated many of the difficulties involved in building up an inventory to meet this highly seasonal demand. If continuous production had not been maintained, it would have been necessary to enlarge the company's production facilities to take care of the great demand of the summer months. Not only would this have entailed a much larger investment in plant, machines, and equipment, but it would have meant that these facilities would have been idle a large part of each year, with the attendant disadvantages of relatively high insurance, maintenance, depreciation, interest, and other burden costs. Continuous manufacture at a relatively uniform level throughout the year brought about much more efficient utilization of plant and equipment.

It also made possible continuous employment of a skillful labor force trained to Jantzen methods and practices.

Continuous operation was considered less risky with the simplified line since experience had shown that there was much less likelihood of accumulating obsolete inventory, and smaller, better balanced stocks resulted.

**13. Other Savings from Product Simplification.** As a result of the foregoing changes, it was found possible to simplify accounting records greatly, with the result that they became more accurate and dependable as well as less costly. Simplification of the line made it easier to detect many points at which small savings could be effected. From an administrative viewpoint, the net result was a greater volume of business at a lower unit cost on a given investment of capital.

**14. Sales Department Objections to Simplification.** Considerable opposition to the simplification program had been voiced by the sales department. The theme of the argument was that since swim suits were a style good they were not suitable commodities for simplification, which tended to make for standardization. It was advanced that the customer desired a wide range of choice in selecting a garment and that if the Jantzen Knitting Mills line did not make such choice possible, the business would go to competitors.

**15. Selling Advantages of the Simplified Line.** Nevertheless, experience had convinced the management that the work of the sales department was much more efficient under the simplification program. It had been impossible for a salesman with a diversified line to concentrate on any one product. The buyer's attention had been divided by an imposing array of samples, with the result that he picked out what he considered a few bargains and let the rest go. With the simplified line, restyled each year, the salesman knew his product much better. He knew that the policy of the company permitted the centering of attention on niceties of style, appearance, and fit. The management believed that advertising was much more effective for a specific product than for a group of products. The rapidly growing extent and intensity of sales seemed an indisputable argument in favor of this position.

**16. General Results of the Program.** In announcing its decision to continue its simplification program, the management stated that, while not all the progress of the company in the preceding five years was the result of product simplification, success could in large measure be traced to adherence to that policy. It was firmly believed that each dollar worked harder under specialization and that opportunities for improvement were far from being exhausted.

**17. Summary and Conclusions.** *Simplification of Product, a Means of Attaining Product Specialization.* A company which makes a variety of products often finds it difficult to get the production economies which result from specialization. Two conditions are largely responsible for this. First, it is not likely that each item in the line can be sold in quantity sufficient to permit employing mass production methods in its manufacture. Second, the skill and effort of the management are divided among a large numbers of items, and no one of them receives maximum attention either from the standpoint of attaining the greatest possible volume of sales or from the standpoint of getting the lowest possible production costs. Thus, while the company may produce and sell a large total volume of products, it does not experience the benefits of economical mass production. Many companies have found the answer to this situation in product simplification programs.

*Limitations to Simplification.* Simplification of product line is not, however, universally possible. The nature of a product may be such that one of its greatest selling appeals is variety. Style goods and novelties are of this class. In other cases the use to which a product is put may be such as to make variety in size and in other characteristics essential if it is to satisfy the major demands of the consumer. Price is another consideration which may make variety in production unavoidable. There is a wide demand for hot water bottles. To meet that wide demand it is necessary to make the article in a variety of qualities to satisfy purchasers who wish to pay prices ranging from $0.50 to $2.50. A company making such rubber goods finds it difficult to confine itself to the production of any one quality. The market demands a variety which the retailer must supply. The distributor will buy from that producer who will furnish him with a complete line and hesitates to buy from one who will not.

Examination of the current product situation of the Jantzen Knitting Mills shows that many changes have been made during the years when the company's annual sales volume has been increased from $2,500,000 to several times that amount. The Jantzen trade-mark now appears on such diversified items as a sun-tan lotion, women's foundation garments, summer play shorts and tops for men and women, and even ski clothing. The reasons for adding each of these items to the swim-suit line differ, but in general the new items are all allied to or spring from the original product. Women's swim suits are more highly styled than they were 10 years ago. General style trends in women's wear have had an effect on this, and the development of new decorative and elastic-type fabrics has made possible the making of form control an in-built feature of many present-day swim suits. This trend made the step from women's swim suits to foundation garments for daily wear relatively easy and natural. The introduction of a separate line of foundation garments was probably motivated by a much more important influence. This was the need for a product closely allied to the modern swim suit which would have year-round demand, thus making it possible to maintain national advertising of the Jantzen name on a continuous 12-month basis. The demand season for swim suits is short. Swim suits are not easily and effectively advertised during the seasons of the year in which the consuming public has little interest in the product. National advertising is most effective when carried on continuously. Thus the sale of foundation garments provided an effective opportunity to advertise "Jantzen" month after month. It is interesting to note that the copy used for advertising Jantzen foundation wear has many of the same characteristics of the copy used for advertising swim suits. Here is a case of a company adding a product to its simplified line largely for the purpose of giving it something to advertise.

Considerations of different, though somewhat similar, nature lie behind the other items of this company's present-day product diversification. Basically they are market considerations, and universally the added products tend to fortify the major line, swim suits, rather than to detract from it or merely add another good product.

What has been the effect of this diversification on the production economies that stemmed from strict adherence to the old simplification policy? Quantitatively it is probably difficult to tell. Sales volume of swim suits has increased, thus maintaining the desired volume status of individual items in the line. This has provided the basic situation requisite for operation specialization. Increased style emphasis within the swim-suit line has thus not necessarily detracted from the production economies of specialization that existed when the company's products consisted solely of swim suits. This economical production situation has been further protected by a company policy of setting up individual, largely self-contained production units (factories) for each of its major added lines such as foundation garments. The company now operates several production units, each of which is basically specialized in the production of one type of product.

By such means as these this company seems to have succeeded in meeting the changing demands of the market and relieving the shortcomings of a very high degree of simplification. At the same time it has managed to retain the production advantages of operating specialization which commonly result from a simplified product line.

Product simplification is frequently limited by another consideration, the existing productive capacity of a company. Shifts in market demand and failure to forecast consumption correctly may leave a manufacturer with idle equipment and plant which can be utilized only by adding products to the existing line. It is, therefore, obvious that there are distinct limitations upon the ability of a company to specialize in the production of one or a few commodities. Occasionally a company will be able to simplify drastically; usually a degree of simplification will be found possible and advantageous; but there are companies making products of such a nature that simplification of output is not advisable.

*Product Standardization.*   Management has displayed much ingenuity in devising means of simplifying product lines from the standpoint of production, at the same time meeting market demand for variety.  This has been accomplished largely by designing standard parts and units which can be combined in a variety of ways to offer a diversified output.  In this way, parts and subassemblies can be produced economically on a mass basis, departure from that basis being necessary only in final assembly.

Recently the *American Machinist* featured an excellent instance of this practice.[1]  The 1948 line of the world-famous Jeep was reported to include eight distinct models:

1. Universal Jeep                   5. Panel delivery
2. Two-wheel-drive truck            6. Jeepster
3. Four-wheel-drive truck           7. Standard sedan
4. Station wagon                    8. Fire engine

Except for the Universal Jeep and the fire engine, which differed only as to equipment, these several models were quite different vehicles.  The line was to include both a four- and a six-cylinder engine.  Three different wheel bases were to be used. Bodies covered a wide range from the strictly utilitarian postwar Jeep to the style-competitive standard sedan.  No automobile manufacturer offered a wider range of vehicle types.  Yet behind this variety was a high degree of parts and components standardization.  Exhibit 1 shows something about how these eight models were to be achieved with no more than three types of any one component.  It is an excellent demonstration of American production ingenuity in having the cake while eating it: gaining the market benefits of variety in end product while keeping the production advantages of product standardization.

The principle of interchangeable parts has long been basic in American manufacture.  Not only does it make for all the advantages of mass production of the parts themselves, but it greatly reduces the cost of assembly, makes for uniformity of the finished product, and enables the user to replace parts which become worn

[1] For details, see "How the Jeep Donned Civvies" by Delmar G. Roos, vice-president in charge of engineering, Willys-Overland Motors, Inc., *American Machinist,* Vol. 92, No. 1, Jan. 1, 1948.

## EXHIBIT 1

### Eight Jeep Models with No More than Three Types of Standard Components

| Component | Jeep and Fire Engine | Two-wheel-drive Truck | Four-wheel-drive Truck | Station Wagon | Panel Delivery | Jeep-ster | Station Sedan |
|---|---|---|---|---|---|---|---|
| Front Axle | A | B | A | C | C | C | C |
| Rear Axle | A | B | B | C | C | C | C |
| Front Brakes | A | B | B | C | C | C | C |
| Rear Brakes | A | B | B | C | C | C | C |
| Wheels | A | B | B | C | C | C | C |
| Clutch | A | B | B | B | B | B | B |
| Engine | A | A | A | A | A | A | B |
| Transmission | A | B | A | C | C | C | C |
| Generator and Regulator | A | A | A | A | A | A | A |
| Starter | A | B | B | B | B | B | B |
| Light Switch | A | B | B | B | B | B | B |
| Dimmer Switch | A | A | A | A | A | A | A |
| Head and Parking Lights | A | A | A | A | A | A | A |
| Tail and Stop Lights | A | B | B | C | C | C | C |
| Batteries | A | A | A | A | A | A | A |
| Distributors | A | B | B | B | B | B | C |
| Instruments | A | B | B | B | B | B | B |
| Radiator Grid | A | B | B | B | B | B | B |
| Bonnet | A | B | B | B | B | B | B |
| Front Fenders | A | B | B | B | B | B | B |
| Rear Fenders | A | B | B | C | C | B | C |
| Cowl | A | B | B | B | B | B | B |
| Dash Assembly | A | B | B | B | B | C | C |
| Windshield Assembly | A | B | B | B | B | C | B |
| Front Door Assemblies | A | B | B | B | B | C | B |
| Forward Floor Stampings | A | B | B | B | B | B | B |
| Chassis | A | B | B | C | C | C | C |
| Gas Tank | A | A | A | A | A | A | A |
| Front Suspension | A | B | A | B | B | B | B |
| Steering Gear | A | A | A | A | A | A | A |

\* The different types of each component are designated by the letters A, B, and C.

in use without the necessity of replacing the entire article. In so designing parts that they can be assembled in different ways to produce a varied line, management has simply extended the principle of interchangeable parts.

In recent years reduction of product variety to a few standard specifications has gone far beyond the efforts of individual companies. Many products have been uniformly simplified by all, or the major portion of, the producers in an industry to conform to a standard variety for the industry as a whole. In the main, two influences have been responsible for this condition. One of the outstanding limitations to simplification of an individual company's line has been willingness of competitors to cater to, in fact sometimes to create, a market desire for variety. In cases where the industry is made up of a relatively small number of large producers it has sometimes been found possible for these manufacturers to cooperate in a general simplification of the lines they produce by agreeing upon certain standards of product to which all conform. In this way an industry can sometimes simplify when one producer alone would be at a serious disadvantage in doing so. A more universal cause of cooperative simplification in terms of standards has been the tremendous growth in industrial interdependence. Items such as bolts, nuts, and machine screws have a wide general demand. Some years ago, largely at the insistence of customers, producers of these articles standardized the sizes and specifications of the product and effected thereby large economies for both themselves and their customers. To the producers the move meant greatly simplified lines and thereby much lower production costs. The consumer gained the advantage of a widened source of supply with greater ease of purchasing. He also found this standardization a great advantage in the designing of his own products.

*Examples of Simplification and Standardization.* In the United States, simplification and standardization have attained the proportions of a movement. The development has been fostered by the Bureau of Standards of the U.S. Department of Commerce, which has provided the machinery for cooperative effort whenever an industry has seen fit to consider standardization. A wide variety of items have been simplified and standardized, the degree of reduction in varieties ranging upward as high as 98 per cent.[2]

The American Engineering Standards Committee is authority for the following statement:

Standardization is today the most important approach to greater industrial efficiency. Actual savings that are now being made in the automobile industry through organized standardization activities are estimated by the industry itself at $750,000,000 a year.

*Social Criticism of Product Standardization.* Social criticism has long been leveled at the practice of production standardization. No attempt will be made here to uphold either side of this argument. Opponents of the practice maintain that it has an adverse effect upon standards of living in that it tends to cast American life into a single mold and thereby dull the imagination, individuality, and initiative of the people. Proponents of simplification and standardization insist that the result has been

[2] The following examples of simplification and standardization practice are taken from *Recent Economic Changes,* Vol. I, pp. 117–118, McGraw-Hill Book Company, Inc., New York, 1929, which lists almost 100 items.

| Item | Reductions in Varieties | | Percentage Reduction |
|---|---|---|---|
| | From | To | |
| Face Brick, Rough and Smooth............ | 75 | 2 | 97 |
| Common Brick....................... | 44 | 1 | 98 |
| Hollow Building Tile (first revision)........ | 36 | 20 | 44 |
| Paint and Varnish Brushes............... | 480 | 143 | 70 |
| Tacks and Nails: | | | |
| Sizes............................... | 421 | 182 | 57 |
| Packing Weights..................... | 423 | 121 | 71 |
| Shovels, Spades, and Scoops (first revision).. | 5,136 | 2,178 | 57 |
| Staple Vitreous-china Plumbing Fixtures.... | 441 | 58 | 87 |
| Solid Section Steel Windows.............. | 42,877 | 2,244 | 95 |
| Woven Wire Fencing.................... | 552 | 69 | 87 |
| Beds, Springs, and Mattresses............ | 78 | 4 | 95 |
| Milk Bottle Caps (first revision).......... | 10 | 1 | 90 |
| Hospital and Institutional Cotton Textiles.. | 575 | 26 | 95 |
| Files and Rasps........................ | 1,351 | 475 | 65 |
| Grinding Wheels (first revision)........... | 715,200 | 254,400 | 64 |
| Range Boilers.......................... | 130 | 13 | 90 |
| Brass Lavatory and Sink Traps............ | 1,114 | 76 | 93 |
| Cotton Duck (first revision).............. | 460 | 86 | 81 |
| Binders' Board........................ | 718 | 10 | 98 |

a great lowering in the cost of consumables and a tremendous increase in the number and variety of necessities and luxuries available to the average citizen. They point to the relatively high standard of living in this country as evidence. It is rather obvious that some articles are much better suited to standardization than others. It is not likely that there are many objections to the standardization of machine bolts and wood screws. On the other hand, the result of standardizing a style good is all too plainly evidenced in the vast number of women's hats of one or a few extreme fashions which make their appearance yearly. Fortunately, each plague is of short duration, which leads us to one aspect of the standardization controversy all too frequently overlooked.

*The American Policy.* It is probably true that in the past a purchaser of an article which is selected on the basis of style, suitability, or aesthetic fitness has found a relatively small variety from which to choose in the American market as compared with the English market. This condition has existed, however, only as regards one instant of time. If the varieties of such an article in the English and American markets were catalogued over a period of five or even three years, the chances are very much in favor of a greater variety in America. The reason for this is to be found very largely in the typical American demand for change. The American producer senses this demand, makes changes frequently, and confines himself to a relatively restricted line at any one time. In analyzing the social significance of specialization and standardization, it would therefore seem necessary to consider rate of change in product design as well as variety at a given time.

*Gains from Simplification.* The American producer has laid out his simplification course, it would seem, largely in terms of economies of production. The first of these, obviously, is intensification of the benefits of specialization: lower labor cost; more complete and intensive utilization of capital invested in plant, machines, and equipment; lower unit costs of supervision. To this first effect must be added, if the experience of the Jantzen Knitting Mills is a guide, better raw materials, less costly purchasing and closer raw materials control, better correlation be-

tween the functions of production and marketing, more effective
control of manufactured product inventory, less inventory risk,
more effective selling and advertising, and simpler, more accurate, and more usable records. Other gains have been pointed
out in detail throughout the case.

*Simplification and Standardization in a Mass Production Pro-
gram.* Thus, the reasons for the accelerating momentum of simplification and standardization in our modern production program must be fully apparent. Likewise, the limitations and
disadvantages can easily be seen and understood. The social
significance of the movement is much less easily readable. Obviously, any economic, managerial, or social study of present-day
industry must treat of specialized and standardized products as
part and parcel of mass production, that industrial concept for
which this nation is world-known.

## QUESTIONS

1. What is the objective of simplification?

2. What advantages resulted from the simplification of the
line of products of the Jantzen Knitting Mills? Be prepared to
explain each.

3. In general, what limitations are there to the simplification
policy? Explain how Jantzen's experience of the past few years
illustrates some of these.

4. How did Willys-Overland Motors, Inc., get variety into its
1948 product line and at the same time gain much of the advantage that comes from product line simplification?

5. What are the advantages to the producer and the consumer
of products made up of standard, interchangeable parts?

6. Are there any disadvantages? Explain.

7. What conditions might cause a company to foster product
standardization for an entire industry?

8. What are the gains and losses to producers which result from
product simplification and standardization for an entire industry?

## GOLDEN CROWN MANUFACTURING COMPANY

The Golden Crown Manufacturing Company of Chicago, Illinois, made and sold men's and boys' shirts. The company was large. It operated 15 factories located in Minnesota and Illinois. It had three sales subsidiaries, each of which sold dress and sports shirts to retailers throughout the United States. Each subsidiary had its own brand, which it advertised nationally. The Chicago office of the parent company sold shirts to chain store and mail order companies, to wholesalers, and for export. At a meeting of the Board of Directors in June, 1948, it was proposed to consolidate the three sales subsidiaries and to make all sales to retailers under a single brand name and discontinue sales to mail order and chain store houses.

Although the shirt business had always been highly competitive, the Golden Crown Manufacturing Company had been profitable and had grown rapidly during the 20 years of its existence until it had become one of the five largest manufacturers of men's shirts. Originally the company's products had been sold exclusively through wholesalers. The company brought out a new line of shirts for wholesalers twice each year. There were never more than 24 different styles in a line, and approximately half of these were in plain white and solid color standard fabrics which did not change from season to season. The other numbers in the wholesale line were conservative patterns in woven and printed designs, mostly stripes. These were changed each season. There were no high-style or novelty items in the company's wholesale line.

The company expanded its sales by the purchase over a period of five years of three smaller shirt companies, each of which sold to retailers. Each sales subsidiary had its own sales force, its own line of shirts, and its own national brand name. One subsidiary made shirts that sold at retail within a price range of

$1.69 to $3.25. Another sold shirts in the price range of $2.95 to $5. The third sold highly styled shirts that were priced at retail from $3.25 to $7.50. The three subsidiaries sold in the same territories. Not infrequently two subsidiaries sold to the same store. A few large department stores bought from all three companies, the low-priced line being purchased for basement departments and the other two for the upstairs men's furnishing departments. Golden Crown salesmen commonly offered a new line to wholesalers about six weeks earlier than subsidiary salesmen offered new lines to retailers. Both wholesale and retail salesmen made two selling trips a year and were on the road for about eight weeks each trip. Retail salesmen sometimes made a third selling trip lasting only three or four weeks. A retail sales line consisted of about twice as many styles as the wholesale line. A large number of these styles were semifancies, fancies, and novelties. The subsidiary selling the highest priced line included the largest number of high-style and novelty items. Although the three retail lines contained a large assortment of style goods, more than 60 per cent of their sales of shirts consisted of standard items that changed infrequently: white and solid color broadcloth, white oxfords, and plain stripes, both printed and woven. Each season there was some duplication of fabrics in the lines of the three subsidiaries, although each had its own designers and fabric buyers who competed actively with one another to produce unique and superior designs that would have strong selling appeal.

The parent company sold large orders of standard styles of shirts to chain store and mail order organizations. While there were only a few of these customers, total sales to them were large and constituted about one-third of the company's total volume. These sales were made by executives in the home office and no salesmen's commissions were paid on them. The customers specified the styles, which were limited to a few numbers.

Production at all the factories was controlled by the home offices. In allotting work to the factories, effort was made to keep all plants always operating at or near capacity and to provide plants with an approximately equal balance of long runs on standard items and shorter runs of fancy shirts. Some of the factories were small and some were large, and it was difficult to provide all plants with an equally desirable combination of large and small production orders. Factory managers disliked small orders because it necessitated rearranging the work of machine operators frequently, and much time was lost before the workers became accustomed to new tasks and could work at top speed. A large number of small production orders in a factory at one time complicated the work of factory supervision.

The proposal to consolidate the three sales subsidiaries and to discontinue sales to mail order and chain store houses came at a time when the company was operating all factories at capacity and still was unable to meet customers' demands for shirts. The discussion was precipitated when quarterly operating statements were being examined by the Board of Directors. These showed that the margin of difference between cost of production and selling price of a shirt sold to a mail order or chain store organization was not over half the comparable figure for a shirt sold to a wholesaler. The reports also showed that advertising costs and sales commissions of the sales subsidiaries were high and tended to reduce the net profit per shirt sold by them to a point that was below the net profit per shirt sold to wholesalers.

## QUESTIONS

1. How would adoption of the proposed change affect the company's marketing problems?

2. How would it affect the company's production problems?

3. How would the effects of the change on marketing affect production?

4. What do you think the company should do?

## Problem 8

## NIKALO SPECIALTIES COMPANY

Analysis of manufacturing costs of the Nikalo Specialties Company showed that novelty items in the company's line were not returning a profit and that on a small group of special-order items sold to college organizations losses were realized. The production manager believed that simplification of the product line would result in lower production costs for the remaining items and would also prevent recurrence of the $50,000 inventory loss realized by the company at the close of the current season. Company executives were considering the advisability of taking such action.

The Nikalo Specialties Company manufactured a line of diaries which included about 300 items. Single diaries were sold direct to individual consumers by means of magazine advertising. Banks and similar commercial enterprises purchased diaries in lots of 500 or more and used them for advertising purposes. College cooperative stores and student body associations bought special designs in larger quantities for distribution to members at the beginning of the school year. The retail trade was supplied largely through jobbers. Sales of different items in the line varied from 200 to 30,000 units per year. Business was extremely seasonal and inventory carried past the first of January was practically valueless.

Four-fifths of the sales of the year just closed were in 200 staple lines which varied little in design from year to year. The remaining one-fifth was evenly divided between a group of 100 styles which were frequently changed in the interest of novelty and a group of 12 special styles which were made up on special order for some college cooperative stores and student body associations.

For several years, production executives of the company had urged the discontinuance of novelty items. When discussing the production program for the coming year, they pointed out that the company then had on hand an inventory which had been produced during the past year at a cost of $50,000 but which, although still carried on the books of the company, was practically valueless. This inventory was about equally divided between novelty items and standard lines designed for the retail trade. The executives strongly recommended that the production of the current year be limited to the 200 staple lines.

The sales manager objected to the proposal to eliminate the novelty styles and suggested that, if the number of items in the line was to be reduced, sales to college organizations be discontinued. Competition for these large orders was very keen and the profit margin on them was relatively small.

To support the argument for discontinuance of novelty lines and retention of the large college orders, production executives prepared figures covering the cost of production for the year just ended. These figures follow in summary form.

|  | College Lines Sold, Cost to Manufacture | Novelty Lines Sold, Cost to Manufacture |
|---|---|---|
| Labor.............. | $ 30,000 | $ 50,000 † |
| Materials............ | 30,000 | 30,000 |
| Burden............. | 40,000 * | 20,000 |
| Total.............. | $100,000 | $100,000 |

\* College lines were produced in relatively large volume which made possible much use of the company's machines and equipment.

† Novelty items were made in small lots and therefore entailed a relatively high hand-labor cost.

These figures were supplemented by the following estimates prepared from the operating statement of the same year by the sales department.

|  | College Lines | Novelty Lines |
|---|---|---|
| Sales........................... | $120,000 | $130,000 |
| Cost to Manufacture Goods Sold... | 100,000 * | 100,000 * |
| Gross Margin.................. | $ 20,000 | $ 30,000 |
| Selling and Administrative Expense | 25,000 | 30,000 |
| Net Profit or Loss................. | $  5,000 (Loss) | $     0 |

\* See preceding table for details of manufacturing costs.

## QUESTIONS

1. Should the Nikalo Specialties Company simplify its line of products? Give your reasons.

2. In your opinion, which of the two lines (college goods or novelty items) might better be eliminated? Explain your reasons.

3. What are the meanings of the terms labor, materials, and burden as they appear in the statement of costs? From the standpoint of elimination of a class of product from the company's line, what is the significance of the proportion of each of these three classes of costs to the total cost of making that class of product?

# CHAPTER V

## STANDARDIZATION

### BEAUTY PREPARATIONS, INC.

## 1. A Company Effects Production Economies by Standardizing Job Methods.

The planning department of Beauty Preparations, Inc., producer of cosmetics, was making a detailed study of factory operations in an effort to reduce production costs. Each job was studied to determine in minute detail just how it should be performed, and once a satisfactory method was devised, it was reduced to writing as a basis for future performance. Prior to the setting up of standard methods of performing the work, every job study involved consideration and standardization of raw materials used, tools and appliances required, machine speeds and feeds, and working conditions. Standard methods of performance so devised had been found a very successful means of reducing costs.

## 2. General Applicability of the Standardization Principle.
Simplification of product lines and concentration on a restricted predetermined variety of output is but one common application of the principle of standardization as found in industry. Standardization may be extended to all factors in the production process. Raw materials are purchased on standard specifications as to form, size, and quality. All progressive manufacturers define standards of similar scope, which are regularly applied and maintained for all work in process. Inspection without standards is of little value. In attempting to attain standard results, working conditions such as temperature, light, and humidity are often standardized. If standard results are to be attained, proper means and methods of work must be employed. Tools, equipment, setup methods, operating methods, operation time schedules, and the speeds, feeds, and cuts of machines all present essential fields for the application of standardization if predetermined results are to be obtained.

Like specialization, standardization is pervasive. As is true of specialization also, its varied applications are interrelated and interdependent. It matters little which of its usual uses one considers first, for the implications in any one endeavor are early apparent and must be understood if any evaluation of the application is to be sound. The following experience of Beauty Preparations, Inc., bears testimony to that effect.

**3. Nature of a Job to Be Standardized.** Beauty Preparations, Inc., produced face creams, lotions, and similar cosmetics. The planning department was making a detailed study of all jobs in the plant. One of the first jobs studied was that of pasting labels on cosmetic bottles by machine.

The task was simple and required little skill. After bottles were filled and washed, they were brought by hand truck to a department in which they were labeled and packed. The operative of a labeling machine picked up a bottle from the hand truck, inserted it in the machine, and withdrew it when the label was affixed. An inspector made certain that labels were straight and in their proper position, after which bottles were packed for shipment.

**4. Causes of Variation in Method of Doing the Work.** As a first step in the study of machine labeling, the time study engineer attempted to formulate the existing routine for doing the job. He found this impossible since the operation was rarely performed the same way twice. One cause of nonstandard routine was variation in size of the labels which were used in the same size of attaching fixture. If the label slipped in the fixture, the machine placed it on the bottle askew, and the operative had to interrupt her routine to straighten or adjust the label. This not only wasted the operative's time but caused the machine to be idle as well. Cleaning and adjusting the machine took considerable time. There was no standard way in which unlabeled bottles were brought and labeled bottles taken away. At times one truck contained the supply of unlabeled bottles and another truck received labeled bottles, although frequently one truck was used for both finished and unfinished work. Sometimes only the top shelves of trucks were used. At other times both top and lower shelves were used. Such variations made it impossible for the operative to perform her task in any uniform way. As a result, production ranged from 1,000 to 1,500 bottles a day, depending much on the number of fixture changes necessary to meet requirements of various sizes of bottles labeled and the diversity in size or design of labels.

**5. Effect of Unsuitable Equipment on Time Required for the Work.** An investigation of equipment disclosed the fact that supply trucks were too high for the operative. This necessitated an awkward upward and lateral reach, and as the supply of bottles diminished, the lateral motion became increasingly difficult unless the operative moved the truck to a more convenient position. Moving the truck took time. Three solutions for this difficulty were suggested: a new truck could be devised, fitted with a revolving turntable so that the operator could move it easily and quickly and always have bottles in a uniform position; present trucks could be remodeled with turntables and lowered to an over-all height of 30 inches from the floor; or present trucks could be lowered without further improvements.

**6. Costs of Equipment Changes in Relation to Savings to Be Effected.** To determine the best solution, time studies were made of workers using the high type of truck and workers using lowered experimental trucks. These studies were made by timing with a stop watch each move the operative made and recording these times in the form of a chart. The entire operation was timed repeatedly until the job-study man was satisfied that data sufficient for accuracy had been obtained. It was found that moving trucks took 2 per cent of the operative's time and that reaching upward took 11 per cent of her time, a total of 13 per cent unproductive time that might be saved if proper equipment were installed.

New trucks equipped with turntables would cost $1,000. If turntables were installed on present trucks, such reconstruction would necessitate 10 days' labor at $32 per day and materials amounting to $200, a total of $520. The trucks could be lowered without turntables for the relatively small cost of $48.

Total earnings of 10 labeling machine operatives would amount to approximately $8,840 per year. Eleven per cent of this amount, $972, could be saved by expending $48 to lower the height of the present trucks. To save the additional 2 per cent, $177, which was now wasted in moving the trucks, would require an added expenditure of $472 if turntables were installed on present trucks, or $952 if new turntable trucks were purchased.

The cost of lowering the trucks would be covered by the savings resulting therefrom in approximately two weeks. It would take almost three years for the additional 2 per cent savings to cover the $472 cost of installing turntables, or 5½ years to cover the cost of new turntable trucks. Because of the small cost of eliminating the 11 per cent waste and the relatively large expense involved in eliminating the additional 2 per cent, decision was made to lower the present trucks to a standard over-all height of 30 inches from the floor.

**7. Use of Helper to Prevent Interruption of Operative's Routine.** The engineer recommended other changes in addition. He urged that a table instead of a truck be used to hold labeled bottles. Inspection could be performed on this table, after which bottles could be packed from it. Substitution of the table for the truck would thus eliminate considerable handling. The engineer proposed also that a helper be provided for the labeling machine operative. This helper could straighten slipped or twisted labels, and thus interruption of the routine of the labeling machine and its operative could be avoided.

**8. Temporary Standard Method of Performance Devised.** In accordance with these recommendations, the inspection and packing table was installed, orders were given for the lowering of the trucks, and a helper was hired for the operative. A temporary standard method for labeling was set up (Exhibit 1). In the new standard motion sequence, the operative used both hands as much as possible. While the left hand deposited a labeled bottle on the inspection table, the right placed an unlabeled bottle in the machine. The left hand grasped the bottle in the machine, and the right grasped a bottle on the supply truck. As the left carried the labeled bottle to the inspection table, the right carried the unlabeled one to the machine. Finally, as the left deposited the labeled bottle on the table, the right placed the unlabeled bottle in the machine. With this method there were no waste motions, and neither hand had to wait for the other.

**9. Results Obtained with the Temporary Standard.** As the operative became accustomed to the new inspection table, to the assistance of a helper, and to the new motions, production increased from the previous 1,000 or 1,500 output to 3,000 or 3,500

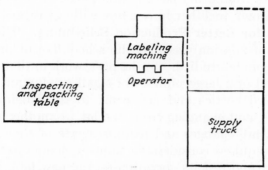

EXHIBIT 1. BEAUTY PREPARATIONS, INC. TEMPORARY STANDARD METHOD OF LABELING BOTTLES BY MACHINE, WORKPLACE LAYOUT, AND MOTION CHART. SIMULTANEOUS MOTIONS ON SAME LINES.

| Left hand | Right hand |
|---|---|
| 1. Release bottle on inspecting table. | 1. Place unlabeled bottle in machine. |
| 2. Go to bottle in machine and grasp it. | 2. Go to supply truck and grasp bottle. |
| 3. Carry bottle to inspecting table. | 3. Carry bottle to machine. |
| 4. Release bottle on inspecting table. | 4. Place unlabeled bottle in machine. |
| Etc. | Etc. |

for the operative and a helper. A further increase was expected when the trucks were lowered to the proposed 30-inch standard. The fluctuation between 3,000 and 3,500 was the result of variation in the number of fixture changes required. Previous to the study, the machines had labeled 32-ounce, 16-ounce, and some 8-ounce bottles. After installation of new methods, all sizes from 2-ounce to 32-ounce were labeled in each machine.

There still remained three studies to be made which the engineer regarded as prerequisite to the adoption of permanent standard methods, motions, and times.

**10. Standardization of Raw Materials and Machine Adjustment.** The engineer recommended that label sizes be standardized. If all labels to be used in the same fixture were uniform, the machine would place them accurately on the bottles without slipping.

He recommended also that a motion study of fixture changing should be made. As a preliminary to this study, he devised a rack with compartments so that each fixture with its parts could be kept separate from other fixtures and parts. Previously they all had been thrown together in one box without regard to size.

**11. Need for Better Production Scheduling.** The engineer's third recommendation was that the scheduling of production in the filling room be studied. In the past, work in that department had consisted of a large number of small production orders. As a result, filled bottles and jars came to the labeling machines in small lots, and changing from one lot to another necessitated frequent fixture changes and readjustments of the labeling machines. It required considerable time to change fixtures, adjust the machine, and test its operation on the new lot. During that time neither the machine nor its operative was productively occupied. Usually the labels on the first bottles of a new lot were improperly attached. They then had to be straightened, and the machine had to be readjusted and tested.

If the work in the filling room was so scheduled that larger lots of one item would come to the labeling machines, fewer interruptions, changes, and adjustments would be required. The engineer believed it was possible to schedule this work so as to keep each labeling machine operating much of the time on one type and size of container with one size of label.

**12. Analysis of Results of Standard Method.** Pending the making of these three studies, the engineer instituted a time study of the temporary standard labeling operation in an effort to improve the motions. The following conditions obtained: the routine outlined for the temporary standard was being followed; a table was used for inspection and packing; the operative had the services of an assistant; but the lowered trucks were not as yet in use. The engineer reported as follows:

## Production Analysis of Labeling by Machine

The total number of minutes actually timed was 490.21. The personal needs of the operative were:

|                    | Minutes |
|--------------------|---------|
| Relief Periods     | 10.00   |
| First Aid *        | 14.23   |
| Lunch              | 60.00   |
| Total              | 84.23   |

\* The operative was underweight, and twice a day she left her machine to drink milk. Her weight soon became normal, and she no longer lost this time.

This left an actual working day of 405.98 minutes, which was divided as follows:

|                                                              | Total Time, Minutes | Per Cent Working Day | Number of Pieces | Unit Time, Minutes |
|--------------------------------------------------------------|---------------------|----------------------|------------------|--------------------|
| Operating Machine Productively                               | 264.19              | 65.0                 | 2,737            | .097               |
| Operating Machine Nonproductively (test running)             | 11.06               | 2.7                  | .....            | ....               |
| Changing Attachments                                         | 40.98               | 10.1                 | .....            | ....               |
| Cleaning Machine                                             | 43.61               | 10.7                 | .....            | ....               |
| Diluting Glue in Machine                                     | .81                 | .2                   | .....            | ....               |
| Adjusting Machine                                            | 5.86                | 1.5                  | .....            | ....               |
| Moving Trucks                                                | 9.05                | 2.3                  | .....            | ....               |
| Miscellaneous Traveling for Help, Labels, Trucks, Rags       | .....               | ....                 | .....            | ....               |
| Waiting for Man to Change Attachment                         | 26.76               | 6.6                  | .....            | ....               |
| Avoidable Delays                                             | 3.66                | .9                   | .....            | ....               |

This shows 65 per cent of the operative's working day productively occupied in using the machine, but at a unit rate of 0.097 minute per piece. The machine, however, is capable of operating at a rate of 0.035 minute per piece. Therefore, although the girl was productively occupied 65 per cent of the day, the machine was so occupied only 23.4 per cent. The difference between the two percentages (41.6 per cent) is in the handling time required, in addition to that handling time available while the machine is in the process of labeling a bottle. A change in method will reduce this extra handling time. Changes in method will also reduce those times other than "Operating Machine Productively."

**13. Summary and Conclusions.** *Job Standardization Involves Many Considerations.* The study just cited is typical of the experience of Beauty Preparations, Inc., in lowering production costs by improving job methods. That the methods of the average operative are inefficient is to be expected if one considers the haphazard conditions under which he works. It is obvious that improvement of work methods can only be superficially profitable unless those factors which condition the performance of the task are controlled. To reduce any task, then, to its most simple, least wasteful, and least fatiguing series of motions involves the study of many factors: the raw materials, surrounding conditions, the workplace itself, the machines and tools, and changes in the nature of the work. If raw materials are standardized and always at hand when required by the operative in standard place, position, and form; if the workplace is so designed as to be convenient for the accomplishment of the task without waste in time and physical and mental effort; if temperature, humidity, light, and noise do not distract but rather recede into the background of the worker's consciousness, leaving only a sense of opportunity for accomplishment; if the proper tools, adequately conditioned, are always at hand in their designated place just at the time they are required by the operative; then, and only then, are conditions such that the skilled observer with stop watch or motion-picture camera [1] can make an analysis of the work to be done, reduce the operation to its essential and nonessential components, and finally synthesize a standard method of performance embracing the fewest, easiest motions,

---

[1] Micromotion study is, in some instances, supplanting the stop watch in job analysis. A clock recording time in short intervals, perhaps 1/1,000 or 1/2,000 of a minute, is set in such position as to be easily read while the work is watched. Motion pictures are then taken of the operation, the rate of exposure being synchronized with the clock which appears in the picture. The developed films so made can be studied at leisure and reduced to a tabular analysis of the motions of the operative in performing the task being studied. Micromotion study differs from stop watch study essentially in that a different tool is employed.

See *Cost and Production Handbook*, pp. 517, 518, 527, McGraw-Hill Book Company, Inc., New York, 1940.

See also Lowry, Maynard, and Stegemerten, *Time and Motion Study* (3d ed.), Chaps. X, XI, McGraw-Hill Book Company, Inc., New York, 1940.

combined in the simplest and most natural sequence to accomplish the task in the shortest, most efficient way.

*Job Analysis Based upon Standardized Operating Conditions.* When standard conditions favorable to the work have been created, the next step is analysis of the job itself and elimination of all unnecessary effort and, so far as possible, of awkward and time-consuming motions. On the basis of such studies a simple, efficient way of work can be devised and tried out. The trial period usually makes possible additional improvement, after which the method can be reduced to writing and accepted as the standard way in which the task will be performed thereafter. In putting such standards on paper it is most essential that all conditioning factors, such as tools, machine speeds, and the like, be made a part of the work standard itself.

*Worker Training in Standard Methods the Next Step.* Determination of the best way of performing a task is the beginning rather than the end if standard work ways are to result in production economies. The essential thing is to make sure that standard practice is followed in the production departments. This means that worker training is absolutely necessary. The methods and means of worker training are many and varied. Conditions in each shop will largely determine whether this training shall be conducted by the departmental foremen, by a training department, or under other arrangements. Regardless of how it is done, however, worker training in prescribed methods is essential if the benefits of job standardization are to be realized.

*Standardization of Worker Training.* The Second World War left two clearly observable impressions on operating management practice and policy in industry: (1) an intensified appreciation of the need and practicability of tighter, more exact controls of all phases of operation and (2) the need and values that come from formalized training of workers. One of the most praiseworthy accomplishments of government attempts to aid industry during the war was its Training Within Industry program. The most effective and finished product of this program was Job Instructor Training. This was a standardized procedure for teaching a worker how to do a specific task. This standardized instructional procedure was taught to thousands of foremen, supervisors, and factory training people. The procedure was simple and effective in accomplishing its purpose. Much of its effectiveness was the result of the rigid standardization of the method that was literally drilled into its practitioners. This standardization extended even to such details as to how the instructor should stand or sit, when he might put his hands in his pockets, and when he must not do so. Such a degree of strait-jacketing is commonly regarded by professional teachers as being thoroughly stifling and obnoxious. Nevertheless it did transform thousands of totally inexperienced people into proficient teachers within a certain limited scope. The proof of that statement is the millions of workers who quickly learned to perform tasks efficiently in war factories under the standardized tutelage of "certified" J.I.T. teachers. This experience is cited here for two reasons: (1) J.I.T. taught and practiced the doctrine that worker training must be preceded by job standardization and (2) that no worker could be expected to be proficient on a job if he were allowed to select or devise his own method or methods of performing the work. Training produces no major gain except in terms of a predetermined standard job procedure. The second reason for calling attention to this wartime practice is that it illustrates the broad range of human activities to which the standardization concept is applicable in industry. The writer of this paragraph is a teacher, and he has been teaching across the time span of two world wars. In 1941 he "took" the standardized 30-hour J.I.T. instructional program that eventuated in his becoming a "certified T.W.I. instructor trainer." He rebelled at the rigid minute requirements to which he had to conform, but he grudgingly accepted, learned, and practiced them. Today he will admit that in this matter T.W.I. was right and he was wrong. There followed many occasions on which he observed certified instructors whose total teaching experience was limited to two or three months producing results by standard J.I.T. methods that were every bit as effective as those obtained by men who had years of successful teaching experience. True, the scope of the teaching task was greatly restricted, but, within its known and accepted limitations, standardized teaching methods did as much as any one thing to enable industry to win its share of the war objective. Standardization of human activity in the factory has wide applicability, and it is recognized in American industry today as a "must" whenever a high degree of operating proficiency is desired.

*Meeting Worker Opposition to New Methods.* Frequently workers oppose such change. It is to be expected that a workman who has spent many years in the performance of a task will be skeptical and sometimes resentful of being required to conform to new methods. Such opposition should be anticipated. Much of it can be allayed through the employment of proper methods and tact in building up the new standard. Intelligent application on the part of the foreman should take care of any remaining resentment. Finally, probably the most constructive method of meeting this situation is to make it worth the worker's while to learn the new method quickly and thereafter conform to it. Incentive wages in the form of bonuses and the like are most effective for such purposes.[2]

It is probably unnecessary to point out that the use of new methods of task performance as a means of exploiting labor is not good. Such a policy distinctly tends to defeat the original purpose of job study, which is reduction in production costs. It is as important to avoid the appearance of such exploitation as to refrain from the practice itself.

*Job Standardization the Basis for Time-study Standards.* Just as worker instruction requires job standardization before it can produce a trained worker, so time study must be based upon a standardized job procedure. The purpose of time study is to determine a standard time for the performance of a specific task. Obviously if the method of performing a task changes, the time required to perform the task will vary. It follows, therefore, that job time standards can be no more reliable than the consistency with which the worker follows a single work procedure. Job standardization must come first. Not until the job method has become standardized and the worker trained to proficiency in the standard method is the job truly fit for the determination of a standard time for the performance of the task. This fact is basically implied in the numerous union-management contracts which state specifically that the time standard on any job shall not be changed except as the nature of the job or the method of performing it are altered.

[2] See Chap. XVI.

*Business Aspects of Job Standardization.* In view of the savings in labor cost that result from job study and the utilization of
standard methods, one wonders that the practice has not had
more universal acceptance. The reason is probably lack of
understanding of the business aspects of the situation on the part
of plant executives and job-study technicians alike. Job study
and task standardization have been regarded as highly technical,
costly procedures suited only to large establishments and applicable exclusively to situations where repetitious tasks on large
volumes exist. As job study has been carried on in the past, these
limitations have probably been controlling factors. More recently it has been realized that job study in the interest of motion
economy need not involve complicated techniques and that economical use of standard methods of task performance is possible
even when the task is performed intermittently and when the
volume of any one run is not great. Much can be done in improving ways of work without using either the stop watch or the
micromotion camera. If foremen and workers are taught to be
motion-economy-minded, improvement in ways of doing jobs
will become a matter of everyday occurrence. In the bottle labeling operation just described, it required no time study to observe
that the label's slipping, which necessitated the operative's
straightening the label on the bottle, was cutting down the output of the labeling machines. Nor was time study essential in
determining the solution. No stop watch was required to see
that idleness of both machine and operative resulted from the
frequent waits during fixture change. Even the need for lowering the trucks would have been obvious to either a foreman or a
worker who had been taught the advantages of standardized access to raw materials and the economy of certain types of arm
and body movements as compared with motions of more awkward and tiring characteristics.

It is common practice in benchwork for the worker to hold
parts or assemblies in the left hand while practically all actual
work is performed with the right hand. In four out of five such
cases the worker's output can be increased greatly through the
devising of a simple, inexpensive fixture for holding the work,
thereby releasing the worker's left hand for truly productive
effort. Opportunities for such improvement in ways of working

are many and become quickly apparent to the observer who is looking for them. They involve no complicated technique, entail no great costs, and arouse no opposition when intelligently carried out and understood by the workers.

In such a program of task improvement by means of motion economy, the worker's attitude and interest must be always considered. It is not difficult to get the essential worker cooperation in such a program, provided that the worker understands the objectives and is given an incentive to take part. In really successful programs of this type, workers have been found the most prolific of all sources of suggestion of improvement. The worker is closer to the job than anyone else, knows what elements of the task are most tiring, where wastes and waits most frequently occur. A large part of the effort in such an endeavor should be directed toward training workers to understand opportunities for task improvement and to recognize the types of ways of work which are bad and those which are good.

When methods which have thus been improved are employed only occasionally because of noncontinuous performance of the task, they can be retained by means of simple written instructions preserved for future use. Such instructions will show clearly how the workplace should be arranged, what fixtures and tools should be used, and the easiest way of performing the task. When workers become accustomed to the use of such instruction cards, it will be found possible to employ standard task methods even on jobs which occur only occasionally.

Task improvement and standardization, when carried out along this line, are sound from the business standpoint. The costs of such improvements are low and the returns are great. That maximum savings are not attained from such "nonscientific" methods should be of no great concern. Maximum returns can be had only by the more technical procedures of the stop watch and micromotion camera. These intensive studies are much more costly, and all too frequently the added economies do not warrant the added costs. When large volumes of work are involved, the total savings mount and the more costly procedures become profitable. The easily discovered and easily remedied errors are the ones which yield greatest returns per dollar expended for improvement. Additional intensive studies will yield less and less returns, and the costs will be greater. These greater costs, however, will be fully justified if the total volume of the task is sufficient to allow the smaller economies to accumulate into large savings.

Job study and standardization can be profitably practiced in their elemental form in almost any business. This simple, common-sense approach will often yield surprising results per dollar of effort invested. This is not to belittle the more elaborate techniques of the time-study and motion-study engineer. From a business standpoint each has its advantages and disadvantages; each has its place and usefulness in industrial management. It so happens that the recent development of the simple approach is more commonly applicable.

*Importance of Quality Standards.* Little has been said in this case about standards applied to quality of output.[3] Obviously, little is accomplished by setting up standard methods of operation which do not result in output of satisfactory quality. It is equally obvious that the word "satisfactory" implies quality measurement. Measurement is only possible in terms of some predetermined standard. An all too frequent practice in attempting quality control is to consider the experience of a foreman or an inspector as a sufficient standard by which to judge current output. It is much better practice to define quality requirements meticulously and to put such requirements systematically into writing. Inspection requirements thus set become true standards. The common use of tolerances in machining operations is an excellent example of such standards. All use of gauges in production is based upon the definition and acceptance of standards.

*Standardization a Fundamental Concept in Mass Production.* Successful mass production is largely dependent on wide application of the standards concept. Such benefits as mass production has to offer practically can be realized only if the offsetting disadvantages are well under control. One of the most effective measures of such control is predetermination of results. At the top of the great organization one usually finds attempts at predetermination in the form of budgets: sales budgets, operating budgets, and financial budgets. These instruments owe their existence chiefly to the predetermination of details. Detailed pre-

---

[3] For discussion of quality control, see India Tire & Rubber Company case, Chap. XXIII.

determination is essentially a matter of development of standards, and, insofar as a dynamic industrial society permits, of adherence to predetermined standards. It is, therefore, to be expected that standardization, like specialization, pervades industry as an essential factor of mass production policy.

## QUESTIONS

1. What was the purpose of the work being done by the planning department of Beauty Preparations, Inc.?

2. Why did the engineers recommend that an "inspecting and packing table" be installed?

3. Why was it recommended that the trucks on which unlabeled bottles were brought to the labeling machine be lowered, but that neither new trucks be purchased nor old trucks be equipped with turntables? Just what part did time and motion study play in reaching that decision?

4. Why was a temporary standard method of labeling evolved? What was its purpose?

5. What was responsible for the increase in output on labeling machines from 1,000–1,500 to 3,000–3,500 bottles a day? What part did labor specialization play in this increased productivity?

6. Why did the engineer recommend that label sizes be standardized?

7. What results might be expected from a job study of fixture changing?

8. What was the object of the recommendation that production scheduling in the filling room be studied?

9. Why was the labeling machine productively occupied only 23.4 per cent of the working day although its operative was productively occupied 65 per cent of the day?

10. What is the objection to this discrepancy? How could it be remedied?

11. Name and explain the essential steps in job study in the order in which they should be taken.

12. Why should worker opposition to job standardization be anticipated, and what preventive measures can you suggest?

13. How is job standardization related to worker training? To time study and to time-study standards?

## Problem 9

## WALTHAM WATCH COMPANY

In common with other watch manufacturers, the Waltham Watch Company was faced with the necessity of catering to market demand for watches which were reliable in keeping time but relatively low in price. Satisfying such demand at a profit to the manufacturer involved a variety of management problems. Certain marketing, inventory financing, and production problems were specific issues with the Waltham Watch Company, having their origin in the changes which had developed in market demand. In considerable degree the management of the company found parts standardization remedial for all three types of issue, marketing, financial, and production.

The Waltham Watch Company, which was started in 1854, had one of the largest watch and clock factories in the world, employing in normal times about 3,000 persons. The company manufactured watch movements but bought cases outside; it had an annual output in excess of 500,000 movements. It produced pocket and wrist watches in eight sizes, ranging from the largest to the smallest sizes commonly manufactured. A watch on the average contained 150 parts, most of which required precision in manufacture.[4] A large portion of the sales were of wrist watches selling at prices which ranged from $35 to $150. In addition to watches, the company manufactured many kinds of clocks, including electric clocks and speedometers for automobiles. It had practically world-wide distribution through wholesalers and retailers. Manufacturing was chiefly in anticipation of sales with standardized parts produced for stock.

For many years the demand for watches had been increasingly in the direction of cheaper yet reliable products. Efforts to meet

[4] Hairsprings ranged in thickness from 0.0015 centimeter to 0.0075 centimeter; mainsprings from 0.009 centimeter to 0.024 centimeter; jewels ranged in hole size from 0.00775 centimeter to 0.0350 centimeter; the smallest screws measured 0.07 centimeter, the largest 0.175 centimeter. Many watch manufacturers are of the opinion that watchmaking is more than a trade, that it is an art.

this demand had developed to a point where a complicated mechanism had been sold for as low as $1. The technical problems of manufacture resulting from this market development were intensified by the trend of consumer demand away from pocket watches to smaller wrist watches. There was a growing shortage of skilled craftsmen for benchwork in production. Furthermore, this shortage had extended to watch repairers in jewelry stores. As a result of this lack of skilled repairmen, the responsibility of manufacturers for their products had been broadened.

Labor cost constituted approximately 85 per cent of the total cost of production of a watch movement. The hairspring is a good illustration of the relative importance of raw materials cost in this industry. Wire for hairsprings cost the Waltham company $8.50 per pound, and from 1 pound were produced 271,360 of the smallest springs, with a value of $73,493.16.

Synthetic jewels were important parts contributing to the reliability of watches. To meet existing assembly requirements it had been necessary for the company to maintain an average inventory in excess of 10 million jewels. With the average jewel representing an investment of 5 cents, the large amount of capital tied up in this inventory constituted a serious financial problem.

Consideration of the marketing, production, and inventory financing problems which faced executives of the Waltham Watch Company seemed to emphasize the need for lowering production costs, and steps were taken to accomplish that objective.

The mechanism of a watch movement consists of a coiled spring, called the "mainspring," which imparts movement to the hands of the watch through a series, or train, of small wheels. The motion of the wheel train is controlled by the escapement, which is actuated by a spring. The wheels of the train are mounted on pinions which terminate at each end in pivots. The pivots are mounted in jewel bearings in the plates of the movement frame, which thus hold the pinions with their wheels accurately in position. Jewels are used for bearings because of absence of friction and resistance to corrosion by oil. To a considerable degree the accuracy of operation of the watch movement is dependent on the fit of the pivots with the jewels which serve as their bearings. Much of the repair work done on watches was necessitated by injury to the pivot as a result of wear or unusual shock.

The Waltham Watch Company made pivots from Stubs wire [5] drawn from high-carbon steel. The dimensions of pivots varied with the size of the wheel, which in turn varied with the size of the watch. There were commonly seven pinions in a Waltham watch, each pinion having two pivots. Fit of pivot and jewel was secured by selective assembly. Women employees tried out jewels of a size approximate to the dimensions of the pivot until they found one giving perfect fit. Manufacturing tolerances caused slight variations in pivot dimensions. This fact, together with lack of standardization of jewel sizes, necessitated carrying a large jewel inventory and was responsible for the costs incurred in the selective assembly procedure.

The general manager of the Waltham Watch Company visited jewel vendors in Switzerland. He pointed out to them the desirability of having jewels made to specified sizes and hole diameters, urged the adoption of uniform methods of stating dimensions, and prevailed upon such vendors to grant price reductions on jewels of standard specifications. On a later trip to Switzerland, the general manager noted that Swiss watch manufacturers had taken advantage of the cooperation of jewel manufacturers in standardizing jewels and, by reducing tolerances, had standardized pivot dimensions to conform to the standardized hole diameters of jewels. Upon his return, he proposed the adoption of a similar policy for his company.

Savings in labor cost in both manufacturing and repairing, increased ease and promptness of repairing, and a very great decrease in jewel inventory were expected to result from jewel and pivot standardization. The company could eliminate the

---

[5] Stubs wire derived its name from a British manufacturer who acquired a reputation for turning out the best steel in drill rod form. It has since become the trade designation for all wire stock of this type, whether manufactured here or abroad.

work of 10 to 15 women engaged in fitting jewels to pivots, since with the standardized pivots a jewel could be assembled without difficulty with a pivot of the particular size specified. The saving in production secured by interchangeability of the parts in assembly not only would reduce costs but also would enable the company to utilize the services of the trained workers for other such work. After pivots were of standard sizes, it would be simple for a watch repairer in a jewelry store to order a wheel for a particular watch with assurance that the pivots would be of satisfactory fit. The facilitation of repairs through the ability to supply parts of standard dimensions and interchangeable characteristics would tend to free the factory from demands for repair service and would increase the sales of Waltham watches because of more timely repair service to customers and a better feeling on the part of retailers.

To standardize the pivots would necessitate changes in production technique. The pivots would have to be produced with closer tolerances than before to ensure interchangeability. Whereas the shop had been working with tolerances of 0.0004 inch, it would be necessary to work with tolerances of less than 0.0001 inch, a degree of precision calling for unusual production technique. Furthermore, the full benefits of standardization might be secured only by a redesign and standardization also of those other parts of the watch, such as the wheel, that would be affected by the change in the design of the pivot. With several designs and sizes of wheels, this was a difficult matter.

Pivots were made in two major operations: (1) turning the stock in a precision lathe and (2) grinding and polishing to size and finish. Drill rod stock ranging in diameter from 0.007 centimeter to 0.35 centimeter was utilized. A pivot was ordinarily less than 0.075 centimeter long. Thus the finishing of so small a part to such narrow tolerances required close attention on the part of the worker to prevent waste of time and material in defective parts. Careful supervision, inspection, and use of inspection gauges were essential to the maintenance of these standards.

The lathe equipment available could be utilized.  The process of grinding and polishing, however, would have to be changed in order to meet the new requirements.  Instead of polishing with a light powder, work performed by women, it would be necessary to secure the finish by burnishing,[6] which would have to be done by skilled workmen using steel burnishers.  New equipment would have to be installed for burnishing.  The unit cost was expected to be approximately 10 per cent greater than under the former method.

Standardization of jewels made possible a reduction of jewel inventory to one-tenth its former size.  The general manager estimated that the net saving secured by the reduction in the inventory of jewels and the interchangeability of the pivots would approximate 25 cents for each watch movement produced.  There were, furthermore, the additional benefits made possible by better repair service.

## QUESTIONS

1. What advantages and disadvantages would result from the standardization program?

2. Explain how the standardization program tended to solve marketing and financial problems as well as production difficulties.

### Problem 10

### KING SAW COMPANY

The King Saw Company, which produced 3,500 types and variations of circular saws and an even larger variety of band saws, employed a graduate of a business school to study the possibility of simplification of its product.  One year later, company executives were considering the reduction of the line of circular saws to 200 items and a proportionate reduction in the band-saw line.

[6] Burnishing provides a finish without removal of material caused by use of an abrasive.  In soft metals and perhaps in the hard steels, the material "flows" or "drags" as a result of the burnishing.  A microscopic examination of the surface shows a different granular structure resulting from the operation.

The manufacture of band and circular saws was highly competitive. Five producers manufactured 98 per cent of the entire output of the United States. The remaining 2 per cent was distributed among a considerable number of small producers. Of these, two had intensively cultivated small local markets to the extent of almost excluding other producers.

Saws for large mills were made according to the individual customer's specifications and stocked for the filling of future orders. A salesman would approach a prospect with the proposition that his company would be glad to produce and stock the particular saw used by the potential customer, and thus be in a position to fill immediately any future orders the customer might give the company. This sort of procedure was typical of the policies of the large saw companies. As a result, saw companies generally carried excessively large inventories. Furthermore, these inventories were of special products, each saw often being salable only to the company to whose specifications it was originally made. Furthermore, two or more saw companies might have special saws in stock for a single mill at one time.

The King Saw Company was generally recognized as one of the leaders in its field. Its business and inventory policies were similar to those just outlined as typical of the industry. The policy of producing special saws for stock had resulted in undesirable looseness in production control. On a few occasions, an order had been put into production and had become lost in process so that a duplicate of the original order had to be produced. The original order usually turned up later and was placed in stock against future orders. Because of the company's inventory policy, neither workmen nor subexecutives had considered such duplication of orders of any great moment.

Another result attributed to the inventory policy was an abnormal amount of defective work. Failure to comply with production specifications could be easily covered up by placing the improperly made saw in stock and producing another which would comply with the specified requirements.

The large inventories and production looseness together with failure to recognize differences in control between special-order production and manufacture for stock resulted in excessive costs.

Such costs were in addition to the usual high costs which result from lack of standardization in product and process.

The management of the King Saw Company was aware of this uneconomical situation and, believing that simplification was the remedy, employed a young college man and assigned to him the task of working out some means of relieving the condition. Being unfamiliar with the industry, this man first made a study of the situation. He found that the existing policy of the company was the result of long development. The band and circular saws produced by his company were sold throughout the United States chiefly to sawmills and woodworking plants. The actual purchasers for large mill saws were the saw filers. As far as sawing operations were concerned, the saw filers were the key men of their respective plants. The ability to cut a volume of lumber depended very largely on the ability of the saw filer to keep his saws in good condition. A saw filer was a highly skilled craftsman who had served a long apprenticeship in learning his job and was well aware of his importance in the mill.

Each saw filer had his own ideas and beliefs as to saws. An illustration was the contention current among filers in the Southern mills that no saw filer from the northwest could possibly be successful in sawing southern pine. In a few instances, saw filers had experimented with different shapes and types of saw tooth and had prepared specifications on the basis of this experience. In the majority of cases, however, the filers' beliefs were the result of personal prejudice, custom, past performance, etc. Frequently, a saw filer's demands changed somewhat from time to time without his being aware of the fact. One explanation of this curious situation was found to be in the continued use of a gumming machine in the filing and conditioning of saws. The gumming machine was so constructed as to follow automatically the outline of the particular saw tooth used at the mill. As a result of continued use, the cams which actuated this automatic mechanism became worn and thus caused the gumming machine gradually to change the shape of the saw tooth. As long as the saw continued to cut properly, the filer was not likely to realize that the tooth shape had been changed. In ordering a new saw, the filer would usually specify that it be made exactly like the one then in use. However, the new saw, though patterned after the gummed saw, would be unlike the specifications according to which the pattern itself had been made. Often the filer was not aware of this fact.

Investigation revealed the fact that there was no scientific knowledge of the art of cutting wood comparable with the work that had been inaugurated by Taylor and his associates in cutting metal. It was established that saw requirements varied with different woods, but there was no uniformity among filers as to the requirements of a saw for cutting a given wood. Investigation also showed that originally saws had been ordered by the filers from four to six months in advance of delivery date. Keen competition among the saw companies had resulted in the development of the existing condition, in which the filer gave his order and expected immediate delivery. If one company would not give instant service, some other company was ready to do so.

After several months of study, the research man of the King Saw Company prepared a list of saws which he believed adequate to supply the actual needs of all users of circular saws and a similar list for band saws. The circular-saw list contained 200 items, a very drastic reduction of the 3,500 specifications then current with the trade.

The following information was taken from the report on the subject rendered the president of the King Saw Company at that time.

This recommendation (that the company simplify its line to 200 numbers) is made as a result of the following conclusions: first, that the saw industry is faced with a permanent, gradual falling off in volume of production as an inevitable result of the future decline of the lumber industry; second, that the condition of the King Saw Company is typical of the industry as a whole; third, that the adoption of the following recommendations would largely rectify the existing undesirable conditions; and fourth, that the King Saw Company is a logical unit in the saw industry to sponsor such a movement.

It is recommended that a conference of executives of the five largest saw producers be arranged. At this meeting our findings as to the condition of the industry should be fully set forth and a tentative program of procedure adopted in order that the movement may start backed by the concerted cooperation of all large interests in the industry.

The program to be adopted at this meeting might well include the appointment of a simplification committee made up of representatives appointed one from each company and a full-time secretary whose function should be the carrying out of the wishes of the committee and active promotion of the simplification movement. The collected materials attached to this report should be turned over to this committee together with the suggested simplified list of standard specifications. The committee should be able to supplement readily the work already accomplished, and at an early date adopt such standards. It is believed that the specifications included in these recommendations would not need great alteration to meet the approval of such a committee.

It is suggested that the operation of the simplification program be controlled through the inventory situation. The committee might well establish a definite time limit for the liquidation of the existing specialized inventories. It is believed that if proper pressure were applied to sales organizations, these inventories could be disposed of within a six-month period. The one point of possible difficulty in this respect is the Pacific Northwest, where it is thought that a supply of saws now exists adequate to care for the needs of that section for a period of 15 months. Even in this case, the loss would not be as great as might at first be expected. Practically all this inventory could be reworked to conform to standard specifications.

At the end of the six-month liquidation period, all nonstandard saws would be scrapped. Thereafter, no nonstandard saws would be produced for stock. Any company would be at liberty to produce special saws according to a customer's specification, but would pledge itself not to manufacture such nonstandard saws for stock. Standard specification saws would be produced for stock and would thus become the only types of saws available for quick delivery. The customer who refused to use standard specification saws would have to await delivery until the special saw could be produced.

To establish confidence among the cooperating companies and assure that all were keeping faith with the program, detailed inventory reports would be placed before the simplification committee at the end of the six-month liquidation period. Company representatives on this committee should have the authority to bind their respective companies to the program of scrapping all nonstandard saws at this time. Thereafter, periodic inventory reports would be turned over to the committee, which should constitute a continuing organization for the administration of the program. These reports would show any departure from the agreement to stock only standard saws and would assure adherence to the established standards. The committee would, from time to time, make any revisions in the standard lists which experience might reveal as advisable.

During the liquidation period, the full-time secretary of the committee should be kept actively engaged as the committee's propagandist, working with both the saw producers and the consumers. His influence should be very effective in assuring that a minimum of nonstandard saws be on hand at the end of the liquidation period.

Following the liquidation of existing inventories, it might still be advisable to keep this secretary in the field for some time as an impartial adviser and as the committee's field representative. This need should not, however, continue indefinitely. The committee would, undoubtedly, always be in need of a secretary, but the work should become less burdensome as familiarity with the new standards became established throughout the trade.

It should be strongly stressed, both in the suggested executives' meeting and in the first meeting of the committee, that all questions of price and price policy are absolutely outside the province of this plan. Such questions as price differential between standard and nonstandard saws, or the effect of simplification upon the general price level, should be carefully excluded from all consideration. It is definitely believed, not only that such questions are undesirable, but that the price consideration is entirely unnecessary to the accomplishment of our aims.

The full report from which the foregoing was extracted was placed on the desk of the president of the King Saw Company with the recommendation that steps be taken to put it into operation.

### QUESTIONS

1. If you were the president of the King Saw Company, would you take steps necessary to the inauguration of this program?

2. Mickelson and Sons was one of the small companies mentioned in the case as having developed intensively a local market for their saws. If you, as chief executive of that company, were asked by the simplification committee to join the group engaged in the standardization movement, what would be your attitude, and what action would you take?

3. What advantages may a company expect to realize as a result of the adoption of a standardization program? What disadvantages might be expected to result?

4. What conditions must obtain to ensure the success of a product standardization program in an industry?

5. In what way does standardization of the product of an industry affect the competitive position of a business in that industry?

# CHAPTER VI

# DIVERSIFICATION

## 1. The Management of a Company Questions the Desirability of Simplifying Output.

The Star-Guard Publishing Company conducted a job printing business in connection with the publication of a weekly newspaper. The yearly gross receipts from the newspaper were approximately equal to the receipts from the print shop. The actual work of producing the newspaper required but two days a week; the remaining four days each week were spent on job work. The managers' time was about equally divided between the newspaper and the job printing work.

The company was owned by two men, one of whom questioned the advisability of continuing the job printing plant. He believed that all profits were coming from the newspaper and urged that the company specialize on that activity. The other partner did not concur in this. He believed that the nature of newspaper production was such that it could not profitably be pursued except in conjunction with a job printing shop. He, therefore, was strongly in favor of the existing diversification.

## 2. Situations Which Demand Product Diversification. The nature of many manufactured products is such that consumers demand variety in form, color, materials, quality, or size. In such cases there are often good reasons why it is desirable for the producer to manufacture the item in variety. Such a manufacturer must expect to pay the costs characteristic of varied production. The losses from this cause, however, will be less than those incurred should the company go counter to insistent market demand for variety and specialize in low-cost production of a few styles and sizes. Under such circumstances, diversification of product seems the obvious course. The extent to which such a program may be profitably carried must be determined by market analysis of probable volume at varying levels of diver-

sification compared with production costs of the volumes obtainable at those various levels.

Another common, though less obvious, cause of diversification is to be found in the nature of some production processes. There are types of production which can be most economically carried on if a somewhat diversified line of products is made. Otherwise wastes occur. These wastes may be of materials, of labor, or often of machine time. Under such circumstances diversification seems the sensible policy. The problem arises in making certain that such a situation does exist, and in calculating the effects of simplification or diversification on costs of production in relation to income. The experience under consideration, that of the Star-Guard Publishing Company, is a typical problem of this sort.

**3. History of the Star-Guard Publishing Company.** The Star-Guard Publishing Company was a consolidation of two small weekly newspapers, the Newport Star and the Weekly Guard. Neither of these two publications had ever been profitable. The Star-Guard Publishing Company was organized by H. A. Hardin, principal of the local high school, and James Marlow, a printer. Hardin became managing editor of the newspaper, and Marlow assumed responsibility for the job shop. They paid $60,000 for the plant equipment, inventories, and subscription lists. Since that time the business had prospered. New equipment had been purchased, the subscription list had been considerably lengthened, and the monthly income had shown an appreciable increase. The table on the following page shows this income by months.

At the time the business was purchased, there were no accounts receivable outstanding. During the first 2½ years that Hardin and Marlow owned and operated the business, this item increased to $13,976.50. Only one-half of the purchase price of the business had been paid in cash. The balance, $30,000, was furnished by a local bank. Monthly payments of $200 had been made to the bank in retirement of this loan. These payments had always been made out of the current income of the business. The partners had each withdrawn $250 per month as salary.

Star-Guard Publishing Company—"Business Done" *

| Year of Ownership | Jan. | Feb. | Mar. | Apr. | May | June |
|---|---|---|---|---|---|---|
| First........... | ...... | ...... | ...... | ...... | ...... | $4,388 |
| Second....... | $5,604 | $6,552 | $5,750 | $5,348 | $9,416 | 5,870 |
| Third......... | 6,848 | 4,706 | 7,068 | 7,958 | 8,082 | 6,776 |

| Year of Ownership | July | Aug. | Sept. | Oct. | Nov. | Dec. | Total |
|---|---|---|---|---|---|---|---|
| First............. | $5,632 | $4,178 | $5,700 | $6,804 | $5,470 | $7,138 | $39,310 |
| Second.......... | 5,694 | 5,528 | 7,634 | 9,340 | 5,798 | 9,278 | 81,812 |
| Third........... | 6,178 | 4,688 | 8,100 | 7,500 | 5,940 | 8,062 | 81,906 |

* This table was compiled from monthly operating statements prepared by the bookkeeper for the use of the managers.

**4. Profits of the Company.** It was the opinion of the managers that the business had been profitable from the time they had first purchased it. The income tax return for the second year of ownership was as follows:

Star-Guard Publishing Company.   Partnership Income-tax Return
January 1 to December 31

| | | |
|---|---|---|
| Total Cash Received....................................................... | | $81,812.00 |
| Depreciation on $40,000 Machinery at 10%............... | $ 4,000.00 | |
| Total Cash Expended | | |
| Wages.................................. | $23,737.56 | |
| Stock.................................. | 14,094.74 | |
| Postage, Freight, and Express............... | 1,419.02 | |
| Rent................................... | 2,400.00 | |
| Interest................................ | 1,344.70 | |
| Water, Light, and Power.................. | 1,164.88 | |
| Miscellaneous, Taxes, etc................. | 6,895.00 | 51,055.90 |
| Business Done............................................... | | $81,812.00 |
| Total Debits................................................. | | 55,055.90 |
| Net Profit Including Owners' Salaries......................... | | $26,756.10 |

In support of this contention, Mr. Hardin pointed out the accumulation of accounts receivable, the steady reduction of the amount owed the local bank, the salaries drawn by the managers, the increased income of the business, and the considerable additions of new equipment. Although there was no record of profits from newspaper operation separate from job shop work, the total annual profits of the business could be computed from the monthly operating statement. Income from each of the two lines of activity had been recorded separately.

**5. Arguments in Favor of Discontinuing the Job Shop.** Mr. Hardin believed that the company should discontinue its job printing business. Other local and nearby city printing companies provided keen competition for this business. The income from the newspaper equaled the income from the job printing. Production of the paper required but one-half the time required to get out the job work. The circulation of the newspaper could be substantially increased if more effort was expended in this direction, but it was doubtful that the circulation could be trebled, or even doubled. Mr. Hardin believed that the profits from the newspaper were now carrying the job printing.

**6. Arguments in Favor of Diversification.** Mr. Marlow was opposed to discontinuing the job shop. He believed that if the paper was operated alone, it would be sure to show a loss. He accepted Mr. Hardin's argument that the paper produced half the revenue while it required but one-third of the time for its production. He even admitted that it was possible that, if segregated, present operations of the job shop might not show much profit. He contended, however, that discontinuance of the job shop would so increase the cost of producing the newspaper that the profits of the enterprise would be greatly reduced, or might even be converted into a loss.

**7. Making Profits by Operating at a Loss.** The basis of Mr. Marlow's belief was simple. If the job work was discontinued, some of the company's equipment would become unnecessary. To prevent its being a total loss it would have to be sold. If it was sold, little could be obtained for it, and the loss from such sale, he believed, would be much greater than any present loss sustained from operating the equipment. If, as he thought, no loss was actually resulting from job shop operations and income from that activity was sufficient to cover the costs of operating the equipment, it seemed foolish to cease operations and take a loss through sale of the equipment.

In event that the job work was discontinued, most of the company's equipment would still be required for the publication of the weekly paper. The costs of owning and maintaining this equipment (repairs, depreciation, insurance, taxes, and interest) would be practically the same whether the job shop was operated or not. If the job work was discontinued, the newspaper would have to support all these costs, whereas in the past equipment had been used much of the time for job work, the return from which cut down, in great measure, these costs as they applied to the newspaper. In this respect, argued Mr. Marlow, it was profitable to operate the job shop just so long as that work absorbed a part of the burden costs which otherwise would have to be carried by the newspaper.

Without the job work, these costs could be kept down to their past level only if the newspaper work could absorb the entire time of the machines. Mr. Marlow did not believe that this was possible, for the nature of weekly newspaper production necessitated a peak of work in the two days immediately preceding publication of each issue. If the circulation was substantially increased, additional equipment would have to be bought. In other words, the nature of the work was such that it could not be spread evenly throughout the week, and specialization on the newspaper was bound to result in idle equipment much of the time. Diversification, operation of both the job shop and the paper, made it possible to keep much equipment busy on job work when it could not be used in getting out the paper. On this one count alone Mr. Marlow was convinced that specialization on the newspaper would bring disaster.

Mr. Marlow pointed out that his argument regarding equipment would apply with equal force to labor costs. If the job shop was discontinued, practically the entire present work force would be required for one-third to one-half of the week to get out the newspaper. The rest of the time there would be nothing for them to do. They could not be laid off, for then they would seek employment elsewhere. Thus the newspaper would be forced to carry practically all the labor costs that had been required to produce both the paper and the job work. Present returns from job work were thus, from the standpoint of labor costs, making the printing of the paper possible.[1]

Mr. Marlow's final argument had to do with the cost of raw materials. If the existing volume requirements for print paper were reduced materially, costs per pound would increase. And here again Mr. Marlow pointed out that as long as income from job work covered the actual raw materials, labor, and machine costs of its production, or was in excess of the additional expenses resulting from continuance of job printing as compared with part-time operations for newspaper production alone, just so long would it be profitable to the business as a whole to continue the job shop.

**8. Diversification to Get Low Costs from Complementary Processes.** All in all, it seemed to Mr. Marlow that the processes operated by the company were of such a nature as to complement each other. He believed that operation of the job shop alone would probably entail a loss. He was also convinced that specialization on the newspaper would, in like manner, prove disastrous. To him diversification seemed the best policy.

Detailed consideration of such figures of cost and income as are available seems to indicate that Mr. Marlow was right in his desire to continue job shop work. If the job shop had been discontinued and the operating costs listed below had been reduced two-thirds as a result, comparison of income from the paper with cost of producing the paper would have shown a net profit for the year of less than half the profit actually realized. The two-thirds reduction is based on the assumption that these costs vary with time of operation.

---

[1] Mr. Marlow might have pointed out with equal force that costs for rent, interest on debt, managers' salaries, office operation, and the like would have become an increasing burden on the newspaper if the job work had been discontinued.

Cash Received from Paper..................... $40,906.00

| | | |
|---|---|---|
| Depreciation...................... | $4,000.00 | |
| Wages............................ | 7,912.52 | |
| Stock..:.......................... | 4,698.25 | |
| Postage, Freight, and Express........ | 473.01 | |
| Rent............................. | 2,400.00 | |
| Interest........................... | 1,344.70 | |
| Water, Light, and Power............. | 388.30 | |
| Miscellaneous, Taxes, etc............ | 6,895.00 | |

Total Costs............................... 28,111.78

Net Profit Including Owners' Salaries.......... $12,794.22

On the assumption that the items depreciation, rent, and miscellaneous had been reduced by half through sale of equipment, reduction of space rented, and similar measures, costs of operation would have been reduced by $6,647.50 to give a total cost figure for producing the paper of $21,464.28.

| | |
|---|---|
| Depreciation................................... | $2,000.00 |
| Rent........................................... | 1,200.00 |
| Miscellaneous.................................. | 3,447.50 |

$6,647.50

Had such cost reduction been possible, profits would have been greater than the computed $12,794.22 by the amount of the reduction.

| | |
|---|---|
| Net Profit as Computed....................... | $12,794.22 |
| Additional Cost Reduction.................... | 6,647.50 |

Net Profit................................. $19,441.72

Using the cost basis assumed above, a 50 per cent increase in income from the paper would have increased total net profit by $11,994.00, giving a total computed net profit for that year of $31,435.72. This is $4,679.62 more than was actually realized and would seem to indicate that the business would have been more profitable if the job shop had not been operated.

Careful consideration of the cost reductions assumed in the foregoing calculations indicates that such an increase in net profit was most unlikely. The reduction of two-thirds in wages assumes that two-thirds of the employees could have been dis-

| | | |
|---|---:|---:|
| Income from Paper, Increase | | $20,453.00 |
| Wages Increase | $3,956.00 | |
| Stock Increase | 2,349.00 | |
| Postage, Freight, Express Increase | 237.00 | |
| Water, Light, Power Increase | 194.00 | |
| Miscellaneous, Taxes, etc., Increase | 1,723.00 | |
| Total Cost Increase | | 8,459.00 |
| Net Profit Increase | | $11,994.00 |
| Net Profit Previously Computed | | 19,441.72 |
| Total Computed Profit | | $31,435.72 |
| Net Profit, Actual | | 26,756.10 |
| Net Profit Increase from Paper Specialization | | $ 4,679.62 |

charged or that the force could have been laid off four days each week. Neither procedure seems practical. It is not at all likely that discontinuance of job work would have resulted in a two-thirds reduction in cost of paper. Even more unlikely is the reduction by one-half of the items depreciation and rent. Such a reduction assumes that one-half the equipment was unnecessary to paper production, that the work of publishing the newspaper could have been carried on in one-half the space required for job and newspaper work, and that rental on the unused space could have been discontinued.

Of great importance is the fact that more than one-third of the computed profit is predicated upon a 50 per cent increase in the income from the newspaper. That such an increase is possible is pure guesswork, and the profits that would result therefrom are questionable, to say the least.

The risks of failure to effect the computed cost savings and newspaper income increase seem far to outweigh the profit increases that might be realized from discontinuing the job shop. The policy of diversification had yielded a satisfactory profit. That a change from that policy would increase profits was most unlikely; the result would probably have been substantial reduction in net income. The nature of the processes and operations involved in job shop and newspaper production were such that diversification seems the sound policy. Most of the work of newspaper production had of necessity to be done in the two days immediately preceding issue.  If the job work was discontinued, the result would have been idle equipment and idle labor. These idleness costs would have had to be carried by the paper, and the result in all probability would have been substantial reduction in profits.

This is a typical case of the need to diversify when lack of diversification results in intermittent operation.  In this instance, the cycle of activity and idleness was complete each week. In other cases, the cycle will often be found to be much longer, the result of seasonal variations or changes in general or specific business conditions.  Intermittent operation is one common cause of diversification.

**9. Cost Records Not Essential to Solution of the Problem.** Both partners were anxious to know the true situation.  They concluded that their records were inadequate for any determination of costs of job shop as compared with newspaper work.  It was decided, therefore, to reorganize the accounting system in such a way as to segregate job shop from newspaper costs.  For raw materials and labor this would be a relatively simple matter.  Burden costs would be much more difficult to allocate.  The problem was not unsolvable, however, and this seemed to both Mr. Hardin and Mr. Marlow the best approach to an understanding of their situation.[2]

After the costs of each line were known it would be necessary to determine the effect which discontinuance of the job shop would have on newspaper production costs.  Of necessity, this would be a matter of estimate.  However, knowledge of the actual costs of each type of activity in the past would make the estimates reasonably accurate.  The managers believed that such records and estimates would provide them with a sound basis

[2] Students who wish to study an explanation of methods of burden distribution should consult a cost accounting text.  The following are suggested:

John W. Neuner, *Industrial Cost Accounting* (3d ed.), Richard D. Irwin, Inc., Chicago, 1947.

Thomas H. Sanders, *Industrial Accounting*, McGraw-Hill Book Company, Inc., New York, 1929.

J. P. Jordan and G. L. Harris, *Cost Accounting*, The Ronald Press Company, New York, 1925.

upon which to judge the advisability of continuing the diversified activity of the company.

The conclusion reached by the partners to elaborate their costs records was probably unsound. There seems to be adequate evidence that the proposal to discontinue the diversification policy was not workable. The better procedure would have been investigation of the possibility of increasing newspaper circulation and the effects of such increase on costs without discontinuing job work. Consideration of the costs incurred in this business would seem to indicate that if increase in newspaper circulation could be obtained without great increase in expense, income from the paper would increase faster than the costs of manufacturing the increased volume. If investigation of the situation should bear out this hypothesis, it might well be possible to increase the profits of this business without running the risks involved in departing from the diversification policy.

**10. Summary and Conclusions.** *What the "Mass Productionist" Thinks of Diversification.* In the eyes of the mass production enthusiast, fortunate indeed seems the manufacturer who produces one product or a few products of such nature that he can concentrate on a small number of types and sizes. His opportunities of effecting low production costs are many. His problems of control are relatively simple.

Less fortunate is his neighbor who makes a line of articles which have been hit by the style craze, or whose product must continually be possessed of novelty.

Then there is the manufacturer who must make or buy for resale certain articles to supplement the product of his own particular interest. The manufacturer of radios is an excellent example of this type. A radio chassis is essentially an electrical instrument assembled from a great number of small parts brought together in subassemblies. Its manufacture is a fairly complicated process. But there is relatively little sale for a radio chassis as such. It must be equipped with tubes, and the manufacture of tubes is a very different type of process, so much so that it is usually carried on as a business in itself. Thus, to supply the market demand for radios, the chassis manufacturer must either make tubes or buy them. Furthermore, as consumers we demand that our radio apparatus be housed in cabinets. Radio cabinets are commonly wood or plastic, the products of a furniture plant or a plastic molder, and again the radio manufacturer must either engage in an activity entirely unlike his main business or buy outside. In this particular case no universal solution has been found.

*Diversification as a Solution to the Problems of Seasonal Production.* Frequently diversification is desirable because of seasonal demand for a product. When demand is peaked in one restricted part of the year, two courses seem open to the manufacturer. He may operate seasonally in anticipation of fluctuating demand and close his plant down, or nearly so, during the slack months of the year. His other choice is to produce at a relatively even level throughout the year, storing the product in dull seasons ready for the concentrated demand later on.

Both of these methods are costly. The first results in idle plant and equipment and the building up each year of a new working force. This labor situation is expensive, for each new crew must be trained and brought slowly up to an efficient producing level. At the end of the season of high activity the workers are discharged, and the next year the building up and training of a labor force must all be done again. In times of high labor demand it may even be impossible to pursue this policy. It is generally recognized that seasonal production is costly production.

The alternative of producing for stock likewise results in high costs, for the accumulated inventories represent large investments of capital idle during that portion of the year when demand is low. Inventory accumulation is also frequently accompanied by great risks. It is not always possible to forecast with accuracy the volume of demand for the coming year, and the danger of underproduction or overproduction is usually present. Furthermore, most consumers' goods are now changed from year to year to conform to style shifts or to provide additional market appeal. This means that steady production for a seasonal market must be based on a forecast of style trends as well as of volume. Production for stock all too frequently entails the carrying over from year to year of inventories which become obsolete and are thereby sources of considerable loss.

In some cases of seasonal demand, solution has been found in a third alternative, product diversification. An additional product is found which is of seasonal nature but with high and low demand points exactly opposite those of the products already being made. The process of making the new product must be similar to that of the old one in order that the same labor force and equipment may be used for both. Diversification along such lines sometimes provides a solution which eliminates the undesirable features of producing for stock or of idle plant and labor which are involved in seasonal production.

*Diversification Resulting from Complementary Processes.* The last situation making for production diversification to be summarized here is that of which the Star-Guard Publishing Company is an example, namely, the possibility of complementary processes. Diversification may grow out of a periodic production situation in which processes complement each other on a time basis. That is true of the publishing case. The records of this company indicate that costs arising from recurring idleness of machines and labor will make diversification through retention of the job printing work essential to profits, even though the job shop itself produces no profits or even entails a loss. The reasons underlying this probability have been fully developed in the case.

*Diversification to Eliminate Waste of Raw Materials.* There are other situations which make diversification advisable. Many of them are quite as important as those here discussed. Diversification is sometimes of great importance if raw materials are to be completely utilized, since otherwise excessive wastes may occur. This is particularly true when the production process is essentially a breaking down of the raw materials into component parts or subdivisions. The meat-packing industry is the example commonly cited. If the packers confined themselves to the production of meat alone, the major portion of the raw materials would be wasted. It is only through conversion of these materials into a wide variety of useful products that costs of meat products can be brought to their existing levels. Diversification as a means of waste elimination is a policy commonly practiced in many industries.

As a policy, diversification works both for and against large-scale production. Where the market demands variety and frequent and rapid change, the smaller producing unit seems to have the advantage. It is more compact, is more easily controlled, is more flexible, and can be made more responsive to changing conditions. Such is the growing opinion. Thus when diversification is largely the result of market demand for variety, mass production methods and policies frequently suffer. On the other hand, when diversification aims at utilization of waste materials, frequently the largest producing units have a volume sufficient to warrant installation of the processes and equipment required for complete utilization. Such is the case of the meat packers.

*Diversification and the Size of the Business Unit.* It might well be mentioned in conclusion that the future of certain small and medium-sized manufacturing units seems rather assured because of the conditions mentioned above. Many businesses are bound to remain small for the sake of retaining the flexibility essential to catering to the market. And, less directly, many small businesses seem destined to thrive on the wastes of larger enterprises that do not themselves wish to take on the diversification involved in complete utilization of raw materials. Frequently, such large enterprises, committed to specialized mass production programs, prefer to sell their waste materials at a figure which compensates them, in part at least, for the waste involved in their specialization. The small manufacturer can operate at a profit because of the advantageous price he pays for this waste, which constitutes his raw material.³ He cannot grow

---

³ An example is to be found in the relatively small manufacturers of metal toys who rely on the scrap from automobile body production for their raw materials. The toys, small wagons, trains, steam shovels, trucks, and autos, are very substantially made because of the excellent quality of the raw materials from which they are fabricated. Yet they can be profitably sold at relatively low prices because of the low cost of these raw materials to the toy manufacturer. The automobile body maker does not wish to diversify output to the extent required in toy manufacture and is, therefore, willing to sell scrap materials at a figure which enables the small toymaker to produce and sell excellent metal toys very cheaply.

indefinitely, however, because his entire producing advantage is limited to the size of the business which makes his existence possible.

In some measure it may be said that specialization and diversification are like the twin weights of the engine governor. They exert reacting forces. Either without the other throws the governor out of balance; vibration sets in, and excessive wear and unsatisfactory functioning results. As complementing influences, however, they tend to regulate smoothly the speed of the running engine.

## QUESTIONS

1. What were the reasons given by Mr. Hardin for wishing to discontinue the job shop?

2. Why did Mr. Marlow oppose specializing on the paper?

3. If, as Mr. Hardin believed, some of the company's equipment was being operated at a loss, would it not be better to sell it or let it remain idle rather than operate it at a loss?

4. How would you go about determining the cost of producing the newspaper when the job shop is operated in connection?

5. What are the items of expense that would have to be considered?

6. How, in your opinion, would the discontinuing of the job shop affect the profits of the Star-Guard Publishing Company? Explain.

7. What would be necessary to offset any tendency toward increased burden cost which might result from the discontinuing of the job shop?

8. The Star-Guard Publishing Company is an excellent example of the utilization of product diversification as a means of cost reduction. Explain.

9. Name three kinds of industry in which failure to practice product diversification would result in raw materials waste.

10. Why has the Jantzen Knitting Mills found a certain amount of diversification of product desirable in recent years?

11. How has Willys-Overland Motors, Inc., succeeded in getting a diversified product line without incurring many of the costs common to diversified production?

## Problem 11

### CLARK BENSON COMPANY

The Clark Benson Company made an extensive line of metal novelties which included more than 20,000 items when variations in size and finish were taken into account. New items were being added to the line at the rate of about five a week. In the past no systematic attention had been directed to the make-up of the line. Suggestions for new items came chiefly from salesmen. If a salesman could convince the sales manager that he could sell a considerable volume of an item and its manufacture was of a nature such that it could be made on the company's machines, it was usually added to the company's line.

The result had been a general increase in the number of items appearing in the company's catalogue. Executives had become convinced that the line was so diversified as to be unwieldy and sought means to control that situation.

Clark Benson Company had been organized for the manufacture of a coinlike screw driver to be carried attached to one's key ring. The company had been successful and had expanded rapidly, adding many new items of small unit value to its line.

No systematic procedure had been developed for the addition of new items to the line or for the elimination of items of which sales had fallen off greatly. The result was that the line became greatly overdiversified, both as to sales appeal and as to economical production.

To provide greater control over product additions, the form in Exhibit 1 was devised.

Daily, all product suggestions were entered on these forms and sent to the executive in charge of production, who signified whether or not the proposed product was suitable for manufacture in the company's plant. If the production manager approved the item for further consideration, the form was forwarded to the cost department, which obtained estimates of the cost of tools required and computed unit production cost for the item.

132

## EXHIBIT 1

### Clark Benson Company
### Product Suggestion Form

| Description of Product | | Suggested by: | | | |
|---|---|---|---|---|---|
| | | Date | | | |

| Article Name | | No. | Size | Finish | Price |
|---|---|---|---|---|---|

| Tool Cost | Estimated | Actual | Amounts Manufactured, Sold, and in Stock | | | | | |
|---|---|---|---|---|---|---|---|---|
| | | | | First Year, 194 | | | Second Year, 194 | | |
| | | | | Made | Sold | In Stock | Made | Sold | In Stock |
| **Production Cost, One Unit:** | | | Jan. Feb. | | | | | | |
| Estimated | Actual | | Mar. Apr. May | | | | | | |
| Labor | | | June July Aug. | | | | | | |
| Materials | | | Sept. Oct. | | | | | | |
| Burden | | | Nov. Dec. | | | | | | |
| Total | | | Total | | | | | | |

After this information had been compiled, it was entered on the form, which was then returned to the sales manager, whose responsibility it was finally to authorize production. Before doing so, that official obtained sales estimates from various salesmen, and, unless they were generally enthusiastic, the sales manager rarely recommended that the new item be produced. If the sales manager came to the conclusion that the item could be marketed by the company's regular sales organization at a price and in such volume as to ensure a fair profit considering probable production costs, he authorized the item into production.

In the past there had been no systematic follow-up of sales of new articles. The new product suggestion form had a space in which was entered the name of the salesman who suggested the item and spaces for recording the amounts made, sold, and on hand monthly for a period of two years. These entries made it possible to check actual sales of the product and periodically to call to the attention of salesmen making suggestions the progress of the items they had originated.

Salesmen were given full credit for all suggestions which made satisfactory sales progress, but were not held fully responsible for items which failed to do so.

### QUESTIONS

1. To what extent will the new plan serve to control diversification of this company's line?

2. What, if any, are its weaknesses?

### Problem 12

### LAMSON & SESSIONS COMPANY

The Lamson & Sessions Company was a prominent manufacturer of machine and miscellaneous types of bolts, nuts, rivets, cotters, and wire rope clips. The company was considering the adoption of a new type of bolt developed by the company's engineers to replace the old loom or carriage bolt. The new bolt was designed particularly with regard to the needs of the automotive industry, but it could be used in other lines as well.

The design of the common carriage bolt was the result of haphazard development rather than of scientific research. Originally it had been hand-forged from bar stock of a square cross section. It was a round-headed bolt with a square shoulder to prevent rotation. Early bolts had shoulders that extended almost to the end of the bolt, with a very short threaded section. On these early bolts the thread was often cut on the square material with little attempt at rounding the segment to be threaded. The long shoulder ceased to exist with the introduction of automatic bolt machinery. It was unnecessary and, in addition, it was hard to make. The raw material was changed to round stock, and the problem became one of producing a square shoulder rather than of rounding off the threaded end of the bolt.

Common carriage bolts had been standardized since 1920. The head of the standard bolt was, in the opinion of the Lamson & Sessions engineers, 2¾ times as high as was needed. The sole requirement of the head was that it would not shear through under tension. Comparison of the carriage bolt with the step bolt and the fin neck bolt also indicated that the head of the carriage bolt was much larger than was necessary.

The designers of the Lamson & Sessions Company had produced a new bolt which they felt would give just as good service as the carriage bolt and would eliminate the disadvantages of the old type. The major change was in the design of the shoulder. This was made in the shape of a diamond with rounded corners. The new bolt retained the head design and proportions set up as standard by the American Standards Association. Any change in the heads would have meant a large expenditure for new tools necessary to fashion them, whereas retention of the old head design meant that the only change in equipment would be new dies to fashion the shoulder.

The Lamson & Sessions engineers believed that this new type of shoulder would eliminate certain difficulties common in the fabrication of square-shoulder bolts. There were two major parts to the operation, the forming of the shoulder and upsetting to give the shape to the head. After these operations, an automatic screw machine produced the thread. With the old type of shoulder, dirt from the raw materials became embedded in the corners of the forming dies. This dirt often accumulated in two hours of operation and resulted in bolts with corners not sufficiently square to pass inspection. In order to remove the dirt, the tools had to be taken apart and cleaned, and this entailed a loss of from 15 to 30 minutes. The corners would be eliminated in the dies used to form the new shoulder. Hence there would be no dirt accumulations, and the time necessary for cleaning would be reduced.

The square die was made by driving a broach, shaped to outline the shoulder, into the die blank. When such dies were hardening, flaws frequently developed in the sharp corners because, in cooling, the crystals that made up the metal tended to arrange themselves in lines perpendicular to the surface. This set up a severe strain in the corners of the dies, with the result that cracks formed at the corners, and at times dies were split. Sometimes the cracks did not appear until the die was in use, and as they became pronounced the die had to be discarded, for cracks of this sort left such noticeable traces on the bolts that they could not pass inspection. In making dies for the new shoulder, it was possible to fashion them by drilling three holes and cutting out the intervening metal. There would be fewer defective dies, and the dies would have a longer life since they were subjected to less strain. Furthermore, less time would be lost in operation since dies would be changed less frequently. The new dies could be produced economically in small quantities.

The proponents of the new bolt also pointed out that it was one means of combating competition. The designers thought that while the company could not monopolize the new type of bolt, nevertheless a considerable amount of prestige would accrue to Lamson & Sessions Company for being the first in the field with the new product.

From the point of view of the consumer, there were advantages to be derived from the new bolt. When in place, the diamond neck would not rotate as early as the square shoulder. Holes to receive the bolt shoulder need not be square, and therefore would be easier to make. When square holes to receive the shoulder had been punched in metal, they tended to crack at the corners; change in shoulder form of the bolt would eliminate this. Tools used to produce holes to receive the new type of shoulder would last at least five times as long as those used to make square holes. The diameter of the new bolt shoulder was 0.02 inch greater than the diameter of the bolt, so that the new type could be used without damage to the thread. In the old carriage bolt, the side of the square shoulder equaled the outside diameter of the thread, and where the bolt was used in a hole punched through metal, the threads were frequently damaged. The volume of material in the shoulder was somewhat less than in the old type of bolt, and the designers believed that this would be in accord with the trend of the automotive industry toward lightness combined with strength.

Tests of the new bolt disclosed that less force was necessary to bring it down flush with the surrounding surface. At the same time, it was shown that more force was necessary to cause the new bolt to rotate.

## QUESTIONS

1. Explain the advantages and disadvantages of diversifying the company's line by the addition of the new type of bolt.

2. Should the new type of bolt have been added? Explain.

### Problem 13

### MITCHELL-SOUTHERN MILLS

In the summer of 1948 the treasurer of the Mitchell-Southern Mills received a suggestion from the company's selling agent that it increase the number of patterns for the coming spring. For several years the cotton-textile industry had enjoyed an unprecedented demand for its products. Prices had risen to previously unknown heights and during 1947 profits had been the greatest ever known in the industry. During this period all mills had emphasized volume of output and in most cases had reduced drastically the number of patterns run as one means of getting the greatest possible volume of output.

During the first six months of 1948 there had been sporadic evidences of buyer resistance to this situation in the piece goods market. There was no over-all decrease in volume of demand, but occasionally buyers for large stores and for wholesale houses would hold off purchasing for a time, apparently hoping that prices would go down. The Mitchell-Southern Mills' selling agent believed that under the circumstances it would be desirable to increase the number of patterns to be produced for the spring of 1949 to approximately the number regularly run before the war. The company treasurer knew that acceptance of this suggestion would entail increased labor cost per yard of cloth and would reduce the output below the volume currently being attained at the mill.

At that time the mill produced gingham in units, known as "sets," of 10,000 yards each. There was at least one set to a pattern. This permitted 84 patterns to be manufactured each season on the 504 looms in the mill. The gingham produced by the Mitchell-Southern Mills was one of the best grades made in the United States. It was sold through a commission agent to wholesalers, cutters-up, and to about 1,500 retail stores. Patterns for the spring season, the period of greatest sales volume, had to be in the loom the first of September.

The line was shown first to the wholesalers and cutters-up and then to the retailers. While orders were being taken, a salesman often made a recommendation that a specific pattern be run, although the full 240 pieces had not been sold. In that instance the company relied upon him to secure orders for the full set on the pattern. The patterns which were found to be poor sellers were dropped September 1, and a suggestion was made to each purchaser who had ordered a pattern which was to be discontinued that, since the pattern was not likely to be in favor, it might be advisable for the customer to change his order to more popular patterns.

The selling agent had recommended that the mill increase its number of patterns by producing ginghams in sets of 5,000 yards each to give department stores as well as wholesalers a wider variety from which to make their selection. The salesmen believed that a line of at least 150 patterns might be necessary. Many buyers, too, particularly in department stores, purchased one or two pieces of 40 yards each of all patterns in a line in order to have variety and also to be sure of having popular patterns when the preference of consumers was manifested.

The Mitchell-Southern Mills ordered ginghams into manufacture in sets. There were usually 10,000 yards to a set; that number seemed most economical and best adapted to the mill's facilities. Greater expense per yard was incurred when the length of the set was decreased. After the threads were spun, it was necessary to determine how many threads of each color were required in the width of the cloth. A 32-inch gingham was made up of approximately 2,500 threads or ends in width. The length of these threads determined the length of a set for a pattern. If five colors of warp yarn were required for the pattern, five separate beams of yarn were made up of the requisite number of threads, each lot being wound on a steel cylinder. For a typical gingham pattern, one beam contained 500 blue threads, one beam 400 red, one beam 600 green, one beam 700 bleached, and one beam 300 black threads. In making each beam, the waste was approximately 1 yard of warp yarn. This quantity of waste was the same whether a set was only 1,000 yards long or was 10,000 yards. Since time was lost in starting and finishing a beam whether it was to be a long or a short one, long beams saved time.

The yarn or threads on these beams next went through the dyeing process, which was generally one of the most expensive processes in the mill. Almost the same quantity of dye liquid was required to run a short set as to run a long one, and the time spent in dyeing each beam was about the same whether the beam was long or short.

After being dyed, the yarn was delivered in rope form to the beaming room where each of the five colors was put on a separate beam again. The stopping and starting of the beam required approximately an equal period of time for a short or a long length. The yarn from all five beams then was wound on one beam in the dressing department. The five beams were placed one behind another. The threads of all five were combined into one sheet 54 inches wide and were passed through a dressing solution in the slasher, which gave them strength to stand the strain and chafing in weaving. After immersion, the yarn was drawn over a drying cylinder and through a harness or comb which spaced the threads of each color to make the pattern, and then it was wound on a beam which went into the loom. This process required about 2½ hours for setting up the beams and running the ends of the thread through the harness, regardless of whether the set was long or short. A 10,000-yard set made six whole loom beams, each beam containing about 1,666 yards of yarn, which, when wound, made 1,600 yards of cloth or 40 pieces each 40 yards long.  A 10,000-yard set thus produced 240 pieces on six looms during a season.

In addition to extra machinery and time spent in this process for making short sets, there were losses in production and waste in the weaving department.  The production time in that department was about 16 weeks.  One loom during this period wove one loom beam of 1,600 yards; thus, if the mill ran one loom beam of each pattern on 500 looms, it produced 500 different patterns.  If, however, it ran 10,000-yard sets, six looms were required for each set and the number of patterns produced during a season was 84.  This was the situation at the Mitchell-Southern Mills when the selling agent of the company made his recommendation.

Although retail and wholesale buyers sought to protect themselves against fluctuations in demand from one pattern to another by having a wide range of patterns in their lines, price also played an important part in the selection of ginghams.  Retail merchants were selling at various prices that ranged from 59 cents to $1.98 a yard and purchased accordingly.  If a manufacturer's price, for example, was set too high to allow a normal margin of profit when the gingham was sold at the retail price of $1.59, a retailer customarily placed the selling price at $1.69 or bought a cheaper gingham from another manufacturer to be sold at $1.59.  The mill was obliged to meet the competition of other domestic producers of high-grade gingham.

To put this recommendation of the selling agent into effect would increase the cost of the cloth 3 cents per yard if the minimum for a set were reduced to 5,000 yards, 3 cents more if it were changed to 2,500 yards, and an additional 3 cents if it were decreased to 1,250 yards.  This extra cost would be caused partly by the loss in waste and by production expenses in the mill and partly by increased fixed charges per yard of cloth produced at the lower volume of output.

The plan also involved the added expense in designing and in providing samples for salesmen and customers if a greater number of patterns were to be made.  Suggestions for patterns were made by the selling agent's designers.  Sample patterns were designed in various color combinations and, after approval by the mill, the patterns were made up in the looms to be used as samples by the salesmen and wholesalers. Annually, 12,000 yards of cloth were manufactured to incorporate designers' suggestions. This requirement necessarily would be increased to 24,000 yards if the number of patterns was doubled, with an additional cost of $10,200 per year at current prices. The mill gave away about 22,000 yards of cloth annually as samples. Doubling the number of patterns would increase the quantity to 40,000 yards, at an extra expense of $18,000 at the current prices.

An alternative plan was to increase the number of patterns by about 16 the first year, to make a total of 100. This could be accomplished by obtaining from the selling agent his selection of 32 patterns which were considered inferior to the remaining 68 that were to be run. Three looms then could be operated on each of the 32 patterns for the production of 120-piece sets. The remaining 408 looms normally could produce the 68 more popular patterns in 240-piece sets. The less popular patterns were to be run in 5,000-yard sets and repeated later in the season if their salability had been misjudged. The second year the number of patterns could be increased again to perhaps 110 and the run of 20 more of the less popular could be shortened. Selection of the patterns to be run in 120-piece sets was to be delayed until sales could be estimated as accurately as possible. The additional cost of short-run patterns would have been prorated to other patterns.

The treasurer of the Mitchell-Southern Mills, however, decided not to increase the number of patterns. He believed that current demand would continue for some time and that the salesmen were prone to exaggerate the need for an extensive variety of patterns, or to use the lack of numerous patterns as an excuse for not making sales. He knew, moreover, that although patterns and style were important considerations to retail consumers, the purchases of retailers and wholesalers also were affected greatly by price. The increase of 3 cents a yard above the present wholesale prices might increase buyer resistance. The primary consideration, however, was the strength of the demand for gingham. Following the war, ginghams were in such demand that the Mitchell-Southern Mills had experienced no difficulty in selling its entire output, with only 84 patterns. It seemed unwise, therefore, to increase the number at that time, especially in view of the fact that an increase would impede production and increase costs.

## QUESTIONS

1. What disadvantages would the Mitchell-Southern Mills experience if the policy of diversification was adopted?
2. What advantages would accrue?
3. Was the decision of the management sound?

# CHAPTER VII

## EXPANSION

### HALMARK BATTERY CORPORATION

### 1. A Company Considers Expansion of Its Production Facilities.

The Halmark Battery Corporation manufactured storage batteries for use in automobiles. Its manufacturing facilities consisted of one modern plant with a production capacity of 2,500 batteries daily. This plant was a most efficient producing unit and at the time of its erection was considered to be of optimum size. Management of the company, foreseeing an opportunity to sell a greater number of storage batteries, considered ways and means of producing an increased output, if the expansion program was undertaken.

### 2. Dynamic Society.
In attempting to explain the operations of modern industrial society, writers on economics sometimes seek to simplify the picture by first portraying conditions as they are assumed to exist in a static society, *i.e.*, an industrial society in which there would be no change but where there would be movement, a society in which business units would neither expand nor contract and yet would all be in active operation. In other words, in a static society each business would be so perfectly tuned to its environment that no further adjustment would occur. It would simply go on functioning in exactly the same manner day after day.

Whatever may be the advantages of using such a basis for an explanation of the principles which underlie present-day industrial society, the hard, cold fact is that the modern business manager lives in a highly dynamic world where change follows change with bewildering swiftness. Sometimes these modifications can be anticipated and prepared for. Occasionally they are catastrophic, catching the business executive unawares, and perhaps even hurling his organization to destruction.

As a result of the highly dynamic nature of present-day industry, a major task of the modern manager is the adjustment of volume of output to market conditions and the maintenance of the size of the producing unit in harmony with requirements of volume of output and variation in volume. In short, a business unit must possess sufficient flexibility to meet changing conditions.

**3. Influence of the Market on the Expansion Problem.** Increase in the output of a manufacturing concern is a many-sided problem. The degree of certainty or uncertainty of outlet is a most important consideration in determining whether or not expansion is advisable and, if it is, the method of expanding plant output to meet the estimated requirement.

Expansion of a plant being operated at one-shift capacity usually entails steps which are not easy to retract. Therefore, size and permanence of anticipated demand increase are very important. Choice of method of increasing output is greatly affected by conditions of demand. If there is reason to believe that the need for increased output is relatively permanent, expansion may take the form of extension of plant facilities through enlargement of buildings or construction of new buildings and the purchase of new equipment. Such action is long range in its effects, and the addition of one or more working shifts utilizing existing physical facilities may be deemed a more sound procedure. Particularly is this likely to be true if demand permanence is somewhat questionable. In some ways the simplest method of increasing output may be overtime work by the existing crew. This method often seems particularly attractive when there is little or no assurance of substantial, sustained increase in demand. It is the method of least permanent commitment inasmuch as it is usually easy to revert to the old rate of output.

**4. Effect of Expansion on Production Costs.** Expansion of output invariably affects production costs. It is a mistake to assume that increase in output will result in lower unit costs. Costs of product may be lower per unit of output or, unless care is exercised, may be higher. This effect on production costs may result from permanence or lack of permanence in the new rate of output. Even though the new rate of production be constantly maintained, the change in processing is very likely to affect costs, and the change is as likely to be an increase as a decrease in the cost of producing each unit of product turned out. Costs, then, are a most important aspect of the expansion problem. Particularly is this true of labor and burden costs.

**5. The Business Aspect of Plant Expansion.** The financing of an expansion program is obviously a business problem. Questions involved in demand determination are likewise obviously of a business nature. Somewhat less apparent are the strictly business aspects of the method of getting the desired physical increase. These business considerations largely grow out of the relation of demand stability to method of operation and the effect of method of expansion on cost of the product turned out. Thus, business considerations are involved even in such technical engineering matters as determination of method of processing and the selection of equipment to be employed.

This chapter deals mainly with the business aspects of the expansion problem. Some consideration of the techniques of production is inevitable, but these are dealt with as the businessman is concerned with them. Production is always a twofold problem. It involves engineering and it involves the business utilization of engineering techniques. Certainly the business executive cannot ignore the engineering aspects of production, and production on an exclusively engineering basis does not ensure profit. The executive of an industrial enterprise may or may not be an engineer. Frequently he is essentially a financier or a man with a market and sales background. Lack of engineering training need not preclude success in this field, provided that there is understanding of the importance of sound engineering technique and ability to utilize such techniques in a business program. In no industrial management problem is this relationship of business and engineering closer than in the expansion of the successful manufacturing enterprise. To ignore the business aspect of this problem is fatal. Failure to appreciate and evaluate soundly the technical aspects of production expansion will defeat the very object of the expansion, profit increase.

**6. Problem of the Halmark Battery Corporation.** The Halmark Battery Corporation had been organized by Thomas

Laboratories, Inc., to undertake the manufacture and sale of lead-acid storage batteries.  The enterprise had been instigated at the request of a large-scale purchaser of batteries that the research organization of Thomas Laboratories, Inc., develop a more efficient battery at a cost comparable with costs of other batteries on the market.  A large contract had been promised Thomas Laboratories, Inc., provided that an improved battery could be designed.  After diligent research a battery that met the specifications of the purchaser had been developed and the contract granted.

Thomas Laboratories, Inc., was a manufacturing company controlling several subsidiaries engaged in the manufacture and sale of products bearing the company name or trade-mark.  The corporation was noted for its research activities in the electrical industry and other industries.  As soon as a new or improved product was developed by its principal organization, so that a fairly stable demand for a quantity suitable for economical manufacture was ensured, it was the policy of the company to organize a subsidiary company to carry on the enterprise.  The Halmark Battery Corporation had been organized in accordance with this policy.

Thomas Laboratories, Inc., executives sought and managed to secure a man to plan and build the new manufacturing unit who was of an open mind and unhampered by traditions of battery manufacture, but who had an adequate background of technical and industrial experience.  This new man, Mr. Demarest, as general manager was given responsibility for the determination of the size of the unit, for erecting and equipping buildings, for redesigning the product to meet manufacturing conditions, and for selecting the executives and personnel.

After a thorough study of the situation, Mr. Demarest concluded that the economical quantity of manufacture was approximately 2,500 batteries per day, and this quantity became the basis for further plans.  This manufacturing quantity was determined in part by the requirements of the assembly plant maintained by the automobile manufacturer who awarded the contract previously referred to and in part by the balancing of labor and overhead costs estimated for several ranges of output that might be secured by sales outside the contract.

A site for the new plant was selected in a growing manufacturing center which attracted labor and service industries. Sufficient land was reclaimed by the filling of a marshy tract to meet the needs not only for a plant of the desired capacity but also for an expansion to four times the original capacity. Concrete buildings were erected in a manner allowing for the construction of additional buildings, either as independent units or in the original line of processing. Careful attention had also been given, prior to the construction of the plant, to the design and construction of both processing equipment and handling equipment, and to their adaptation to each other.

As a result of the careful preplanning of the enterprise, the manufacture of 2,500 batteries per day was undertaken on a most efficient basis. Particularly noticeable to a visitor at the plant was the small number of men working at jobs other than direct operation or supervision of machines. This situation had resulted from a coordination of equipment for handling raw materials and work in process with the various production machines and from an analysis of jobs in order to secure an effective division of labor both between individuals and between the operative and the machine. Production was on a straight-line basis. The sequence of operations was planned so that the various groups of workmen reported for work at different hours in accordance with the process schedule. Similarly, each group finished at a different hour in the afternoon. The plant was manned and equipped for a daily production of 2,500 batteries without recourse to a night shift or overtime except for three processes. Grid casting was accomplished by three shifts working continuously during a three-day week because of the saving in gas, labor, and material losses due to drossing of the metal when melting pots were shut down and started up. Forming and charging were also continuous processes on three shifts because of the small amount of labor involved and the desire to save time in processing. Had it not been for the forming and charging operations, it would have been possible for the plant to have a complete turnover of 2,500 batteries each day, the parts passing through the various operations and emerging as completed batteries to be shipped at night.

Waste in motion, effort, time, and material was minimized. Among the achievements of the new management which were indicative of its diligence and inventiveness were the piping of molten lead to different points in the process, the designing of automatic equipment for the casting of lead parts, the "pasting" of plates by machine, the designing of new features to provide extra capacity, and the developing of devices to ensure and control the quality of production. To safeguard the worker, furthermore, since lead-battery manufacture presented hazards to health from lead poisoning, the management developed tests for applicants for jobs, maintained a medical department with a nurse in attendance, protected the workmen's street clothes from contamination by a washing process which made it impossible for an employee to avoid responsibility in this connection, provided workmen with respirators, and installed a ventilating system.

The existing plant required a force of 150 men in turning out 2,500 batteries daily.[1]  The batteries were produced in various sizes, the number of plates varying from 7 to 21, and in four grades, varying as to materials and workmanship. The retail prices of the four grades in the 13-plate size were $6.95, $8.95, $13.95 and $17.95. Approximately 65 per cent of the cost of producing a battery was represented by the cost of materials, and 35 per cent by the labor and overhead.

**7. Battery Manufacture at the Halmark Battery Corporation Plant.**  The manufacture of a storage battery is a combination of fabrication and assembly. The parts which go to make up a storage battery are the case, the cell covers, the vent plugs, the plates, the separators, the plate straps or posts, the connectors, the sealing compound, and the electrolyte. The Halmark Battery Corporation purchased cases, cell covers, vent plugs, and separators. Its major fabrication operations were those of manufacturing the plates (see Exhibit 1). The main operations in

[1] The plant of a well-known Middle Western battery company had a daily capacity of 15,000 batteries. Production at this volume required a force of approximately one thousand men. The Toronto and Los Angeles plants of the same company had capacities of 1,000 and 2,000 batteries per day.

making the plates were grid casting, grid trimming, mixing the paste with which the grids were filled, applying the paste to the grids, grid drying, and giving the plates a forming charge.

The grid or framework of latticelike construction was cast from a lead alloy in molds. At the Halmark plant, standardization of design and perfection of equipment made it possible to cast grids for both positive and negative plates for all sizes of the battery by mechanical means. The equipment automatically controlled the temperature of the metal which was mechanically poured into molds resembling waffle irons. The castings were automatically cooled, removed, and conveyed to a trimming and inspection station. Two men supervised three casting machines.

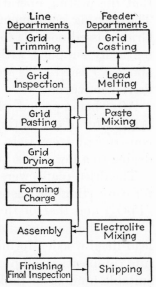

After being cast, grids were trimmed and inspected by examination for broken bars, cracked lugs, and other imperfections. Defective grids were remelted and recast. Perfect grids passed on to the pasting operation.

The mixing of the paste that constituted the active material was done by machine. Cranks of peculiar shape, revolving in opposite directions within

EXHIBIT 1. HALMARK BATTERY CORPORATION. PROCESS DIAGRAM.

a drum, mixed thoroughly the various components that made up the paste. Scientific control through rigid adherence to formulas and constant testing of materials made possible the best of active materials in well-conditioned pastes, both positive and negative. The mixing machines were located on a mezzanine directly above the pasting machines. Materials used in making the paste were conveyed in drums to bins and thence to the mixing machines. Mixed paste flowed by gravity to the pasting machines on the floor beneath them.

The pasting of the grids was done by machine. The principle of the machine operation was quite similar to the hand method employed in some shops. The puttylike active material was spread over the grid and worked thoroughly between the latticed members. The paste was compacted into the grids by mechanical means so regulated as to produce uniform plates by subjecting each area to the same pressure. As the life of a storage battery is partly contingent upon the conductivity ensured by a proper bond between the active material and the grid, it was essential that the pasting operation be performed in an efficient manner. The pasting equipment formed a part of the production line. Grids passed on rolls to the pasting machines, which were automatically supplied with paste from the paste-mixing machines above. Pasted grids were mechanically discharged onto power-driven conveyors.

After being pasted, plates were dried. In the open air, drying is a matter of one to three days. At the Halmark plant specially constructed ovens were used which reduced the time required for drying to a few hours.

The dried plates were given an initial charge (forming charge) for converting the paste of the positive plates into lead peroxide ($PbO_2$) and that of the negative plates into sponge lead (Pb). To give the forming charge, plates were hung on racks in lead or lead-lined wooden forming tanks containing electrolyte of a definite composition, all plates being connected to a common bus. A suitable number of tanks were then connected in series, and the line connected to the corresponding busses from the generator which supplied the forming current. In forming the positive and negative plates, various charging rates and time cycles in regulation of current were used, depending on the size of the plate. There were also controlled variations in the density of the electrolyte. By virtue of standardized materials and usage, the forming charge at the Halmark plant was subject to close scientific control by an operative in a glass-enclosed room with instruments to keep him informed of the progress of all units. The forming process had been reduced to 30 hours.

Upon completion of the forming charge, the plates were drained and then burned into groups. This was accomplished by setting up the single plates in fixtures and welding their lugs to posts by means of torches. As a result of this operation the so-called "groups" were obtained, consisting of a definite number of positive or negative plates joined to a plate strap (or post) and so spaced that they could be meshed or leaved together with a corresponding group of opposite polarity with separators inserted between the opposing plates. Such a pair of groups with the inserted separators composed an "element," the unit placed in each cell of a battery being assembled. An element having been placed in each cell of a given battery, the cell covers were slipped over the posts, a sealing compound poured in the space between the covers and the cell walls, and connectors burned on in such a way that the cells were connected in series. The assembled battery, after being subjected to various inspections, was filled with electrolyte of the proper strength and was given an additional charge known as the "conditioning" charge. At the Halmark plant, the assembly took place on a series of roller conveyors by which the battery passed from one station to the next, each worker performing one of the several necessary operations. Capacity production required nine workers on the assembly line. The oxyacetylene flame for burning on connectors was turned off and on by an automatic switch as each unit passed down the line.

The finishing operations consisted of smoothing out irregularities in the assembled unit, marking terminal posts, painting on trade-marks, placing vent plugs in the filling holes of the cell covers, and various inspection operations, including a final inspection just prior to packing for shipment.

**8. Possible Methods of Increasing Halmark Battery Corporation Output.** When the Halmark Battery Corporation had been in operation for three years, the executives of the company foresaw an opportunity to increase the demand for its batteries. Increased output, they believed, could be obtained through an extension of the sales made to outlets other than those resulting from the original contract. It was quite possible that total production might need to be increased from 2,500 to 5,000 batteries per day. Company executives considered and investigated several methods of increasing output. Night-shift operation of the existing unit was obviously worthy of consideration. The management was firm in its belief in the efficiency of the existing unit.

This suggested as an alternative setting up a second complete unit duplicating the present one. If this was done, two courses would be possible: (1) increase in the size of the present plant to accommodate the new unit or (2) construction of a separate building to house the second unit. Another method of expansion would be extension of the present line by the installation of machines of larger capacity, or by duplicates of present machines used in the various operations throughout the process. Still other methods of increasing output were possible.

**9. Advantages and Disadvantages of a Night Shift.** Seemingly, a second shift would be the easiest and simplest method of increasing output. By operating the lead-melting and grid-casting units continuously, investment in new facilities could be limited to additional equipment for forming charges, which would consist of more tanks with their control devices. The result would be more intensive use of existing equipment, which would tend to reduce unit burden costs both for present output and for the added volume. While burden costs in battery manufacture were commonly much less than raw materials costs, nevertheless they represented a substantial element in cost of production, and the effect of any expansion proposal on burden costs was an important consideration of Halmark executives. The more intensive use of equipment would tend to reduce risks of equipment obsolescence. As the lead-acid storage battery and its production process were well past the stage of rapid development, these obsolescence risks would probably be of less importance than if the product and its manufacture were newer.

The greatest disadvantage of a second shift was thought to be difficulty in obtaining suitable labor. Night operation was not common in the locality, and transportation would be inconvenient for the men. Certainly a higher hourly wage would have to be paid than was necessary for the day shift, and even then it was likely that spoilage would be increased. It could be argued that mechanized production of this type calls for little skilled labor and that unskilled labor could probably be found and trained. It might also be pointed out that, like burden, labor costs were not a large percentage of total costs. This would tend to minimize the importance of higher wage rates. Some difficulty might well be expected in providing good supervision. While it is true that supervision would be less difficult than in some industries, protection of the company's reputation for high quality without greatly increasing spoilage would call for efficient supervision. This would probably entail transfer and promotion from the day shift.

It is unlikely that the installation of a second shift would result in lower unit production costs for this business. Depreciation and obsolescence costs would be lower, but labor and supervision costs would be higher. The net effect on unit costs would probably be an increase rather than a decrease.

The most attractive feature of the plan is its responsiveness to volume change. Should the increase in demand prove temporary, it would be possible to return to one-shift operation without greatly increasing operating costs. Nightworkers could be laid off, and there would be little idle equipment as a result of output curtailment. Also, if the increased demand should prove to be fluctuating on a seasonal or other basis, the extra-shift method is probably best suited as to flexibility.

**10. Advantages and Disadvantages of Duplicating the Existing Unit.** Company executives were convinced of the low-cost operating efficiency of the 2,500-batteries-per-day unit. This suggests the desirability of expanding by building a second unit, a duplicate of the existing one. Such a plant would incur none of the developmental costs incurred when the first plant was built. Furthermore, experience with a similar unit would make it possible to avoid much of the lack of smoothness which is usually costly when a new plant goes into operation. Finally, the costs of operation would be known in advance.

If a duplicate plant was erected, it would be operated as a separate unit on its own orders and under the control of its own executive personnel. Results of operation would be subject to check against those of the older plant, and the competitive situation thus developed might well prove a valuable continuing incentive throughout the organization from top to bottom. A second complete unit would avoid most of the objections to a night shift. It would have no disturbing effect on existing operations, and results would be accurately predictable.

The building of a separate 2,500-batteries-per-day unit is obviously a long-time commitment, possessing little flexibility to meet volume change. It is true that any fluctuation in the added volume would have no effect upon the operation efficiency and production cost of the present unit. This does not mean, of course, that the profits of the business as a whole would not suffer if the new unit was idle. This lack of flexibility is the most obvious objection to the building of a duplicate unit. The plan calls for the same sort of demand assurance that was requisite to the construction of the original plant.

**11. Expansion of Present Production Lines.** The chief argument in favor of a separate duplicate of the present unit is the proved efficiency of the 2,500-batteries-per-day unit. At the time the existing plant was constructed, a unit of this size was judged to be of optimum size. As the management still holds that opinion, it would seem that increasing capacity of the various parts of the existing plant would be undesirable. It would tend to upset existing operating efficiency and increase production cost. Operation might well be so inflexible as to affect adversely costs of all batteries produced if volume of output was substantially below capacity.

There is another aspect of this situation, however, which is probably of major concern. When the size of the existing unit was determined, two types of influences dictated, market demand and technique of production. If the demand situation has substantially changed, this alone might call for a departure from 2,500 batteries per day as the optimum output. Also, it is unlikely, even in so simple a process as the one involved, that optimum size for each and every operation would be the same.

It can be readily demonstrated in this case that optimum size of the process as a whole was the result of compromise as to capacity of the various operations making up the complete process. Although the plant as a whole operated six days a week, the lead-melting and grid-casting operations were carried on only one-half of that time, three days a week. This means that insofar as these two operations are concerned, a process capacity of 5,000 batteries per day is more nearly optimum as to technique of operation and production cost than is a capacity of half that output.

This does not mean that the capacity of the lead-melting and grid-casting equipment installed is excessive. Nor does it mean that the process as a whole has submaximum efficiency. It only demonstrates that inevitably optimum capacity of a plant as a whole does not mean that each step in the process will be carried on at optimum rate of operation.

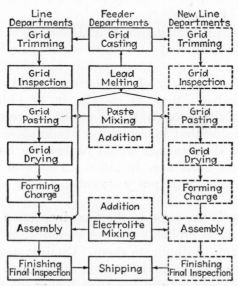

EXHIBIT 2. HALMARK BATTERY CORPORATION. DIAGRAM TO SHOW PROPOSED CHANGES IN PROCESS.

This situation is of considerable importance in determining a method of expanding plant facilities of the Halmark Battery Corporation. There is substantial argument in favor of increasing output by means of a combination of duplication of certain steps in the process, increasing the capacity of some steps without duplication, and utilization of the excess capacity that already exists in certain operations as now carried on. The diagram in Exhibit 2 is indicative of the possibilities of processing economies inherent in this method of securing increased capacity.

In the diagram no additional facilities for lead melting and grid casting are indicated. It is proposed to operate existing equipment six days a week instead of three. The result would be a unit cost for these operations less than the existing cost. This reduction would be effective for both the new volume and the present output. Variation in output would affect these costs but would never increase them above unit costs prior to expansion, and would tend to decrease existing costs to the extent that output is in excess of the 2,500-batteries-per-day level. This proposal seems to be the most likely method of treatment for lead melting and grid casting.

The equipment for mixing paste and electrolyte might well be displaced with equipment of greater capacity. The nature of these operations indicates this procedure in the interest of lower labor costs. Careful study of the operations and equipment involved might indicate that the installation of additional equipment similar to that already in use would be preferable. However, it is probable that investigation would show that costs of operating these departments would be less per battery if new, larger equipment units were installed. This would be likely to hold true even though output were substantially less than 5,000 units per day.

The situation is the same in the final inspection and shipping departments. It is probably more economical to expand these departments than to duplicate them. Quality standards should be more uniform in a single inspection department and shipping costs should be substantially less than if two complete shipping organizations handling the same products were maintained.

The nature of the other operations of the process indicates that these steps are now carried on at an optimum rate. If this is true, these units should not be disturbed, and greatest efficiency at maximum and submaximum rates of operation could be obtained by setting up separate duplicates of the existing units. Operating costs at capacity output would probably be close to present unit costs for these operations. Output at less than 2,500 product units per day would be less disturbing than if other methods of expansion were employed. As long as output was up to 2,500 batteries per day, one line could be operated at optimum efficiency, and only unit costs in excess of 2,500 batteries and less than 5,000 batteries would be adversely affected. Furthermore, this adverse effect would probably be less than if equipment of greater capacity was designed or than if duplicate units were installed in a single line of operation.

The foregoing is a recommendation for investigation rather than a definitely indicated solution to the problem. The possibilities of such a procedure should be carefully considered, and studies should be carried out for each step of the process. It is rare indeed that optimum rate of operation for a complete process will coincide with optimum rate for each and every step in the process. This clearly indicates that expansion in excess of over-all optimum operating rate may make possible reduction of costs for some operations. The possibilities inherent in this situation should never be neglected.

**12. Summary and Conclusions.** The case of the Halmark Battery Corporation is an excellent illustration of the management problems involved in increasing the output of a manufacturing business. These problems are essentially of two types: engineering and business. The engineering problems have to do with changes in methods of processing and design and installation of the equipment involved. The business problems have to do with market demand for the product and cost of production as affected by variation in market demand and change in method of production. The engineering and business aspects of expansion are so interrelated as to be practically incapable of isolation. Neither is more critical than the other. Neither will alone provide a solution. The important principle is that neither should be neglected.

*Methods of Expansion—Overtime Work.* The common methods of securing increase in output are overtime work, night shifts, and increase in physical production facilities. Overtime work is best suited for temporary increases of short duration. Usually no increased permanent investment is involved, and return to normal rates of operation is thus relatively easy. The existing work force is not expanded, and no costs of hiring and training operatives and supervisory personnel are involved. However, overtime work can never be more than a means of satisfying temporary, short-lived increases in demand. Hourly wage rates or base rates are usually 50 per cent greater for overtime work. Men cannot efficiently work long hours for any protracted period of time. Modern efficient operation calls for speed on the part of operatives that precludes this. Overtime work runs up labor cost, increases spoilage, and tends to increase costs of supervision. Its most desirable attribute is its flexibility. Its outstanding limitations are its costs and its temporary nature.

*Night Shifts.* Recently, short hours for men and long hours for machines has become almost a battle cry in industry. The intensive use of equipment is often very attractive from a business standpoint. In industries where product, methods, or machines are in process of rapid development, night operation frequently is an excellent means of forestalling the high costs of equipment obsolescence. Even when the product and process have attained a rather stable state, intensive use of the equipment aids materially in lessening the risk inherent in the long-time capital commitments of mechanized industry. Machines cannot distinguish between day and night, and machine efficiency usually is just as high after sunset as it is during the daylight hours.

Nightwork for men is of more questionable desirability. It is a matter concerning which there are "schools of thought." Undoubtedly, nightwork is commonly somewhat more costly than daytime labor. While this is not always true, there is a tendency for night hourly wages to be somewhat higher than daytime wages. If there is a difference in labor efficiency between day and night shifts, the margin is in favor of the day shift. Commonly, men would rather work a day shift than a night shift.

This does not mean that night shifts are undesirable. First, the machine cost savings frequently much more than offset the higher labor costs. Furthermore, in some industrial communities, night operation of mills is common to the extent that there is little or no wage differential between day and night shifts. Many manufacturers are today demonstrating that with proper supervision night labor can be just as efficient as day labor in many industries. It has frequently been proved that, given favorable conditions, spoilage by the night shift need be no greater than that by the day shift. In certain locations, night atmospheric conditions are actually superior and more conducive to efficient processing. Continuous operation often tends to reduce cost per unit of power used in processing, particularly when power is purchased. Not all men object to working on night shifts. Occasionally workers actually prefer night-shift work, either because of higher wages received or because of greater freedom during daylight hours. From the labor standpoint, practically the only generalization that can be laid down with regard to nightwork is that there is a definite tendency for it to be less satisfactory and to compare less favorably with daywork than is the case with machine costs.

The social desirability of nightwork is a debated issue. Some states prohibit nightwork for women in certain industries. Some authorities urge that men do not like nightwork and that it results in undesirable social conditions. The answer in a given case seems to depend on the community. If night operation of plants is common in the vicinity, the social effect of any one plant's adding a night shift is quite different from what it would be if the life of the community were not adjusted to a considerable amount of nightwork. While the absence or prevalence of nightwork in a community is no index of the general social level of the community, it is an important factor in the building up of a suitable night labor supply.

The major advantages of the night shift as a means of increasing plant output are its tendency to reduce physical investment risks and costs and its responsiveness to demand fluctuation. In this latter regard, it is more rigid than overtime work. Increase in output on this basis entails the building up of the work force with its attendant costs of hiring and training. Overtime work avoids these costs. Discontinuance of a night shift is a more serious decision than is discontinuance of overtime work. Nevertheless, the night shift is flexible as to capital commitment.

The outstanding disadvantages of the night-shift method have to do with personnel. Labor supply is not always available or of the best. Wages may be higher for nightwork. Transportation may be difficult. Workers may be less efficient. Quality of output may suffer.

Obviously there is no one answer to the night-shift problem. The nature of the product and the process, the quantity and characteristics of the labor required, site and location—these things, and others, vary as between cases. Thus the answer must be based upon the particular situation with due regard for both the business itself and the environment in which it operates.

*Plant Expansion.* Commonly, where overtime work and night shifts are weak, expansion of physical facilities is the strong method of increasing output. Conversely, plant expansion is likely to be weak where long hours of operation of existing facilities are strong. Plant expansion is likely to be advantageous on the labor side; its most frequent weakness is in its permanence of capital commitment and inflexibility in changing conditions.

These generalizations do not always hold. There are times when very large capital expenditures tend to discourage competition. Particularly is this true when the utilization of machines and equipment of greater capacity tend to reduce operating costs. All too frequently this expectation is overdone. Many gigantic producing units exist today that have failed to live up to expectations of low unit producing costs. The economies of size are much less than is commonly thought. In many processes, the point of balanced returns is reached rather early in the expansion process. Much ill-advised financial promotion fails on this account. It is inefficient production capacity rather than excessive production capacity that afflicts much of industry today.

When physical plant facilities are increased, the method of expansion is just as important as the question whether to expand or not to expand which preceded it. This is demonstrated in the Halmark Battery Corporation case. Engineering skills and techniques pervade this problem, but, as we have already seen, the business aspects of the situation are of equal importance.

Probably all too little attention has been given the idea of optimum size of the producing unit. When management has this concept under consideration, it should always be remembered that even this is subject to the influences of change. Undoubtedly, certain businesses have characteristic size optimums, large units conclusively more efficient than small, or small units possessing all or most of the advantages of large units and at the same time escaping many of the difficulties of large unit administration. But within these limits, change in production technique or market characteristics may drastically alter the output level at which production is most economically attained. Also, the limit characteristics themselves are not permanently fixed. Extension of recent labor organization activities seems already to be making for a tendency toward smaller decentralized producing units in some industries. Also, technical production changes do occasionally result in production economies for small units which bring them up into the class of relatively low-cost producers. Optimum size of producing unit is a worth-while management goal. It should be remembered, however, that optimum size changes, that the dynamic characteristics of industrial society have their impact here as elsewhere, and that today's optimum may be obsolete tomorrow. A management to succeed must be forward-looking in the areas of market demand and production technique if its control of size of producing unit is to be most efficient. As a corollary, it is a mistake to believe that because a clever management has brought into existence a plant of size such that operating costs are at a minimum, increase in output beyond the capacity of that unit will of necessity be a matter of simple duplication. The situation of the Halmark Battery Corporation is a case in point.

Increase in demand for a product already in production is not the only condition which may initiate consideration of production expansion. As we shall see when we come to consider the selection and layout of production equipment, obsolescence of existing production facilities may well raise this issue. Occasionally, inefficiencies of marketing at an existing production level may bring expansion or contraction of production facilities into consideration. Market demand for variety in output also often brings the question up for discussion. Under the latter condition, the problem may become acute, as the desires of the production group may well be in distinct conflict with the aims of the production executives. This problem receives consideration in the chapters on diversification and integration of production.

*Effects of General Economic and Social Change on Current Problems of Expansion.* Immediately following the cessation of the Second World War hostilities, industry set about the reconversion of its facilities for the production of peacetime consumables. This change-over was accompanied by an unusual expansion of industrial production capacity. Billions of dollars were spent for new plants and new equipment. Two major motives were behind this activity: (1) Accumulated technological improvements called for replacement of existing equipment if a producing unit again was to become competitive in its field. (2) For two decades production capacity had not kept pace with growth of population. These conditions were basic long-run influences; they were obvious and were powerful spurs to the industrial expansion that followed the war.

Perhaps more immediate influences were such factors as the tremendous unsatisfied demand for all kinds of manufactured products that had accumulated during the war, the foreseeable demand for American goods abroad during the years of foreign reconstruction, and the rapid rise in wages. The first two of these considerations were clearly of temporary duration. The future level of wages was less readily determinable. The great increase in wage rates, particularly for the large numbers of unskilled and semiskilled industrial workers brought about a shift in cost balance at many points. With high wages, it was frequently desirable to mechanize an operation that had been more cheaply done by hand before the war. Automatic machines could produce more cheaply with wages up than could semiautomatic machines. In many instances semiautomatic machines replaced manually operated machines.

Periods of rapid wage rise have usually been followed by periods of wage recession. Seldom have wages been reduced in these periods to the point from which they started. In the postwar period there was unusually strong reason to believe that wages never again would return to anything like prewar levels. The war period and the postwar years saw great growth in size and strength of labor organizations. Many industrialists believed that these huge powerful unions of national scope would successfully resist any reduction in wages that would result in a labor cost level at all approaching that of the 1930's. Thus the risks of large capital expenditures for increased mechanization seemed less than the risks of loss of competitive position that might result from failure to mechanize. This situation was less certain than was the influence of population increase. On the other hand, it was probably of more lasting effect than consumer demand backlogs that had accumulated during the war.

Many industrial concerns entered the reconversion period with substantial accumulations of resources that made expansion possible. On the other hand, costs of new equipment rose rapidly following the war and the cost of new plant construction more than doubled. These latter adverse influences caused substantial hesitation on the part of management, but the net balance of the many factors involved was a very substantial increase in industrial capacity brought about by expansion of plant and facilities. Insofar as industry is concerned, the forces of social and economic change are irresistible. The decade of the 1940's has seen such changes occurring at an unprecedented rate. There was little that a manufacturer could do but shiver and take the plunge into a stream of developments, the temperature or depth of which could be but little known.

## QUESTIONS

1. Why should the modern business unit possess flexibility?

2. What are some of the conditions which may cause consideration of the expansion of the output of a plant?

3. What are the common methods of increasing the output of a plant which is operating at one-shift capacity?

4. What are the elements of strength and weakness of each method?

5. Under what conditions is each method most likely to be successful?

6. What is meant by the term "optimum-size unit"?

7. When a management has achieved a producing unit of optimum size, what is the nature of its problem of rate of output?

8. What is the best way of meeting this problem?

9. In your opinion, what is the best method of increasing output for the Halmark Battery Corporation? Explain fully.

10. Should the management of the Halmark Battery Corporation come to a conclusion as to whether or not to expand output

without previously reaching a decision as to the method of production increase to be employed if expansion is undertaken?

11. What is the contribution of the mechanical engineer in reaching conclusions on expansion problems?

12. Will engineering considerations provide a satisfactory solution to an expansion problem? Why?

13. What were the causes of the industrial expansion that followed the Second World War?

14. Be prepared to discuss the problems of the manufacturer who had to decide whether or not to expand his plant capacity during that period.

## BELFORD CORK COMPANY

The plant of the Belford Cork Company was operating at less than capacity, and company executives believed that as a result production costs were relatively high. An increase in output would entail increased selling expense, which it was expected would increase more rapidly than the volume. The management was not sure whether or not decreases in production cost resulting from the greater volume would more than offset the increase in selling expense necessary to market the additional output.

Sales of the company in its principal line, which comprised about 90 per cent of its business, were $188,000 for the year. On this portion of the sales it made a net profit of $9,000. Productive materials amounted to $84,000; direct labor, $35,000; indirect labor and all other overhead, $50,000; and selling expense, $10,000.

Plant capacity was sufficient to permit an increase in sales volume of one-third. Additional working capital would be needed to finance any increase in operation and was available at 4 per cent. New markets would have to be solicited, and these could be reached only with an increase in the percentage of selling expense to total sales.

It was expected that if sales increased, the cost of materials and direct labor would rise in proportion to the increase of output. Of the indirect labor item and all other overhead, it was estimated that $15,000 was fixed and would not increase or decrease with volume. The balance of the item, however, was variable but would increase only one-half as fast as the volume. Selling expense for the extra volume was expected to be not less than 15 per cent of the amount of the increase in sales and might be even greater. Working capital necessary to finance the new volume was expected to have a turnover of twice a year.

## QUESTIONS

1. Should the Belford Cork Company have attempted to increase its sales to enable it to operate at capacity?

2. What is the maximum additional selling expense that could be profitably supported by the added volume of business?

### Problem 15

### RAVENCROFT MANUFACTURING COMPANY

The Ravencroft Manufacturing Company had more business than it could handle by operating only during normal hours. Consequently, executives of the company faced the task of selecting some means of increasing output. The three devices under consideration were systematic overtime work, establishment of a night shift, and building an addition to the plant.

The products of the Ravencroft Manufacturing Company were metal specialties of wide variety used in many different industries. The company's plant was located on the outskirts of Trenton, New Jersey, and consisted of several buildings which had been erected at different times as the company's business had increased. Growth had been steady and in recent years rapid. One large unit had recently been added to the plant, but the company had already outgrown the facilities thus provided. Some temporary relief was being obtained by the erection of a new office building, which released a considerable space in one of the factory buildings heretofore occupied for office purposes, but need for increased production was still pressing, and the company had under consideration three methods of providing for it. These were overtime work with the present force, organization of a night shift, and the erection of another manufacturing unit.

The company employed about 600 men, many of whom lived in Trenton and nearby towns. Some of the employees had their own automobiles, but the majority were dependent on reaching the plant by means of a railroad which ran close by, or by trolley. The business was not seasonal to any appreciable extent, and the manufacturing load was consequently very nearly uniform.

Overtime work was the method which involved the least change in organization, facilities, and overhead costs. It had frequently been necessary for the employees to work overtime, but if the increase in business was to be permanent it would be impossible to continue this practice indefinitely. In the past, working until ten o'clock at night three days a week was as much as the management had felt it could ask the men to do, and the probabilities were that at least four or five nights a week would be necessary. In addition there was the expense of paying time and a half for the work, and a tendency toward decreased production per man per hour because of fatigue. Going home late at night was an annoyance to the men, since there were no trains at that hour and trolley service was infrequent.

The proposal to organize a night shift, at least for certain departments, offered a more permanent form of relief, and the outlook for the company's business seemed to warrant the expectation that the overload would continue for an indefinite period. With a night shift, however, there would be the usual disadvantages of nightwork, and also some additional drawbacks in this particular case. It was difficult to get good men who were willing to work on a night shift. The matter of supervision would have to be taken care of by placing foremen or assistant foremen of the day shift in charge of the nightwork. The company felt that this would be a difficult matter to arrange satisfactorily. The night crew would probably have to be organized by partial dilution, *i.e.*, by placing on the night shift a number of the day-shift workers and replacing them by inexperienced men to complete the force of the day shift. In the judgment of the management, the night shift would not be so efficient as the day shift, and there was always some lost motion and a certain amount of spoiled work when one shift had to pick up the work which the other shift left. Many operations would be incomplete when the whistle blew, and in many cases there would be chance for excuses for spoiled work, making it difficult to fix responsibility. The efficiency per man-hour could not be determined in advance, but the management felt that it would be lower than that obtained by the day shift. Furthermore, in the case of this particular company many of the operations required a considerable degree of skill, and the training and organizing of a night force presented more than ordinary difficulties.

It was estimated that a new building and equipment suitable to provide for the immediate needs of the company would cost about $100,000. The expenditure of this amount of money was a serious matter. Such a capital outlay might call for increased borrowings at the banks at times or might necessitate the reduction of dividends, and the investment would add to taxes, insurance, and depreciation. Some economies in operation might be expected from the opportunity to install the latest type of machines and to arrange a layout unhampered by restrictions. There was plenty of land on which to build, and the new unit could be located with proper reference to the flow of work.

The location of the plant was a good one for the purpose, ready access being obtainable both to raw materials and to markets. The wide diversity of the company's product made it susceptible only to general business conditions, and while a considerable portion was sold to certain particular industries such as the automobile industry, the management did not believe that depression in any one line would seriously affect the output.

Power was generated by the company for part of its requirements, and exhaust steam was used for heating. Outside current was purchased for the balance of the power requirements and would have to be purchased for the new unit.

### QUESTIONS

1. What were the advantages and disadvantages of each of the three proposals: overtime, night shifts, or plant additions?

2. Explain in detail the effects of each of these plans upon the various production costs of the three types: labor, raw materials, and burden.

3. What action should the company have taken?

## Problem 16

### EVER-GLOW OIL COMPANY

The Ever-Glow Oil Company, an independent refinery, had difficulty in disposing of sulphuric acid after it had been used to purify kerosene and gasoline. The problem became acute whenever the acid manufacturers were unable to accept return shipments of the impregnated acid. Other refineries which experienced the same difficulty had constructed plants to convert the acid into usable condition. A new method of purifying acid had recently been perfected, and the management of the Ever-Glow Oil Company was considering the advisability of expanding the scope of the company's operations to include reclamation of sulphuric acid.

The company converted annually about 500,000 barrels of Mexican crude petroleum into gasoline, kerosene, and various grades of oil and asphalt. The annual consumption of acid for conversion purposes was 1,800 tons. This acid was bought on contract and shipped in tank cars to the plant, where it was stored until needed. If gasoline and kerosene were to be marketed for motor and fuel use, it was essential to treat them with sulphuric acid in order to remove the impurities. A definite quantity of acid was pumped into an agitator filled with either gasoline or kerosene and the two liquids were mixed. The quality and strength of the acid and the length of time required for mixing depended on the type of oil that was being treated. After the agitation, the acid was allowed to settle and was drawn off into storage tanks. In this condition it was of no value to the company, since it could not be sold and could not be turned into sewers or emptied into the ocean. In order to dispose of it, the sludge acid was pumped into tank cars and returned without charge, freight prepaid, to the acid manufacturers. There it was atomized in a hot coke fire and the products of combustion, chiefly sulphur dioxide, conducted into lead chambers to be regenerated into sulphuric acid. The product reclaimed by this process was not returned to the company, since it could not be used for treating petroleum compounds because of the detrimental effect of the nitrogen it contained.

By returning impure sulphuric acid to the chemical manufacturer, the company avoided the necessity of maintaining a re-
converting unit, which was a public nuisance because of the
offensive odors that escaped.  This method of disposal, however,
was not entirely satisfactory to the company.  Not only was the
acid of value when reclaimed, but the manufacturers frequently
were unable to accept the old acid immediately because of limited
storage facilities.  Freight shipments were often slow.  When
there was a shortage of old tank cars, it was necessary to use new
ones, which necessitated careful cleaning, an expensive operation,
before they could be used again for new acid.

When the management of the Ever-Glow Oil Company previously had considered the installation of the reclaiming plant, it
had decided against it because of the offensive odors which escaped and because the chemical process did not reconvert the
acid into a form usable in the refinery.  A new method of purifying acid was perfected which consumed the obnoxious gases and
left no nitrogen in the reconverted product.  The cost of a reclaiming unit of this kind with a capacity of 10 tons a day was
$30,000.  The annual depreciation on such a plant was low, and
small floor space was required.  The total cost of regenerated acid
would have been approximately $8 per ton.  With one of these
units, the company would have been independent of acid manufacturers except for 25 per cent of its total requirements, which
would have been needed to mix with the reclaimed product.  The
reclaiming apparatus could have been managed by the company's
chemists, and little unskilled labor would have been required.
It would have lessened the amount of capital invested in acid
but would have increased the investment in plant equipment.

The monthly supply of fresh acid which the company bought
cost $2,550; the return freight of $250 on used acid brought the
total cost of the acid up to $2,800.  If the waste acid was re-
claimed in the Ever-Glow Oil Company's plant, it would have
cost $1,200 per month; to this would have been added about 38
tons (25 per cent of 150 tons) of new acid which would have cost
$646, making a total monthly cost of acid of $1,846.  Conservative estimates showed that a saving of $1,000 per month was
possible.

Should the company have expanded its operations by installing an acid reclamation unit?

## Problem 17

### GULL ISLAND FISHERIES COMPANY

The new manager of the Gull Island Fisheries Company wished to expand the company's production. For years the company had processed and sold fresh fish, slow-frozen fish, and cured fish. To meet the developing demand for fish fillets and to exploit the Middle West as a market for fish, the new general manager installed a quick-freezing unit and began filleting a large portion of the company's output. Filleting increased waste until it approximated 55 per cent of the total weight of the fish. He wished to add to the company's products fish flakes, fish-meal, glue, isinglass, and cod-liver oil.[2] He believed that this diversification of the company's products would decrease waste and make the company more profitable than at any time in the past.

The banking firm, Kendall and Thompson, held in its portfolio $60,000 in notes of the Gull Island Fisheries Company. A substantial portion of this amount was overdue and the company was asking for the extension of additional credit. The bank's credit department had in its files financial and operating statements of the company covering a period of five years. Upon failure of the company to meet its obligations, the usual credit investigations were made, and the credit manager spent considerable time in endeavoring to determine what action the bank should take.

Kendall and Thompson had obtained the Gull Island Fisheries Company account five years earlier at the time Mr. W. K. Williams had acquired control of the Gull Island Fisheries Company and had become its president and general manager. Mr. Williams had known executives of Kendall and Thompson for many years and had done considerable business with that institution. The bank had great confidence in Mr. Williams and was glad to get the account of the Gull Island Fisheries Company. Under Mr. Williams's management the company prospered, and the

[2] See Appendixes A, B, C, and D, pp. 180–182, for descriptions of these processes.

bank found the account very profitable. The bank advanced funds to supply periodic current needs of the company. These loans rarely had exceeded $50,000 at one time. They always had been paid promptly, and the bank considered the company an excellent credit risk.

Mr. Williams had operated the business for two years when he was fatally injured in an automobile accident. The management of the business was then taken over by its treasurer, Mr. Perry, a young man who had been brought into the organization by Mr. Williams. During the first year of Mr. Perry's management the business of the company declined somewhat, but to a much less extent than the decrease in volume experienced by the business of the country as a whole. Profits shrank to a greater extent than did business volume, and in the last quarter of the year the company experienced a loss, although the last three months of the year were normally the season of greatest profit. During the early months of the following year, bank borrowings increased and in April of that year the treasurer of the company asked for extension of time on $20,000 of notes then maturing. In view of the operating record of the company and its seemingly sound basic financial condition, as exhibited in its January 1 financial statement, the extension was granted. The credit manager of the bank had the records concerning the company transferred to a file in his personal office in which were segregated those accounts which he deemed should receive his constant attention.

By midyear, payment of the major portion of the Gull Island Fisheries Company notes held by the bank was in arrears, and the company was asking for credit in addition to the $60,000 already extended. Though small, the credit department of Kendall and Thompson was efficient and exceedingly well managed. The volume of business did not permit the maintenance of a staff adequate for the making of an investigation such as the credit manager now believed advisable in the case of the Gull Island Fisheries Company. The treasurer of that company had explained his present situation as growing out of changes in the fish-packing business. He stated that if the bank would give him additional financial assistance, the business would become more profitable than ever before. The market was demanding fish fillets rather than whole dressed fish. The company had recently installed facilities which would provide for quick freezing and the management wished to acquire equipment which would make possible the utilization of the increased waste which resulted from the filleting process. The company's treasurer believed that if this were done the business would not only regain its old profit-making ability but would become a better paying proposition than at any time in the past.

The bank's credit manager was satisfied with the ability of his department to pass on the usual credit problems that came before it. However, he was not familiar with conditions in the fish industry nor with the operating and management problems of the Gull Island Fisheries Company. The death of Mr. W. K. Williams further complicated the situation. The credit manager believed that it would be impossible for him to make a satisfactory analysis of the company's situation from its financial and operating statements without an understanding of the situation in the industry and the operating problems of the Gull Island Fisheries Company. Accordingly an experienced industrial research man was employed who, after making a comprehensive study, reported his findings as to the fish-packing industry with particular reference to operating conditions within the Gull Island Fisheries Company. The following information extracted from his report provided the basis for his recommendation to the credit manager of Kendall and Thompson.

*General History of the Gull Island Fisheries Company.* The Gull Island Fisheries was started as a single fish pier in the early 1850's by Josiah Hibbard and Ebenezer Allen. It specialized on ground fish,[3] including cod, haddock, hake, and cusk. Production activities had been gradually expanded to include slow-frozen, cured, dried, and smoked fish for domestic and export trade, as well as frozen bait for fishermen. Over a period of years, equipment, processes, labor force, internal control, contact with fishermen, marketing and financial programs were built around the specific products to be sold. The business continued in the hands of the descendants of the founders until Mr. W. K.

---

[3] Ground fish are fish which live on or near the floor of the ocean.

Williams bought practically all the stock of the company and assumed active control.  Under his leadership the company continued to return a handsome profit on the money invested.  Larger fish companies often referred to Gull Island Fisheries as one of their most respected and profitable small competitors.  Mr. Williams continued the drying and salting of fish as the main activities of the company, although he was aware that public demand in regard to fish was changing.  The market was demanding fillets [4] to an increasing extent.  The introduction of quick-freezing processes appeared to be giving a greater impetus to the filleting business.

Mr. Williams often talked this situation over with Glen Perry, a young man whom Williams had taken into the business as treasurer of the company.  Williams believed that Perry would become a successful businessman.  He had a good mind.  He was energetic and was a tireless worker.  He had had no previous experience in the fish business.  From the beginning, Perry was enthusiastic over the possibilities of filleting fish.  The more he studied the matter, the more he became convinced that the company should at once install a quick-freezing unit and begin active competition for the fillet trade.  On every possible occasion he urged such a course upon Williams.  He pictured the entire Middle West as a market for fillet exploitation.  Mr. Williams was intrigued by the possibilities of a wide distribution of fillets, but because the company was still selling its present products at a good profit he hesitated to make the change.  When Mr. Williams died, Perry took over active charge of the business.  One of the first major changes which he inaugurated was the installation of a quick-freezing unit.

*Plant, Buildings, and Equipment.*  At the time Mr. Williams bought a controlling interest in the business, the plant, buildings and equipment included the following:

Ground space: 3½ acres
Wharf frontage: 350 feet with 16 feet of water at low tide
A four-story cold storage plant: capacity, 200 barrels of fish daily; storage capacity, 1,000,000 pounds

---

[4] Fillets were slices cut from the sides of the fish and contained the choice meat.

Salt house: capacity, 3,000 hogsheads

Smoke house: capacity, 15,000 pounds of finnan haddie daily

A two-story main fish factory: capacity, 2,000,000 pounds

Curing sheds: "flakes," coal bunkers, boiler house, storage and repair shops, and freight sheds, adjoining which was a steamboat landing

The plant now embraces 100,000 square feet of floor space, lighted by electricity and with ample hydrant and fire protection. There is sufficient space and hogsheads enough to salt 2,000,000 pounds of fish at one time.

The plant, which is valued at $200,000, was built out of earnings of the business; and while the total investment is not large in comparison with many industrial establishments, it is, nevertheless, considered a satisfactory unit of its kind and, except for one or two periods of unfortunate management, has always been a very profitable enterprise. However, no appreciable reserve has been accumulated and any such major expenditures as might arise with contemplated changes will call for additional financing.

*Difficulty of Production and Market Correlation.* There are certain difficulties that seemed inherent in the fish business. The managers of the Gull Island Fisheries Company, for instance, find it exceedingly hard to coordinate effective marketing and production programs. The demand for fish is not continuous like that for beef or bread. To an amazing extent it is controlled by social, racial, and sectarian customs; it is neither steady throughout the week nor does it conform to seasonal changes in the industry. In summer, when fish are abundant and conditions propitious for catching and packing them, demand is weak; in winter, when fish are scarce and fishing conditions hazardous, demand is strong. The Lenten season usually more than exhausts normal local supplies. The most effective correlation between production and distribution is obtained in those fish-packing plants which have large amounts of working capital. These concerns purchase large quantities of fish when the runs are at their peak and hold the finished product until the market is strong. Companies which are so situated financially that they can follow this policy are almost certain of realizing handsome profits.

*Influence of Raw Material Supplies.*  A steady predetermined flow of raw materials, that is, of fish, to the factory is impossible. The fisherman has to make his catch while fish are abundant or he will lose it altogether.  Thus he works long, hard hours when the run is on, but no one can forecast exactly the time, length, or size of a season's run.  As a result of this situation, the factory has to purchase its fish when they are available even though such purchases may not be best suited to the wishes of the company.  The extreme perishability of the product adds to the acuteness of the situation and makes for a condition whereby at times the factory is taxed to its fullest capacity; at other periods it operates only part time, and at still others it shuts down production altogether.  Production programs must be flexible in the extreme.

*Production Processes.*  Production processes in the plant are relatively simple.  Fish are unloaded onto the company wharf where they are weighed and sorted according to size and kind. The processing operations from that point on depend on the kind of product into which the fish is to be converted and the extent of dressing operations (if any) which already have been performed.

If the market seems favorable, fresh fish (iced) are dispatched to Boston and New York City.  If the fish have not been previously worked on, they are headed, gutted, and thoroughly washed, after which the fish are wheeled to the freezing room for thorough chilling (which takes from two to three hours).  The fish are then wrapped in parchment paper, packed in iced boxes, and hurried to the market.  The company can dispose of a small percentage of its product in this manner.  A larger portion is slow frozen and put into cold storage to be shipped when prices are favorable.

If the fish are to be cured, the head and back are split until the fish is flat like an open book.  After gutting and thorough rinsing, the fish are placed in butts (hogsheads) and saturated in brine.  The curing process consumes from a few days to three weeks, depending on whether or not the fish have been cleaned and salted on shipboard, but the fish can remain in the butts for long periods without injury. Shipment is made in barrels, kegs, or wooden pails.

When fish are to be dried, they are first cleaned and washed, after which they are piled in the open on wooden racks called "flakes." The length of time they must remain in the sun depends on weather conditions and on the use to which the dried fish are to be put. Each night they are collected and covered as a protection against the cold, damp atmosphere. If weather conditions are unfavorable, the fish are sent to the drier after they are removed from the flakes. Fish for export are generally sent back to the flakes for a second hard finish, after which they are packed in drums for shipment. If the product is to be salt-dried, it is either packed directly in drums or made into cakes or bricks. The latter process means that fish so used have to be skinned, boned and cut, and each cake or brick wrapped in parchment paper. Fish are also shredded and made into prepared fish cakes.

The particular operations through which smoked fish pass depend, as in other products, on the ultimate product sought, whether it is to be finnan haddie or plain smoked fish and whether it is for domestic or export use.

*Development of Filleting Business.* The successful production of fillets has depended upon the introduction of quick-freezing processes.

The fillet differs from the older method of preparing the fish in that it includes only two large slices out of each fish. These are the choice meat, and if properly cut contain no bones. They are thus not only better in quality but also easier to handle in the kitchen. They can be cooked more easily and are much more attractive on the table. There is nothing particularly new in the fillet idea. The very select trade has demanded them for years, but most fish packers have assumed that this demand would be limited to the small class of buyers who are willing to pay extra fancy prices. However, the demand for fillets now appears to come from everyone, and if the prospective purchaser cannot get what he wants, there is abundant evidence to show that he turns his choice to meat, fresh fruits, and green vegetables. The more progressive fish-packing concerns recognized the situation.

Since the filleting process was introduced by the Gull Island Fisheries Company, fish are still received at the wharf as heretofore. The cutting, however, is different. Only the fillets are removed. The process essentially is simple, but it requires dexterity and cannot be entirely standardized because each fish has its own characteristics and presents an individual problem. The shape and size of the fish and the thickness and desirability of the fillets are matters governed by such factors as the season of the year, the kind of food upon which the fish has been feeding, and the depth at which it has been living. A carefully cut fillet from a first-class fish brings more in the market than a fillet cut from the same fish in a haphazard manner. On the other hand, if a fish is naturally inferior, careful cutting cannot make a first-class product.

A fundamental objection to the general production of fillets is the fact that until recently no successful methods of marketing the product have been developed. The slow-freezing process has meant that the fillets can be shipped only short distances, but the new quick-freezing processes seem to hold out great possibilities for the fish industry. They open the entire Middle West as a potential market for fresh fish, a territory which heretofore has been but little exploited by the New England fisheries. It was to secure the advantages of entering the Middle West with fillets while the market was still unexploited that was the outstanding consideration in the new president's mind when he decided to install a quick-freezing unit.

*Labor Supply.* The labor needs of the packing plant vary, of course, with seasonal activities. Except for the shipping department, watchmen, etc., the plant is virtually shut down after the first of each year, and continues that way until late spring when the season's run starts. The plant continues in active operation until well into the fall. The number of employees vary from 10 to 70, depending on the extent of operations to be performed.

The labor supply of the company has always come from Littletown, a small village near the plant. The type of labor available is the kind usually found in small country villages, although the inhabitants of Littletown seem more provincial than the residents of most small places. They distrust innovations of all kinds and pursue the even tenor of their way just as their fathers and grandfathers did. The number of men available in Littletown is more than ample for the needs of the factory.

*Raw Materials Waste.* Raw materials waste is an annoying problem for the Gull Island Fisheries Company. No matter whether the product is fresh-frozen, cured, dried, or smoked, there is a considerable part of the fish that cannot be used. In fact, from 30 to 35 per cent of each fish is not utilized. This waste include heads, livers, bones, parts of the skin, and the entrails. In some cases, companies have installed machinery to utilize some of these products; but the Gull Island Fisheries Company has never operated such units, and its waste, except livers, has always been dumped into the ocean. Residents living nearby have recently petitioned local health authorities to have this practice stopped.

The introduction of the filleting process has made the above situation more acute because of the fact that when a fish is filleted, what remains cannot be smoked, salted, dried, or cured for market. This means that the new process is more wasteful than the old; in fact, it has increased the waste to about 55 per cent of the fish.

The greater waste resulting from the filleting process has brought before the Gull Island Fisheries Company the whole question of effective utilization of such materials in the form of salable by-products. The new president has made a survey of the problems which are involved. He reports that other fish concerns have installed successful units for the production of fish flakes from the flesh remaining after the fillets are cut; of fish meal from the bones; of glue from heads, bones and skins; of cod-liver oil; and of isinglass from the sounds. He believes that similar units would be successful in his own plant. He points out that with the utilization of the entire fish the Gull Island Fisheries Company will be in a position to realize the fullest benefits of the filleting process. The company will receive a top price for steaks, and make a good profit on the remaining parts of the fish. He is of the opinion that the only thing which stands in the way of a realization of his plans is lack of adequate finances.  The installation of the quick-freezing unit has strained the credit facilities of the company.

On the basis of the foregoing findings and the following process descriptions, what would you as an industrial engineer have advised the credit manager of Kendall and Thompson?

### APPENDIX A

#### FISH FLAKES AND FISH MEAL

The process of making fish flakes provides a relatively simple way of utilizing the edible parts of the fish that are left after fillets have been cut.

After the fillets have been removed, the fish are put into large retorts filled with hot water and cooked for 20 minutes.  They are then removed from the water and shaken by hand until the flakes of flesh fall from the bones.  The flakes are put into cans and again cooked for a short time, after which the cans are put on an endless belt and passed to the sealer.  The sealed cans are immersed in another retort and subjected to intense heat in order to complete the process of sterilization and to test the cans for leaks.  They are then labeled and packed for shipment.

Another by-product is meal made from the bones.  Such meal finds ready sale in the Middle West, where it is used as a chicken feed.  After the flakes have been removed, the bare skeletons are put through a grinding process and reduced to a fine meal which is then ready for packing and shipment.

Fish meal may also be made from the heads, tails, and fins.  After the oil has been taken out, this meal has a high protein content which makes it desirable food for cattle, swine, and poultry.

### APPENDIX B

#### FISH GLUE

Fish glue is made from the heads, bones, trimmings, and skins of fish, chiefly of cusk, haddock, hake, and pollack.  The product is graded commercially on the basis of the raw materials; head glue is least valuable, bone glue next, and skin glue of greatest strength and value. Fish glue is used in the shoe trade, in book-binding, and for flexible adhesives, such as court plaster, labels, and stamps. Cheaper grades are used in joinery work and sizing operations. Fish glue is marketed in liquid form. The color depends on the material. Head and bone glues are turbid and brown but may be bleached to a light yellow. Skin glue is clear and light in color.

Cod and cusk skins yield 60 to 80 gallons of glue per ton of stock; hake, haddock, and pollack, 35 to 45 gallons; trimming and bones, 25 to 30 gallons; heads, 12 to 18 gallons.

In order to make glue profitably, the supply of raw materials must be abundant and steady. The manufacturing processes, however, are very simple.

The raw material is sorted according to the kinds of glue to be produced. It is then put into wash mills and washed with fresh water to remove dirt, blood, and salt. From four to six changes of water are used. For this purpose, an abundant supply of pure water must be available. Frequent tests must be made to ascertain the salt content of the stock, which should be kept below 1 per cent. The material is then put into tanks and cooked for about two hours at a temperature just below the boiling point. After being tested, the glue liquor is drawn off into other tanks and run through a filter. It is next run to the evaporator and evaporated to the desired consistency, usually about 50 per cent solid to 50 per cent liquid. The glue may be bleached, if necessary, before evaporation. When the right consistency has been obtained, the glue is pumped into storage tanks where it stands for a day before being put into containers for market. Here, preservative chemicals may be added, and frequently wintergreen or sassafras to disguise the odor of the glue. The production of high-quality glue requires the careful use of chemicals as clarifiers and preservatives. Higher grades of glue are put into tubes and bottles, and other grades into barrels or cans.

### Appendix C

#### Isinglass

Isinglass is a collagen in the fibrous layer of the "sounds," or swim bladders, of fish. The sound is a hollow sac containing a gas and located just beneath the backbone. By compression and expansion of this sac the specific gravity of the fish is changed.

The best quality of American isinglass is prepared from the sounds of hake caught off the northeastern coast. If the fish is dressed on shipboard and the vessel is to remain at sea for several days, the sounds are taken out and salted down in barrels. One ton of hake will yield from 300 to 500 large sounds which will weigh from 40 to 50 pounds.

When the sounds are brought in to be processed, they are split and dried in the open air. Later they are soaked until soft, chopped into fine pieces by a cutting machine, and macerated between a set of iron rollers. The material is next passed through the sheeting rollers and pressed into sheets from $\frac{1}{8}$ to $\frac{1}{4}$ inch thick and from 6 to 8 inches wide. These sheets are reworked by another set of rollers into ribbons about $\frac{1}{64}$ inch thick and still 6 to 8 inches wide. The ribbons are dried quickly and wound on wooden spools in pound lots.

Isinglass has various commercial uses. It is used as a clarifying agent for white wines. It is no longer used in the preparation of jellies and confectionery, but it is of value in the sizing of silk, in making cement for mending china, as a waterproofing compound for textiles, and as a dressing for leather.

### Appendix D

#### Cod-liver Oil

Oil is extracted from the livers of cod for medicinal and for technical uses. The nonmedicinal oils are of two grades; the higher grade is taken from cod livers alone and the lower from a mixture of cod livers with the livers of haddock and other fish. The medicinal oil is taken from the livers of fresh-caught cod in prime condition. The vitamin content of the oil depends on the condition of the fish, the season of the year, and the locality in which the fish is caught. In certain areas, minute marine vegetation grows on shallow banks and ledges where sunlight penetrates. Such areas are found off Newfoundland and on the Atlantic Banks. If the cod has fed on the small fishes which subsist on such vegetation, the vitamin content of the oil is high.

The oil is extracted from the livers in steam-jacketed pans or by direct steaming. The stearin, which is said to make the oil unpalatable, is removed by a chilling process, the crude oil being pumped through cooled pipes from which the clear, nonfreezing oil flows into containers ready for shipment. There are many variations in the process and equipment used in extracting the oil, and changes and improvements are still being made, the chief object of all of them being to protect the oil from oxidation by contact with the air, which increases the unpleasant flavor.

The residue of the livers after the oil has been extracted may be utilized as chicken and cattle feed since it also has a high vitamin content.

# CHAPTER VIII

## CONTRACTION

### QUEEN PAPER MANUFACTURING COMPANY

**1. A Company Contracts Its Scale of Operations.**

The Queen Paper Manufacturing Company operated two paper mills, one at Anderson and the other at Biltonville. During a period of business depression, the decline in volume of business so increased the unit costs of products manufactured that the management of the company thought it wise to close the mill at Biltonville and transfer all activity to the Anderson plant.

**2. Nature and Causes of Plant Contraction.** The forces of our dynamic society frequently make contraction of manufacturing operations desirable. Shifts in market demand, alterations in production methods, and changes in general business conditions, one or all of these influences may have an impact on a particular producing unit that results in reduction in sales with concurrent lessening of plant activity.

The buying public is notoriously fickle. Random changes in demand result from style shifts and the rise and fall of fads. A few years ago, a trend to shorter skirts for women and lower shoes gave the hosiery producers a tremendous increase in business, but at the same time curtailed the demand upon manufacturers of dress and shoe materials to such an extent as practically to wreck some producers of such goods. The ramifications of style changes have brought to industrialists many sleepless nights. Fads frequently soar to unexpected heights and then even more quickly disappear. The jigsaw puzzle flashed into popularity and then as quickly disappeared. Today, bicycles are "in," for how long no one knows. Occasionally fad changes are predictable, but more often their rise and fall are nearly impossible to understand. Nevertheless, manufacture in industries affected by such influences must be carried on with expectation of such rapid change, and knowing when and how to contract operations is a definite responsibility of industrial managers.

Fully as important for studied consideration as random changes are seasonal shifts. Much of American manufacture is subject to this type of influence. Cosmetics, radios, textiles, automobiles, building materials, and even foodstuffs are subject to the influence of changing seasons. Under such conditions, the manager squarely faces a dilemma. He may manufacture for stock during seasons of low demand, thereby accepting all the costs and risks of large inventory investment, or he may operate at alternately high and low rates of activity. The latter course involves the costs of a noncontinuous labor force, congestion of work, and idle plant and workers, which are problems of great import from a profit standpoint. Fortunately, seasonal variations in demand can usually be foretold, and, thus warned, manufacturing executives can plan. The methods of attack upon this problem are many and varied. Some concerns produce continuously and warehouse the excess output of dull seasons. Others expand and contract manufacture seasonally to correspond with the swings of seasonal demand. Still others go part way, curtailing somewhat during months of slack demand and accumulating some inventory beyond current needs. More recently, managements have searched assiduously for products of opposite seasonal characteristics to absorb the inactive capacity of plant and labor during slack times. The problem is difficult and there is no one answer. The following factors are among the major considerations in finding a suitable solution to the individual problem: the availability of labor supply; the relative importance of labor, raw materials, and burden costs; the predictability of forthcoming demand; and the importance of style elements.

Development of competitive products is a common cause of decreased demand. Phonographs became popular, and piano manufacturers had to curtail their activity. Radios produced a like effect upon phonograph manufacturing. Rayon influenced both cotton and silk demand. Wide-awake management will usually foresee such change and be prepared for it. Occasionally, however, the influence is so indirect, or management so obstinate in its faith in the existing order, that disaster follows.  Under the best of administration the problem is a serious one, and the degree and method of curtailment almost always constitute puzzling problems.

Shifts in consumer demand are not the only cause of production fluctuation.  Improvement of a production process may throw a hitherto low-cost producer into the high-cost class. Under such circumstances, management has but two choices: follow suit and attempt to regain competitive position or accept the fact of relatively high cost and depend on various means of maintaining a profit at a somewhat lower rate of output.  On the surface, the former course seems the more sensible.  There are times, however, when the gains of process modernization may not be entirely worth the cost, and the clever manager may then well accept the change in status, reduce his scale of operation, and look for some other way out.

Process change is only one production cause of volume change. Product improvement and equipment improvement are others. Unfortunately, from the standpoint of the outmoded producer, advancement in products and machines may often be made more binding by means of grant of patent rights.  While it is probably of less import than is usually supposed by the novice, still the monopolistic aids of patent protection under sound management are upon occasion ruinously destructive of volume of the less fortunate producer.

Governmental activities not infrequently make for changes in rate of operations of this or that producer.  The possibility of tariff reduction sometimes constitutes a threat of output decrease.  Since 1936 the reciprocal trade agreement program has brought about decreased demand for some producers as well as increases for many others.  Certainly, the various controls exercised with increasing frequency by the Federal government have occasionally brought this or that manufacturer face to face with the necessity of contracting his output.

Last, and perhaps the most serious of the changes affecting rate of output, must be considered the influence of general business conditions.  The phenomenon of the business cycle is familiar to all, as likewise are its effects upon the rate of output of the individual manufacturer. Unquestionably, the most critical aspect of this problem to an individual management is the question of how to cut down operations so as to minimize the long-time adverse effect upon the business. The greatest difficulty is inability to read the future. The experienced executive knows that far greater change takes place in a five-year stretch of depression than in a like period of prosperity. Simply to shut up shop and wait for the sun to shine again is suicide. Even to curtail at all is a difficult decision psychologically, and as a result the early months of a generally declining demand commonly see producers turning out unneeded volume at the old rate. The cause is probably fear of the effect of reduced operation on costs and profits. The result is gradual accumulation of excessive inventory and acceleration of decline in price to the breaking point.

That the decision to reduce or cease operations cannot be made lightly, no one will deny. The considerations and effects thereof are many and widespread, and rare indeed is the executive who can foretell the result with accuracy. The experience of the Queen Paper Manufacturing Company, discussed briefly here, illustrates the nature of the problem and the considerations involved. Essentially, it is typical of what a management faces when depression exists generally.

**3. Situation in the Mills of the Queen Paper Manufacturing Company.** The Queen Paper Manufacturing Company operated two paper mills. One mill was located in the city of Anderson and the other in Biltonville, 100 miles distant. Anderson was a city of 40,000 inhabitants, with a variety of manufacturing establishments. Biltonville had only 2,000 inhabitants, and the paper mill was its only manufacturing enterprise. When operated at capacity, the Anderson mill produced 1,306 tons of paper and the Biltonville mill 478 tons of paper during a four-week period. Only one grade of paper was produced at the Biltonville plant, whereas this grade and several other grades were manufactured at the Anderson mill.

Because of a reduction in orders during a period of general business depression, the mills had been manufacturing chiefly for stock. Production was only 61.5 per cent of normal capacity at the Anderson mill and 50 per cent of normal capacity at the Biltonville mill.

An investigation by officials of the company showed that when the rates of operation at the two mills were decreased, production costs per unit of output were increased. Production costs were made up of three classes of items: raw materials, labor, and burden. The raw materials charges of the Queen Paper Manufacturing Company were an important item, for the company had long-term contracts for pulpwood, drawn up on the basis of anticipated normal annual needs. Thus, when production at Anderson and Biltonville was reduced to 61.5 and 50 per cent, respectively, there was an immediate piling up of raw materials inventories in the storage yards of the company. Since these raw materials could not be put into production at once, a large amount of capital was tied up in a nonliquid investment from which the owners could secure no immediate return.

Labor costs were also an important consideration. If the two plants were to operate at less than normal capacity, the number of workers would have to be considerably reduced. The production managers, however, were reluctant to make substantial cuts in the working force because it is expensive to organize an efficient factory personnel. If, for example, one-half of the workers at Biltonville were laid off, these men would doubtless seek work elsewhere, and many of them would eventually be lost to the Queen Paper Manufacturing Company. The company had made a real investment in these workers. It had paid out money to secure them and train them into an effective organization. If these men left Biltonville, the company would pay out more money in securing, training, and adapting other workers to fill vacancies when business again returned to normal.

An expedient commonly adopted to meet a situation such as that which the Queen Paper Manufacturing Company was facing is to shorten the workday or the work week. In this way each employee secures his proportionate share of work even though it is not a full day's or a full week's work. But the problem at the plants of this company was complicated by the fact that papermaking is a continuous process. The costs incident to stopping and starting paper machines make it imperative that these machines be kept constantly running.[1]

The Queen Paper Manufacturing Company could meet this situation in part by reducing the speeds at which the machines were operated, since rates of machine operation were controllable within certain limits. When the speeds of the machines were reduced, however, certain disadvantages at once appeared. The entire system of planning and operation was thrown out of adjustment and had to be reorganized to meet the new conditions. Many of the former benefits of a high degree of specialization were then no longer applicable. Furthermore, the management soon discovered that employees working at less than normal speeds easily fell into slovenly habits, and the problem of quality control of product quickly became important. These disadvantages obviously tended to increase the unit cost of production.

Burden charges at the two mills were made up of such items as insurance, taxes, power, heat, light, steam for fire pumps, and depreciation on buildings and equipment. The costs due to these items went on day after day and bore no particular relationship to the rate of production at which the mills were operated. The normal way by which the management of the Queen Paper Manufacturing Company secured funds to pay these costs was by producing goods for sale. Each unit of goods produced had to bear its proportionate share of total factory expense. If the number of units was reduced by 50 per cent, as was true at the Biltonville mill, then the unit burden costs of production at that mill would be approximately doubled, for there would be only half as many units over which to distribute the fixed cost of production.

It is clear, then, that labor and burden costs at both the Anderson and Biltonville plants tended to remain constant and bore no fixed relation to the rates at which the plants were operated. This was due in part to the nature of the labor re-

---

[1] There is waste involved in the shutting down of paper machinery because it takes considerable time to put a paper machine into operation and to start the paper running through it. There is waste in cooling and reheating the drying cylinders, and the paper which is run immediately after a shutdown is not marketable.

quirements, which made it highly desirable to keep the working force together if possible, and in part to the fact that the majority of the items listed as burden charges were constant expenses of production irrespective of whether the mills operated at capacity or only 50 per cent of capacity.

**4. Advantages of Closing One Mill.** After watching the situation carefully for a number of weeks and seeing no likelihood of immediate relief from the depression, the general manager of the Queen Paper Manufacturing Company suggested that in his opinion it would be more profitable for the company to close down the Biltonville mill entirely and to transfer all production to Anderson until such a time as business showed evidence of picking up. He believed that in this way overhead expenses might be reduced at the Biltonville plant and the output of the Anderson mill raised from 61.5 to 80 per cent of normal capacity.

The general manager estimated that when manufacture was carried on at the existing rate, the overhead costs for a four-week period were $135,191 for the Anderson mill and $70,039 for the Biltonville mill. If the latter was shut down and its tonnage transferred to the Anderson mill, the overhead costs would be $141,757 for the Anderson mill and $30,893 for the Biltonville mill. Overhead costs for the Biltonville plant when it was shut down would consist of taxes, insurance, depreciation, power for lights, steam for fire pumps, and salaries for superintendents, including foremen.

**5. Disadvantages of Closing One Mill.** The plan, however, was not without certain drawbacks. Beginning operations when business revived would involve expense for initial repairs, recruiting labor, and building up the organization. After such a suspension, only an inferior quality of pulp could be produced, and paper made while adjustments were being set was not of the first grade. The expense of starting the Biltonville plant after a four-week shutdown was estimated to be $33,000. This expense would increase $2,000 for each consecutive four-week period during which the mill remained idle.

If the Biltonville plant was closed, the employees could not find other work in the town and many of them, undoubtedly.

would leave. Such a condition would cause the whole community to suffer. Workers would have to be imported when the plant resumed operations, and it would probably be difficult to build up a new crew as capable and loyal as the existing one. The management had experienced no labor troubles in the plant, but there was a possibility that the imported workers might be of a radical frame of mind, and thus labor agitation might be started. It was possible to retain a portion of the more skilled workers by offering them an opportunity to go to the Anderson mill, but only a limited number could be so accommodated. To close the Biltonville mill involved a loss of prestige, since the work of the service department there had been held up to the whole paper industry as a favorable example.

**6. Why the Biltonville Mill Was Closed.** In spite of the objections which stood in the way of shutting down the Biltonville plant, executives of the Queen Paper Manufacturing Company believed it imperative to reduce unit burden costs. Consequently, the Biltonville mill was closed and all production transferred to Anderson. The increased number of units then produced at Anderson (80 per cent of normal capacity) made it possible for the management of that plant to reduce unit burden charges from what they were when the plant operated at 61.5 per cent of capacity. Under the new arrangement the number of units produced in the Anderson plant was increased 19 per cent, while the overhead costs at that plant increased less than 5 per cent. This meant that there was a larger number of units over which to distribute the costs of operation, and consequently the cost per unit of the product manufactured was lowered. Lower unit costs of production make possible a lower price to the consumer.

As month after month went by and no cessation of the depression appeared, the costs of keeping the Biltonville plant idle accumulated rapidly. The only means by which the Queen Paper Manufacturing Company could offset these losses was by the sale of products produced at the Anderson mill. In other words, this mill had to carry a double load. This finally proved too great, and the executives of the Queen Paper Manufacturing Company decided to sell the plant at Biltonville and to give their undivided attention to the operations of the Anderson mill. Only by so doing were they able to weather the severe depression.

The decision to close the Biltonville mill seems sound. Had the depression been of short duration, the reduction in costs resulting from the shift would have been insufficient to cover the expense of putting the Biltonville mill into operation again. As time elapsed, the resultant savings accumulated more rapidly than did the growth in reopening costs, and the wisdom of the management's action became clear.

The desirability of selling the Biltonville plant is not so obvious. It was a highly specialized unit and probably possessed substantial production economies for the manufacture of the type of product for which it was designed. Unless the future showed that demand for this particular paper had become permanently curtailed, return of prosperity would find the Queen Paper Manufacturing Company at a disadvantage. However, company executives had little choice in this matter, since the company seems to have been financially unable to withstand the drain of losses on the idle plant until such time as it could again be placed in operation. Even if the company had possessed adequate resources to retain the Biltonville plant, the sale of it might have been an act of wisdom. As we learned in the 1930's, depressions can be of long duration, and the losses of retaining an idle mill might have become so great as to require many years of successful management after business again became active to wipe out depression losses. In the field of finance the principle of quickly cutting losses has long been recognized. In the area of manufacturing, management commonly has been less quick to grasp its force. The experience of the Queen Paper Manufacturing Company is an excellent instance of the need of farsighted management, exercise of judgment, and sound decisions in terms of an unknown future.

**7. Summary and Conclusions.** *Effects of Subcapacity Operation on Costs.* A common weakness of American management has been lack of appreciation of the effects of subcapacity operation on burden costs. The diagram (Exhibit 1) is designed to show graphically the effects of subcapacity operation upon the production cost elements: raw materials, labor, and burden. In the diagram the process is represented by the continuous conveyor, the process flow being from right to left. Raw materials are put in process at *A*, labor is applied at *B*, and burden at *C*. The frequency with which raw materials are put in process is under the control of management. This control is represented by the gate valve at *A*. By means of some device, such as piece

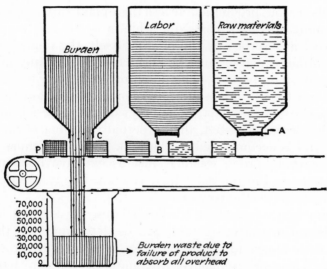

EXHIBIT 1. DIAGRAM TO ILLUSTRATE CHARACTERISTICS OF COST APPLICATION.

rates or variation in the size of the work force, raw materials may be made to carry a relatively uniform amount of labor cost even though the volume of production, determined in this case by the rate of release of raw materials, is not uniform. The valve at *B,* automatically tripped by the raw materials as they reach that point, represents such control. At the outlet of the burden reservoir, *C,* no such controlling device exists. That outlet is always open, and the burden flow is therefore continuous. When work in process is passing beneath the outlet, it absorbs burden. If no work in process is beneath the outlet, the burden flows on just the same. It is in this respect that burden costs are so greatly different from labor and raw materials costs. The latter two are usually largely under the control of the operating personnel. Burden is not so flexible or so readily controlled; it tends to be constant. Its volume flow is somewhat affected by the rate of plant operation. As the rate decreases, certain burden items tend to fall off and certain items tend to increase, but the greater portion do not vary. Therefore, in the diagram, the outlet of the burden reservoir is shown as always being wide open.

For this reason, production at less than plant capacity tends to increase unit operating costs, for while a decreasing portion of burden cost is absorbed by the product itself, the remainder, the wasted burden expense, must be borne by the company and is a charge against its profits. This unabsorbed burden is shown in the diagram by the unabsorbed burden accumulation tank beneath the conveyor system. When no work in process is beneath the burden reservoir outlet, the perpetually flowing burden falls through and is accumulated in the tank below. It must be remembered that burden waste is just as effective in increasing unit costs as is the burden which is immediately absorbed by work in process on the conveyor.

It is apparent, then, that in the diagram the level of burden accumulation in the waste tank will be determined by the frequency with which raw materials are released into process at point $A$. The more frequently raw material units are fed upon the process conveyor, the smaller will be the spaces between the product units in process. The smaller these spaces between product units, the less burden will leak through into the waste tank. The larger these space intervals, the greater will be the flow from burden reservoir into burden waste. The ideal condition would be shown in the diagram if the product units in process were tightly packed against each other on the conveyor. Then all burden flow would be absorbed by the product flow and none would escape into the waste collector.

In practice such an ideal is rarely, if ever, attained. Few plants operate through the 24 hours of the day. It is no easier to shut off burden in the dark than it is in daylight. Most products are subject to seasonal demand. There are periods of depression and periods of business activity. Competition causes further variations in the already irregular product flow. It is often difficult, even impossible, to determine just how large a plant should be. Thus, unabsorbed burden is to be expected; provision for its accumulation must be made, and its depressing effect upon profits anticipated.

Though inevitable, this condition is not hopeless. Informed management knows of and understands the situation, and effective management will keep waste burden at a minimum. The level of waste burden in the diagram tank will provide a means of measuring the efficiency of management in this respect. Who is responsible for this control of burden waste? This question can be answered by an analysis of the factors which tend to raise or lower the level in the waste tank. By providing an outlet for the company's products, good sales management will tend to reduce the level. Sometimes the best of sales management cannot dispose of a plant's maximum output. A general business depression might be responsible for such a situation. Again, existence of demand does not ensure maximum output. Factories do not run themselves; careful production planning and supervision are necessary all the way down from the plant superintendent to subforemen and stockroom clerks. Materials do not automatically release themselves into process. Control of this function at point $A$ in the diagram is a management job. The degree of excellence with which this work is carried out will have a direct effect upon the amount of burden that is wasted. Released raw materials will seldom pick up automatically an efficient labor application at point $B$. The longer it takes to make the necessary labor application, the more the process is slowed up and the greater is the burden waste. Effective utilization and motivation of labor are management jobs. Burden control is not the responsibility of any one executive in an organization. It is a problem that can be solved only through the cooperation of all who are concerned with management functions. In fact, under certain circumstances, its solution may in considerable measure be beyond the complete control of the management of any single business unit.

This does not mean, however, that the point in the diagram scale at which the level of waste burden rests cannot be used as a means of measuring management efficiency. It is possible, with a considerable degree of accuracy, to isolate the effects of plant management upon burden utilization and thus place responsibility for profit fluctuations arising from changes in volume of operation. Continuous operation at maximum plant capacity, 24 hours a day, 365 days a year, has been pointed out as the ideal condition so far as unit burden costs are concerned. This ideal is rarely obtainable or advisable. A study of the past operating experience of the company will give what may be termed a normal rate of operation. This normal rate will consider good years and bad years as well as average years. The number of labor dollars expended during such a normal period can be determined, and the ledger accounts of the company will show the total burden incurred during that period. The burden cost per labor dollar, or burden rate, at normal production is determined by dividing the total burden cost by the number of labor dollars paid out. This normal burden rate can be used as a standard just so long as it can fairly be considered normal. In practice it is possible to set a standard that will operate successfully over a period of years without revision. This standard provides a means of measuring current efficiency in burden control and to a considerable extent makes possible the determination of responsibility therefor.

To use such a standard it is first necessary to determine the actual current burden cost for a period of time: one month, three months, six months, or a year. This current cost can then be compared with the standard cost for that period.[2] Variations from normal are thus revealed irrespective of changes in volume. When the current unit cost is greater than standard, burden is said to be underabsorbed. (Burden in excess of the normal

---

[2] The standard cost can be obtained by totaling the burden charges on the cost sheets of the period. On each cost sheet the burden entry has been calculated by taking the labor cost and multiplying it by the standard burden rate. Example: Labor costs on a cost sheet amount to $148. The standard burden rate in use in that department in 80 per cent. Multiplying the labor cost, $148 by 0.80, will give the standard burden cost, $118.40, for the production covered by that cost sheet. Totaling these standard burden costs for all cost sheets for the period under consideration will give the total standard burden cost for the period. Not infrequently, the regular accounting procedure is designed to show the relation of actual to standard burden costs at frequent predetermined periods.

amount is escaping through the production line into the waste tank.) When current unit burden cost is less than standard, burden is said to be overabsorbed. (Production processes are absorbing more than the predetermined normal amount of burden flow, and the waste level in the accumulation tank is below the normal point in the scale.)

Causes of and responsibility for underabsorbed and overabsorbed burden can be determined through study of current volume in comparison with normal volume, existing general business conditions, individual burden cost items, and the like. To be effective, such a device must distinguish between plant burden and burden arising from the exercise of other managerial functions, such as marketing and finance. A better analysis may be obtained in a company operating more than one plant if the total plant burden is distributed among the individual operating units. Likewise, within a single plant, standard unit burden may be set for the various departments operated and products produced. Such detailed analysis and comparison make for better determination of causes, fixing of responsibility, and remedy of unsatisfactory conditions. It should be remembered, however, that the collection of detailed cost information in itself tends to increase the very cost which the use of the device seeks to control, namely, burden, and therefore such data should be gathered and used with discretion. Cost information is expensive to gather and in itself has no virtue. It is only when such information is effectively used in the hands of competent management that it will pay its way. If it is properly compiled and consistently utilized, it will increase profits.

There are many ways of furthering the use of information about burden absorption. One of them will suffice as illustration at this point. The effect of burden fluctuation upon operating costs and profits can be made to appear in the periodic operating statement as prepared for the use of the management. Outlines of two methods of presenting the same set of operation facts are given on p. 198. The first, Profit and Loss Statement A, does not show the effect of burden fluctuation. Profit and Loss Statement B does better in that respect.

In Statement A, underabsorbed burden is included as a part

### Profit and Loss Statement A

| | |
|---|---|
| Net Sales............................................. | $2,000,000 |
| Less, Cost of Producing Goods Sold................. | 1,300,000 |
| | |
| Gross Operating Margin.............................. | $ 700,000 |
| Less, Selling and Administrative Expense............. | 600,000 |
| | |
| Net Profit........................................... | $ 100,000 |

### Profit and Loss Statement B

| | |
|---|---|
| Net Sales............................................. | $2,000,000 |
| Less, Cost of Producing Goods Sold (at standard burden cost)............................................... | 1,200,000 |
| | |
| Gross Operating Margin (at standard)................. | $ 800,000 |
| Less, Underabsorbed Burden......................... | 100,000 |
| | |
| Gross Operating Margin—Actual...................... | $ 700,000 |
| Less, Selling and Administrative Expense............. | 600,000 |
| | |
| Net Profit........................................... | $ 100,000 |

of the item "Cost of Producing Goods Sold," and the reader is given no indication of the true situation as to burden costs. The separation of the underabsorbed burden item, as in Statement B, calls the reader's attention immediately to the fact that burden in excess of normal has cut profits to one-half of what they would have been if the burden costs of the period had been no greater than normal. While the example given is a very simple illustration of methods of use of burden cost data, it is typical in that it is a device which tends to make cost data valuable as a tool of managerial control. When effectively and economically used, such data are very valuable. Unless so employed, their collection is one common element which makes for excessive burden cost.

*Management Approach to Contraction Problems.* As management understanding of burden has grown, there has come to be too great reliance upon volume as a means of keeping costs down. When demand slackens, management too frequently accepts unprofitable business on the theory that it tends to absorb overhead. The reasoning is that just so long as the return is greater than the out-of-pocket costs, acceptance of business at less than total cost is desirable in that it lessens the burden which must be carried by each unit of output. Within limits, this reasoning is accurate. It is important, however, to consider further and to realize that a widespread following of this practice among competitors tends to make more acute the conditions responsible for lack of profit in the first place. The acceptance of nonprofitable business simply to help absorb burden when volume is subnormal is lazy management. It should be practiced only as a last resort when all other means of reducing costs, both of operation and of idleness, have been completely exploited and exhausted. It is common knowledge that businesses are less efficient in prosperity than in continued depression. The opportunities for cutting nonessential costs, for becoming more efficient, are greatest at the beginning of a period of slack demand. Sound management is that management which foresees the necessity of contraction early, management that aggressively puts the production house in order, that effects changes which reduce the total of burden costs as well as materials and labor costs. To accept burden as a completely noncontrollable cost and supinely to do business at less than total cost on the theory that it absorbs burden is not good management. It is more characteristically the course of a little man with a little knowledge—knowledge that is actually dangerous in its long-run effects. Many businesses can be made to operate successfully at less than accustomed volumes. However, such result occurs only from the activities of courageous individuals who recognize change, accept the new order, and plan for profit on that basis.

Not all contraction in demand upon a particular manufacturing unit is permanent or necessarily of long duration. Obviously, a major responsibility of manufacturing executives is determination of the character and probable duration of demand contraction. Action can be taken wisely only when this question has been determined. Once convinced of the nature of change in status, it is then incumbent upon executives to take remedial action as directly and quickly as possible. It is frequently difficult psychologically to accept change and to shift unhesitatingly to the most suitable gear. But good management demands just that, for the industrial order is essentially an order of change and calls for adaptability in those directing business.

*Causes of Dynamic Society.* An analysis of the development of American business shows that at all times our industrial society has been highly dynamic. Business units always seem to be either expanding or contracting. Also, as a whole, business is either going forward or receding. Scarcely ever does it appear to stand still. The causes making for this condition are many and varied, and some of them are but little understood.

In the last hundred years of our history we have had several major cyclical variations which have brought ruin to thousands of industrial establishments. It would be foolish indeed to try to give a single explanation of these occurrences. The earlier ones were closely associated with unrestrained speculation in land coupled with unsound systems of banking and currency. Others have been the aftermath of the destruction of economic wealth in wars. The one which started in the latter part of 1929 was probably caused in part by the destruction of economic goods in the First World War; in part by an inflated standard of living built upon artificial demands caused by the First World War; in part by the failure of consumption to stay in line with increased production; and in part by an almost childlike faith that there was no necessary relationship between the prices for which securities should sell and the immediate capacity of the capital represented by such securities to earn a profit.

Just how soon and to what extent the combination of high volume of output, high prices for agricultural and manufactured goods, and high level of employment and high worker earnings that followed the Second World War will change certainly is not known at the present time of writing, 1948. Two things do seem certain, however. The conditions which have made for a continuing balance of these four factors are themselves clearly subject to change. Any change in any one of the four factors will affect the others, and few people believe that the condition of balance can be maintained indefinitely. How long the present high prosperity of American industry will continue no one knows. The present is the best of times to think of problems of recession and even of depression and to prepare for them.

Aside from these general fluctuations, individual industries and enterprises are subject to changing influences. Many business units have pronounced seasonal characteristics. This is true of such products as automobiles, radios, electric refrigerators, oil burners, and the like. In the garment industry, in addition to seasonal characteristics, there are style changes which are often so profound in character as to change entirely the type of raw materials needed, the process used, labor requirements, and the basis of wage payment. Sometimes dynamic conditions are brought about by competition between industries such as bituminous coal on the one hand, and gas, oil, and electricity on the other, or as seen in the long-drawn-out conflict between lumber and lumber substitutes.

In the maze of complex relationships which these conditions influence, the individual business enterpriser must so set up his plant as to be able to take advantage of every favorable development and to circumvent changes which would mean lessened profits. The task is not an easy one. It requires a keen knowledge of human nature, of economic principles, of technical processes, and of sound business organization.

The question often arises as to how much the dynamic conditions above described are susceptible to control by business executives. To what extent are these men responsible for such occurrences? One is safe in concluding that the present-day executive has a responsibility which extends beyond the mere securing of dividends for his stockholders, important as this task may be.

The business executive holds a particular responsibility to his labor group for their welfare. Their well-being is intimately affected by practically every decision which he makes. One questions the soundness of a business policy, for example, which ruthlessly throws workers out of employment simply because a machine has been invented which can take their places. It is certainly not sound social policy to permit such workers to be thrown out of employment in vast numbers, and there is much evidence on the horizon to indicate that if the business executive does not effect the regulation of employment made necessary by the introduction of laborsaving machinery, society will attempt such regulation for him.

On the other hand, there are times when the only sound policy is to reduce rigorously the costs of production. This was true in the case of the Queen Paper Manufacturing Company. Doubtless there were very real hardships for employees involved in the closing down of the plant at Biltonville. When it came to a choice, however, between shutting down the plant on the one hand, and jeopardizing the entire future of the company on the other hand, executives could come to but one conclusion. The decision to close the plant was sound, not only from the point of view of the stockholders, but from the point of view of society as well. If the plant had attempted to continue in full operation, the company would doubtless have been forced into receivership, and thus the social gains which the company hoped to bring about would have been permanently lost.

## QUESTIONS

1. Why should the modern business unit possess flexibility?

2. Was there anything about the plant at Biltonville which would make it less suited for concentration of production than the mill at Anderson?

3. Explain why it is that when the rate of operation in a plant decreases, the cost of operation per unit of product tends to increase.

4. Who was responsible for the increased unit cost of production at the Biltonville and Anderson mills when they were operating at 50 and 61 per cent capacity—the president of the company, the mill superintendent, or the workers?

5. Why do production managers often dislike to discharge part of their personnel in times of slack business?

6. How did the type of pulpwood contract used by the Queen Paper Manufacturing Company affect profits in a period of depression?

7. What reason is there to think it was a wise plan to shut down the plant at Biltonville?

8. What would be the nature of the costs incurred when the Biltonville mill was reopened?

9. In what way did the Anderson mill have to carry a double load after the mill at Biltonville was closed?

10. Name any circumstances you can in which you think it might be wise to operate a plant at a loss.

11. Explain, by use of the diagram, how subcapacity operation affects production cost elements: raw materials, labor, and burden.

12. Explain the difference between Profit and Loss Statements A and B on page 198.

## PLANTATION MACHINE WORKS

For 5½ years the Plantation Machine Works had been experiencing continuous decline in the amount of business obtained. During the second half of the current year the total volume of business was expected to consist of two orders for a total of 18,000 domestic water-supply systems. These orders were sufficient to keep the plant operating at 60 per cent of capacity for two months. The management considered the alternative of operating the plant continuously throughout the six-month period at 20 per cent of capacity.

The Plantation Machine Works originated as a job shop doing special-order foundry and machine shop work. The shop was equipped with general-purpose machines suitable for such diversified work, and employed a considerable number of all-round mechanics. The character of the business had changed greatly. Output had become specialized and was confined largely to small, pressure water-supply units for rural domestic use. These were manufactured on order for mail-order houses and other large buyers. As a result of this change in the nature of product, the plant had been reequipped and the type of workers employed had changed also. The foundry had been discontinued, and all parts were purchased. Production operations at the plant were departmentized into three major divisions: machine shop, assembly division, and testing and shipping department. Parts were machined, then passed to the assembly division where the complete units were assembled, and finally sent to the testing and shipping department, where each unit was given a trial and thoroughly inspected before shipment. All production was for accepted orders; no finished parts or complete units were manufactured for stock.

During a period of 5½ years the business of the company had fallen off steadily until on July 1 the company had on hand only two orders, a large one calling for 12,000 units and another for

6,000 units. The contract amount of these orders was $702,000. Delivery was to be made in monthly shipments totaling 3,000 units. In the opinion of the management, there was little likelihood of obtaining more business before December 31, and plans for production of the 18,000 units were to be based on the assumption that no other orders would be obtained before that date.

The average rate of plant operation during the previous five years had been 60 per cent of capacity, and, if production was carried on at that rate, the 18,000 units could be produced in two months. It would then be necessary to close the plant down for four months. It was hoped that at the end of that time additional orders would have been secured.

Production executives of the company foresaw many objections to such a shutdown, some of which would not become effective until after the plant was reopened. As an alternative to operating the plant at 60 per cent of capacity for two months, executives considered the advisability of continuous operation throughout the six-month period at 20 per cent of capacity. This would result in an output of 3,000 units per month, a rate sufficient to provide for deliveries on the dates promised.

Company executives expected that costs of producing the orders on hand would be somewhat greater for continuous operation at 20 per cent of capacity than for operation for two months at 60 per cent of capacity. Following are careful estimates of anticipated costs.

*Raw Materials* (parts ready for machining)

The cost of parts delivered to the Plantation Machine Works ready for machining would be the same, $162,000, whether the order was completed in two months or six.

*Labor*

In the machine shop and the testing and shipping department, hourly wages were paid. Assembly was set up as a continuous, conveyorized process, and a group piece rate was paid for each accepted unit coming off the conveyor line. This was divided

Monthly Direct Labor Cost when Plant Is Operated at Various Rates and when Idle

| Plant Division | Rate of Plant Operation | | |
| --- | --- | --- | --- |
| | 60% of Capacity | 20% of Capacity | Idle |
| Machine Shop..................... | $54,000 | $18,900 | $0 |
| Assembly Division................. | 40,500 | 13,500 | 0 |
| Testing and Shipping Department.... | 13,500 | 6,750 | 0 |

among the workers along the line on a predetermined basis. The speed of the line was variable so that the number of men employed on the line could be changed in accordance with the rate of output. Regardless of the number of men on the line, the rate paid for each unit assembled and passed by inspectors was the same.

*Burden*

In computing unit production costs, it had become the practice to consider operation at 60 per cent of capacity as normal, and on that basis standard burden rates as a percentage of direct labor costs had been established for each department. On all cost sheets burden was charged at 62 per cent of direct labor cost for the machine shop, 48 per cent of direct labor cost for the assembly division, and 100 per cent of direct labor cost for the testing and shipping department.

By applying these standard burden rates to the estimated labor costs, and adding the raw materials and labor costs, the accounting department prepared the following cost sheet for the order.

In addition to the cost information thus developed, production executives cooperated with the plant cost accountant in preparing a schedule of estimated actual burden costs for the six-month period. The following summary of that schedule includes monthly estimates based on operation at 60 per cent of capacity, operation at 20 per cent of capacity, and shutdown of the plant.

Cost Sheet to Show Total and Unit Costs of Producing the 18,000 Units at 60 Per Cent and 20 Per Cent Capacity Operating Rates

| Elements of Cost | Rate of Plant Operation | |
|---|---|---|
| | 60% of Capacity | 20% of Capacity |
| Raw Materials............................ | $162,000 | $162,000 |
| Labor.................................. | 216,000 | 234,900 |
| Burden................................ | 132,840 | 149,688 |
| Total.............................. | $510,840 | $546,588 |

Number of Good Finished Units Produced.................. 18,000
Cost per Unit, If Produced at 60% of Capacity Rate.......... $28.38
Cost per Unit, If Produced at 20% of Capacity Rate.......... $30.36

Burden Charges, One Month, when Plant Is Operated at Various Rates and when Idle

| Rate of Plant Operation | Fixed Burden | Variable Burden | Total Burden |
|---|---|---|---|
| 60% of Capacity............... | $9,180 | $58,320 | $67,500 |
| 20% of Capacity............... | 9,180 | 35,720 | 44,900 |
| Idle......................... | 9,180 | 14,580 | 23,760 |

## QUESTIONS

1. Should the plant have been operated at 20 per cent of capacity for the six-month period, or should the 18,000 pressure water-supply units have been made during the first two months and the plant shut down thereafter for the remainder of the year?

2. What are the risks and costs of manufacture for stock in periods of seasonally low demand?

## HUMBOLT-CLATSON COMPANY

Humbolt-Clatson Company of St. Louis, Missouri, manufactured and sold direct to retailers boys' underwear of a type not subject to rapid style change. The management effected drastic revision of the company's sales and production policies, which resulted in a significant improvement of company earnings.

Demand for the product of the Humbolt-Clatson Company was seasonal, with peaks in the spring and fall. Garments required for the fall trade differed from those demanded for spring in type and weight of fabric as well as cut of garment. Although the company was a relatively small unit in the industry, years of catering to the individual requests of a large number of retail stores had resulted in a wide line of types and sizes of the garments in the production of which the company specialized. During a protracted period of business depression, volume fell off rapidly in spite of increased effort by the sales department. Currently sales were less than $300,000 annually, and there was every indication that volume would become still less. Past experience had shown that when annual sales volume fell below $600,000, operation resulted in a loss.

Briefly, the manufacturing process carried on by Humbolt-Clatson Company was as follows:

Threads and yarns purchased from specialist producers were knit into tubular fabrics in the knitting room. This was a machine process. Knitting machines were automatic and needed only intermittent attention while in operation. Such attention as was necessary required the services of skilled specialists. The machines were complicated, and the nicety of precision adjustment essential to satisfactory operation called for men trained in the setting up and adjustment of work in the machines.

Fabric from the knitting room went to the bleachery in the basement. There it was bleached, finished, pressed, and wound into rolls. The rolls were either stored or sent direct to the cutting room.

Cutting was done by men skilled in the use of electric knives which cut many layers of fabric at one time. Cut parts were bundled and assembled for complete garments in hand trucks.

Stitching of cut parts into complete garments was the next step. The stitching process was divided into a number of detailed operations, such as sewing a single seam, stitching on a label, and attaching buttons. Equipment in the stitching room was light and relatively flexible in use and arrangement. This department employed more workers than any other step in the process.

After the garments were completely sewed, they were pressed, folded, and packed into cardboard containers, which were labeled and placed in stock. The shipping room filled orders by withdrawals from the stockroom. There orders were assembled, packed in cartons, and dispatched for shipment by parcel post, express, or freight.

Having become convinced that sales of the coming year would be less than ever before, the management of Humbolt-Clatson Company decided upon certain drastic changes in policy. Only changes in production are given here. Those included the following:

Reduction of the product line by the elimination of all types of items that had not sold in volume during the past year. Approximately two-thirds of the items in the line were dropped. All items retained were made in the usual sizes demanded by the trade.

Refusal of all special orders except those for models which appeared to be improvements on existing items and would probably replace them.

Division of the year into two six-month production periods, one for the spring line and one for fall.

Budgeting and detailed planning of each six months' production in advance. Manufacture for stock.

Production at a steady rate throughout each period.

Replacement of foremen with working bosses who spent most of their time at processing tasks. These working bosses were responsible for inspection of work in process.

Elimination of three of the four clerks engaged in scheduling and cost work.

Replacement of a job cost system with a simple cumulative daily statement for the manager. This statement showed daily production, payroll, orders, and shipments, with weekly summaries. Standard costs for raw materials and burden were developed.

Repricing of piece-rate jobs at lower figures. Practically all workers had been paid piece rates.

Closing of one finishing room.

In all departments, operation of only the fastest and most modern equipment. Older, less efficient machines were stored in a manner to protect them from physical deterioration.

Handling of all operations by two executives: the president, who also served as sales manager, and the mill superintendent.

## Results of the changes were reported for the following year as follows:

Budgeted sales, $275,000.

Actual sales, $254,000.

Practically no seasonal finished goods inventory at the end of either the spring or fall season.

Profit which, if continued, would wipe out all bank obligations within three years.

Lowest production cost ever attained by the company.

Lowest selling cost ever attained.

Production and selling savings of approximately equal amounts.

Highest earnings workers had ever received from the company.

Best satisfied and most contented group of employees in the vicinity.

Best service ever rendered to customers.

Less effort required of the executives than for many years.

### QUESTIONS

1. Were the contraction policy and program of Humbolt-Clatson Company sound?

2. Explain how the action taken produced the results indicated.

# CHAPTER IX

## INTEGRATION

### LOST MOUNTAIN COPPER COMPANY

## 1. An Example of Integration.

The president of the Lost Mountain Copper Company was endeavoring to bring under one management five companies which operated copper mines in contiguous territory. Although the companies competed, there was some interlocking ownership of stock. Three of the mines were high-cost producers. Because of the declining price of copper, the companies were finding it difficult to realize profits, and in the case of the three high-cost mines substantial losses were being experienced.

The president of the largest of the five companies, the Lost Mountain Copper Company, believed that if all the mines could be placed under one management, such a consolidation would result in economies in financing, marketing, management, and production. Accordingly, he proposed such a program. After going into the matter thoroughly, the stockholders of the five properties were convinced that integration held advantages for all, and the proposed consolidation became effective.

## 2. Development of Integration.

Ever since the advent of the factory system of production, there appears to have been an irresistible tendency for business units to coalesce and form new and larger units. This process of combination is generally spoken of as integration of industry. In economic literature there is much discussion as to what constitutes integration. Some writers distinguish between aggregation of industry, integration of industry, and consolidation of industry. As the term "integration" is used in this chapter no such refinement of distinction is attempted. Integration is used in its generally accepted meaning —the formation of a whole from constituent parts. In some cases this whole is the result of combining small units. In other instances both small and large units are brought together. In still others several large units are combined to form a new organization. Always, however, one fundamental is present—combination of units previously regarded as entities to gain anticipated benefits.

No one can glance at the industrial development of the United States during the past 75 or 100 years without being profoundly impressed by the fact that, for better or for worse, American industry, decade after decade, has moved in the direction of bigger business units.

**3. Kinds of Integration.** While this chapter attempts no refinement in defining the integration of industrial units, nevertheless, the more common types of integration should be readily distinguishable, for they have grown up through attempts of American business managers to gain the benefits of consolidation.

An integration which is the result of consolidating producing units which perform similar functions is often referred to as horizontal integration. International Harvester Company is frequently cited as an example of this type. That company was formed in 1902 by combining the McCormick Harvesting Machine Company, the Deering Harvester Company, the Warder, Bushnell and Glessner Company, and the Milwaukee Harvester Company. These competing companies made similar products, and as a result of the combination, the integrated corporation produced three-fourths of the total harvesting machines manufactured in the United States.[1]

When an organization seeks to control all the steps in producing and marketing a product from ownership of raw materials to distribution of finished goods, the situation is characterized as vertical integration. The United States Steel Corporation, for instance, owns vast deposits of raw materials, railroads, steamship lines, blast furnaces, rolling mills, and other finishing units; and it is generally regarded as a typical example of vertical integration.

More recently a third type of integration has attracted considerable attention in this country, and many people believe that this new type will become increasingly important in the years immediately ahead. This third form differs from both horizontal and vertical integration in important respects. There is not

---

[1] See *Report of the Federal Trade Commission on the Causes of High Prices of Farm Implements,* Washington, D.C., 1920.

necessarily an attempt to combine in one organization units operating on approximately the same level, nor is there necessarily any attempt to control production operations from the point of raw materials through the distribution of the finished product. Rather, an attempt is made to combine products in one plant on the basis of either their likeness in the productive process or their complementary nature in a sales program. This type of combination is sometimes spoken of as circular integration; for example, some companies which manufacture oil burners for household use, a business which is highly seasonal in nature, have found it distinctly advantageous to manufacture electric refrigerators. On the face of it there appears to be little in common between these two products, but underneath the surface the situation appears quite different. The seasonal demands for oil burners and refrigerators are such that they complement each other. The raw materials entering into the two products are much the same, similar machinery may be employed, and workers of the same type are needed in making both products. The resulting benefits in purchasing raw materials, in utilizing plant, equipment, and labor under such circumstances are many. Sometimes circular integration takes place because of marketing advantages. A company may produce two products unlike from a production standpoint but of such a nature that they can be advantageously distributed by the same sales organization.

**4. Goal of Integration.** Integration, in whatever form it takes, seeks to avoid some of the obvious limitations of specialization, simplification, standardization, unwise diversification, and waste, and it must be regarded as one of the basic concepts underlying mass production.

**5. Need for Close Integration in This Case.** The Lost Mountain Copper Company produced about 3 per cent of the world's output of copper. Contiguous to the mines of the company were those of four other producers in each of which the Lost Mountain Copper Company owned from 25 to 51 per cent of the capital stock. Each of the five companies was operated independently, although sales were made exclusively through the distributing organization of the Lost Mountain Copper Company. The president of the Lost Mountain Copper Company proposed a consolidation in order to operate the five mines as a unit and thereby effect certain economies which he believed would be beneficial to all concerned.

The properties of the Lost Mountain Copper Company and of the other companies, the High-Low copper mines, the Luster Mines, Inc., the Boyd Copper Mining Company, and the Dickeson Mining Company, were situated along the outcrop of a vein of copper. The Lost Mountain Copper Company had been in operation for over 60 years; the others, from 20 to 50 years. In this region copper was mined at costs ranging from 8½ cents to 14 cents a pound, and averaging 10½ cents. This average was relatively high; in some mines in Chile the cost was said to be only 7 cents a pound, and it was rumored that as the result of discoveries of vast deposits in Africa, low-cost copper from that territory might become an important factor in the markets of the world.

At the prevailing price of copper the Luster Mines, Inc., the Boyd Copper Mining Company, and the Dickeson Mining Company, which were unable to produce and sell copper profitably at less than 13, 14½, and 13½ cents, respectively, were closed. Their properties were smaller than those of either the Lost Mountain Copper Company or the High-Low mines. Consequently, they had no opportunity to gain the benefits of large-scale production. The president of the Lost Mountain Copper Company believed that the depressed condition of the copper market was likely to continue for a considerable period. The only hope which he saw was to put the five mines under one effective management and operate them as a single unit. If such a step was taken, he believed it would be possible to secure many of the economies of mass production which were now denied to the individual mines. Some of these economies would result from production advantages; others would come from marketing, financial, and managerial savings.

**6. Production Economies.** There were several production economies which the president was certain he could obtain in the event that the proposed consolidation was effected, for example, a state law required that at least two connected shafts be maintained on the property of each mining company. Some of the mines in question did not need two shafts for effective operation. This was particularly true of the Luster and Boyd mines. The president planned, if the amalgamation was consummated, to connect one shaft in each mine with a shaft in one of the adjacent mines. Because of the nearness of the shafts, such a plan was entirely practical and would, he pointed out, permit the closing of one shaft in each of the mines.

If all the adjacent properties were under one engineering staff instead of five isolated groups, many other economies would be possible. Blind drifts could then be extended into adjoining properties wherever feasible. Ores could be hauled to the nearest shaft for transportation to the surface. Twenty-foot barriers between properties, as required by law, could be eliminated. A unified system for pumping compressed air into all the mines could be devised. Company geologists and company engineers could plan the work of the five properties as a whole, whereas under existing conditions the geologists and engineers of one mine had no reliable information as to conditions existing in any of the four others. In some of the mines the ores contained a smaller percentage of deposits of copper than in the other properties, and in some mines it was necessary to sink shafts much deeper than in other properties. The executive believed that if the properties were integrated under one management, an operating program could be worked out whereby the high-cost ores would be taken out only when the demand for copper was strong.

The Luster, Boyd, and Dickeson mines did not have stamping mills. They sent their ores to either the High-Low or the Lost Mountain mills to be crushed. Under such arrangements, every consignment of ore from each mine had to be kept separate. This increased costs of handling. In case of consolidation no such separation of ores would be necessary.

After the stamping process was completed, all five companies had their ores refined in the smelters of the Lost Mountain Copper Company. Here again it was necessary that each consignment of ore be handled as an individual lot during the refining process. This manner of handling not only increased refining costs, but it also resulted in a distinct waste, since ores from some of the mines contained inadequate amounts of fluxing agents such as iron and silica, while ores from other mines contained a superabundance of these agents. So long as the ores of the different companies had to be kept separate during the refining process, no advantage could be taken of the excess supplies of fluxing agents. The president believed that it would be a simple matter, under a unified control, to remedy this difficulty by combining in correct proportions the ores which were deficient in fluxing materials with those which possessed a superabundance.

The production manager of the Lost Mountain Copper Company pointed out to the president that if such an amalgamation was completed it would probably be wise to replace the present 30,000-pound furnaces with others of 250,000-pound capacity. A small number of large furnaces could be operated more economically than a large number of small ones, provided that control of all ores was under one management.

Each mine, when operated individually, had to maintain its own shops, pumps, air compressors, etc. During periods of curtailed production, the cost of maintaining these separate lines of equipment was much greater than would be the case if there was but one set of each type of equipment, since five separate establishments resulted in duplication of equipment, supervision, and labor forces.

When all the mines were in operation, the supply of labor in the region was inadequate to man the shafts fully. The employees' homes were distributed throughout the district where the five companies were located, and the men naturally preferred to work in the nearest shafts, although they were willing to go farther away if the nearby shafts were closed. During periods of high prices for copper, when all the companies required laborers, the more profitable mines could not obtain a sufficient number of men to operate at maximum capacity. Under a consolidated management, if such a labor shortage occurred, the available men could be assigned to the shafts where ore was mined at low cost, in order to operate such shafts at capacity if this action was thought desirable; while in the higher cost shafts only the available remainder of the labor supply would be employed.

Under one management, not only could the labor force be distributed at the most profitable points, but also a degree of labor specialization could be obtained such as was not possible under individual management. Crews specializing in certain mining operations could be transferred from place to place as occasion arose.

Each of the five mines had considerable equipment which was used only at infrequent intervals. A single management, by careful planning, could reduce the total amount of this equipment, thereby cutting down the fixed investment.

These production advantages were so impressive that the president of the Lost Mountain Copper Company felt certain that integration would be beneficial to all the five companies.

**7. Marketing Advantages.** For a number of years the total sales of the five companies had been made through the sales organization of the Lost Mountain Copper Company. The copper had been sold under two brands. That which came from the mines of the Lost Mountain Copper Company proper was sold under the Lost Mountain brand and commanded a price from ⅛ of a cent to 1 cent higher than that of the T-C copper, which was taken from the properties of the four other companies. Analysis of the metal, however, had shown almost no difference in quality between the two brands.

The demand for Lost Mountain copper had been built up over a period of years through uninterrupted service. Many customers, especially those who manufactured fine-drawn wire, were reluctant to accept the T-C brand even at a lower price when supplies of the Lost Mountain brand were inadequate. The use of the Lost Mountain name on the entire product would, therefore, be advantageous.

The five companies customarily mined about 3,000,000 tons of ore per year. This ore was hauled to the smelters over the Cuba & Southern Railroad, which had been built for public freight service. Its line was not well adapted to the specific needs of these mines, and as a result transportation costs were uneconomical because of heavy grades and roundabout routes. Lost Mountain Copper Company executives believed it would be entirely feasible in event of consolidation to build a private railroad which, if constructed to meet the individual needs of the mines, would, according to the estimates of company engineers, reduce the cost of handling ore from the prevailing 18.5 cents per ton to 11.25 cents per ton.

**8. Management Economies.** The president was also of the opinion that there would be resultant economies in management. One president would be needed instead of five. Subexecutives could be specialized according to their capabilities. Existing office forces could be consolidated, specialized, and reduced. One planning department could do the work for all five mines. Only the superior foremen would have to be retained. All along the line managerial activities could be revised so as to be more effective and economical in operation.

**9. Financial Considerations.** Several stockholders of the Lost Mountain Copper Company objected to the consolidation on the ground that it provided for the inclusion of three relatively high-cost mines whose stockholders were to receive dividends from profits in the making of which they had had no part. The president pointed out, however, that these properties were situated between the others in such a way that their inclusion in the consolidation was essential to the attainment of the economies outlined. He stated that the varying earning powers of the companies were reflected fairly in the market prices of their common stocks. The terms on which the companies should join the merger, therefore, could be determined on the basis of comparative common stock quotations. In the less profitable mines, furthermore, the average life of the shafts was estimated to exceed the average in the other mines by three or four years. The president computed the savings at $1,000,000 per year, and the earnings at slightly over $2 per share on 2,000,000 shares, with copper at 14½ cents.

The executive also pointed out that there would be some financial saving due to the fact that the new company would have to pay but one corporation tax, whereas under the existing organizations five such taxes were paid.

At the end of several weeks' investigation and conference, a consolidation was effected on the basis proposed by the president of the Lost Mountain Copper Company.

**10. Summary and Conclusions.** *Strength and Weakness of Horizontal Integration.* The experience of the Lost Mountain Copper Company is a typical illustration of the advantages accruing from intelligent horizontal integration. Better utilization of facilities was obtained; labor was employed to the greater advantage of both employees and the company; raw materials were more completely and economically used; equipment investment per pound of product was reduced in amount even though better equipment was employed; improvement in administrative personnel and organization made management more effective. Throughout the production process, waste was reduced and efficiency of operation was improved. In addition, financial and marketing advantages were forthcoming.

Unfortunately not all horizontal integrations have produced comparable results. Great size itself is not the key to low-cost production. Size frequently tends to make unwieldy and complicated the problems of business management. Particularly is this true in the absence of careful specialization. That this tendency toward the ponderous is not a necessary concomitant of horizontal integration is demonstrated by the Lost Mountain Copper Company experience. Horizontal integration is sound business policy when it tends to reduce production costs without saddling management with business problems of such ramifications as to render foresight difficult or lull management into a feeling of lethargic content in monopolistic advantage.

*Forces Making for Vertical Integration.* The forces which from time to time motivate management in American industry to vertical integration policies are often quite different from those which result in horizontal integration. The most common influence is a desire to eliminate the risks of dependence on supplies of raw materials or fabricated parts, or outside channels of product distribution. To ensure uninterrupted inflow of requisite raw materials, ownership of such sources is undertaken. To provide properly aggressive outflow of finished product, a distributing organization is acquired or built up to place the product in the hands of the ultimate consumer. When the urge to integrate grows out of the desire to avoid risks of this type, emphasis is upon maintenance of profits accruing from the original production activities of the business. The acquisition of dissimilar properties in the undertaking of new functions is essentially for the protection of the original purposes of the organization.

Vertical integrations have frequently resulted from the desire to supplement the profits of original functions by adding thereto the profits which others have enjoyed from the performance of facilitating functions. The reasoning involved is simple. The Ginwan Company makes a product that incorporates gray iron castings. During a period of years the output of this company has grown until the volume of gray iron castings required is great. Throughout this period the outside foundry from which the castings are procured has increased its profits just as the prosperity of the Ginwan Company has grown. Ginwan Company executives know this, and as competition narrows the margin between costs and profits on the machines they make and sell, the management looks somewhat covetously upon the profit the foundry makes from Ginwan Company castings. As a result, the Ginwan Company erects a foundry and makes its own gray iron castings. The company has embarked upon a program of vertical integration in an attempt at profit accretion. Continued pursuit of such a policy would involve the Ginwan Company in blast furnace operation to supply its foundry with pig iron, in the mining of coal and iron ore to provide the requisite raw materials for the blast furnace, and, perhaps, rail or water transportation from mine to furnace to foundry. These activities as here cited would be undertaken for the purposes of adding to Ginwan Company returns the profits from related though dissimilar activities.

It is not unknown for a company to pursue a vertical integration policy in furtherance of competitive price advantage in the market. Some years ago an automobile company with a venerable name in the manufacturing field advertised its product as "the one-profit car" produced by "the great independent." The idea behind such advertising lies in the implication that the company carries on many activities upon which it makes no profit. The advantage held out to the consumer is price reduction resulting from the manufacturer's selling a substantial part of the product at cost of production and distribution. Many automobile manufacturers do not make the bodies for the cars they sell. These bodies are produced by specialized body makers who, of course, are in business for profit. The "one-profit car" manufacturer would make these bodies himself, and the assumption would be that the selling price of the car would be loaded by the cost of producing the bodies with no profit element on this activity included. The consumer would then be led to understand that a car purchased from this "great independent" would cost less by the amount of the profit foregone on these profitless activities. In this way the vertically integrated manufacturer might plan for himself a competitive price advantage.

Manufacturers enjoying a market reputation for dependability and high quality of product occasionally embark upon a vertical integration program in an attempt to spread that quality reputation over a wider range of products. Almost no automobile manufacturer makes the storage batteries with which cars are equipped. In the past, however, at least one of the best known automobile trade names was placed upon batteries used by the company. The automobile manufacturer made these batteries, which undoubtedly received some popularity from the placing of the automobile manufacturer's name upon them. The brand was expected to extend to the battery the reputation for quality enjoyed by the automobile itself.

*Strength and Weakness of Vertical Integration.* Probably more attempts at profit increase by means of vertical integration have failed than have succeeded. As has been noted, the objectives sought through such activity are varied and include control of materials supply, ensurance of market channels, finished product price advantage, and enhancement of quality reputation. Lack of success is not peculiar to any one of these, although the case for vertical integration may well be stronger with certain objectives in mind than with others.

Ownership of sources is no panacea for the elimination of risks of raw materials and parts supply. The company which embarks upon a program of materials or parts production actually exchanges one group of risks for another. Commonly the processes and problems of materials production are quite unlike those with which the integrating company is familiar. The risks of inefficient raw materials production are undoubtedly greater when an inexperienced manufacturer undertakes their production. The major advantage enjoyed by a materials producer when owned and controlled by its product user is assurance of demand for at least part of its output.  This market backlog often does not eliminate, however, the need for developing other outlets in competition with experienced producers in the field.  It is not to be expected that optimum size of a materials producing unit will usually coincide with the materials requirements of the parent company.  Thus, more often than not, the materials producing unit is subject to disadvantages of uneconomical size from a production standpoint, or must actively undertake competitive marketing of a portion of its output.

Integration in the direction of raw materials production increases in number and complicates in nature the problems of management.  Attention of executives usually must be divided between activities of quite unlike nature.  This dilution may have an unfortunate effect upon the affairs of the parent company.  To whatever extent the raw materials supply problems of the integrating company are relieved by such action, the increase in management difficulties is somewhat offset.

More often than not it is a mistake to think that satisfactory control of materials requirements cannot be attained through buying in the open market.  Active market competition is an effective safeguard to the buyer in most cases.  Stability of supply can usually be increased through the establishment of close relations with a small number of carefully selected suppliers.  Essentially, what was said at the beginning of this discussion serves well to summarize it.  Vertical integration to secure control of raw materials and parts supply is basically a situation in which management attempts to relieve itself of one set of risks by accepting another set of dissimilar risks.  Occasionally, this decision is a display of wisdom.  All too frequently management is ill equipped to cope with the new problems undertaken, and the result is cost of materials in excess of market price plus the cost of procurement.

To the extent that there is soundness in our analysis of weakness of materials production to ensure supply control, there is danger in the vertical integration program undertaken to add to profits accruing from established activity.  Much of American industry is highly specialized industry.  There are specialized producers of watch and clock hands, of valve guides for automobile engines, of the vacuum tubes with which radios are equipped, of wooden chair legs, and of thousands of the parts that go into the simplest and the most complicated things we use in everyday life.  These specialist producers have developed great efficiency as communication and transportation have become lightning-fast and gravity-sure in a great economic area unhampered by man-made trade restrictions.  Likewise, technical progress has been driving manufacturing executives into narrower lines of activity through constant acceleration in the rate of change.

For the Ginwan Company management to assume that it could make a profit from the operation of its own foundry just because the company from which it had been buying castings had made a profit would be a serious mistake.  Perhaps profits would result; perhaps losses would be entailed.  A hundred conditions might be effective determinants.  Suppose the Ginwan Company is subject to severe seasonal fluctuations in its volume.  In that case its foundry operation might be highly intermittent.  Non-constant operation is costly operation.  The merchant foundry from which Ginwan Company has purchased parts need not be subject to this adverse seasonal effect, for it can balance the seasonal Ginwan demand with business solicited from sources with demand peaks offsetting those of the Ginwan Company.  If the latter company is to produce castings as cheaply as the merchant foundry, it must take steps to meet this disadvantage of its own seasonal operation.  It might make castings for stock, but that would involve inventory costs to which the Ginwan Company is not now subject.  Furthermore, it would accept the risks of inventory obsolescence, which it now escapes.  If production for stock was unwise, about the only way open for Ginwan Company to obtain basic efficiency parity with the merchant foundry would be to obtain outside business during the seasons when its own demand was slack.  This might be easy, or it might be almost impossible.  To assume that no problem is involved certainly would be a fundamental mistake.

Economical operation of a foundry normally calls for either

exclusive production of heavy castings or carefully considered balance between heavy and light castings. When the output of a foundry is limited to intricate lightweight castings, the cost of production per pound of product turned out is usually excessive. The merchant foundry producing castings for a variety of customers is always careful to maintain a volume of relatively profitable heavy casting business to offset loss or absence of profit on its lightweight casting. The ability of the Ginwan Company to produce its own castings economically is thus greatly influenced by the nature of the castings it requires. If it is buying a reasonable balance between light and heavy castings, its position in that respect would be quite comparable with that of the foundry that has been supplying it. If its needs are for a preponderance of heavy castings, it might well be in a better position than its supplier. If, however, its needs are mainly for light castings, its costs will tend to be greater than those of the supplying foundry unless sufficient outside heavy casting business is found to balance the high costs of producing its own lightweight requirements. To ignore this aspect of the problem of making its own castings is simply inviting disaster.

Seasonal variation and lack of foundry balance are only two of many possible difficulties that the Ginwan Company management might encounter. The specialized materials and parts producer has become dominant in American industry largely because he possesses real economic advantage. There are occasions when these specialists do not have a net advantage but more often than not they do. Any notion that the existence of profits in the business of materials and parts supply offers an opportunity to the buyer to obtain those profits for himself simply by undertaking production of such materials and parts is gross error. There are occasions upon which the manufacturer can increase his profit by vertically extending the area of his activity. To determine when these occasions actually exist and when vertical integration would be unprofitable is a management problem of considerable magnitude.

Obviously, if vertical integration results in uneconomical production, the management which seeks price advantage through such activity is headed for disappointment. No more need be said on that matter. The one-profit-car notion, though closely related, is slightly different. If it is assumed that the integrating company can carry on the diverse affiliated activities exactly as economically as they were carried on prior to integration, the ability thereby to pass on to the consumer the profits of the non-integrated producers is questionable. There is little to indicate that integration of these activities will result in reduction of capital essential to the conduct of the affiliated enterprise. The suppliers of such capital, whether they be stockholders of the parent company or not, will expect, and in the long run insist upon, a return on their investment commensurate with the amount of the commitment and the risk involved. It has just been pointed out that there is little likelihood that either the amount of capital required or the risk entailed inevitably will be lessened by vertical integration. It would seem, then, that only to the extent that the nonintegrated unit had been able to return an abnormally liberal profit through exceptional efficiency would it be possible to reduce the capital costs of production through integration. The more efficient the production has been in the past, the more difficult the job of making integrated production successful, and, thus, the less the likelihood that new management can maintain the past profit level. The one-profit-product idea may be good advertising. On rare occasions it will certainly have basis in fact. That, however, will be the exception.

The advantages likely to result from vertical integration in the interest of extending brand values depend on marketing considerations that are essentially outside the immediate concern of this text. No such marketing program should be undertaken, however, without careful study of the production problems involved. Many production problems inherent in vertical integration have already been discussed or pointed out, and these must be satisfactorily settled if any market advantages are to be net advantages, not offset by production difficulties or inefficiencies.

*Circular Integration.* That type of combination which is sometimes known as circular integration has its origin in the desire to eliminate costly characteristics of either a production or a marketing situation. The most common condition from which relief is sought by combining the production of seemingly dissimilar products in one plant is seasonal demand. When the nature of a highly seasonal product is such that a specialized marketing organization is required for its distribution, marketing costs are likely to be excessive. If a product of like nature (in the sense of marketing organization requirements) but with off-setting seasonal peaks and lows could be made available to the sales organization, distribution costs should thereby become much more nearly normal. The addition of such a product would involve either manufacture or purchase outside for resale. If conditions seem to indicate the desirability of manufacture, the problem of circular integration immediately becomes pertinent. It would be purely fortuitous if the addition of the new product to the one already manufactured resulted in production economies. If the process, materials, and labor requirements are essentially unlike those being employed, the result is likely to be an increase in existing costs. If the opposite is true and basic likenesses exist, the resulting ability to eliminate seasonal hiring and firing and periodic idleness of equipment and supervisory personnel should bring about lowered cost of production of the line already produced and low cost of production of the added product.

The economies of production under such circumstances may be so substantial as to dictate circular integration even though no marketing advantages result. While the two products involved may be basically complementary as to production characteristics, from the standpoint of marketing they may have widely different characteristics. Under such circumstances it is imperative to make sure that the increase in marketing costs does not wipe out production economies gained. Likewise, when seasonally complementary products will reduce selling costs, it is important to make certain that production costs will not increase to such an extent as to eliminate market gains. The most fortunate of circumstances is, of course, a situation in which two products are seasonally complementary in both marketing and production.

While seasonality is the most common cause of circular integration, it is not the only one. Whatever the urge may be, the same need for considering both the market and the production aspects of the situation exists. Truly startling economies have resulted from some integrations of the circular type. It must be remembered, however, that the record shows equally startling disasters. The difference between success and failure is managerial consideration of the problem as a business issue rather than from a more exclusive viewpoint of technical production or marketing. The two technical aspects are important, but the businesslike reconciliation of the two is absolutely essential to success.

*What Is Integration?* Like all business management, integration is essentially the creation of business relationships. This holds whether the relationship is between similar products or activities, dissimilar products, or products and raw materials. Effective integration is based upon management perception of the existence of natural relationships. It is probably impossible at the present time to produce either domestic oil-burner equipment or electric refrigerators alone as cheaply as it is possible to produce them together in the same plant. From the production standpoint and, to a somewhat lesser extent, from the marketing point of view, these two products are inherently complementary. Management has commonly recognized this characteristic of the two products, and they are usually made together in the same factory. Whether the combination be in the nature of circular, horizontal, or vertical integration, success is the result of recognition of the opportunity to create advantageous relationships, intelligent setting up of such relationships, and the continued maintenance of them in the interest of low costs of the use value finally produced.

*Results of Integration.* In spite of the somewhat drab picture which has been painted here of the dangers and pitfalls of integration, anyone who will read that part of the industrial history of the United States which covers the last half of the nineteenth century and the first quarter of the twentieth cannot fail to be impressed by the ever-present movement toward integration. A study of the size of the average manufacturing establishment by decades since 1850 shows clearly what has taken place in American industry. Large organizations are the order of the day. In some industries, such as iron and steel and meat packing, although the value of the product and the number of workers employed have increased tremendously since the early 1880's, the number of producing establishments has either remained practically stationary or actually decreased. For factories as a whole throughout the country, the average amount of capital invested in 1919 was fifty times greater than it was for the establishments that existed in 1850. The gains which have been responsible for this degree of integration are those which were seen to operate in the Lost Mountain Copper Company, namely, financial, marketing, managerial, and production economies. The particular advantages that will be outstanding in any given case of integration will, of course, depend entirely on the circumstances surrounding the consolidation. Sometimes the most obvious gains will come because of some new method of distribution. In other cases, financial benefits are outstanding; in still others, managerial and production gains are most important. It should be emphasized, however, that financial reorganizations which are not in the last analysis based upon sound economies in marketing, management, and production may be the cause of profound industrial disturbances.

One can conclude the whole subject of integration by the more or less obvious statement that if consolidation is used intelligently and for the best interests of society, as well as for those of the manufacturer, its benefits are outstanding. Where, however, products which are not naturally complementary in nature are integrated, or where the ultimate object is financial manipulation or monopoly rather than the legitimate advantages of mass production, then the result may easily spell disaster and eventually ruin. Just how far business units should be allowed to integrate in order to gain the benefits of mass production is one of the most baffling of all questions which the American people face today.

*Integration during the Second World War and the Postwar Period.* One of the most serious problems of the manufacturer during and following the war was the obtaining of adequate raw materials. Government control of materials through the use of priority allocations limited materials for nonmilitary use to a small fraction of prewar volume. In attempts to bolster these inadequate supplies many manufacturers purchased mills that produced the raw materials they required. Users of cotton cloth such as the larger manufacturers of men's and women's clothing purchased spinning and weaving mills. Much of the output of such a "captured" mill went to the government, but whatever was left over was available to the garment manufacturer who had the cloth finished for his use by custom bleacheries and printworks. Many of these mills were old and inefficient, and the purchasers often paid two or three times their prewar market worth. However, these mills did provide the garment manufacturers with some cloth when none was available from their usual source, the piece goods market.

Whenever a garment manufacturer purchased a cotton mill, a certain amount of fabric which regularly had gone from that mill to converters was no longer available to those business houses. Converters regularly bought gray goods from mills, had them finished and dyed, and then sold them to garment manufacturers. To protect their position in the market, some converters purchased cotton mills, and to ensure finishing capacity also they likewise bought bleacheries and printworks. Sometimes cotton mill owners enviously eyeing profits that were being made by finishers and converters stepped out and acquired their own bleacheries and printworks. The result of all this was a new structure within a substantial part of the raw-cotton-to-finished-garment industry. Over many past years this old, established industry had reacted to the influences of the techniques and economics of the business and had developed a highly specialized structure. This consisted of independently owned and operated gray goods mills, finishing plants, converting houses, and consumer products manufacturers. There were only a few instances where vertical integration had worked well. These were producers of standardized nonstyle products, such as sheets and pillow cases, gauze bandages, and the like. Pequot sheets and the Kendall Company's products are examples. Attempts to integrate from cotton to garment had never worked out well when any substantial style element was involved, and management in the industry had come to believe that independent specialized producers at the various steps in the process constituted sound organization for the industry.

When wartime controls of materials were removed, competition for cotton goods by garment manufacturers increased because of the need to get back quickly into the civilian market. The trade journals reported more mill purchases, and again the motive was the securing of needed materials.  Just how long this integration will last is difficult to foresee, but insofar as style goods are concerned it is unlikely to be permanent.  Many managements of integrated textile operations expect to dump these purchased mills someday.  Their ownership, as sources of supply during a most abnormal period, has been exceedingly profitable. In many cases the entire purchase price has been "written off the books" already.  When profit margins begin to shrink and the industry again competes on a price basis, many of the captured mills—often old and inefficient—will not be economical sources of supply to their owners.  When that day arrives, the managements will have two courses of action before them: to sell these mills or to modernize them.  The mills then will bring less in the market than was paid for them, but this loss will have been foreseen.  To modernize these mills will be expensive.  Usually this cost will be greater than the original purchase price. The most experienced executives in this industry believe that in a few cases where the materials are standard and subject to little change, denims for example, the garment manufacturers may retain and modernize the mills.  These men believe, however, that in the case of style goods the mills will be dumped for what they will bring and that the industry will resume its old prewar non-integrated form.

There are those who question this conclusion.  They think that changes such as the wide introduction of new fiber combinations in fabrics will cause gray goods mills and bleacheries and dye works to retain a close relationship via ownership or contractual control.  This view is not generally held, and the arguments that the industry will revert seem persuasive.

This wartime story has been told here at some length to illustrate the impact of the dynamics of industry on the practice of one of its principles, integration.  A temporary drastic change in the industrial scene called for a basic change in operating policy.  The management that recognized early this need for change and acted on it profited from foresight.  Likewise, managements that recognize the writing on the wall as the situation again changes and have the judgment and fortitude to change with the times again will profit. As yet there is no indication that the prewar setup of the textile industry is permanently a thing of the past. There are now in existence one or two organizations that are being managed on the theory that the wartime changes in the textile industry are here to stay. However, the odds are against them, and there seems to be good reason to believe that vertical integration in the textile field will again prove to be unsatisfactory.

The textile industry is not the only one in which the desire to control supplies of raw materials has motivated managements to buy suppliers' mills. In early 1948 the Studebaker Corporation announced the purchase of a steel mill. All automobile manufacturers were being handicapped by lack of steel sheets for car bodies. Both Ford and Kaiser-Frazer owned steel mills, and the Studebaker purchase was not surprising. Whether or not such ownership proves permanently advantageous will depend on what transpires in the steel industry and on the ability of an automobile manufacturer to produce steel in a relatively small mill in competition with the large producers.

Other examples of war-born integration can be cited. Just so long as these vertical combinations are harmonious with existing industrial conditions they can be sound. Managements of such combinations must be alert to changes and shifts in the related industries concerned. They should be as quick to undo that which they have done as they were in originally promoting the integrations.

## QUESTIONS

1. What were the specific advantages which the president of the Lost Mountain Copper Company expected to gain in marketing, management, and production?

2. In just what ways would the labor advantages be obtained in the Lost Mountain Copper Company case?

3. In the case of the copper companies under discussion, what would be the economies of the operation of a few large furnaces as compared with the operation of a large number of small ones?

4. Against what disadvantages should the management be

prepared to safeguard itself in case the larger furnaces were installed?

5. Of the anticipated production economies in the Lost Mountain Copper Company case, which ones are characteristic of industrial consolidation and which are peculiar to an extractive industry such as copper mining?

6. What is the current price of copper?

7. How would you expect the action taken by the Lost Mountain Copper Company to affect the company profits under today's conditions?

8. What is meant by the term "integration"?

9. How would you differentiate between horizontal, vertical, and circular integration?

10. What are the advantages of each of these three types?

11. What are the disadvantages of each of these three types?

12. Be prepared to discuss the causes and the future of the vertical integration that took place during and immediately following the Second World War.

## BRANDON BATTERY COMPANY

The Brandon Battery Company manufactured dry cells, from which it made dry-cell batteries in varying sizes and for a variety of purposes. The company had found that in buying batteries for use in flashlights, the trade, especially the retailers, wished to buy the flashlight cases in which the batteries were to be used at the same time and from the same source. Accordingly, the company extended its activities to include the production of flashlight cases. The case department, however, never operated at a profit, and the Brandon management was faced with the problem of either putting this department on a paying basis or discontinuing it and buying cases from outside sources.

The Brandon Battery Company was primarily known as a manufacturer of dry cells and of batteries made up of a number of cells. When running at normal capacity, it manufactured 500,000 cells of all varieties per day. The manufacture of dry-cell batteries was essentially a chemical process. The work had to be planned and supervised by persons who had an understanding of the chemical problems involved, although many of the actual tasks in the productive process were simple and could be performed by girls who had the requisite agility, provided that they were properly supervised.

The case department in the plant was equipped with machinery sufficient to produce parts for and assemble flashlight cases in 35 styles. The production of flashlight cases was not a chemical process. Rather it involved stamping out, punching, plating, and polishing or lacquering the brass sheets which were the basic material from which the cases were made, followed by the assembly of parts. It required a different type of workmanship from that in the dry-cell department.

Distribution of company products was national in scope with some foreign business obtained through agents. Sales were made to both wholesale and retail trade. The company's distributing organization sold batteries, lamps, and flashlight cases. Cases

were considered a necessary item because dealers, especially retailers, wished to purchase both cases and dry cells from the same
source, and it would have been almost impossible to sell one without the other. The company acted as a jobber of lamps merely
in order to complete its line.

In their report, officials who investigated the situation stressed
the fact that the supervisor of the case department was also the
head of the machine shop, which cared for equipment maintenance, developed new machinery, made dies, etc. This man had
been employed by the company for his ability in maintaining and
developing dry-cell manufacturing equipment, and his problems
along this line were constant and urgent. The general superintendent and the manager of the company were also principally
interested in the dry-cell part of the plant.

The investigation showed that the supervision of the case department was inadequate, that the dies used in the department
were poorly designed, and that manufacturing methods were inefficient. Most of these difficulties appeared to grow out of the
small volume of production required of the case department.
The volume was not sufficient to warrant the employment of
specialists necessary to place the department upon a proper basis.
The investigation further revealed that the conditions in the case
department were not peculiar to the Brandon Battery Company, but were experienced by most dry-cell manufacturers who
attempted the manufacture of flashlight cases.

The report recommended that the president of the company
choose one of three possible solutions: (1) Outside stamping contracts might be secured and thus increase the volume of the department to a point where it would be possible to add the needed
specialists. (2) The case department might be discontinued and
flashlight cases purchased from outside sources. (3) The company might purchase the Manson Company, a concern which
had manufactured flashlight cases for a number of years with outstanding success. The Manson Company sold cases under its
own trade name, manufactured for battery companies under contract, and possessed valuable contracts for other stampings which
served to balance its production. Its records indicated a flourish-
ing and profitable business.

The Manson Company had an excellent reputation, and was able to produce evidence to the effect that several of the competitors of the Brandon Battery Company had already tried to purchase it. It was common opinion in the trade that the Manson Company manufactured the best flashlight cases on the market at a cost lower than any other producer. Although it had no selling organization, the company possessed a number of good chain store contracts, a field which up to that time the Brandon Battery Company had been unable to enter. The Manson Company had become financially involved, however, and was willing to sell out at a reasonable figure. In the event that a change of ownership was made, the present management of the Manson Company was willing to continue in active charge of production operations.

What action should the management of the Brandon Battery Company have taken to eliminate losses on flashlight battery cases?

### Problem 21

## NEW BUILTWELL BURNER CORPORATION

The New Builtwell Burner Corporation, a producer of oil-burning equipment, considered the desirability of adding a line of domestic quick-freezing units in an effort to reduce fluctuations in production.

The factory of the company, a three-story brick building, was located at Binswood, Illinois. The framework was of steel, the floors were concrete, and the total amount of floor space was approximately 190,000 square feet. Railroad connections included the Big Four, the Nickel Plate, the Illinois Central, and the Chicago and Alton. When the factory was operated on one shift of eight hours per day, the productive capacity was 40,000 oil burners annually.

Burners were manufactured in five sizes for use in heating buildings ranging from large apartment houses, hotels, and churches to small one-family dwellings. The company's normal labor force numbered 200.

Products were distributed in the United States by 2,000 dealers and in the rest of the world by 18 general distributors. The company assisted in the sale of its products by national advertising and radio programs. Dealers were also given help in making sales, for example, the company's sales department developed standard methods of approaching various distribution problems. Dealers were supplied with this material and given assistance in its use. The latter task was both simple and effective because all dealer helps were set up on a basis of a standardized approach. Training courses in the efficient servicing of products were maintained, and an annual sales convention was held at Binswood, which was attended by representatives from all over the world.

There was a strong company *esprit de corps,* which extended to active cooperation between plant workers and the sales force. Employees frequently assisted in selling burners in the Binswood area, going as far in some instances as to close the deals themselves. Twice a week a get-together was held during the lunch hour in the company cafeteria, attended by foremen and workers from each of the production departments, as well as by representatives of the sales force and the management. Programs on these occasions included music, "pep talks," and discussions of mutual interest. If any company dealers were visiting the plant on the days when the meetings were held, they were always present at the gatherings, where they received special recognition.

The company employed both skilled and unskilled workers, although a large proportion of the jobs were performed by skilled mechanics and machinists. The unskilled workers were paid on an hourly basis, and the skilled operators received day wages. The essential operations involved in the construction of burners consisted of high-grade machining, sheet-metal operations, and expert assembling.

Each of the major components of the product required several operations, and factory production was laid out on a process basis rather than by product. Machines of like character were grouped together. Thus, a man tending a given machine could very likely operate any other in his department. The chief production units in the plant were as follows: heat-treating, normalizing, machining, sheet-metal working, assembly, inspection, painting, and shipping.

There was little attempt made at specialization in production. No conveyor belts were used in the assembly process, and special-purpose tools and equipment were few. Most of the machines and tools were general-purpose equipment, installed with a view to achieving flexibility of output. There was no standardization of job performance, nor were incentive wage plans used; but foremen were thoroughly trained to exercise very careful supervision over both employees and the work in process.[2]

There was a pronounced seasonal fluctuation in the manufacture of oil burners, which the company had been able to lessen somewhat by intensive cultivation of markets below the equator where the cold season occurred during the summer of the Northern Hemisphere. At best, however, monthly sales varied widely. Accordingly, production of burners was high from August through November, fell off slightly in December, continued to be good in January, and fell gradually through March. The low months were April, May, June, and July.

After a great deal of research in which the possibilities of several products were investigated, the management decided that it might be possible to eliminate the undesirable features of seasonal operation by the introduction of a line of electrical quick-freezing units for home use. This product would have a seasonal fluctuation counter to that of oil burners, since the peak season for production of this newly popular product occurred from January to July of each year.

An experimental food freezing and storing unit which used a new refrigerating agent was designed. The use of this chemical presented definite advantages. The boiling point was lower than many refrigerants in use, and the gas that formed on evaporation was nonpoisonous in the quantities used in a home freezer. Any moisture that collected in the mechanism when the machine was serviced was removed by a calcium chloride dehydrator. As a result of this dehydrator feature, it was possible to perform servicing in the home of the owner unless repairs had to be made on

[2] For a more detailed description of the manufacture of oil burners, see Exhibit 1, p. 238.

the piston. Sulphur dioxide, a common refrigerant, was noxious in the quantities used in a freezer. Thus it was deemed unsafe to break the gas-line seal unless the serviceman wore a gas mask, and whenever the seal was broken the unit had to be subjected to a 48-hour dehydrating baking. Any moisture in excess of 0.0005 per cent in a sulphur dioxide freezer formed sulphurous acid and "froze" the working parts of the machine. The chief disadvantage of the new chemical was that it filtered through an ordinary casting to such an extent that the charge soon evaporated. This difficulty was eliminated by the use of special nickel-steel alloy castings.

After extensive tests to establish the mechanical efficiency of the various units, the company put into production a complete line of home quick-freezing units which ranged from a capacity of 4 cubic feet for apartment use to 20 cubic feet for use on farms and in rural communities.[3]

EXHIBIT 1

MANUFACTURE OF OIL BURNERS

Essential parts of an oil burner, of the type made by the New Builtwell Burner Corporation, were the motor, shaft, oil circulating pump, fan, air volume control, atomizing device, oil feed metering unit, automatic shutoff valve, oil strainer, draft pipe, nozzle, ignition device, and transformer. Moving parts were designed so that one shaft on the motor supplied all necessary power.

The cycle of operations of the burner was as follows: In response to a thermostatic contact when room temperature fell, the motor started; current flowed through the transformer causing a spark to jump the gap at the ignition device at the end of the draft pipe; pressure built up in a centrifugal vane pump discharged oil and acted on a bellows which opened the shutoff valve; this valve allowed a flow of oil from strainer to metering device; an oil pump on the motor shaft sucked oil from the tank into the strainer and a gravity line prevented any overflow of the

[3] For a detailed description of processes and work involved, see Exhibit 2, p. 240, on the production of quick-freezing units.

strainer. Usually the ignition spark was regulated to run for 20 seconds only and then shut off. Once power was turned on by thermostatic closing of the contact, it flowed through a heat element switch which was designed to carry the load for two minutes only. If combustion took place, heat from it reached a stack safety device which made a positive contact diverting the power flow from the heat-element switch. If, however, the fire failed to ignite in two minutes, the heat-element switch would cut out and open the circuit, and the unit could not start again until it was manually adjusted and the trouble corrected. Another safety device was a gauge which broke the power circuit (in case the thermostatic contact failed to open) when water, steam, or flue temperature reached a predetermined height. Ordinarily, however, the thermostat broke the contact, the burner stopped, the shutoff valve closed, the ignition switch made contact for the next flow of current, and the stack safety switch broke contact.

In large part processes through which raw materials went were determined by type of raw material. Gray iron, brass, and alloy castings were first normalized by a heating operation in which stresses and strains within castings were equalized. They then proceeded to the machine shop where they were turned, milled, drilled, tapped, and ground on general purpose machine tools. After these operations, parts were ready for a test in which high pressure was applied to make certain that there were no weak places or leaks in them.

Parts made from steel bar stock were heat-treated. Essential steps here were carburizing, quenching, or tempering. Bar stock of brass did not undergo heat-treatment, but, otherwise, steel and brass bar stock were subjected to similar operations. Ordinarily, these bars either went through automatic screw machines and hand screw machines or were milled, drilled, tapped, and inspected.

Sheet metal was subjected to square shearing, blanking, piercing, rolling, stamping, and breaking. Some sheets were seamed to form the pipe which conducted oil and air to the combustion chamber. There was also some spot welding done in the sheet-metal department.

Casings for various units that made up the burner were fabricated from castings. All units were enclosed. The centrifugal vane pump, the air fan, the diffuser, the oil meter, parts of the housings, and the strainer were fashioned from sheet metal. The shaft, parts for valves, toggle arms, and the like were made from bar stock. Brass castings and steel castings were used for various small parts.

Certain items featured by specialty companies, such as oil cups, pipe fittings, gauges, and special fittings were purchased from independent manufacturers. In addition, standard lines of hardware universally catalogued and made by specialists were purchased. Finally, the New Builtwell Burner Corporation purchased motors, die castings, and transformers.

### Exhibit 2

#### Production of Quick-freezing Units

The chief parts of the refrigerating unit of the freezer were two motors (one for the compressor and one for the fan), a condenser, float valve, fan assembly, dehydrator, various shutoff valves, oil trap, crankcase, dome, flapper valve, liquid receiver, condenser housing, cooling unit, and thermostatic control.

One cycle of refrigeration occurred as follows: As the temperature in the freezer rose above the desired point, thermostatic contol actuated a switch which closed the circuit and started the compressor; low-pressure gas in the top of the cooling unit was drawn to the compressor through the suction line and the dome into the compression chamber when the piston reached the reverse end of the stroke; on the following forward stroke these low-pressure vapors were compressed and forced through the discharge flapper valve and into the oil float chamber; this chamber separated lubricating oil from methyl chloride, and was fitted with a float so that when the oil on the bottom reached a certain height, the outlet opened and pressure of the gas drove the lubricating oil back to the compressor. The high-pressure gas was forced through finned condenser tubing which cooled it under pressure with the result that the gas liquefied and flowed down to the liquid receiver; as suction removed the low-pressure vapor from the top of the cooling unit, pressure was lowered and this allowed more methyl chloride to vaporize with an accompanying absorption of heat; as gas vaporized, the level of liquid methyl chloride in the cooling unit was lowered so the float valve opened and allowed more liquid methyl chloride to enter the cooling unit through the dehydrator from the liquid receiver. When the necessary amount of heat had been absorbed, the thermostatic switch broke the contact and the whole operation ceased until the temperature was raised to a point such that the thermostat again made contact.

Raw materials for parts manufactured were similar to those used in production of oil burners. All castings which came in contact with gaseous methyl chloride had to be made of a special nickel alloy steel. Gray iron and brass castings were used and bar stock of steel and brass.

Parts made from castings included the dome (or motor housing), the condenser housing, the eccentric for the piston, the piston, and the cylinder. The cylinder was made of cast iron with a special steel lining. Parts made from bar stock included valve stems, seats, fittings, and motor shafts. Sheet-metal parts were the oil trap housing and float, the liquid receiver, and the fan. The connections were made with copper tubing.

Castings were normalized to equalize internal stresses and strains, and were then turned, milled, drilled, tapped, and ground. They were then subjected to pressure tests. Bar stock of steel or brass was either run through automatic screw machines and hand screw machines or it was milled, drilled, tapped, and inspected.

Sheet metal required was square sheared, blanked, pierced, rolled, stamped, and broken. In case of steel stock, it was heat-treated and in this process underwent carburizing, quenching, and tempering.

Parts purchased by the company included two types of induction motors, condenser, cooling unit, and various specialties which could be manufactured by independent producers at a far lower cost. In addition, all cabinets were purchased from outside manufacturers who specialized in refrigerator and freezer-cabinet production.

## QUESTIONS

1. What advantages should the New Builtwell Burner Corporation realize from the addition of quick-freezing units for domestic use to its oil burner line?

2. With what disadvantages should the company be prepared to deal?

3. Was the decision to add the new line sound?

# PART II

## FACTORS OF PRODUCTION

# CHAPTER X

## RAW MATERIALS SUPPLY

### KINGSLEY SHOE COMPANY

### 1. A Typical Example of Purchasing Raw Materials.

To offset decreasing profit margins in a period of decreasing activity in the industry, the Kingsley Shoe Company adopted a retrenchment program. One step in this program was to centralize in the hands of one executive all control of manufacturing stores and purchasing of raw materials. This official adopted as a general policy the plan of purchasing on a routine basis. In buying linen thread, however, conditions soon arose which made it advisable for the purchasing executive to depart from his established policy. The results obtained by modifying the purchasing program were not entirely satisfactory.

**2. Factors of Production.** In explaining the operations of our present industrial organization, economists point out that there are four fundamental factors of production: land, capital, labor, and enterprise. The business manager works with these same four agents although the terminology he uses in referring to them is usually different from that employed by the economist. The equivalent of land, he refers to as raw materials. Capital is spoken of in terms of plant, buildings, and equipment, or working capital. Labor is often called personnel. Enterprise is known as management.

**3. Nature and Definition of Management.** The task of management is to control the three other factors of production to the end that they may be united to form an effective producing unit. This involves the formation and putting into effect of definite policies of managerial control. In other words, management consists of the creation of the proper relationships between the production factors of a business unit within an industry and the maintenance of those relationships in terms of changing conditions.

The popular picture of a high-salaried American executive as a man who sits at his desk simultaneously dictating to a stenographer, talking over the telephone, pressing electric buzzers, and listening to words of advice from his private secretary is something more than a caricature of what is actually taking place. Every day the manager faces the task of coordinating and maintaining proper relationships within his business unit. Externally these relationships concern the competitive position of his unit in the industry of which it is a part. Internally the relationships are associated with the proper correlation of plant, buildings and equipment, raw materials, and personnel, all of which are conditioned by highly dynamic surroundings. An unexpected stoppage in source of raw materials supply, for example, may easily throw normal relationships out of adjustment to such an extent as to paralyze temporarily the functioning of the plant. One of the manager's many duties is to see that a condition of this kind does not arise.

**4. Importance of the Purchasing Function.** The chapters which follow are an analysis of various means by which executives exert managerial control, so as to maintain relationships on as nearly normal a basis as possible.

Just as the economist considers land indispensable if goods are to be produced, so too the modern manager looks upon a supply of raw materials as essential. The executive in charge of purchasing must know his sources of raw materials, foreign and domestic, potential as well as actual. He must be able to characterize a given choice of supply in respect to quality, service, and price, and do so in terms of the specific needs of his business. In short, he must know where to purchase, when to purchase, how to purchase, how much to purchase, and how much to pay.

**5. Conditions in Kingsley Shoe Company.** The Kingsley Shoe Company, a prominent manufacturer of women's and children's high-grade shoes, was experiencing a period of decreasing demand. This condition was general throughout the industry. Executives of the company became convinced that they should adopt a plan of rigid retrenchment, embracing all possible economies. As a part of this program a competent executive was placed in charge of the central storeroom and of the purchasing of manufacturing materials.

Purchasing of raw materials was an important function in the operating program of the Kingsley Shoe Company. In the period of abnormally high demand which had preceded the current recession, the chief task of the purchasing agent had been to secure a sufficient volume of raw materials of proper kind, delivered when needed. Cost of raw materials had been of secondary importance because prices of shoes constantly had been rising, and this made it possible for the manufacturer to pass any increased charge on to the consumer.

The recession reversed conditions. Prices of shoes stopped their upward swing and started downward slightly. Prices of raw materials also began to fall a little, but these changes were irregular and could not easily be forecast. Coincident with the lowering of price, there appeared to be a tendency on the part of many producers of raw materials to lower quality. Such a situation was particularly serious for the Kingsley Shoe Company, which had long jealously guarded the quality of its shoes. Furthermore, the sales department, in attempting to check declining sales, was insistent upon the adoption of a large number of style changes. By this means the sales manager hoped to stimulate a new buying interest on the part of his customers. As a result of frequent style changes many of the raw materials which would, under normal conditions, be bought in large quantities now had to be purchased on a hand-to-mouth basis. Otherwise, raw materials inventories would pile up.

Furthermore, the new styles resulted in a need for many new items such as new styles of heels, toes, tips, counters, bows, buckles, and many fancy leathers such as snake skin, alligator skin, and the like. The task of estimating the exact requirements for such items was very difficult in itself, and style shifts might leave the company with a considerable amount of money invested in materials which, if not entirely unusable, would at least be very slow moving.

Because of unsettled conditions in the shoe industry and the resultant policy of retrenchment adopted by the Kingsley management, the executive in charge of purchasing adopted a policy of routine buying; *i.e.,* he bought only according to actual current needs, and so far as possible in stipulated amounts at regular intervals.[1] The new plan had been set up on the first of January. In the following August the purchasing agent had to decide whether to continue buying linen thread on a routine basis or to contract for at least a year's supply.

**6. The Problem of Linen Thread.** Under the new plan, purchasing and raw materials stores control were separated completely from the control of the manufacturing departments. The latter placed requisitions with the storeroom for materials and were charged therefor on the stores department records. Beginning in January the purchasing executive kept charts covering internal information of interest to him in purchasing—factory production, sales, orders from salesmen, and materials on order. He received also sales and production estimates made by the management. In the storeroom, balance-of-stores cards were used. On the basis of records of materials turnover, and through his knowledge of the delivery period on orders, the purchasing agent worked out a graduated system for ordering. When withdrawals, as shown on the balance-of-stores sheet, brought the quantity in stock to a point predetermined from the above information, this condition served as a warning to buy the necessary quantity. The new system, however, was not inflexible. The purchasing executive used his judgment as to purchases, even if the quantity on hand was below the specified limit, since by waiting he frequently obtained a lower price.

By June, production in the factory was approximately 3,500 pairs of shoes daily, of which 50 per cent were welt-soled. The linen thread used in the manufacture of a pair of shoes was less than 1 per cent of the total cost. Thread required to sew uppers to welts was an eight-cord linen thread. This measured approximately 800 yards to the pound, and an average of 3 yards was required per pair of shoes. Linen thread was manufactured from

---

[1] The new purchasing executive did not have charge of buying upper leather, which, because of the large volume needed and the frequent style changes, required the entire time of a specialist. Since upper leather constituted the largest single item of cost in the production of a shoe, effective purchasing of it might easily represent the difference between profit and loss for the Kingsley Shoe Company.

flax raised in Ireland, Belgium, and Russia. The Russian crop, however, was not used in American production, and most of the flax imported for this eight-cord thread came from Belgium. In Belgium, flax harvested in the fall underwent processing which took approximately eight months before it was manufactured into thread. This Belgian method of preparation gave a fineness of quality such that American thread manufacturers contracted for a year or more ahead of requirements in order to ensure continuity of supply. In July, the purchasing agent learned from trade reports that the Belgian crop which had been used in current thread manufacture was practically exhausted and that the on-coming crop, then being marketed, was likely to be less satisfactory and might make a weak thread. The thread in current use was of exceptional quality.

The purchasing executive had made exhaustive tests of linen thread for tensile strength, for frictional wear, and for yardage per pound, and he realized that quality was a preeminent factor. A break in thread on the shoe machinery in course of production involved ripping uppers from welts with the possible destruction of welts as well as uppers, and the extra time required for ripping and resewing. After the shoe was sold, poor wearing qualities were sure to reflect on the reputation of the Kingsley Shoe Company. As a matter of policy, all shoes were sold under brands, and the quality of brands was maintained rigidly in order that women who bought any brand might know exactly what to expect on a second purchase.

Production from the thread in current use might continue for another three months, after which thread from the new and supposedly inferior crop would be used. On a routine basis, each purchase was one case of 168 pounds; below this unit, no quantity discounts were allowed by thread manufacturers. During the period of greatest demand, the price of linen thread had been abnormally high and in June of the current year had been $2.85 per pound. In August, the price dropped to $2.70 per pound, and further decreases were not unlikely.

An analysis by the purchasing executive of each six-month period of the previous year and of the first half of the current year showed that the factory had used 1,000 pounds of eight-cord linen thread each six months. Estimates by the sales department indicated a normal production of shoes for the ensuing year. However, production of women's shoes was highly uncertain because of increasing change in styles. Purchase of materials in advance of needs or contract for future delivery was contrary to the general policy of the purchasing executive and might leave on hand either material or contract for material which could not be used immediately. In either case a portion of the company's capital was tied up in slow-moving inventory. One of the chief tasks of the new purchasing agent was to avoid situations of this kind.

Although linen thread represented a small percentage of production costs and a marked changed in its price was not likely to be reflected noticeably in the cost of producing shoes or in the selling price, the total sum involved, approximately $5,400 for a year's supply of 2,000 pounds, was substantial. Investment of capital in slow-moving assets was generally considered undesirable as tending to reduce company profits. However, there was no question of deterioration of material on hand, for linen thread could be stored indefinitely without loss of quality in properly humidified warehouses. So anxious were thread manufacturers to sell that if the purchasing executive bought or contracted for a year's supply of thread, he could secure a January 5, following, dating on bills covering deliveries during the remaining five months in the current year, although no additional discount for quantity could be secured.

On the other hand, continuation of routine purchasing released capital for active use, allowed the advantage of possible fluctuations downward in price, and reduced the risk of loss on possible changes in production. In addition, low inventories saved such charges as government taxes. It was not entirely certain that the quality of thread from the on-coming flax crop would be as unsatisfactory as was estimated.

The purchasing executive decided that in spite of his established policy of routine purchasing, the quality of thread was of such paramount consideration as to warrant purchase in advance of immediate needs. He placed his order for 12 cases of 168 pounds each of eight-cord linen thread to be made up from the flax crop in current use. One case was to be delivered each month at $2.70 per pound, and the buyer arranged for a January 5, following, dating on the invoices covering the first five months' deliveries.

**7. Effect of Style Changes.** During the winter in which the new purchasing department was established, 50 per cent of the shoes marketed had welt soles. Welts were stitched to uppers and the soles then were sewed to the welts by outside stitching. The purchasing agent estimated his need for thread on the 50 per cent basis when he signed the contract in August. During the following winter, demand became active for shoes with turned soles. Turned soles were stitched with the uppers inside out and then the uppers were pulled over to their final shape. A lighter thread was used than for welt sewing. In the fall following the signing of the contract for a year's supply of thread, production was approximately only 30 per cent welt shoes, and the purchasing executive had in stock at the end of the period covered by his contract 1,000 pounds of linen thread. The market price, after a gradual decrease, reached $2.60 per pound.

**8. Summary and Conclusions.** *Experience of Kingsley Shoe Company.* The experience of the purchasing executive of the Kingsley Shoe Company illustrates some of the difficulties involved in effective purchasing of raw materials. The task of purchasing the required items in such a manner and at such a price that they flow into the factory economically when, and only when, needed is far from simple. For instance, the purchasing agent of the Kingsley Shoe Company made a genuine effort to analyze the problem before him. In the last analysis he had to choose between supply of the desired quality and price. There seemed to be no reasonable way in which he could protect his company against unfavorable fluctuations in both these factors. He finally decided that quality supply was paramount and proceeded accordingly. He lost money by so doing and on the face of it appears to have gone contrary to the general spirit of the company's retrenchment program. A discerning general manager would, however, look beneath the surface, and would probably conclude that, although the purchasing agent had lost money, he had actually safeguarded the reputation of the firm as a quality producer and that the money lost in the purchase of linen thread should be considered in the nature of insurance for quality.   On the other hand, the purchasing agent of the Kingsley Shoe Company could not make many mistakes of this kind without encountering serious objections from the general executives.

*Objectives in Raw Materials Control.*   The objectives of the business manager in controlling his raw materials supplies are clear and unmistakable.   He wishes to have his company ensured a minimum, adequate supply of the proper quality of raw materials at the machine or workbench at the exact time they are needed for processing, at a price which (over a period of time) will ensure quantity, quality, and service at the lowest cost per unit of product.

*Raw Materials as a Cost Factor.*   The necessity of accomplishing this result may be readily appreciated when one stops to consider the relative importance of raw materials as a factor in the cost of production.   For the year 1904, the total value of manufactured products in the United States was $14,794,000,000.   The cost of the raw materials from which these products were made was $8,500,000,000, leaving as value added by the manufacturing process only $6,294,000,000.   The total value of goods manufactured in this country in 1929 was estimated at $70,420,000,000. The cost of the raw materials was $38,520,000,000, and the value added by the manufacturing process was $31,900,000,000.[2]   Since 1929 this relationship has remained roughly constant.   Raw materials, then, are seen to be a major item in cost of production. Their economical purchase and effective handling are, therefore, matters of first importance in practically every factory.

On the surface there is a vast difference between the purchasing problems in a steel mill which annually uses thousands of tons of ore and those of a manufacturer of watches who makes thousands of delicate hairsprings from a block of fine steel.   The tasks in the two purchasing departments in question vary in many important respects, but underneath the surface the need

[2] Source: Bureau of Foreign and Domestic Commerce, *Statistical Abstract of the United States,* 1931.

for the right quality, quantity, service of delivery, and cost is present in each case.

*The Purchasing Function.* Performance of the purchasing function involves several things: (1) a knowledge of world sources of materials supply, (2) the adoption of an effective policy as regards the utilization of the sources of supply, (3) choice between suppliers in carrying out the policy, and (4) control of materials inventory after the materials have once reached the factory. The third and fourth of these activities will be dealt with in subsequent chapters, the third in the chapter which immediately follows, and the fourth in Chap. XXII, Raw Materials Inventory Control.

*Importance of Knowledge of Sources of Supply.* Knowledge of world sources of supply is very important in the case of many materials. This was true of linen thread in the Kingsley Shoe Company case. The United States and many other countries produce flax. Investigation will show, however, that most flax grown in the United States has too short a fiber to make linen thread suitable for sewing shoes. Even in those parts of the country where long-stemmed flax is grown, the amount annually marketed is uncertain, and retting and processing have not been well developed. It would be unwise for a purchasing agent to depend on such sources for flax. Russia produces good flax, but political conditions there have been such as to make an American thread buyer skeptical of the acceptability of that source. Belgium, on the other hand, has been producing flax for many generations. Reliable stock has been developed. Exactly the right kind of seed is planted in the right soil to give the desired stalk. The retting process, while perhaps appearing antiquated according to American industrial methods, produces a fiber that makes first-class thread. Information of this kind is a necessary part of the equipment of any executive who is required to purchase linen thread. Exhaustive knowledge is necessary for every purchasing agent. He must know sources of supply, both domestic and foreign.

*Types of Purchasing Policies.* The policies which purchasing executives use in utilizing sources of supply are many and varied. Sometimes an executive adheres to one policy; other executives follow more than one.  Just what the individual agent should do will depend, of course, on the circumstances facing him.  Some of the more typical purchasing policies will be discussed.

*Materials Purchase vs. Materials Production.*  One of the first questions that presents itself to company executives is: Can this company develop its own source of supply to greater advantage than it can purchase from others?  Some years ago the high price of crude rubber convinced certain American tire producers that they should not be dependent on foreign sources for raw materials.  Notwithstanding the fact that rubber has not yet been grown in this country on a suitable commercial basis, millions of dollars have been spent in attempting to develop sources under the immediate ownership and control of individual American companies.  It would appear that a clearer, more intensive analysis of the world rubber situation might have indicated what experience has since proved, namely, that the high prices then existing were the result of temporary conditions.

On the other hand, a large manufacturer of cotton goods decided to use rayon as a complementary material.  The idea proved sound, and soon the question arose as to whether or not this company should erect its own rayon plant.  After a critical investigation, company executives decided that because of the large initial investments required, the differences in processing rayon and cotton, the difficulty of securing proper supervisors to run a rayon unit, and the great likelihood of revolutionary changes in rayon making, the erection of a rayon plant would be unwise.  Accordingly, this company has continued to purchase its rayon yarns from rayon producers.

The factors which must be considered in deciding whether to produce or purchase raw materials are so many and varied, and differ so widely as between companies, that individual decisions always must be reached on the basis of specific circumstances surrounding a given manufacturer.  Much of the discussion in Chap. IX in regard to vertical integration is pertinent in this connection.

*Long-time or Short-time Contracts.*  Many purchasing agents insist upon written contracts when buying raw materials.  Such documents, if properly drawn, are legal and enforcible in courts of law.  When purchases are being made on contract, the length of time covered by the contract is always important.  For several years a certain purchasing executive had contracted for an annual supply of cans according to need as each year's canning season approached.  The plan had the advantages of permitting the company to profit by any favorable price changes and any new sources of low-cost supply that might develop.  It had the disadvantages of not securing such efficient service from the can manufacturers as could be secured if a long-time contract was entered into.  The need of quick service from the manufacturer was an important item, for the cannery found it difficult to estimate its requirements exactly.  The solution of the difficulty was the signing of a three-year contract with prices to be adjusted on the basis of market price of tin plate at the beginning of each year.  The cannery was thus ensured service and protected in part from undue price advances.  The price tended to be relatively low, for the manufacturer's cost of selling the account was less because of the three-year contract.  Long-time contracts are also of advantage to materials suppliers in that they help to assure volume of output.  Factors such as these influence suppliers to grant favorable consideration to buyers who are able and willing to enter into long-time purchase contracts.

*Purchase on Specification.*  Some buyers prefer to purchase on specification; *i.e.,* they draw up a long list of details covering every possible phase of the purchase transaction.  These specifications, when signed by both parties, are enforcible in courts of law.  Purchasing by specification has many advantages in securing for the purchasing agent exactly what he wants in the way he wants it.  The great weakness of such a plan is that it is very difficult to include in written specifications all the factors that are normally understood as a part of a purchase transaction.  Often unforeseen changes make modification of the original plan advisable.  The omission of any details or the violation of any specification, however trivial, may invalidate the whole transaction.  A shirt manufacturer, because of a rush of seasonal orders, sublet the making of a large consignment of shirts to another manufacturer under a rigid specification contract.  The required raw materials were furnished by the original manufacturer. The manufacturer who had subcontracted to make the shirts did not fulfill the terms of the agreement. The manufacturer who had sublet the contract insisted that the contract be fulfilled, only to wake up one morning to discover that his company was the defendant in a suit for damages instituted by the subcontractor, who alleged violation of the original contract. Investigation brought to light the fact that when the head of the manufacturer's stock department had shipped the raw materials called for in the contract, he had substituted number 52 thread for number 48. He did this because at that time the company had no number 48 thread on hand but did have a large supply of number 52. The difference in thread was probably an inconsequential matter insofar as quality of workmanship of the shirts was concerned, but the substitution of one size for another constituted a violation of the contract.

The setting forth of materials specifications in writing has the obvious advantage of fostering clarity and understanding. However, complete dependence on such written instruments has decided shortcomings as compared with their use as a means of supplementing established friendly relations between buyer and seller.

*Maintenance of Two or More Sources.* To maintain adequate sources of supply many purchasing executives follow the policy of always purchasing from two or more sellers of a given material. Some executives believe it is unwise for their companies to depend on only one source since an untoward situation might arise which would render that source unusable. Neither is it considered good policy from a price standpoint to be at the mercy of one supplier. Competition, so the argument goes, leads to better prices.

The decision to use one or more than one source of supply is not always simple. It depends on a consideration of such factors as price trends, the possibility of buying in the "spot" market, the location of the suppliers in question, and their reliability as to quality, promptness of delivery, and capital and credit ratings, as well as upon past experience with the suppliers. Many of these same factors must also influence actual choice of suppliers.

Sometimes these numerous factors as a whole will be almost

equal as between suppliers. The purchasing executive of one company which normally maintained three sources of supply found this to be true, except for one thing. One of the suppliers furnished the executive with advance information as to price changes. This was a very important service, for it enabled the agent to make substantial savings in his purchases. Month after month this service continued without any lowering in quality or increase in price of the product. Gradually the buyer shifted more and more of his purchases to the company that gave this superior service. General business conditions and conditions within the specific industry concerned will influence in considerable measure the importance attached by the purchasing agent to the maintenance of more than a single source of materials supply.

*Speculative Purchasing.* The market for certain raw materials is highly dynamic. This is especially true of such commodities as cotton, wheat, wool, corn, and leather. Not infrequently, in fact altogether too frequently, purchasing agents for companies using large quantities of such products make their purchases upon a speculative basis. If they believe that the market is going to rise, they purchase or contract to buy two or three times as much raw material as they actually need. Then during the year as prices strengthen they sell the surplus to less farsighted competitors.

Speculative purchasing has two outstanding weaknesses. To the extent that profits are made from this source, there is a seemingly irresistible temptation on the part of management to ignore the problems of production, substituting for profits from careful management the gains which result from speculative purchasing. Speculation at best is a highly uncertain venture. The purchasing executive cannot always guess correctly, and when he misjudges, his mistake may be so serious that it brings heavy losses, if not eventual ruin, to his company.

A large textile plant, which followed the plan of speculative purchasing, reorganized its productive processes and during a 12-month period effected economies which resulted in savings of a half million dollars, only to find that during this same period its purchasing department had misjudged the market and had incurred a raw materials inventory loss of a million dollars.

A certain shoe company had a purchasing agent who specialized in the purchase of sole leather. He became convinced that the market price was going to go up. Since none of the purchasing executives in competing firms was preparing for such a change, he thought he saw a chance to make money for his company. He purchased a million dollars' worth of sole leather, expecting to sell portions of the supply to competitors when prices rose. Instead of increasing, the market weakened month after month, and the shoe company was soon facing severe financial embarrassment due to excessive investment in raw materials.

Speculative purchasing of raw materials (purchase in excess of production requirements) by the average factory buyer probably has little or no justification. The chief function of a manufacturing plant is to produce goods, not to gamble in the raw materials market. Unfortunately, the practice of speculative purchasing at times has been widespread. Attempts of purchasing agents to make speculative profits during the months that followed the stock market crash of October, 1929, on the whole proved so ill-advised that they in turn became contributory causes to a continuance of the depression. In any event, a company which speculates in raw materials should so organize its books of account and its statements that they show profits or losses resulting from trading in raw materials separate from the profits or losses incurred as a result of manufacturing activities.[3]

*Use of Specialists.* Many companies, especially the larger ones, find it advisable to specialize certain purchasing functions. Shoe factories frequently have men who do nothing but buy upper and sole leathers, or sometimes only one of these. A factory which uses hundreds of tons of coal annually may have an agent who buys nothing but coal. A large manufacturer of absorbent cotton and gauze products has found it advisable to specialize the purchase of raw cotton. To just what extent specialization will enter into the purchasing function depends on the circum-

[3] Some purchasing agents must deal in highly speculative markets. In such cases the device of "hedging" may often be used to safeguard legitimate purchases that must be made.

stances surrounding the individual company. The nature of the materials purchased, the character of the markets in which they must be bought, the dollar volume of material required, the relative importance of the raw materials element in total cost to manufacture, matters such as these are the determinants.

Enough has been said to make it obvious that the control of raw materials is a major managerial task in the average factory. As stated at the beginning of this summary, proper control of raw materials involves four things: knowledge of sources of supply, adoption of a well-defined purchasing policy, choice between suppliers in carrying out the policy, and some means of inventory control of raw materials once they are in the factory. Sufficient discussion has already been given to show the importance of the first two of these items; purchasing will be discussed in the following chapter, and inventory will be dealt with in Chap. XXII.

## QUESTIONS

1. What are the four major factors in production?
2. What terminology does the businessman apply to them?
3. What is the job of management?
4. Define management.
5. From the standpoint of costs, what is the importance of raw materials purchasing?
6. What is the work of the purchasing agent?
7. If thread represented less than 1 per cent of the cost of producing a pair of shoes, why did the purchasing executive of the Kingsley Shoe Company place so much emphasis on the matter of correct purchase of thread?
8. How were changing styles related to the purchase of thread?
9. Do you think the purchasing agent of the Kingsley Shoe Company followed a wise course in his thread purchase? Explain.
10. Why is a comprehensive knowledge of sources of supply important?
11. What are the objectives of raw materials supply control?

## Problem 22

### SUPERSEAL COMPANY

When the Superseal Company established a materials-testing laboratory, the purposes of which were drawing up specifications for the purchase of materials and comparing purchased materials with the desired
standards, one of the first problems of policy was to determine how rigid
the standards which were to be included in purchase specifications should
be. The superintendent in charge of the new testing laboratory consulted the production manager, who agreed that the problem was of
major importance and who asked the superintendent to study the problem from all points of view and report his recommendations as to what
policy should be adopted.

The laboratory superintendent was considering two policies
followed by buyers of his acquaintance. The first was to make
specifications rigid, including requirements more exacting than
those absolutely necessary for the particular use to be made of the
material being purchased. The second was to make the specifications equally rigid but to include in the specifications only those
requirements that were absolutely essential to the proper use
of the material in manufacture.

An advantage attributed to the first method was that the
vendor in attempting to comply with the specifications would be
sure to deliver a product which would be entirely satisfactory
to the company's use. Moreover, since specifications were more
exacting than necessary, materials that did not attain the standards set could still be accepted upon occasion. Another advantage was said to be that materials would be secured which were
equal to or above manufacturing requirements, thus ensuring
high quality of manufactured product.

The second policy was based on the concept that a purchase
specification was a mutual agreement to which both parties
assented and with which full compliance was expected.

Which of the two policies should the superintendent of the
testing department have recommended for adoption?

## Problem 23

## EAST SIDE GARMENT MANUFACTURING COMPANY

The president of the East Side Garment Manufacturing Company was notified that his company had been made defendant in a suit for damages of $5,000 for injuries received by the Dunlap Manufacturing Company in connection with a contract the company had made six months earlier.

The East Side Garment Manufacturing Company manufactured and distributed shirts of medium price. At certain times of the year a part of the work was let out to garment workers [4] under contract. In October, the rush season of the year, the East Side Garment Manufacturing Company had asked for bids for work necessary in the manufacture of 5,000 shirts. The specifications in this instance called for the working up of material furnished by the East Side Garment Manufacturing Company in accordance with certain definite standards of workmanship. The material, the cloth and thread, was to be furnished to the garment workers and to be returned in lots of 500 shirts at the rate of 1,000 shirts per month. Of the bids received, that of the Dunlap Manufacturing Company was by far the lowest. The bid was slightly more than half of the next lowest bid, and considerably lower than any bid received on similar contracts. In view of the abnormally low bid and lack of previous relations with the Dunlap Manufacturing Company, the president of the East Side Garment Manufacturing Company sent his representative to the shops of the Dunlap Manufacturing Company to determine whether the latter was competent to fulfill the contract in the event that it was awarded.

The representative reported that the Dunlap Manufacturing Company was a manufacturer of shirts of a lower quality than those of the East Side Garment Manufacturing Company, that a modern shop was maintained in a locality where wages were somewhat lower than ordinary, and that it was his opinion that the company would be able to do satisfactory work. After receiving this report, the president of the East Side Garment Manufactur-

---

[4] A small group, usually women, working under the direction of the owner of an establishment.

ing Company informed the Dunlap Manufacturing Company that its bid was out of line with others received and requested assurance of full performance of the work in strict accordance with the specifications. The president of the Dunlap Manufacturing Company stated that he had not bid on previous contracts for such work but that his force was familiar with the work and he was confident that it could be done satisfactorily. The contract was then awarded to the Dunlap Manufacturing Company.

The first lot of shirts received by the East Side Garment Manufacturing Company in November failed to meet the standards of workmanship called for in the specifications. The work had been very carelessly done. The sewing was poor and loose threads had been left. A chain stitch was used in lieu of the lock stitch which was specified. The entire shipment was rejected, and the Dunlap Manufacturing Company was notified of the failure of the shipment to pass inspection. Attention was called to the defective workmanship, and the entire lot was returned for reworking.

Of the next lot received, approximately 20 per cent was accepted; the balance was rejected for faults similar to those of the first lot. The president of the Dunlap Manufacturing Company visited the East Side Garment Manufacturing Company and protested against the rigidity of specifications. He stated that it was practically impossible to meet such rigid requirements. It was pointed out to him that he had accepted the contract with a full knowledge of the specifications, that the difficulties and requirements had been purposely brought to his attention when the award was made; and that he therefore had to fulfill his contractual obligations.

During the period between December 1 and December 15, the president of the East Side Garment Manufacturing Company advised his inspectors, however, that a less rigid policy might advisably be adopted in judging future shipments from the Dunlap Manufacturing Company. His reason for this decision was largely his desire to secure some of the product at an early date in order to meet deliveries on accepted orders and also his feeling that the specification requirements were rigid and that the inspectors might have been too rigid in their inspections.

The entire shipment from the Dunlap Manufacturing Com-

pany on December 15 was accepted.  Approximately one-half
of the shirts received had been reworked from the initial lot.

On January 1, a lot of 500 was received which was unsatisfactory even from the standpoint of the less rigid inspection
policy.  The lot was returned and further delivery of material
refused until the Dunlap Manufacturing Company had completed
the work which was already assigned.  No further work was
delivered by the Dunlap Manufacturing Company although the
East Side Garment Manufacturing Company wrote several letters requesting information as to the status of the reworked
material.

In its action for damages dated March 1, the Dunlap Manufacturing Company complained that the material received by it
had not been in accordance with the specifications.  The specifications had called for number 48 thread, and 52 thread had been
furnished.  An examination of the stores' requisitions showed
that the complaint was founded on fact.  The stockkeeper at the
East Side plant had on hand, in November, a large supply of
number 52 thread, and had substituted it for the number 48
thread specified.  The company further claimed that inspection
was too rigid as shown by the reinspection and acceptance of
garments previously rejected.  The action carried a further complaint that other shirt manufacturers had inspected the rejected
garments and had pronounced them to be good workmanship.

The president of the East Side Garment Manufacturing Company decided to cancel the existing contract, if possible, and to
let the work out to one of the companies with which it had
formerly satisfactorily contracted for similar work.  He felt that
number 52 thread was less suitable for the work, but was not an
important factor in the poor workmanship, and that other first-
class shirt manufacturers would be likely to concur with his
judgment that the workmanship was far below the standard
called for in the specifications.  He felt also that the Dunlap
Manufacturing Company was unfamiliar with the requirements
of specifications contracts, that it had undoubtedly suffered a
considerable loss, and that the contract had been entered into
without due consideration of the requirements and costs.  The
president believed that the Dunlap Manufacturing Company

was in the wrong and that it was seeking to obtain relief from an unfavorable contract.

## QUESTIONS

1. Should the East Side Garment Manufacturing Company have accepted the bid of the Dunlap Manufacturing Company and awarded the contract to it?

2. Should the company have endeavored to arrange a settlement?

### Problem 24

### DICKLAND COMPANY

Twice during the current year the Dickland Company, a manufacturer of filing equipment located in Columbus, Ohio, received advance information of price increases in cotton cloth from the Bown Company, which supplied it with 50 per cent of the cotton cloth used in the manufacture of tabs for index cards. The purchasing agent of the Dickland Company considered whether this service on the part of the Bown Company was sufficient to warrant giving that company 100 per cent of his orders.

The cloth used by the Dickland Company was the product of a manufacturer who distributed through wholesalers located in the principal cities of the United States. The prices quoted by these wholesale distributors were identical in the same territory. The company's annual requirements of cotton cloth were about 25,000 yards. It maintained an average stock of 2,000 yards. A new supply was ordered each month about four weeks in advance of actual use. For 15 years the Dickland Company had bought its total requirements of cotton cloth from the Rodas Company, a wholesale distributor also located in Columbus, Ohio.

During the last three years, a salesman of the Bown Company, a wholesale distributor of cloth located in Chicago, had called upon the purchasing agent of the Dickland Company in an effort to obtain orders to supply that company with its requirements of cloth. He had not obtained the orders because he had been unable to offer higher quality or lower price than competitors.

During a visit to the Dickland Company's plant in the preceding June, he noticed an idle machine which had been installed to manufacture an article which the Dickland Company had found unprofitable to market. He offered to find a purchaser for this machine at the price asked by the company if the purchasing agent would give him a part of the orders for cotton cloth. As the machine had been idle two years, the company was anxious to dispose of it. The purchasing agent, therefore, told the salesman that 50 per cent of the company's requirements would be ordered from him if he sold the machine and if the service given by the Bown Company was as satisfactory as that of its competitors. Three weeks later the machine was sold, and the Dickland Company gave 50 per cent of its orders for the remainder of the year to the Bown Company.

During the remainder of the year, the manufacturer's price of the cloth that the company used was increased twice. This increase affected equally the quotations of the two distributors then supplying the company. On both occasions the salesman of the Bown Company notified the purchasing agent of the Dickland Company about a week in advance that an increase in price was expected and stated that the Bown Company was prepared to fill any requirements of the Dickland Company at the old price if the order was placed before official notice of the increase was sent out. The Dickland Company took advantage of this advance information, and in each case the price increased. The Rodas Company, however, did not notify the purchasing agent of the Dickland Company until several days after the advance in price took effect. The purchasing agent of the Dickland Company was uncertain whether or not this effort to give extraordinary service was sufficient to warrant giving the Bown Company 100 per cent of his orders.

Service of the Rodas Company always had been satisfactory to the Dickland Company. Deliveries were made punctually, and the company could expect to receive shipment within a maximum period of 10 days after placing the order. The Dickland Company maintained a stock more than sufficient to last over such a period. The Rodas Company had filled all orders in a businesslike manner, especially in regard to correspondence, prompt invoicing, and adjustments. Its location in Columbus, Ohio, was an advantage because the purchasing agent of the Dickland Company could communicate with the salesman or executives personally in a short time. Since the purchasing agent had bought all his requirements for several years from the Rodas Company, a relationship was established which made it probable that the Rodas Company would continue to give as good service as it had in the past. There was a possibility, moreover, that with advancing prices and increasing difficulty of obtaining materials it would be advantageous to have two sources of supply for the cloth. The purchasing agent could use the information furnished by the Bown Company to advantage in purchasing from the Rodas Company.

Service of the Bown Company in the matter of delivery and of carrying out the routine of each transaction was equal to that of the Rodas Company. The special service given by the Bown Company might not be continued after it was assured of the continuance of orders from the Dickland Company. The purchasing agent, however, believed that purchases should be made from the company which gave the better service on the basis of equal price and quality. Therefore, the proportion of orders placed with the Bown Company was increased gradually until two years later it reached 70 per cent. In order to ensure that the forecasts of price changes sent out by the Bown Company would continue, especially in a period of declining prices, and would remain as trustworthy as they had been in the past, the purchasing agent did not give the Bown Company 100 per cent of the orders. During the following year notices of declines in prices were received from the Bown Company in the same way that had characterized those of advancing prices. The Dickland Company was able to take advantage of every decline in price. When prices began to increase, the service was continued. No notices of impending price changes were received from the Rodas Company. Thereafter the purchasing agent of the Dickland Company began to purchase all the company's requirements of cotton cloth from the Bown Company.

Was the purchasing agent's action sound?

# CHAPTER XI

## PURCHASING

### CONTRACT FURNITURE COMPANY

### 1. A Furniture Company Centralizes Purchasing.

The assistant to the general manager of the Contract Furniture Company was acting as office manager. He had had experience in production and as part of his office duties undertook to install centralized control of purchasing. Within two months he faced difficulties inherent in the craftsmanship type of production and the old-time personnel.

**2. How the Small Business Buys.** The current chapter will discuss two aspects of the purchasing function: who should do the buying, and from whom purchases should be made. As a business grows in size, more attention is commonly given to purchasing. Up to the point where the time necessary to do the buying is sufficient to absorb all the energies of one person, one of two methods of getting the purchasing job done is usually followed. Frequently an officer of the company does the buying as one of his several duties. That officer may be the president of the company, the general manager in charge of both production and selling, the plant manager charged with manufacturing operations, the company treasurer, the office manager, or even the head foreman out in the shop. In the slipper manufacturing business occasionally the sales managers of small shops buy the necessary supplies of leather, fabrics, and findings in addition to their responsibility for selling the products of the shops. Where the business is small, almost any officer of the company may have as one of his duties the purchase of required raw materials and supplies.

Another situation often found in a small business is decentralization of the purchasing job. The office manager, treasurer, or head bookkeeper buys the stationery and similar supplies required for the office. In the shop each foreman buys the materials used in his department. Maintenance and repair supplies are purchased by whatever man has the maintenance job. Each responsible individual buys what he needs when he thinks he needs it, where it seems to him best, subject only to the general or specific approval of his immediate superior. Under such conditions suppliers usually know the company and its customary methods, honor the requisitions with which the various buying individuals are armed, and bill the company periodically. The financial relationships of buying are usually arranged by the treasurer or head bookkeeper under such circumstances. When so decentralized, purchasing will obviously be subjected to much looseness of control and will be restricted to local suppliers.

**3. How the Larger Business Purchases.** Even in businesses of substantial size, buying is frequently decentralized to some degree. It is quite common for the office manager to buy the stationery, forms, and office supplies for the entire plant as well as for his own office. The superintendent or foreman in charge of maintenance and repairs frequently buys the materials and supplies needed by his department. This is particularly true of repair items which are infrequently required and not commonly carried in stock. Purchases for the machining departments are often made by a clerical assistant of the machine shop foreman, and the foundry superintendent may well buy the pig and scrap iron, coke, and sand he uses.

While such decentralization is frequently found in manufacturing units of substantial size, the trend with growth is toward centralization. One individual is made responsible for providing all materials and supplies required. Buying is his major task, and he spends all or most of his time at it. Because of past experience and the specific nature of the supplies required, the office manager may buy his own requirements even after all other materials purchases have become the responsibility of some one man. Sooner or later, however, he is likely to go the common way and pass on to the purchasing agent the job of buying office supplies. This centralization of authority for the performance of the purchasing function has disadvantages as well as advantages.

**4. Specialization within the Purchasing Organization.** There comes a time with the growing business when one man can no longer do the entire purchasing job. The task becomes too big and he has to have assistance. Usually the organization which develops is based upon functional specialization. Contact with suppliers and salesmen is made a separate job. The routines of handling shop requisitions and placement of orders are specialized. The work of the department is broken up on a functional basis.

Departures are sometimes made from this type of organization. Cotton textile mills usually have one man who buys nothing but raw cotton, other requirements being procured by a general purchasing executive. A shoe factory is quite likely to have an executive whose sole job is the purchase of upper leather. A soap or cooking compound manufacturer may well have a specialist buyer of vegetable oils. In such cases the raw material so purchased is usually needed in large volume. Frequently its cost is a large part of the total cost of manufacture. Also the organization of the market in which the material is bought may be of such complexity as to call for expert knowledge and constant careful attention to change in market supply and demand. Such situations require specialists and give rise to departures from the more usual method of subdividing the work of the purchasing department.

It is interesting to note that the trend toward centralizing authority in one man for materials procurement, which so often accompanies growth of a business unit, may eventually reverse itself. It should be pointed out, however, that when decentralization develops in a large business, a quite different set of executives share the responsibility as compared with the group that divides the purchasing activities of the small business.

**5. Who Should Buy.** General characteristics and trends cannot be depended on to provide the answer as to who should do the buying in a specific situation. The conditions that govern the various situations which give evidence of trends are important considerations in getting an answer to a new problem. Definitely, however, the trends and general practices are not answers themselves, nor do they provide ready-made answers. Such matters as personal characteristics of the individuals concerned, past practices, and the nature of the finished product and method of processing it bear directly on the problem and at times are determinants. No better illustration of the need for carefully appraising such elements of the situation will be found than the experience which follows.

**6. Characteristics of One Furniture Company.** The Contract Furniture Company was founded in 1800 for the manufacture of high-grade furniture according to the specifications of customers. Sales were made to interior decorators or directly to clubs, private homes, fraternal organizations, and hotels in all parts of the United States. Yearly production in number of pieces was constant; sales approximated $300,000. The company secured two or three contracts each year which totaled about $125,000.

The furniture produced by the company had the reputation in the trade of being excellent in quality. This excellence was the result of the skill of the employees, all of whom were craftsmen. Many of them had been with the company 25 years. The foremen were workmen who, because of exceptional ability or long service, had been made the heads of their departments. However, the general manager, who had been employed by the company for 40 years, did not place full responsibility upon them. He walked through the plant many times each day, greeted workmen by their first names, made decisions on details, and assisted foremen in the solution of problems which they brought to his attention.

Thirty per cent of the total cost of production was for materials; labor represented almost all the remainder. The final cost of labor, however, was difficult to estimate in advance. Consequently, prices quoted by the company varied from 50 per cent less than actual cost to 50 per cent more than actual cost.

**7. Purchasing Methods of the Contract Furniture Company.** When an order was received, drawings of the piece of furniture to be constructed were made in the designing department. Upon the basis of blueprints of these drawings, the head of the designing department, the mill superintendent, and the general manager quoted prices. Under the company's system of independent purchasing, the foreman of each department then placed orders for the materials required for his part of the production. A few materials, such as office supplies, nails, designers' materials, art material for the decorators, varnishes, shellacs, oils, glues, burlaps, cotton cloth for upholstery, and a few types of hardware, were purchased for stock. Paints, varnishes, and oils were purchased, regardless of price, from one or two companies who furnished a definite quality. Tapestry of the required quality, which was imported material, was obtainable only from a few companies. The lumber used was purchased air-dried and then kiln-dried in the company's own kilns. Most lumber was of standard quality. Orders which amounted to more than $2,000 each were approved by the general manager. The foremen checked materials received and were held responsible for their conformance to specifications and quality.

**8. Centralizing the Company's Purchasing.** The office manager of the Contract Furniture Company made changes from the established method of purchasing. He had come to the company from a larger business in which he had some experience with various aspects of production control. He recognized the looseness of the practice of foreman purchasing and believed that he could purchase many materials at lower prices than had been obtained by the foremen, who had grown accustomed to buying from one or two companies. If the foremen described to him their needs, he could do the actual purchasing and thereby save the time of the foremen, whose attention should have been given to production. This would make it impossible for foremen to obtain commissions on materials which they ordered and also would bring matters of price paid and quality received directly under control of the office.

The office manager realized that only an expert of long experience could judge by observation the water content of lumber. Therefore, since he would be unable to determine whether or not vendors supplied him with the grades specified, he did not undertake to purchase lumber.

**9. Results of the Centralization Program.** During the first two months of his attempt at systematized purchasing, the office manager found that the foremen were spending much more time in describing their materials requirements to him than they had previously taken in writing and placing orders. The office manager was not himself a master craftsman and found it difficult to visualize the details of an artistic production and its place in a scheme of interior decoration. He was told by one foreman that a successful independent purchasing agent for this plant had to have the combined knowledge of all the foremen.

Under the centralized buying plan, when orders were placed specifically at the direction of the foremen as to what and where to buy, the latter were responsible for quality. However, when the office manager decided with whom the order was to be placed, he alone was responsible. No instance occurred when the foremen openly objected to usurpation by the purchasing agent of what they considered their responsibility, nor did they object to his criticisms of their orders. However, an atmosphere of hostility developed, and when mistakes occurred for which the office manager might be considered responsible, such errors caused much open criticism among the workers.

A typical occasion for such comment in the two months of systemization was as follows: Shellac purchased at a lower price than that previously paid was applied to a table which was to sell for $500. Total shellac used was worth about $1. It became clouded, and the table had to be refinished at an approximate cost of $50. The quality of shellac previously purchased would have cost approximately $1.50.

**10. Appraisal of the Situation.** The office manager realized that his attempt at improved materials procurement had not been entirely successful, but he hesitated to go back to the old method of foreman buying. True, return to the old order would restore the friendly atmosphere which was essential where production was so distinctly of the craftsmanship type. He was quite certain that in the past foremen had not been receiving substantial commissions on purchases. He was quick to admit the disastrous results of buying and using unsuitable materials, particularly when the materials were a small item in total cost of the product. Furthermore, he came to the conclusion that the undercover antagonism of the foremen to what they considered an unwarranted usurpation of their authorities would cause these men to avail themselves of any opportunities of upsetting

his program and of making its operation difficult.  These arguments seemed definitely to indicate return to the old established
routine.

At the same time he did not believe these arguments to be
entirely conclusive.  He had made a little progress in familiariz-
ing himself with the precise nature of some of the materials requirements.  In this respect his greatest difficulty grew out of the
lack of concise specifications.  In many instances foremen were
not able to define their wants in terms other than a company
trade name, or some similar individual company designation.
While he believed that in all cases the foremen had been buying
good materials, he had evidence that there were alternative
sources of equally good materials, and in some instances he was
convinced that the foremen themselves did not know what the
market had to offer them and therefore were not getting the best
for their purposes.  It was dangerous to rely upon too few sources
of supply, and lack of market knowledge would tend to lessen
efficiency in purchasing.  As to price, the office manager concluded that while he had overestimated its importance, there
were worth-while opportunities for savings through the development of potential competitive sources of supply.

**11. Summary and Conclusions.**  *What Should Have Been
Done.*  It seems that some adjustment of the purchasing practice
of the Contract Furniture Company should have been made.
That the office manager would eventually succeed with his program was unlikely unless changes in it were effected.  In time he
undoubtedly would become more familiar with the requirements
of the various foremen, but there seems little likelihood that
these needs could be reduced to precise specification.  The nature of many of the raw materials would preclude such precision.
This would limit the possibilities of buying on the basis of competitive bidding or the like.  It would probably be wise to allow
the foremen to specify their needs in much the same fashion as
when they were themselves doing the buying.  In many cases
this would include specification of the supplier from whom purchase would be made.  The office manager gradually might be
able to persuade foremen to specify alternative sources.  He could
also accomplish much by suggesting specific sources to the fore-

men as warranting their investigation and consideration. In this way the office manager might broaden somewhat the supply area. The actual selection of what to buy, and in many cases choice of where to buy, would revert to the foremen. Responsibility for quality would then rest squarely with that group.

The actual placement of practically all orders would be made by the office manager. This would give a centralized check on the foremen's performance of their part of the purchasing function, would tend to discourage commissions to foremen, and would tighten up somewhat such looseness as existed under the old decentralized system. The office manager could give considerable attention to developing new sources and could bring new or better materials to the attention of the foremen. Placement of all orders by the office should help somewhat to keep prices in line, and, above all, the irritation of the foremen resulting from complete centralization of purchasing would in large measure disappear. If modifications of this nature were made, the plan ought to work and would probably pay well for the time and effort required of the office manager.

*Basis of the Conclusion.* Recognition of common buying considerations is always basic in making purchasing decisions. Nature of the material, use to which it is to be put, need for quick or unforeseen delivery, possibility of substitution, importance of quality characteristics, number of potential sources of supply, nature and location of sources of supply, importance of raw materials cost in relation to cost of labor and burden, these are the types of consideration upon which answers to questions of purchasing should be based. In the Contract Furniture Company situation it was essential to recognize that the most important purchasing consideration was quality. There seemed to be little question of delivery service and the like, and often price was of secondary importance. This matter of relative weights of factors should have been recognized as a guiding principle in determining who should do the buying and from whom purchases should be made.

*Choice of Suppliers.* It is usually desirable that alternative sources of supply be available. Sometimes many sources should be developed and maintained; in other cases two or three sources will be adequate. There are situations in which it seems advisable to confine all purchases of one commodity or part to a single source of supply. In general, the question of number of sources comes down to the effect on risks of price, quality, regular and emergency delivery, and other "service," such as information on forthcoming price changes, promptness in adjustment of errors, and accuracy and rapidity of billing. Reduction of these risks, individually and collectively, should be the objective in deciding from how many sources to buy.

The question of which sources to utilize involves consideration of the same factors. Decision here usually requires careful weighing of the advantages and disadvantages of one source against the advantages and disadvantages of one or several others. It is usually a case of relative merit. The answer, then, involves, (1) careful determination of just what characteristics are most important and (2) judgment of the relative desirability of various suppliers measured in terms of the required characteristics. The trend seems definitely toward the creation and maintenance over a period of time of desirable relations with a few reliable suppliers. This will sometimes mean some temporary sacrifice in immediate price. But here again we must remember that trends are not answers, and that the answers implied in general practices and trends may be dangerous.

*Scope of the Purchasing Executive's Function.* When purchasing activities are functionalized and responsibility for them is placed upon the shoulders of one major executive, we normally think of him as buying the raw materials, parts, and supplies needed to keep the plant in operation. There has been recent evidence of a tendency to expand the scope of the purchasing function beyond these common bounds.

The purchasing department may buy such equipment as typewriters, adding and calculating machines to be used in company offices, and drinking-water coolers to be used throughout the plant. When a company decides to install an intraplant communication system, should the purchasing department decide whether the system will consist of telephones or telautographs, what types of these to buy, and where to buy them? Should the purchasing department buy the small tools and devices needed in the shops? If the answer to this is yes, should the purchasing department select the specific tools and devices and decide from whom they shall be purchased and the price to be paid? Should the purchasing department go further and upon requisition of the operating departments select and buy the machines, large and small, with which the plant is equipped?

Occasionally a purchasing department buys all these things, and there are cases where the responsibility of the department has been extended to the procuring of the company's advertising. Some purchasing departments buy part of the items here listed but do not buy others. Most departments buy few or none of them. In practically every case the answer depends largely on considerations similar to those which influenced the office manager of the Contract Furniture Company to omit lumber from the list of materials he proposed to buy when he took over the purchasing work for that company.

The answer for any specific item is not obvious and in many instances is not easy. Usually there is little objection to the purchasing department's selecting and buying drinking-water coolers. In the case of office typewriters, there may be more objection. However, the purchasing department should have no difficulty in ascertaining and giving due consideration to preferences of the office organization as to writing machines, and the arguments for having such equipment bought by the purchasing department are frequently very strong.

Successful purchasing of tools and heavy plant equipment by a general purchasing department is much more difficult. Of necessity this involves cooperation of several groups of interested individuals. In most instances selection of such equipment and source of purchase will be dictated by engineering and production executives, and rightly so. In that event the task of the purchasing department becomes routine and clerical in nature, and the opportunities for the purchasing department to make much contribution are not great.

*Scope of the Procurement Problem.* In recent years industrial procurement has been receiving much more nearly the executive attention it deserves than was true 10 years ago. During the Second World War and for several years following that conflict, inability to get adequate quantities of raw materials and fabricated parts was the most restrictive influence faced by industry. Because of this abnormal situation the attention of top executives has been focused on the procurement problem. Today it is recognized that the problem is important, the field is broad, and the opportunities for executives working therein to contribute substantially to the profits of a manufacturing concern are considerable. The future is likely to see a continuation of management's interest in this area.

## QUESTIONS

1. What are the relative merits and shortcomings of the two methods of purchasing commonly found in small manufacturing businesses?

2. Why does growth of a business frequently result in change in methods of purchasing?

3. Is centralization of purchasing responsibility and authority sound in the large organization?

4. What is meant by functional organization within a purchasing department?

5. When is the use of buying specialists for one or more raw materials sound?

6. What characteristics of the Contract Furniture Company situation should have been considered by the office manager of that company before he made any changes from the established practice of foreman buying?

7. Which of these did he consider and which did he neglect to consider? To which did he fail to give proper weight?

8. Why did the program he put into effect fail to accomplish what he wished it to?

9. Are the suggested changes in the office manager's practice sound?

10. Would the accomplishment of the revised program be worth the effort and time involved? Explain.

11. Why is it usually desirable to have more than one source of supply for each raw material or part?

12. What conditions might indicate that a policy of concentrating all purchases of one item from one source would be sound?

13. What factors are commonly important in selecting companies from which to buy?

14. When a company has an experienced, well-managed purchasing department, who should purchase the following items?

    *a*. Ice for cooling drinking water

    *b*. Glass to replace broken windows

    *c*. Carbon paper for office use

    *d*. Bookkeeping machines

    *e*. Intraplant communication apparatus

    *f*. Fire-protection apparatus

    *g*. Fire insurance

    *h*. Credit insurance

    *i*. Time clocks

    *j*. Motor trucks for use outside the plant

    *k*. Scrap iron for foundry use

    *l*. Coal

    *m*. A special-purpose machine costing $3,000

    *n*. A drawing press costing $10,000

    *o*. Land for the erection of a warehouse

    *p*. Billboard space for outdoor advertising

    *q*. Files purchased in large quantities for use in the plant

    *r*. Crude rubber used in large quantities

15. What are the personal qualities requisite in a materials receiving clerk in a purchasing department?

16. Who would make the better chief purchasing executive, an assistant sales manager who has been in the employ of the company for several years, or a graduate of an engineering school who has been an assistant to the head of the company's product designing department for the same length of time?   Explain.

## Problem 25

### ZOOK COMPANY

The Zook Company, which manufactured footwear, was located in Akron. In December the purchasing agent estimated that the company's requirements of box shooks for the next three months would amount to about 1,500,000 board feet. Quotations were secured from five reliable sources of supply. Of the bids received, those of the Gummeree Box Company, located in Cleveland, and the Myers Box Company, located in Akron, were the lowest. The quotation of the former was $102 per 1,000 board feet delivered, and that of the latter was $100 per 1,000 board feet delivered. Since the purchasing agent of the Zook Company always maintained more than one source of supply, he had to determine the proportion of the company's requirements which should be ordered from each of these companies.

Requirements of 1,500,000 feet of box shooks during a period of three months necessitated delivery of four or five carloads per week. A carload usually contained from 25,000 to 30,000 feet. From one to two weeks' supply of shooks was maintained at the plant of the Zook Company.

Subsequent to the receipt of the quotations, the purchasing agent informed the Gummeree Box Company that its price was high. The president of the Gummeree Box Company stated that the company was operating at a loss when it sold shooks at $102 per 1,000 feet, and that it would be less unprofitable to shut down the plant than to sell at a price of $100 per 1,000 feet.

The Zook Company had secured about 70 per cent of its requirements of box shooks for 25 years from the Gummeree Box Company. Its prices always had been as low as those of competitors and frequently even lower. During the past two years, when the price of other companies, including the Myers Box Company, had risen as high as $190 to $200 per 1,000 board feet, prices quoted by the Gummeree Box Company to the Zook Company never had been higher than $140 per 1,000 feet. Frequently when the Zook Company had needed shooks to meet an emergency, the Gummeree Box Company had given the order preference over others already received or had operated its factory at night in order to make immediate shipment. At such times, it never had taken advantage of the Zook Company's position by increasing its prices. The executives of the Gummeree Box Company had made a practice of advising the purchasing agent of the Zook Company of the probable trends in prices of lumber and box shooks. The purchasing agent usually followed such advice, since he realized that the executives of the Gummeree Box Company knew more about the lumber market than he. Their statements in regard to price movements always had been reliable. Although a few mistakes had occurred, the purchasing agent was convinced that no effort ever had been made to take advantage of the Zook Company in the purchase of shooks.

Although the purchasing agent believed that the shooks furnished by the Gummeree Box Company were of the highest quality obtainable, he knew from experience that the quality of the products of the Myers Box Company was excellent. The latter company was favored over the former on account of its location, but it had not given more prompt delivery. The account of the Zook Company with the Myers Box Company never had been important enough for the latter company to favor the Zook Company over other customers. During the past two years, the Myers Box Company had taken advantage of the demand for box shooks and raised its prices considerably above those quoted by the Gummeree Box Company.

While prices had been rising, the purchasing agent of the Zook Company had had difficulty in securing as prompt and punctual delivery from the Myers Box Company as he desired. During the coming winter, failure to receive prompt and punctual delivery from any manufacturer of box shooks was improbable on account of decrease in demand caused by changing conditions. Although the price of the Myers Box Company was lower than that of the Gummeree Box Company in December, the purchasing agent had been advised by the Gummeree Box Company that the situation probably was temporary, and that, with the renewal of the demand for shooks in the spring, the price quoted by the Gummeree Box Company would be no higher than those of its competitors.

How should the purchasing agent of the Zook Company place his order, or orders, for 1,500,000 feet of box shooks for the first three months of the coming year?

### Problem 26

### LUNA COMPANY

The Luna Company, of New York, manufactured soap. Each year it required about 50,000,000 cartons printed from steel-faced plates by a color process. The purchasing agent usually contracted for the company's requirements twice a year. In July he secured bids from four companies which he knew to be reliable.

The purchasing agent of the Luna Company always had maintained at least two sources of carton supply in order to protect the company against inability of a supplier to fulfill a contract. An inventory of not less than five weeks' supply of cartons was maintained at all times. The company's requirement of about 1,000,000 cartons per week could be filled by the operation of one press. Each of the supplying companies had several presses and operated at a different time on orders of the Luna Company. The purchasing agent notified the supplying companies when they should start their presses, and they operated continuously until their respective orders were completed. The purchasing agent followed this practice in order to ensure deliveries when required. The specifications of the Luna Company were detailed and exacting.

In July the Mixter Company, located in Boston, quoted a price of $2.91 per thousand f.o.b. New York; the Damon Company, located in Trenton, $2.85 per thousand f.o.b. New York; the Rushmore Company, located in Cincinnati, $2.83 per thousand f.o.b. New York; and the Holzman Company, located in Philadelphia, $2.81 per thousand f.o.b. Philadelphia, freight allowed to New York. Freight deliveries to New York were made direct to the company's siding. These prices were to apply to shipments made during the last three months of the current year and the first three months of the following year.

Since the price quoted by the Mixter Company was much higher than quotations received from other reliable sources, that company was given no further consideration.  Satisfactory purchases had been made previously from all companies except the Rushmore Company.  The Rushmore Company never had been given an order prior to the current year since its price always had been out of line.  Practically all the requirements of the Luna Company had been supplied in the past by the Damon Company and the Holzman Company.

The quality of cartons supplied by the Damon Company and the Holzman Company had always been excellent. Because of their location near the plant of the Luna Company, it was possible for Luna Company executives to keep continuously informed regarding the manufacture and shipment of the cartons.  The Damon Company was able to make deliveries by truck in one day from date of shipment.  The Holzman Company, since it shipped by freight, required one week in which to make delivery.  The purchasing agent believed that the Damon Company was the more reliable source of supply.  Its price, however, was 4 cents per thousand higher than that of the Holzman Company.

Because of the distance between the plant of the Rushmore Company and the plant of the Luna Company, two weeks would be required for effecting delivery.  Among other purchasers of cartons, the Rushmore Company had an excellent reputation for the quality of its work and service.  Its price was 2 cents per thousand lower than that of the Damon Company and 2 cents per thousand higher than that of the Holzman Company.

Shortly after receiving quotations from the four companies mentioned, the purchasing agent of the Luna Company was solicited for business by the sales manager of the Commercial Printing Company, Inc., New York.  The Luna Company had never purchased from this concern, nor had it previously received bids from it.  The purchasing agent furnished the representative of the Commercial Printing Company, Inc., with specifications of the work being considered and was told that the printing company was very anxious to submit a bid.

Two days later the sales manager called again and said that his company would furnish cartons exactly as specified by the Luna Company at a price of $2.51 per thousand delivered at the soap company's receiving platform, provided that an order for not less than 20,000,000 cartons was forthcoming. He showed the purchasing agent many samples of excellent color printing that had been done by his company and said that work of equal quality would be guaranteed. He told the sales manager that the $2.51 quotation would return his company absolutely no profit. The company's plant had practically no work on schedule and an order for 20,000,000 cartons would enable it to keep its work force employed for several weeks, during which time the sales manager hoped to obtain additional business for his company. Also, it happened that the Commercial Printing Company, Inc., had in stock a large amount of material of the exact specifications required for the Luna Company order. The printing company was willing to sacrifice all profits on a large order which would enable it to keep its plant operating and its working force occupied, particularly when the order made possible the liquidation of some of its inventory of raw materials. The sales manager went so far as to show the Luna Company purchasing agent detailed cost estimates for the order, and also pointed out the desirability of furnishing New York workers with employment by keeping the work in that city.

The purchasing agent visited the plant of the Commercial Printing Company, Inc. He found it to be a small, well-equipped establishment. Inspection of the materials to be used in his order revealed them to be of good quality. Similar work then being done was excellent in appearance, and there seemed to be no reason why the company could not satisfactorily produce the Luna Company order.

While at the plant, he met the president of the printing company, who told him frankly that the order for cartons was of critical importance to the Commercial Printing Company, Inc., and when he declined to place the order then and there, the president offered a cash discount of 2 per cent in addition to the terms originally extended.

How should the purchasing agent of the Luna Company place his order or orders for 25,000,000 cartons?

## Problem 27

### SOUTHERN BAKERS, INC.

Southern Bakers, Inc., a baking company in a Southern city, was faced with the necessity of supplying new personnel for its purchasing department. Resignation of the purchasing agent and his assistant had left no one familiar with the problems and routine of the department, nor was there anyone in the employ of the company experienced in purchasing the materials and supplies required for daily operation of the company. It would take some time to find a man with the requisite ability and experience to head the department, and, since it was essential to make provision at once for supplying the constant day-to-day requirements of the company, a young man was transferred from the accounting department and temporarily put in charge of purchasing activities.

Southern Bakers, Inc., was an old and well-established company which had been built up as a family business and was not connected with any large baking combine. It had established a reputation for high quality of a wide variety of bakery products, and its sales amounted to over $2,000,000 yearly. The major portion of sales were made from house to house.

The purchasing department was responsible for buying all the materials and supplies used by the company. These were of several types and consisted of hundreds of items. The principal baking materials were wheat flour, other wheat products, special flours and meals, sugar, salt, shortening, butter, eggs, milk, and various fruits and flavorings. Wrapping materials of many kinds, office supplies, general plant supplies, and repair materials were also purchased. Practically all the principal purchases were made on the basis of contracts with local brokers and manufacturers. These contracts stipulated that the volume covered must be taken by a certain date, that deliveries would be made at times requested up to that date, and that each delivery would be billed on the date of shipment. The terms were usually f.o.b. Southern Bakers, Inc., plants or nearby railroad terminals or piers. Commercial truckmen were hired to bring goods from piers and railroad terminals.

After the resignation of the purchasing agent, company executives discovered a serious inventory situation which required immediate attention. The warehouse was full of flour, and large quantities were still in freight cars and lying on piers, accumulating heavy demurrage charges and in danger of damage. Furthermore, some of the contract time limits apparently were overdue since mills were demanding that flour be taken. Storage facilities of the company were already overtaxed, and it seemed undesirable to have more flour shipments coming in.

The president of Southern Bakers, Inc., decided to place a young man, Albert Clinton, from the accounting department, in temporary charge of the company's purchasing. Effort immediately would be made to find an experienced purchasing executive, but until such a person was employed Clinton was to endeavor to keep the material needs of the company supplied and to settle such other problems of the purchasing department as required immediate attention.

Mr. Clinton was a young man with some business experience. He had spent one year at a graduate school of business administration and had been employed by Southern Bakers, Inc., for the summer. In the fall he was going to return to school to complete his business training. Mr. Clinton was not experienced in purchasing, nor had his few weeks in the company's accounting department enabled him to become very familiar with the material needs of the concern. However, he expressed willingness to accept the job and was at once transferred to the purchasing department.

In addition to the growing surplus of certain raw materials, other immediate difficulties faced Mr. Clinton. In some instances he was unable to locate copies of important contracts in the files. In the past, shipping instructions had been given over the telephone, and he could not locate complete notations of the facts. Freight shipments were arriving in quantities larger than were called for by such notations as were available, and Mr. Clinton believed that some dealers were making larger shipments than had been ordered. However, he had no means of substantiating that belief.

Information as to the condition of inventory of materials was meager. Each day the chief receiving clerk would look at his stocks to estimate the quantity on hand and amounts of each item needed. With so many varied items, such visible control was difficult, and it was inevitable that he would make occasional mistakes necessitating special trips into the city for small orders; on the other hand, too much of one article was sometimes ordered. The production department sent weekly reports of the consumption of the major materials to the accounting department for cost records. Mr. Clinton had to apply to the accounting department if he wished these figures.

There had been no detailed system of inventory control. The receiving clerk, of course, remembered many pertinent facts from past experience. He knew, for instance, that bread wrappers had to be ordered at least two weeks in advance to allow time for printing, while some supplies could be obtained immediately from local dealers.

Certain materials required even more advanced purchasing. For instance, blueberries, a seasonal crop, had to be bought and taken to a refrigeration plant, from which they could be withdrawn throughout the year.

One detail to which the purchasing agent had to give attention was the testing of each load of flour as it arrived. Southern Bakers, Inc., used only unbleached flour. No shipment of flour could be put in process until samples had been taken to a local food testing laboratory and the results of the test received. This testing took two or three days.

In reaching solutions to these and other similar problems, Mr. Clinton had to consider that his work would soon be taken over by a permanent purchasing agent. Whatever he did would be largely temporary in nature and his policies, therefore, should be such as to give the new executive a relatively free hand in the permanent reorganization which was to be his job.

What steps would you suggest that Mr. Clinton take to provide Southern Bakers, Inc., with suitable supplies of raw materials at minimum inventory cost until such time as a permanent purchasing agent was obtained?

# CHAPTER XII

## PLANT LOCATION

### AUTO-STOKER COMPANY

**1. A Company Considers Relocation of Its Manufacturing Facilities.**

The Auto-Stoker Company, located in Portland, Oregon, manufactured a patented coal burner under the trade name "Auto-Stoker." In working out an expansion program, the company purchased a plant in Cleveland, Ohio, for $100,000. Several years later exact utilization of the company's manufacturing properties was still under consideration.

**2. Importance of Plant Location.** A mass of published material is available to those who are interested in plant location.[1] Some of it is historical, much is explanatory, a little deals with basic theory. Here we will confine ourselves to a consideration of the business problems immediately faced by an executive who is considering the location or relocation of proposed or existing manufacturing facilities.

It is the scope of the location problem that establishes its importance. A plant location problem, like most business problems, points directly toward profits. To get the full impact of location on profits, one must commonly include for consideration far more than the conversion process that goes on within the walls of one factory. Location influences begin with the sources of raw materials and do not end until the finished product is finally in the hands of the consumer. Effects of location on earnings must be projected beyond today's profits into a future commensurate with the physical life of the manufacturing facilities

[1] See Dexter S. Kimball and Dexter S. Kimball, Jr., *Principles of Industrial Organization* (6th ed.), McGraw-Hill Book Company, Inc., New York, 1947.

Lawrence L. Bethel, Franklin S. Atwater, George H. E. Smith, and Harvey J. Stackman, Jr., *Industrial Organization and Management,* McGraw-Hill Book Company, Inc., New York, 1945.

involved, and occasionally far beyond that. Foresight must also frequently be applied to the life probabilities of raw materials sources and the future shiftings of market areas and concentrations of industry. Few executives or organizations are fully prepared to make such complete projections. Usually the permanence of whatever solution is devised is the most important characteristic of the location problem. Industrial executives are both fortunate and unfortunate in that the question of plant location is of infrequent occurrence.

**3. Why Factories Are Located Where They Are.** The location of a particular factory may be the result of sheer accident or the culmination of many months of study on the part of highly paid specialists. A plant may be located in a town simply because it is the home of a promoting management. Plants so located are not necessarily poorly located. The promotion and location may be the result of recognition of local need.

Nor does the expending of much time and money in the making of highly technical location surveys always ensure excellence in location. An actual case in point is a blast furnace which, because of poor location, has been in operation less than half the time since it was built. Several months and much money were spent in investigation of the suitability of the location finally recommended in a lengthy technical report. The recommendation was accepted and over $4,000,000 spent in the erection of a plant. The location soon proved far less satisfactory than was expected. The reason was a change in transportation methods and rates for pig iron from Southern furnaces into the market the new plant had expected to serve. Other examples of similar nature have forced the conclusion that careful investigation, while important in selecting good plant location, is not absolute assurance of permanently satisfactory results.

Study of engineers' reports on plant location quickly reveals a general pattern. They commonly consider the nature of the product and its processing in relation to such matters as nearness to market, accessibility of raw materials, labor supply, power supply and cost, fuel requirements, climatic conditions, and availability of capital. In addition to such common factors, almost any specific case presents certain peculiar conditions.

Examples that can be cited are local tax concessions, availability of specialized technicians for consultation, advertising values of a location, or need of providing specialized engineering services to the market. It may be trite to say that each location problem should be looked upon as peculiar in itself. Nevertheless, it is important to emphasize that fact. There is no general formula. There are common factors which are important. Correct solution more often than not is to be determined by characteristics of a specific situation which are less common than the old standby, distance to the market.

**4. The Experience of the Auto-Stoker Company.** The Auto-Stoker Company paid $100,000 for an industrial property in Cleveland, Ohio, consisting of three buildings containing 65,000 square feet of floor space located on a three-acre tract of land. At that time the company's output was being manufactured in a small, modern plant in Portland, Oregon. The product was shipped by rail to Pacific Coast points, by water to the Atlantic Coast, and by rail or rail and water to interior points.

**5. Nature of the Product.** The Auto-Stoker was a device for forced underfiring of furnaces. It was described in the advertising circulars of the company as follows:

The Auto-Stoker is so simple that anyone can easily understand it. You simply fill the hopper with cheap coal; beneath the hopper is a screw shaft like that in your food chopper, but much larger. This carries the coal into the furnace, feeding the fire from below; the same quiet little motor which feeds the coal to the fire also operates the ball-bearing fan which supplies air in just the right proportions to produce the greatest heat.

The Auto-Stoker principle of forced underfiring does away with ashes. The intense heat which the Auto-Stoker produces (500 to 1,000 degrees hotter than hand firing) melts the ashes and fuses them into solid pieces easily lifted out with tongs at the same time you fill the hopper—about once a day.

In forced underfiring a constant supply of slack, screenings, or buckwheat coal is fed to the fire from below. The exact amount of air necessary for complete combustion is forced into the fire. The whole machine starts and stops automatically to keep the exact steam pressure desired, regardless of variations of load or outdoor temperature.

The burner wherever installed had resulted in a saving of from 15 to 50 per cent of fuel costs, and the company had received ample testimonials from customers to prove this saving.

**6. History of the Company.** Prior to the formation of the Auto-Stoker Company in 1923, the burner had remained an obscure product for lack of adequate capital to push the device on the market. In 1923, a new company, adequately capitalized, introduced the product in the eastern markets and after three years' pioneering work began to experience a rapid growth.

National advertising was started in the fall of 1923 in greenhouse magazines, and a similar and slightly larger campaign was conducted in the fall of 1924. In 1925 advertising was started in the *Saturday Evening Post,* and use of this medium was continued with increased space each year. Other national publications were added to the advertising schedule each year, such as *Time, Better Homes and Gardens, House and Garden,* and *House Beautiful.*

A business of $630,000 was done in 1926, and in 1927 the amount doubled. Distribution in 1928 was through approximately 300 dealers chiefly in the Middle West, New England, and the Middle Atlantic states, with one branch office in St. Louis and another in Cleveland. There were 15 missionary salesmen, operating out of the branch offices and Portland, whose business it was to assist the dealers in pushing the product. As an additional aid, the sales manager made an annual tour with other executives of the company to hold sectional sales conventions attended by dealers. In 1928, less than 4 per cent of the burners were sold in Oregon and over 75 per cent of the company's market was east of the Rocky Mountains. The company was well on its way to becoming of national importance in the stoker industry.

Dealers usually sold the product on an exclusive agency basis. In 1940 the cost of the burner installed varied from $425 for private homes and small furnaces to $2,500 for the large buildings.

**7. Production Methods.** The Auto-Stoker was made up in three units: a sheet-metal hopper with air blower attached, a patented driving-gear mechanism enclosed in a gearbox, and a cast-iron burner with feed pipe and spiral feed screw attached. The whole mechanism was electrically driven. No special equipment was required for the production of either the hopper or the burner units. The hopper could be readily produced at any sheet-metal works. The burner, feed pipe, and screw, which were heavy castings requiring little finishing, could be easily produced in almost any foundry. The important unit was the driving mechanism. Its economical production required a well-equipped machine shop and heat-treating ovens. None of this equipment, however, needed to be of special design except the dies, jigs, and tools. The cost department records at the Portland plant showed that the cost of producing the driving mechanism was approximately 50 per cent of the entire cost of manufacturing the stoker.

**8. Why the Auto-Stoker Company Plant Was Located in Portland, Oregon.** The production of the Auto-Stoker had been started in Portland chiefly because its promoters lived there and had other interests in the city. There was no difficulty in securing skilled workers. The patented part of the stoker was not expensive to ship to the eastern market, but the hopper and castings were bulky and carried heavy freight charges. Differential prices according to location were charged by the company, since little competition had been experienced and the device paid for itself many times over in fuel saving. The management had not been troubled by patent infringement. It expected to cover the field so thoroughly and to operate so economically as to hold its own against prospective competitors. The executives of the company observed that so far as administration of the enterprise was concerned, the company could operate efficiently from Portland. However, the shipping costs became an increasingly greater problem as the business grew.

Because the company was located on the Pacific Coast, it had the advantage of low shipping rates by water to New York City. The management had considered Chicago as a location for its central plant, but shipping costs from Portland to New York by water were very little more than from Chicago to New York by rail. Hence there would be little gained by such a move so far as the Atlantic Coast trade was concerned. Cleveland was more nearly the center of the company's business, and the management had, in 1926, considered establishing a plant there. It had abandoned the idea, however, and instead had made arrangements there for the local manufacture of some of the bulky castings for the burner in order to save shipping costs.

An addition to the Portland plant was constructed in 1927 and modern machines were added. These included automatic gear cutters, shapers, and lathes. The plant then covered approximately one-quarter of a city block. A careful departmentization of the production process was worked out. The lower floor was about equally divided between the assembly and shipping department and the machine department, which produced, set up, and tested the driving assembly, the patented part of the machine. The sheet-metal department, the toolroom, and the experimental laboratory were located on the second floor. In the basement were a boiler and furnace fully equipped with testing instruments for experimentation. Castings used at the plant were purchased from local foundries. The plant was well organized and was fully equipped with modern tools. Active research, engineering, and cost departments were maintained.

**9. Expansion Before the Second World War; the Location Problem.** With growth in business the shipping problem had become increasingly vital, and the executives were, in 1928, again considering the problem of expansion. However, no action was taken at that time. Shortly before the Second World War, the company announced the purchase of a plant in Cleveland, Ohio.

This property had been acquired after executives of the company had carefully surveyed the problems involved in its utilization. These concerned the immediate and future use to which the Portland plant was to be put. Should all production be shifted to Cleveland and the Portland plant closed down? Should the Portland plant specialize on the production of the driving mechanism and the Cleveland plant confine its activities to the production of the sheet metal and cast iron parts and to assembly of the complete units? Should the Portland plant continue producing as in the past but distribute its output in adjacent territory only and the Cleveland plant become a complete producing unit distributing to its natural geographic territory? Should the Cleveland plant produce its own castings, or should it follow the policy adopted for the Portland plant and purchase them from merchant foundries? Or would some combination of the foregoing possibilities be best suited to the company's situation?

In developing sales of newer types of product there was always the possibility of competition to be considered. This factor would vary between the different types of installation. A complicating factor was the steadily increasing demand for small home installations of the company's product. It was anticipated that this type of business would be highly competitive. Another consideration was the development of installations for ovens to be used in bakeries, ceramic industries, and the like. These opportunities were in addition to the already occupied fields of apartment houses, hotels, schools, greenhouses, office buildings, and industrial establishments. The management believed that the business would continue to expand and was prepared financially to meet this expansion.

**10. Analysis of the Situation.** Centering of production of the Auto-Stoker Company in Portland, Oregon, is open to question. Major considerations favoring that location include the existence of an efficient, smooth-working plant and organization, availability of a suitable labor supply, low-cost transportation to the Pacific and Atlantic Coast markets, personal preference of company owners and executives for living in the Pacific Northwest, adequate established banking connections, and opinion of the executives that they could manage the business satisfactorily at a distance from the major market. Against that location are the growth of the Middle Western market with its relatively high cost of finished product shipment, increasing competition in home installations in the area most conveniently served from Cleveland, relatively high cost of many materials which had to carry transportation costs from the East to the Pacific Northwest, difficulties of maintaining close contact with the growing market, restriction of the geographic areas that could be economically served from Portland, Oregon, and problems of rendering developmental and technical service for industrial and commercial installations when factory and market were so widely separated. It appears, then, that in the main the urge toward change of location came largely from changes that were taking place in the market and were foreseen as likely to take place.

**11. Relative Efficiency of the Portland Plant.** Any production change which included lessening the output of the Portland plant was likely to disrupt the efficiency of that unit. This would mean increased cost of production. In view of anticipated increase in competition, cost increase would seem particularly undesirable. Given the best of plant facilities, labor, and management, it takes time to adjust an organization to smooth-working order. It should be expected that any new producing unit set up by the Auto-Stoker Company would be less efficient for some time than the experienced organization at the Portland plant.

**12. Labor Supply.** The existence of a skilled, experienced, stable labor supply is an asset to any company. Of particular importance is a dependable and efficient labor group when labor costs constitute a substantial portion of total production costs. Labor supply at the Portland plant was excellent. Skilled labor in that area tended to be conservative and not easily stirred to radicalism. Company workers were mostly native Americans who had families and, therefore, a sense of personal responsibility. There is reason to believe that the company was obtaining relatively high productivity from its labor force and that each dollar expended for wages was yielding a high return in value of product.

The management should have experienced no difficulty in obtaining labor of the requisite type and skill in the Cleveland area. There was some possibility that labor obtainable in that area would be somewhat less productive and substantially higher in cost than that available to the company in Portland. Of particular concern was the lack of assurance of labor stability such as was characteristic of the company's Portland employees.

**13. Transportation Costs.** Transportation costs on raw materials would be lower at the Cleveland location than at Portland. Cleveland was nearer the source of supply, both geographically and in terms of transportation costs. Finished product comparison is not quite so simple. Shipping costs to the Pacific Coast market would be greater from Cleveland than from Portland. However, the Pacific Coast volume was much less than that which centered around Cleveland. Transportation costs to the Atlantic Coast areas were about the same from Portland as from Cleveland. This is an excellent illustration of the fallacy of measuring nearness to market entirely in terms of miles. Portland is three times as far from New York as Cleveland. Relatively low costs of water shipment through the Panama Canal neutralized the greater distance and made transportation cost to the Atlantic Coast from Portland no greater than rail shipment cost from Cleveland. Cleveland's great advantage as to finished goods transportation cost was in the inland territory between the west and east coasts. This advantage assumed particular significance in the light of the trend toward greatest volume expansion in that inland territory.

**14. Personal Preferences of Company Executives.** The importance of personal preferences of the executives should not be underestimated. They had established themselves in Portland. They preferred to stay there. From a cold efficiency standpoint one might say that such preference should have been of little or no consideration. As a matter of economics that position might hold. Practically, and probably socially, such an economic attitude is not entirely adequate. In the first place, there was some doubt as to the actual possibility of transferring these executives. If they were prevailed upon to transfer in face of their own opposition, it would very likely result in an increase in cost of supervision. That should be calculated. Also there is the question of objectives. One may say that economical production is the matter of first concern, that the preferences, the likes and dislikes, of the servants of the business are of secondary importance. But are they? Do these men exist to serve this business or is the business there to serve its owners and executives? Practically no business can succeed beyond the abilities of its management, and corporate directors who form the practice of sacrificing the thoughtful desires of employed executives to the seemingly immediate demands of corporate success are building a reputation that is very likely to hamper the enterprise in the future.

**15. Nearness of Management to Market.** The opinion of company executives that they could manage the business as well from Portland as they could from Cleveland is open to very serious question. During the early years of the company's development they were able to do so. After that, changes occurred which made the management problem essentially different.

In the home-heating field the severity of competition increased. Under such circumstances, close contact with the consumer becomes very important. It is important to know quickly and accurately what the consumer wants and what he does not want. It is equally important to know what your competitor is doing, and is going to do, to influence what the consumer thinks he wants and does not want. Consumer reactions are frequently influenced far more by what competition has taught the consumer than by logical thinking on the consumer's part.

At this point is it natural to say that the Auto-Stoker Company could gain this desirable contact with the market by moving its marketing and selling organization east, that such a change does not necessitate transfer of production as well. Such action would probably be better than making no attempt to get closer to demand. It should be pointed out, however, that this gain would be at the expense of isolation of the marketing function from the production function.

In the field of industrial and commercial use of the company's product there was even greater reason for bringing the factory closer to the consumer. These installations were sold with emphasis on continuity of operation of the product. Unfailing service of the product requires continuously available servicing of the product. The Auto-Stoker Company could set up fully equipped servicing facilities for its products in the eastern territory. There were, however, two objections to this method of meeting servicing requirements: it would involve costs of non-resident management, and from a sales standpoint it would be less convincing to many prospective buyers than would the nearby location of the factory itself. Particularly would this be true of special installations calling for engineering adaptations of the product to peculiar requirements. Thus, from the sales and service standpoints, there is much to be said for locating the plant close to the major market in this case.

**16. Influence of the Future Market.** Thus far it has been assumed that the company faced a growing demand and that such increase would tend to be greatest in a territory contiguous to Cleveland, Ohio. Management should make no such assumption. Future demand for the company's product should be studied carefully and thoroughly. It is not the province of this book to study the methods and techniques of market analysis. It will suffice here to point out that in addition to competition of other automatic coal-stoking devices, actual and potential, this company would face the competition of other fuels possessing comparable appeals; oil, gas, and electricity are all actual or potential competitors of the Auto-Stoker. The future of this company would be greatly influenced by the development of these fuels. Obviously, one of the first and most important problems which faced the executives of this company was determination of the character and location of future demand. Solution of both expansion and location problems should wait upon the results of such studies.

**17. Summary and Conclusions.** *Recommended Action in the Case of the Auto-Stoker Company.* The following recommendation is based upon an assumption that the company was sound in its conclusion that the big future market for the company's product was easily reached from Cleveland. Manufacture of the driving mechanism should be continued in Portland for the time being. Heavy castings for the eastern market should be purchased from Cleveland merchant foundries and finished at the Cleveland plant. The seasonal demand for the company's product came at a time when Cleveland foundries were experiencing slack demand and would be likely to quote prices at least as low as costs of production in any foundry the Auto-Stoker Company would build. The Cleveland plant should be equipped to produce sheet-metal parts for the eastern market. A service department should be set up at the Cleveland plant, complete even to product engineering service. As soon as the market most cheaply served from Cleveland developed a volume sufficient to permit relatively economical production in Cleveland for that market alone, production of driving mechanisms for that market should be transferred from Portland to Cleveland. This would leave the Portland plant serving the Atlantic and Pacific Coast markets with driving devices. If the volume of business then available in the seaboard markets was too low to permit economical manufacture in Portland, all driving mechanism production should be transferred to Cleveland and the Portland location used as an assembly, sheet-metal working, and service plant only. Manufacture in the Portland plant for the Atlantic and Pacific coasts should be continued until the increase in costs due to low-volume production is higher than the freight differential of gear case shipment from Portland.

*Reasons for the Proposed Action.* The recommendation that for the time being production in the Portland plant be continued turns on the relatively low costs of a going organization, the comparatively high productivity of the labor force, and the personal desires of the owners and executives to remain in that location. The recommendation to transfer production to Cleveland when volume in the central territory increased is made on a quite different basis. It is doubtful whether unit production costs would ever be lower in Cleveland than at Portland. It is questionable whether they would ever be low enough to make the transportation saving of the Cleveland plant to its natural market a net saving. It should be possible, however, to reduce costs of production at Cleveland so that production plus transportation from that plant to the adjacent market would be as cheap as production at Portland plus transportation from there to the Cleveland market. But even if this goal should not be entirely attainable, the shift should be made as indicated. The decision rests on belief in the importance of physical proximity of this factory and the market it served, largely from the marketing standpoint. In commercial and industrial stoker installations, nearness was imperative for sales and service. For the home installation market, nearness was important if the Auto-Stoker Company was to continue to meet and keep ahead of competition within the Cleveland market as it developed. It is this aspect, rather than the seemingly obvious transportation differential, which controls in this case.

One other argument must be disposed of. What of the personal wishes of the owners and managers? This factor might rightly reverse the action outlined here. On that score a matter of major policy had to be decided, and no one but those men immediately concerned could make the decision. It seems likely

that the Auto-Stoker Company could continue its present policies from Portland and remain a profitable business. That
might be the sound decision for company executives to make,
a sound personal decision. It is doubtful whether the future
profits of this company would be so great if it continued all production in Portland as they would be if the company aggressively established itself in Cleveland. From the strictly business
standpoint, one would wish for the Cleveland development.
From the standpoint of greatest satisfaction to ownership and
management, there is reason to believe that Portland might
well be the sounder location.

*Nature of Plant Location Problems.* While all industrial location problems consist of selecting a place for plant facilities,
they appear in a variety of forms. Our consideration of the
Auto-Stoker Company was limited to the relative merits of geographical areas. This was because the specific sites within those
areas had already been determined upon. Site within a given
area constitutes a distinct type of location problem. Selection
of site involves many of the same considerations that are of importance in selecting general locations. Emphasis is likely to be
somewhat different. Accessibility of transportation for materials, product, and workers is a common factor. Land cost and
construction costs as affected by land characteristics must be
considered. Tax rates and assessment values are important.
Municipal restrictions on uses to which real estate may be put,
and local reaction to smoke, fumes, odors, and risks of fire and
explosion must not be overlooked. Usually the problem of site
selection is not difficult. Methodical, careful approach to the
situation with a forward look to consider the effects of change
in any or all of the factors involved will yield satisfactory results.

Another form which the location problem frequently takes is
the question of relative desirability of locating where the industry already congregates or away from concentration areas.
There is no ready-made answer here. That there are both advantages and disadvantages can be demonstrated by considering
briefly labor supply. Where an industry congregates, there can
be found trained, experienced labor. At the same time the
existence of a number of similar businesses in close proximity

creates competitive demand for that labor. Whether or not concentration makes for an advantageous or a disadvantageous labor supply for a specific company can only be told by careful appraisal of the elements in each particular situation. The same is true of many other location factors upon which concentration has an effect. It is more profitable to study these factors in each specific case than to approach a location problem with a preconceived notion that concentration is likely to affect one element in this way and another element in that way.

Another way in which the location problem is sometimes approached is in terms of the urban versus the suburban or the rural location. Here again, generalizations are of no great profit. The factors upon which choice is based are commonly similar to those taken into consideration in the Auto-Stoker Company case. Procedure along the lines followed there will determine the relative desirability of a particular city location as compared with a particular country site.

At present, there is said to be a trend toward rural location. Perhaps that is true. The tying up of industrial with agricultural occupations assumes a prominent place when this particular trend is being discussed. Just how practical this combination is for any given company has little to do with whatever trend may exist. As conditions change, the relative importance of location factors changes, and, of course, such shifts in importance must receive careful consideration in a search for a location solution. The widespread ownership of automobiles has changed the location picture of some businesses insofar as worker transportation and worker supply factors are concerned, although excellent electric trolley service is still of great importance to most large business units and to many small ones. Motor trucks have sometimes made the existence of a railroad siding at the plant less essential. However, it is hardly accurate to say that development of the automobile has completely changed the nature of the location problem.

During the reconversion and expansion of manufacturing facilities that has followed the recent war, there has been something of a tendency on the part of some large corporations to decentralize manufacturing activities. The result has been the location of medium-sized specialized factories away from large urban industrial concentrations. It has been hoped that these locations would prove attractive to labor, which might be somewhat less under the constant purview of labor organizations. If this resulted, the daily operating management and supervision of these plants might be somewhat less hectic. It would be foolish to expect that these branch plants would not be subject to organized labor influence. Since the war there has been a great increase in the negotiation of corporation-wide labor-management contracts. No suburban or rural plant will be beyond the scope of these arrangements. It is true, however, that if labor finds such locations more acceptable than the highly industrialized centers the tasks of management may be somewhat less burdensome in these branch plants.

The day may come when plant location problems are radically different from what they are now. However, any drastic difference is likely to be the result of slow change in the importance of this or that element rather than of some startling innovation that repaints the whole picture overnight. The major problem of the executive responsible for choice of location of an enterprise is to foresee the probable nature of such change and the effects of change during the business life span of the physical facilities involved. Industries in this country have migrated and are still in slow process of doing so. Suitability of a location 10 or 20 years hence may well be of greater importance than suitability today. Consideration of the future within practical limitations is more often than not the critical determinant in the problem of plant location.

## QUESTIONS

1. What factors are commonly considered when a proposed plant location is being studied?

2. What were the factors considered in reaching a solution to the Auto-Stoker Company's location problem?

3. Is the solution suggested in the text sound?

4. How was that decision reached?

5. Foundries and ice manufacturing plants tend to cater to local markets. Why?

6. For a company manufacturing 6-volt storage batteries that it sells nationally, which would be the better, a single large plant located near Detroit, or several smaller plants located at such points as New York, Detroit, St. Louis, Denver, and San Francisco?

7. Would Boston, Massachusetts, be a good location for a manufacturer of automobile tires if it sells its product

   a. As original new-car equipment?
   b. Through retail outlets?
   c. Through mail order houses?

8. How is plant location influenced by

   a. The nature of the product?
   b. The characteristics of the production process?
   c. The dynamic characteristics of industrial society?

9. Wherein does geographical location choice differ from site selection?

10. Why do different manufacturers in an industry sometimes tend to locate near one another?

11. Why do industries migrate?

12. Why is plant location an important business problem?

## FRENCH MOTOR CAR COMPANY

The French Motor Car Company with plant and main offices located in Cleveland, Ohio, manufactured passenger and commercial cars of medium price. Cars were produced with chassis standard, or nearly so, in each car. Automobiles were delivered to dealers situated in cities of the United States and foreign countries from the main plant and from an assembly plant at Toronto, Canada. All cars were priced f.o.b. Cleveland. Company officials were considering the advisability of establishing other assembly plants at some points on the Atlantic and Pacific coasts for the purpose of reducing the cost of the car to dealers in these localities. One city selected for analysis was Newark, New Jersey.

The total freight charges on cars shipped to Newark were estimated for the current year at $3,800,000. An assembly plant located at Newark would supply 96 dealer cities. Estimated distribution of cars for the current year to Newark was 78,040. The plant engineer estimated that an assembly plant of sufficient capacity to meet the requirements at Newark would necessitate a capital investment of $3,500,000. This estimate was based on the most up-to-date assembly methods and on the effect of seasonal operation upon annual production. Freight rates from Cleveland to Newark were obtained from the traffic division as follows: average per assembled car, $48.75; average per car disassembled, $16. Loading costs were estimated by the plant engineer to range from $6.50 to $7 on assembled cars and $8.50 to $9 on disassembled cars, the cost depending on the number to be loaded. Costs at assembly plant including fixed charges were estimated at $12 per car, assuming a daily plant output of 280 cars.

In the past cars had been shipped from Cleveland direct to dealer cities in the Newark territory. Driveaway costs from stations of receipt to dealer agencies had been nominal. If an assembly plant was located at Newark, all cars assembled there would be driven from the assembly plant to the dealer agencies.

Driveaway costs were approximately 10 cents per mile.  The longest driveaway from Newark would be 260 miles.

Does it seem advisable for the French Motor Car Company to erect an assembly plant at Newark, New Jersey?

## Problem 29

### FLEXUNIT BODY COMPANY

The Flexunit Body Company, with moderate capitalization but with ample resources available, was formed in Boston to take over patents and development of a unit truck body.  The body could be rolled or lifted onto or off a truck chassis, and similarly could be rolled into a freight car or lifted onto a flat car.  These cars would each hold seven units.  The technical features were worked out through five experimental installations involving 40 bodies.  It was expected that this form of body would eventually play a tremendous part in systematizing less-than-carload transportation, and that the manufacture of such bodies would assume great proportions.  This removable body would also simplify the shipping problems of users of motor trucks in local hauls where loading and unloading time is considerable.  Backers of the company were confident, therefore, of a large local business in each large city.

The bodies were of such design that the sills and certain bottom framework members, cut and assembled from standard structural steel rolled shapes, and the cast bronze and malleable iron rollers, all covered by patents, could be standardized and made at one factory.  These parts could be shipped in carload lots to points of assembly.  On the other hand, the problem of the bodies proper was that met by truck manufacturers in general; truck bodies are very bulky, and local requirements differ, so that a large number of trucks are sold as chassis only and the bodies are made in local plants, usually independent.

After the earliest stages, the Flexunit removable body was developed in a truck-body plant in the Boston district.  The Flexunit bottom frame would fit a large variety of bodies and most standard chassis, the method of adjusting and fastening being one of the patented features; but this adaptability was not without limits. Best results would require some control or some influence over the bodybuilders looking to standardization of body designs to a few forms.

The company was preparing to establish a manufacturing plant, small at first, to do three things: (1) To make frames and rollers, and later when the volume of business warranted to establish a brass foundry, and still later to establish an iron foundry for making its own castings; (2) to make a line of suitable standard bodies for local short hauls, and for demonstration of railroad possibilities wherever such demonstration could be arranged; (3) to organize and develop an engineering department and a developmental department for the purpose of taking care of all the design and developmental work of the company at that time and in the future.

The company expected a large growth and a country-wide business. It expected that the earlier and easier field would be in local transportation, but that the great growth would be in transportation including a railroad haul of less-than-carload lots. The bodies could be loaded and trucked in one city, railed to another, there transferred to trucks at the freight terminal, and trucked to destination, where the body would be rolled off, unloaded, sent to some shipper in that city for reload, and again railed to another destination.

It was expected that the local business would be more than self-supporting, and that it would supply working funds for the more ambitious plan of truck-rail-truck transportation. The greatest hopes of the company, moreover, were based upon its belief in the possibilities of the latter. The initial problem was the selection of a city for the first plant, which was to become the engineering base for the whole enterprise.

What should the company do?

# CHAPTER XIII

## PLANT LAYOUT

### SIMONDS SAW AND STEEL COMPANY

**1. A Large Manufacturer of Saws and Knives Plans an Improved Layout of Plant Equipment.**

The Simonds Saw and Steel Company, one of the oldest and largest manufacturers of circular wood and metal saws, machine knives, band saws, band knives, files, and hack saws in the United States, was preparing to consolidate and reorganize its two plants in Fitchburg, Massachusetts, and its Chicago plant. All three of these plants were laid out in general for functional operation. Company officials were considering the desirability of laying out the new consolidated plant for line production.

**2. Fixed Assets.** The selection of equipment for use in the production process and the arrangement of this equipment in the plant have considerable effect on the profits of a manufacturing establishment. Selection and layout problems are somewhat similar to plant location problems in that they tend to constitute long-time commitments.

When the manufacturer prepares a statement to show the condition of his business, he lists among the things to which the business holds legal title a group of physical possessions to which he gives the caption "Fixed Assets." Plant, machines, and equipment are characteristic items of this category. The heading "Fixed Assets" seems to endow these items with the quality of permanency, and that is the characteristic which the average reader of a financial statement ascribes to them. They are the permanent, tangible attributes of the manufacturing business which any claimant against that business, be he creditor or stockholder, may see, touch, and observe at any time if he will go to the point at which these physical aids to the production process have their place of fixity. This is an important consideration from the standpoint of attracting funds to the business.

**3. Fixed Assets That Are Not Fixed.** It is not the province of this volume to discuss financial problems as such. Our interest in fixed assets lies in their usefulness in production, and from that point of view there is no such thing as a fixed asset in the sense that it does not change or disappear. Essentially, plants, buildings, and equipment are just like all other assets used in the production process. They are continually changing, being used up. The essence of the productive process is conversion of assets, be they machines or raw materials, into marketable goods, usually of an entirely different form and designed to serve an entirely different purpose.

**4. Depreciation and Obsolescence Defined.** The only difference between machines and raw materials from the standpoint of production is that the former are usually converted into finished product more slowly than are the latter. We define depreciation as the physical wearing away of a fixed asset. Obsolescence we define as the economic wasting away of a fixed asset. Depreciation has to do with the mechanical ability of a machine to produce. Obsolescence refers to the efficiency of operation of a machine as compared with some other newer device of greater productivity. We are concerned with obsolescence only when it takes place at a more rapid rate than does depreciation.

**5. Depreciation and Obsolescence a Part of the Production Process.** It is important to know the meanings of these two terms and their significance. It is far more important for an understanding of the basic principles of production to realize that depreciation and obsolescence of operating machines are nothing more or less than the conversion of fixed assets into finished product. This is a concept which might, upon occasion, prove of value to the financially minded.

**6. Importance of the Rate of Depreciation and Obsolescence.** A major problem of the manufacturing executive is to keep his costs of production low. Frequently some of his largest costs are those which arise from the utilization of machines in processing. These costs include depreciation, obsolescence, repair, maintenance, taxes, insurance, and interest. Depreciation and obsolescence assume major proportions in this list. Under such circumstances much executive attention is given to the rate at which machines are converted into finished product. If obsolescence is a large item of cost, the more rapid the rate of conversion of fixed into current assets the better. In other words, the manager will wish the machine to depreciate, to wear out, as quickly as possible—provided that the wearing out is actually a conversion of the machine into marketable product.

Even when obsolescence is not an important element of cost, it may be desirable to depreciate a machine by productive wear quickly. When wage rates are relatively high and output is in proportion to the speed of the machine, obviously the more rapid the machine operation, the lower will be the labor cost of the operative per unit of product. Much cotton textile equipment in use today was designed at a time when wages were lower than they are now. In consequence, it was built to run at speeds entirely unsuited to modern, high-wage conditions. The low speeds at which these machines have been run have given them a long physical life, but the rate of conversion of these machines into cloth has been far too slow for present-day high wage rates.

It is important to realize that a consideration of machine speeds in relation to wage rates in any specific case must concern itself with many factors; the type of wage payment is an example. Hourly rates and piece rates will have quite different effects. The ability of the operative to influence the rate of output will likewise be important.

The relative slowness with which buildings and equipment are commonly used up in processing makes errors in their selection for production costly. Ordinarily machines and equipment are used up more rapidly than factory buildings. Nevertheless, in making new installations or replacements, consideration must be given to trends within the particular industry involved, effects of cyclical swings in business, seasonal fluctuations in volume, technical progress, and many similar influences in addition to the usual consideration of immediate cost to produce with the new equipment as compared with the old.

**7. Plant Layout Types.** Proper plant location, advantageous site, and suitable equipment are important business considerations of the industrial executive. In operation, the combination of these factors should be such as to make possible plant and machine layout which will ensure rapid and economical process flow and low labor, inventory, and supervision costs. Plant layouts are of two general types, namely, line and functional. Neither of these types is commonly found in pure form. Most plants incorporate both in some degree with emphasis placed on one or the other. Strictly functional layout is less rare than strictly line type.

**8. Functional Layout.** A plant is said to have a functional layout when each type of operation is performed in a separate department on all types of product. For example, consider a factory manufacturing taps, drills, reamers, and milling cutters. All these types of tools have four principal operations in common, *i.e.*, they are all turned, milled, heat-treated, and ground. For a functional layout, therefore, the factory would have a turning department, a milling department, a heat-treating department, and a grinding department, through each of which all four types of product would pass.

**9. Line Layout.** A plant is said to have a line layout when each type of operation is performed in such sequence as to require no backtracking or deviation of material. For a line layout in the factory manufacturing taps, drills, reamers, and milling cutters there would be a reamer department made up of groups of machinery devoted entirely to work on reamers. A group of lathes to turn reamer blanks would be followed by milling machines to square the shanks and others to mill the flutes, then hardening and tempering furnaces continuously maintaining the correct heats for reamers, and lastly, grinding machines to do the finishing. Other groups of machinery would be set up in a similar manner for the other products. This line layout would thus comprise a tap department, a drill department, a reamer department, and a milling cutter department.

**10. Development of the Simonds Saw and Steel Company.** In general the plants of the Simonds Saw and Steel Company were laid out functionally. In part this had been the result of years of development and growth.

The company was founded in Fitchburg, Massachusetts, in 1832, for the manufacture of mowing-machine knives. It was managed and controlled by the Simonds family from the first.

From time to time new lines of product were added, and during 1905 and 1906 a new plant was erected on North Street in Fitchburg. The size of this plant was increased as additional production space was required, until it had reached a total of approximately 300,000 square feet of floor space. The following items were the principal products of the North Street plant:

| | |
|---|---|
| Solid tooth circular wood saws | Band knives |
| Inserted tooth circular wood saws | Circular cutters |
| Solid tooth circular metal saws | Planer knives |
| Inserted tooth circular metal saws | Paper knives |
| Dado saws | Hog knives |
| Planer saws | Veneer knives |
| Saw bits and shanks | Tobacco knives |
| Narrow band saws | Printers' steel rules |

In 1892 the management, realizing that most of its customers for wide band and crosscut saws were located in the northern and southern central states, had opened a factory in Chicago for the manufacture of those products. This was considered a more desirable location than Fitchburg for supplying the lumbering interests in Louisiana, Mississippi, Wisconsin, and Minnesota. Production of these items in Fitchburg was discontinued at that time.

In 1905 the Fitchburg File Company had been purchased by the Simonds Saw and Steel Company. The product of the Fitchburg File Company, files and hack saws, combined well with the company's other lines from a distribution point of view. In addition, the Simonds Saw and Steel Company was a large user of files and felt that it was more economical to make them than to buy them.

**11. Methods of Distribution.** The products of the Simonds Saw and Steel Company were distributed directly by the factories and by branch offices located at various points throughout the United States and Canada. Salesmen worked from these branch offices and sold directly to consumers as well as to dealers. Several small shops for the repair and servicing of saws were maintained at strategic points in connection with the branch offices. These shops were equipped to make up an occasional circular saw from hardened blanks when special service was required. Their principal work, however, was refitting and retensioning saws returned for that purpose by the customer. A complete manufacturing branch plant was maintained in Montreal.

**12. Seasonal Aspects of the Business.** Wood saws were a decidedly seasonal product, being in greatest demand during the winter. Metal saws were less seasonal, and the demand for many of the knife lines was unusually even throughout the year. The complete Simonds line, therefore, was not badly balanced, although some slackening in production was usual during the summer months.

**13. The Existing Plant Layout.** The North Street plant in Fitchburg was the largest of the company's plants, and its layout and organization were typical of the condition which obtained in the others. This plant was laid out in general along functional lines. It had a heat-treating department, where the whole product was hardened and tempered; a milling department, where most of the milling machine work was done; a smithing and straightening department, where all types of saws were tensioned and blocked and where knives were straightened; and several other departments devoted to one or two functions applying to several of the products. Additions of new products from time to time had complicated the organization, and, in several cases, parallel departments had been set up to perform the same type of operation on newly added lines of product. For example, one grinding department finished circular wood saws and large circular metal saws, whereas another grinding department finished small metal saws, and a third department finished knives. With the gradual growth of the plant and increase in product lines, it had become difficult to avoid these duplications in departments.

Another complication arose through the tendency of nearly all foremen to acquire as much responsibility as possible by adding allied operations to their departments. This tendency had been combated to a large extent, but there had grown up, nevertheless, a few instances where departments with one main function included several varying side lines.

**14. Objections to Existing Layout.** As a result of this plant layout, the management was faced with increasing production difficulties as volume of business grew. It was impossible to

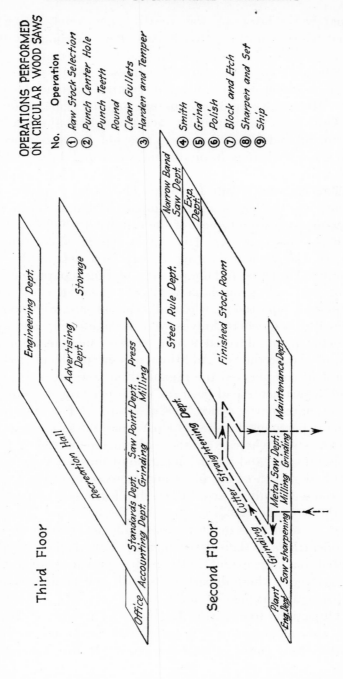

OPERATIONS PERFORMED
ON CIRCULAR WOOD SAWS

No.    Operation

① Raw Stock Selection
② Punch Center Hole
   Punch Teeth
   Round
   Clean Gullets
③ Harden and Temper

④ Smith
⑤ Grind
⑥ Polish
⑦ Block and Etch
⑧ Sharpen and Set
⑨ Ship

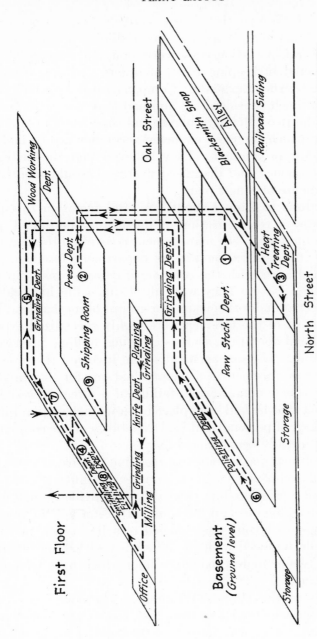

EXHIBIT 1. SIMONDS SAW AND STEEL COMPANY. DIAGRAM TO SHOW THE EFFECT OF FUNCTIONAL DEPARTMENTS IN THE OLD PLANT ON PROCESS FLOW OF CIRCULAR WOOD SAWS.

route material through the shop effectively because successive operations were widely separated (see Exhibit 1, pages 312 and 313). Shop transportation costs were high, and much difficulty was encountered in keeping track of orders. All these factors added to the overhead expense. Company executives had given this problem much consideration and had tentatively decided to consolidate the two Fitchburg plants and the Chicago plant in a new building which company engineers recommended be laid out for straight-line production. They believed that the increased production efficiency and decreased overhead would more than offset the expense of a new plant.

**15. Objections to Line Layout.** A vital factor in this plan was the necessary reorganization of the factory personnel, particularly the foremen. The management recognized the fact that the heart of its organization was its department foremen. All these men had been with the company for many years, in two cases more than forty. They were all of unusually high caliber and had collected under them superior groups of mechanics. Unfortunately most of the foremen were highly specialized experts in one functional operation, such as grinding, milling, presswork, or heat-treating. The management's plan involved the problem of utilizing these foremen in a factory laid out for line production. Under a new organization, failure of a foreman would be due to the fact that he had been placed in a wrong position rather than to any lack of personal ability. Capability of the company's foremen had already been proved by years of trial.

Under the functional layout, one machine was usually used to perform similar operations on a number of different lines of product. One type of product alone did not provide enough work to keep the machine busy all the time. Therefore, if the present functional type of layout was changed to a line type, the management would be faced with the possibility of having identical machines in two or more production lines which were busy only part of the time.

**16. Details of the Proposed Layout.** The company's engineers had proposed a layout wherein the product was to flow from the raw material storage at one end of the building to the finished stock storage at the other. Production was to be carried on in seven lines comprising the entire output (file, hack saw, saw point, knife, circular wood saw, circular metal saw, and band saw), and progress of work was to be assisted as far as possible by automatic conveyors.

Exhibit 2, pages 316 and 317, shows the proposed machine layout of the new plant. Exhibit 3, pages 318 and 319, groups the machinery shown in Exhibit 2 into sections within which machines perform similar operations, and indicates flow of the seven production lines through these sections.

**17. Description of the New Building.** The layout proposed was to be housed in a one-story building 360 by 560 feet, with no partitions. The building was without windows of any sort. The lighting fixtures were a new development of the General Electric Company, combining the mercury-vapor arc of the Cooper-Hewitt with large incandescent lamps. The effect produced was that of sunlight. Temperature and humidity were regulated by means of air washers and steam coils through which currents of fresh air were circulated by large ventilating fans. This apparatus could be controlled to give uniform temperature and humidity at all times both in winter and in summer. A roof of sound-absorbing material and possibly later installation of sound-absorbing baffles around the noisest machines were expected to deaden atmospheric vibrations to such an extent as to permit ordinary conversation in any part of the plant. Roof ventilators, ventilating curtains in the roof trusses, and insulated hoods connected with the flue gas exhaust system were expected to make the area occupied by the heat-treating equipment as comfortable as any other part of the plant.

An observation walk was installed in the building. It was raised 11 feet above the working floor and made a complete circuit of the room at a distance of 90 feet from the walls. This permitted the inspection of the plant by supervisors and visitors without in any way hindering production. Railroad sidetracks were built to the delivery and discharge doors at the ends of the building.

It was the management's purpose to produce uniformly agreeable working conditions and, in return, to demand a high degree of production efficiency from its workmen.

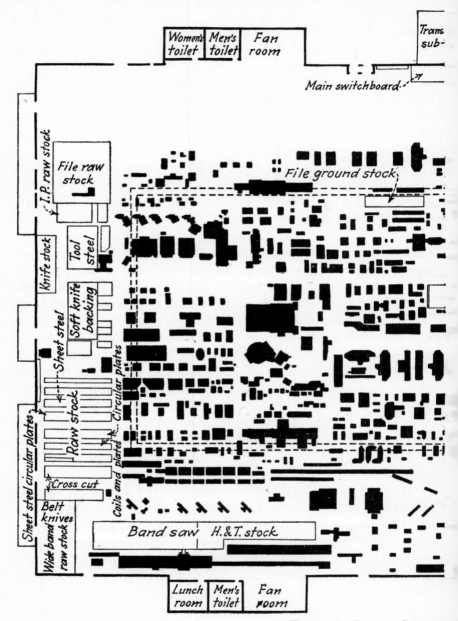

Exhibit 2.  Simonds Saw and

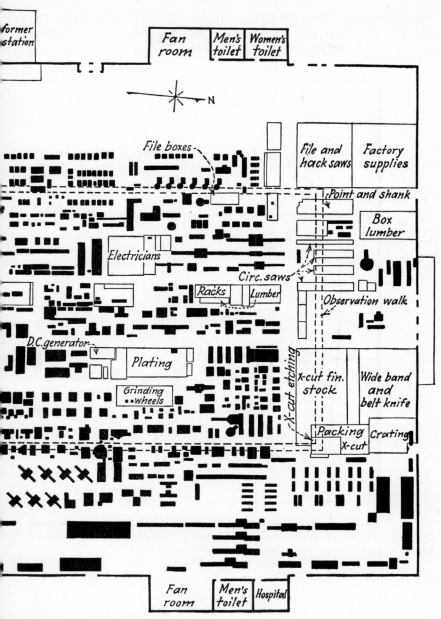

STEEL COMPANY. NEW PLANT LAYOUT.

**18. Effect of Two-shift Operation.** Company officials expected to operate the new plant on the basis of 80 production hours a week. There would be two eight-hour shifts a day, five

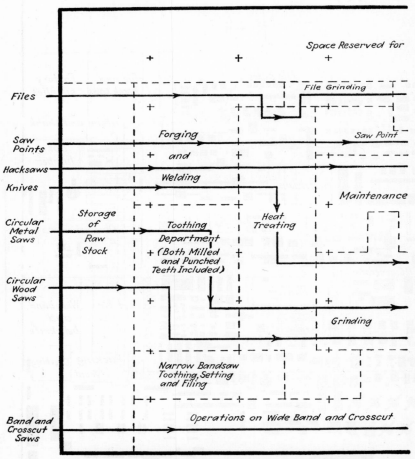

EXHIBIT 3. SIMONDS SAW AND STEEL COMPANY. DIAGRAM TO SHOW PROPOSED LINES OF PRODUCT THROUGH THESE MACHINE GROUPINGS.

days a week. The Fitchburg plants were operated 50 hours a week, and since the object of the change was to increase operating efficiency rather than to increase the volume of production, the more intensive utilization of the new plant would make it possible to eliminate much of the company's existing equipment.

It was urged that greater production efficiency of the new line
layout would further reduce the equipment necessary to maintain output.

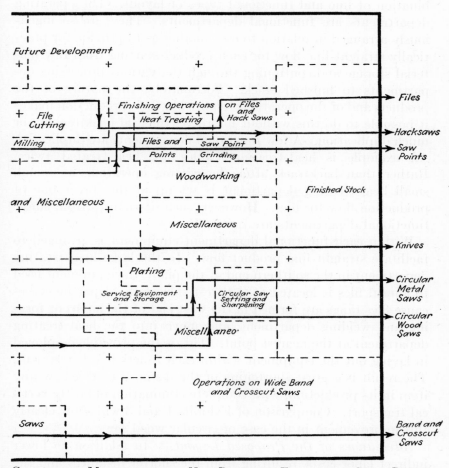

GROUPINGS OF MACHINES IN THE NEW PLANT AND FLOW OF THE SEVEN PRINCIPAL

**19. Summary and Conclusions.** *What Should Have Been
Done.* If the production carried on in the three Simonds Saw and
Steel Company plants was to be concentrated in one new plant, it
would seem desirable to adopt the principle of the proposed new
layout shown in Exhibits 2 and 3. Substantial advantages would

be gained, and questionable aspects of the plan could be foreseen and probably eliminated or provided against.

*Nature of the Proposed Plan.*  The plan as proposed is a combination of line and functional types of layout.  The operating departments are functional departments.  They are so ingeniously arranged in relation to one another as to provide for practically straight-line flow for each product starting from raw material storage and continuing through the various processing departments to finished stock.  Fortunately, the nature of the products and of the operations required in their production makes it possible to do this without interdepartmental backtracking or much duplication.  A few functional departments are duplicated.  An example is heat-treating.  Files are heat-treated twice.  Rather than backtrack after the cutting operation, a second, small heat-treating department is set up in the direct line of production flow for files.  However, such departures from single functional departments are rare.

Within each functional department equipment is arranged to facilitate straight-line product flow.  In the large heat-treating department in the southern end of the plant, the equipment used to anneal files is located at the west side of the department because files tangs are formed in the west end of the adjacent forging and welding department, and move into the heat-treating department at the nearest point.  This is the principle employed in laying out the equipment within each functional department.  The result is a great shortening of the distance traveled by any item in its production, with complete elimination of costly vertical transport.  Comparison of Exhibits 1 and 3 will show clearly this improvement in the case of circular wood saws.

*Advantages of the Proposed Layout.*  In addition to lower indirect labor costs, resulting from the shorter distances and the possibility of using conveyor equipment, the proposed layout presents other substantial advantages.  Shorter transport would shorten the time required to produce an item and therefore would lessen work-in-process inventory and make more rapid the turnover of capital invested in work in process.  Supervision would be easier because routing is largely predetermined by the new layout, and less moving instruction and follow-up of orders in process would be required. This should enable the company to make deliveries more quickly and surely, for the time required to process an order would be more accurately known. Finished goods inventories could be safely reduced because of the shortening of processing time and greater accuracy of forecasting it. The proposed layout lessens the possibility for orders to become lost in process or for workers to cover up defective work. Decrease in work-in-process inventories and shorter transportation make it possible to reduce floor space without restricting output capacity. This would result in less plant depreciation and lower costs of heat and light, insurance, taxes, maintenance, and watchman service. These gains will be intensified by the change from one to two operating shifts. Two-shift operation also cuts down the amount of equipment required and operating and ownership costs.

The particular layout devised tends to gain many of the advantages of line layout without sacrificing certain of the desirable features of the old functional arrangement. One of the greatest gains from functional organization is the skill it engenders in both workmen and foremen. Simonds Saw and Steel Company executives recognized the importance of retaining the skills built up in the old plant. The proposed layout seems to make this possible. Workers will be doing the same jobs that they have done. Foremen will be called upon to perform no substantially new tasks of supervision. This characteristic of the proposed layout is evidence of the thoroughness and care with which company engineers have devised a plan suited to the needs and characteristics of the situation it was designed to meet.

*Questionable Aspects of the Proposed Layout.* The plan does not entirely escape adverse criticism. Line layout tends to be inflexible. It is best suited to situations where there is little change in products turned out or variation in volume of output. When a company is subject to seasonal or cyclical ups and downs in the rate of operation, line layout tends to make for drastic fluctuation in the cost of producing a single unit of output. In other words, line layout is inflexible as to accommodation to volume change. When production for stock is carried on to keep line production costs down during slack periods, inventory costs and risks increase.  When production for stock is not deemed wise, idleness costs increase.  The same is true to a lesser degree of functional layout, but the characteristically lower investment in equipment in the functional department and the ability to expand and contract the work force more readily tend to make functional layout more responsive to volume shifts.

Likewise, the functional department is more adaptable to change in product design and type.  Machines are more likely to be usable for a number of purposes.  Their arrangement bears no close relation to any one product.  Labor is more likely to be able to operate different types of machines or to do a variety of jobs on any one piece of equipment.  The functional department is usually far more able to change from the making of one product to the making of a substantially different one, or to effect quickly and inexpensively changes called for by alterations in product design.

Usually it is not difficult to increase the capacity of a plant which is made up of functional departments.  New machines can be readily added and increased floor space arranged.  It is far more difficult to increase the capacity of a line production plant. In line processing, the capacity of each machine must be related to the capacities of every other machine on the line.  A line can be no faster than its slowest unit.  To increase the output of the line, various alterations must usually be made.  Of course, it is possible that the only change required would be an increase in the speed of every unit in the line.  Such adaptability is rare, however.  Usually it will involve a combination of many things: some machines will be run faster; some machines will be replaced by machines of greater capacity; some operations will be brought up to the new rate by duplicating the equipment at that point. Inevitably the whole layout will have to be readjusted.  This is obviously a more difficult and costly procedure than the relatively simple additions of machines and floor space for functional departments.

All these generalizations apply to some extent to the Simonds Saw and Steel Company situation.  In the main, the difficulties have been foreseen and protection provided in the recommended plan.  Within each department there would be more of functional

layout than of strictly line layout. Volume change would therefore be accommodated to a considerble degree without incurring
high costs of production. If it was desirable to expand capacity,
it could be done within the departments in much the way that
functional departments usually expand. A limiting factor here,
however, might be difficulty in obtaining the needed additional
floor space without upsetting interdepartmental location relationships.

Because the departments in the proposed plan would be essentially functional, reasonable changes in product design could
be accomplished without great difficulty. New sizes and designs
of files could be readily introduced and old items dropped without
substantially disturbing layout.

The plan makes some provision for addition of entirely new
products in the unused space along the west side of the building.
Expansion or change of this nature would be definitely restricted,
however.

Analysis of the foreseeable requirements of this company
would lead one to the conclusion that as far as layout is concerned the proposed plan provides for essential flexibility. The
carefully interrelated arrangement of departments in terms of
the process sequences of the various products would be a limitation. However, the company did not make a style product, or
a product which was likely to be subject to rapid technological
change. It would seem reasonable to conclude, therefore, that
the gains from superior layout would fully justify the risks inherent in the questionable aspects of the proposed plan.

*Problems Growing Out of the Proposal.* One must not over-
look the fact that the proposed changes call for large initial out-
lays of money. Just what weight this should carry in making a
decision in this case cannot be determined here; requisite information is not available. It is not likely, however, that so obviously important a matter would be overlooked.

The new layout would give rise to certain supervision problems.
A foreman's job would be just what it was before, with one difference. The scheduling of work into and out of the department
would no longer be a responsibility of the functional department
foreman. To secure the gains inherent in the proposed layout,

centralized authority for scheduling would be required. This is because in most instances several products would go through each operating department. If the work is to flow smoothly along the lines planned, someone with a knowledge more extensive than that of any one departmental foreman would have to have the authority to say what should be done in each department and when each job should be completed. Such centralization of scheduling impinges on the authority exercised by the departmental foreman under the old layout. This change is imperative and while it may not seem radical it might well prove difficult for some foremen to adjust themselves to the new status. In this one respect the foreman no longer would plan. His job would be to execute the orders of a central planning department. It might be more of a mental wrench than offhand judgment would anticipate. Definitely, this change in supervision must be worked out. Definitely, it should be expected that some difficulty in adjustment of foremen to the change will result.

*Conclusions.* The layout proposed for the new plant is superior to that of the old. It is superior to either a pure functional or pure line layout for this company. It should result in substantial production economies. It involves certain risks. It gives rise to problems which must be solved if the gains inherent in the plan are to be realized. Considering the nature of this company's product, the character of its demand, and the types of process involved, it would seem desirable to adopt, at least in principle, the plan devised by company engineers.

*Relation of the Process to Plant Layout.* The process of manufacture largely governs layout. In a plant which specializes in the continuous production of a few standard products, it is natural that machine groupings should be of the direct line type. When a large and diverse line of products is intermittently manufactured, the advantages of this type of organization are more than offset by its weaknesses, and the functional type of layout seems best fitted to process requirements.

*The Efficiency of Straight-line Layout.* Given suitable processing conditions, straight-line layout has many advantages. There is a tendency for work to proceed rapidly from operation to operation, with the result that the total time required for production is lessened and investment in work in process is lowered. The planning of work schedules and the movement of work from operation to operation are facilitated. Once a product is started at the beginning of the line, it tends to progress without interruption from operation to operation, and without the supervisory attention required in the functionally arranged plant. The straight-line method also has the advantage of eliminating backtracking of work in process and rehandling of worked materials. It is always costly for a product to retrace its path during the process of production, and it is likewise expensive to handle and rehandle materials and work in process. The straight-line type of setup often utilizes many automatic materials handling devices, such as gravity and power conveyors, which tend to reduce handling costs to a minimum. The extent to which straight-line layout facilitates the use of handling equipment makes it economical of floor space, a saving which comes through elimination of the wide aisles required for hand trucking and storage space at the machines. Once a direct line layout is properly effected, bottlenecks do not develop, and the bottleneck is one of the major problems of the plant organized into functional departments. One further advantage of direct line layout should be mentioned. It is common practice so to lay out and locate production lines that the final operation on a part occurs in close proximity to the point at which the part enters into the assembly process. This yields additional savings in low inventory, handling, and supervision costs. The development of the flexible overhead monorail, however, has brought physically separated points within a plant into close contact so as to lessen greatly the need for laying out production lines in such manner that they empty directly into the assembly flow.

*Objections to Straight-line Layout.* The most unsatisfactory characteristic of direct line layout is its relative inflexibility. Changes in product necessitate change in the layout of production lines. Even minor changes in design, improvement in methods of processing, or changes in raw materials used may require a rather complete change in machine arrangement. Unless production volume between changes is relatively large, such alterations are expensive.

Fluctuations in the rate of production likewise make line manufacture costly. When equipment is not occupied in producing the particular part or product for which it is laid out, it is idle. Its layout makes it essentially a special-purpose device, and as such it is subject to all the objections to specialized equipment for purposes of diversified manufacture.

*Advantages of Functional Layout.* The functional type of equipment arrangement is weak where the line type is strong and strong where the line type is weak. It adjusts itself to change in product and design of parts and in volume much more readily than does the line type. Often a higher percentage of productive machine operating time is obtained. Where the output is varied, it is often possible to accomplish a certain volume of finished work with less investment in equipment. Sometimes skilled workers can be utilized to better advantage, and in the opinion of many foremen, skill is likely to be greater and to increase in the functional department.

*Disadvantages of Functional Layout.* At the same time, the functional department possesses certain definite weaknesses. Control is more difficult, and supervision inside and outside the department is more costly. The work of each department and of each man and machine within each department must be planned and supervised for every hour of every day. Delays are much more frequent, and predetermination of results, though usually possible, is difficult and therefore costly. In addition, the functional department possesses little of the machine-pacing incentive to labor productivity which is frequently found in the line type. Materials and work in process are commonly moved from machine to machine, from operation to operation, by hand or by truck. Thus transport is relatively costly and much more space is required for aisles and temporary storage.

In brief, one may say that line type of layout has the advantage of high productivity with little supervision at low cost of operation—given suitable conditions. Functional layout has the distinct advantages of relatively great adaptability to change and a high degree of machine utilization even under rapidly varying conditions.

## QUESTIONS

1. What is the so-called line type of plant layout?

2. What are its advantages?

3. Why is it desirable to keep inventory of work in process at a low level?

4. What are the objections to the line type of layout?

5. Under what conditions is the line type of layout likely to result in low costs of operation?

6. Explain the functional type of plant layout.

7. What are its strong points?

8. What are its weaknesses?

9. Under what conditions is functional layout likely to result in low costs of operation?

10. How would you characterize the layout proposed for the Simonds Saw and Steel Company?

11. In what respects is it superior to the old layout?

12. Has it any weaknesses, objections, or dangers?

13. Do you think the company should adopt the proposed layout?

14. Under what circumstances is the type of combined line and functional layout sound?

15. What is depreciation? Obsolescence?

16. What is the business significance of depreciation and obsolescence?

## CADILLAC MOTOR CAR COMPANY (A)

In view of the success of experimental departures from commonly accepted ideas regarding plant layout, executives of the Cadillac Motor Car Company decided to rearrange the equipment in the connecting-rod department.

The production of a Cadillac connecting rod involved 63 machining operations, and 155 machines were in use within the department. These machines were laid out for line production. Exhibit 1, on page 329, shows the arrangement of one group of 12 of these machines on the production line. These 12 machines performed four operations, designated in the diagram as operations 15, 16, 17, and 18. Machines and operations designated as 16 and 18 were similar.

Three types of machines were included in this group, and four machines of each type were required to effect the desired output. The nature of the job was such that the operations could be performed in almost any desired sequence.

A roller conveyor between the two lines of machines supplied parts to each of the 12 workers on the line. This conveyor aided transportation but made it necessary for workers to turn completely around in order to secure or deliver material. Machine time computed by time-study men disclosed the fact that a worker could easily operate two machines performing similar operations if materials handling time was reduced. Such a situation could be brought about by rearranging machinery so that a minimum of effort was required to secure and deliver material. Time-study men and layout engineers were hampered by the fact that no additional space could be allowed the department.

Prepare an improved layout for the connecting-rod line of the Cadillac Motor Car Company. Tracing templates, one for each

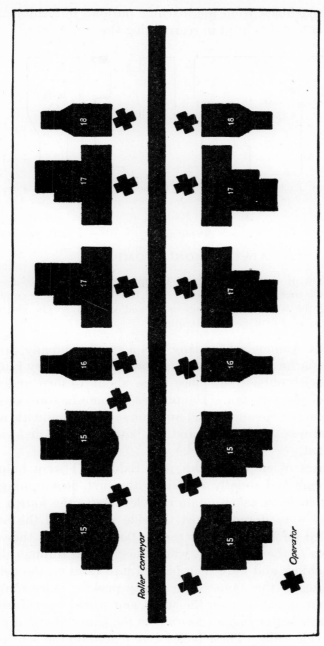

EXHIBIT 1. CADILLAC MOTOR CAR COMPANY. ARRANGEMENT OF GROUP OF 12 MACHINES ON THE CONNECTING-ROD LINE.

of the 12 machines, from the machine outlines in Exhibit 2, below, will be found helpful in rearranging the equipment.

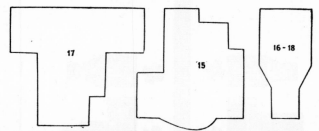

17

15

16 - 18

EXHIBIT 2.   CADILLAC MOTOR CAR COMPANY.   MACHINE OUTLINES.

## Problem 31

### AJAX AMMONIA COMPANY

The plant of the Ajax Ammonia Company was seriously congested. Inefficient layout, unused equipment, and lack of "plant housekeeping" prevented the work from flowing easily and smoothly. The situation called for careful management attention.

The Ajax Ammonia Company was a small company producing ammonia for household use. It owned a four-story building and employed, outside the office force, about 15 men under the direction of one foreman. The process of manufacture consisted of the mixing of chemicals and an ammonia solution with water. This liquid was then bottled and the bottles labeled and packed for shipment.

The crates of empty bottles (see Exhibit 1) were unloaded from the cars and usually stored on the first floor temporarily until they could be taken up on the elevator to the fourth floor. There they were stored against the side walls, until the bottles were needed for filling. After the bottles were filled, they were taken down to the third floor, where they passed through the labeling machines and were then packed into cases on the benches in the center of the room. The empty packing cases were unloaded from auto trucks on the street and stored temporarily on the first floor before being taken up to the third floor and placed along the side walls. These boxes were placed on the benches for packing the bottles as needed, and, after the covers had been nailed on, the full cases were piled alongside the benches, ready to be shipped. The water was run into the tanks through pipes, and the ammonia was added, when needed, by a pump. The routing, therefore, was very simple.

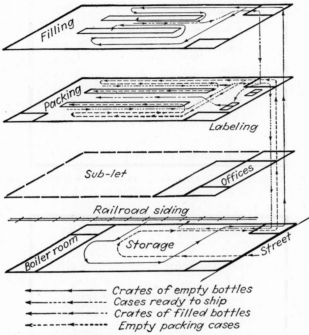

EXHIBIT 1. AJAX AMMONIA COMPANY. LAYOUT OF PLANT.

Crates of empty bottles (see Exhibit 2) were stacked against the walls in places that were difficult of access, and broken bottles and refuse of all kinds were piled high in front of the window. Two good bottling machines were set in line, end to end, as shown. Ventilation was poor, and men were unable to work on the bottling machines for more than three or four months at a time because of the effect of ammonia fumes on the lungs. The labor turnover was consequently very high. After the bottles were filled and corked, they were taken down the elevator on trucks. Breakage resulting from rough handling was heavy. Two men bottled the liquid, another corked the bottles, while a fourth was used frequently to bring up cases of empty bottles and to sort out the broken glass.

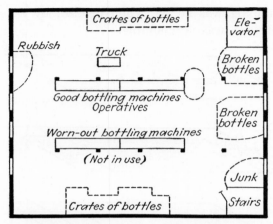

EXHIBIT 2. AJAX AMMONIA COMPANY. DETAIL OF FOURTH FLOOR LAYOUT.

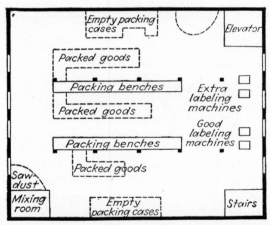

EXHIBIT 3. AJAX AMMONIA COMPANY. DETAIL OF THIRD FLOOR LAYOUT.

The filled bottles came down from the fourth floor (see Exhibit 3) in crates. They were run through the labeling machines, replaced in the same crates, and set on the floor near the machines. The packers then walked down the aisle between the packing benches, picked out a half-dozen bottles, and walked back to put them in the packing cases. This operation was repeated until all the bottles were packed. Sawdust was then scattered over the bottles, the covers to the cases were nailed on, and the packed goods were moved off the benches. An obsolete set of labeling machines stood near the elevator. Work frequently was congested at the elevator, and the process of manufacture was often delayed because the elevator was being used to bring up empty bottles or packing cases when bottled goods were waiting to be taken down to the next floor for labeling and packing.

## QUESTIONS

1. Prepare an improved layout for this plant.
2. Are there other suggestions you would make to the management of this company?

### Problem 32

### THE N-W MACHINE COMPANY

The N-W Machine Company manufactured machines. The oldest and principal product of the company was a turret lathe, which had been invented in 1892 and which had been the only product of the company from 1892 to 1905. A new design of this lathe and additional sizes of the old design were introduced in 1905. By 1948 an automatic lathe and an automatic die opener had been added to the line. In addition to the manufacture of machines, the company was engaged in repair and special work related to the service of machines that had been installed in the shops of customers.

The company had devoted considerable effort to the increase of speeds and feeds, to the improvement in methods of doing the work and controlling it, and to other developments of scientific management. The net result of several years' effort was decidedly profitable. The total machining time and total direct labor cost of the product were noticeably reduced and, in addition, the earnings of the men were considerably increased.

The management next became concerned about the overhead

costs. With only a moderate increase in output there had been
a noticeable increase in the number of foremen, functional and
others, and a great increase in the amount of clerical work that
they were called upon to do. The general statistics of the plant
showed that the direct labor cost of the product was very small,
as had been hoped, that the material cost was much higher, and
that the manufacturing overhead was the largest of all. This
overhead was so large that, even with a moderate selling expense,
profit was doubtful.

The overhead cost had not grown to its present dimensions
suddenly or through carelessness. It was the result of slow ac-
cretions of small expenses, each added to take care of some real
difficulty in management in what appeared at the time to be
the simplest and least expensive way. An examination of the
various details did not indicate that individual treatment could
be improved. It was decided, therefore, that a complete rearrangement of all the elements of the business was necessary so
that difficulties in management could be avoided.

One difficulty had arisen because of the arrangement of the
shop. The shop was arranged by process. All milling was done
in a milling department, all drilling in a drilling department, and
all turning in a lathe department. By specializing in a given
operation, the foreman and workman became highly skilled in
that work and could do it more cheaply than if they were concerned with a wider range of operations. The variation in design of the product made it impossible to arrange the machines
in a continuous line. Constant movement of work from department to department, with its consequent slowing up of the work
flow, however, had brought division of responsibility, difficulties
of control, and increased overhead expenses.

The manufacture of turret lathes was divided into two classes
of work: the manufacture of new machines and a rather large
service business in the supply of replacement parts for the machines now in the users' hands. One of the most perplexing difficulties had arisen in the control of the special and repair work
related to the service business. Repair orders, both for customers and for the tools, fixtures, and special machines used by

the company in production, were irregular and unpredictable. New machines were produced at the rate of 75 per month.

A reorganization was proposed whereby the products were segregated in manufacture. The shop was to be rearranged on a basis of departments by products. Arranging the department by product meant that an individual piece or part would stay in a single department until it was completely finished and ready for assembly. Such a department might be arranged to complete all parts of a similar nature, no matter where found in a machine, or all parts of whatever nature belonging to a given assembly unit of the machine. Both arrangements are to be found in automobile manufacture, where departmentalization by product is the rule in the larger and more successful shops.

In the turret lathe shop, it was decided to departmentalize primarily on the basis of the unit assembly, and only secondarily by similarity of parts. This arrangement was expected to prove strongest where the layout by process was weakest. Turret lathes were built in three styles: 2¼-inch, 3-inch, and double-spindle. These machines were designed on the same general plan, and many of the parts of the 2¼-inch and 3-inch styles interchanged, but this was not true to any extent of the latest design, the double-spindle turret lathe.

Major castings entering into the assembly of a turret lathe were headstocks, spindles, beds, turret slides, and turrets. Certain parts for a 2¼-inch lathe, with its higher spindle speed and less powerful drive, were lighter than those for the 3-inch lathe, and specialized manufacturing equipment was necessary to care for this difference in weight.

The space available was 275 feet long by 100 feet wide (as shown in Exhibit 1), divided by columns lengthwise into 10-foot aisles and crosswise into 25-foot bays. The width of shop and width of cross bays had been satisfactory under the previous arrangement. The building was of steel-frame, saw-tooth roof construction, and was fireproof.

Exhibit 1 shows the new arrangement. Incoming material passed north up a long aisle extending the full length of the shop. In the aisle on the left, next to the west wall, were the bins for raw material storage. The center of the shop was occupied by

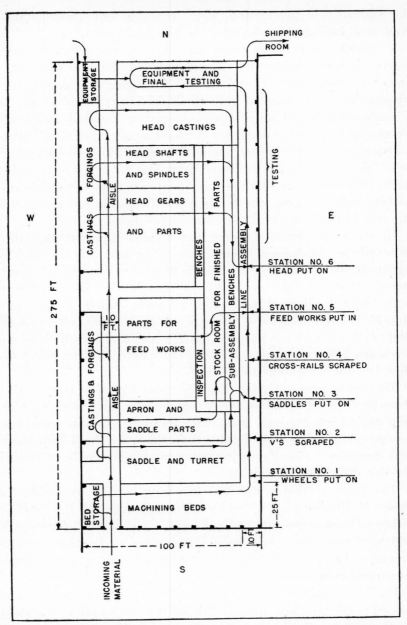

EXHIBIT 1. THE N-W MACHINE COMPANY. LAYOUT FOR TURRET LATHE SHOP.

the various manufacturing departments, with the equipment and final testing department at the north end. In successive aisles, toward the east, and running for practically the full length of the manufacturing section, were the inspection benches, storage of finished parts, subassemblies, and line assembly. From the line assembly the finished machines detoured into the bay for equipment and final testing and thence out into the painting and shipping room.

The flow of material was from the southwest corner north to the appropriate department, thence directly east across the width of the shop to final inspection and storage, and thence to subassembly and line assembly. The line assembly moved north on the eastern side and out at the northeast.

Castings for the bed were stored at the west of the aisle. They were taken first to an Ingersoll mill, where the pads on the bottom were milled off, after which the bed was turned over and the crossrails milled. The bed then went to the roughing planer, then to the horizontal boring and milling machine, and then to the radial drill. After drilling, the bed went to the finishing planer for removal of the "wind" so that the hand-scraper's job could be one of finishing the surface rather than of removing material. The bed was then mounted on wheels instead of on its regular legs, and was ready to start up the assembly line. The bed machining department was under the supervision of the foreman of the line assembly.

Certain departments and operations could not be included in the rearranged layout. The following processes remained departmentalized: steel storage and cutting off; casting, snagging, cleaning, and filling; painting, boxing, and shipping; automatic screw machining; hardening and heat-treating. This last process caused the main break in the orderly flow of work through the shop.

Be prepared to discuss the desirability of the proposed layout.

# CHAPTER XIV

## POWER

### FOSTER YARN, INC.

**1. Changes in Power Application Help a Company to Meet Changing Business Conditions.**

Foster Yarn, Inc., manufacturer of worsted yarns used for knitting purposes, was experiencing difficulty in maintaining its earning position. Much was done to reduce costs of operation. Among the items of operating expense scrutinized was the cost of power, which the company always had generated. Changes made in supply and application of power brought about substantial economies. Essentially, these changes involved doing away with central steam-engine drives and installing a well-considered combination of individual and group motor drives.

**2. Management's Relation to the Power Problem.** Every factory management faces the problem of providing power for the operation of machinery. The generation, transmission, and application of power have been continuously developed until today they constitute technical problems of great intricacy. In the large plant which uses much power a staff of highly specialized experts is employed to take care of power problems. In the small plant such a specialized technical staff is too costly, and all too frequently the power situation is not given the attention it deserves.

The employment of power technicians does not relieve management of responsibility for considering power problems. The power engineer knows the technique of producing power and applying it to machines and equipment. Usually he can translate these technical considerations into dollars. Often he can make suggestions to the management as to action to be taken in terms of his technical knowledge and cost findings. Such advice is of great value to management and should be regarded and used just as management uses the work of experts in the more familiar fields of accounting, statistics, and product design. Management should not expect the power engineer to have complete grasp of the business implications of power problems. Thus, management should assume the same attitude toward power specialists that has long been held in relations with other specialized technicians. The final decisions on power problems must be made by management. Executives cannot escape this responsibility. They are often better equipped to weigh and judge the short-range and long-range business implications in power supply and application than is the technician who is specialized in the field.

**3. Purpose of This Chapter.** The experience of Foster Yarn, Inc., is included in this text because it is an excellent illustration of the point that the selection of power equipment and its installation has business aspects that call for managerial consideration. No attempt will be made in this chapter to discuss such typical power problems as choice between produced and purchased power, or choice of fuels when a manufacturing company generates its own power. The discussion will attempt to establish two points only, namely, that many power problems are business problems and that as such they are the concern of management.

**4. Foster Yarn, Inc.** As the result of reorganization of an older firm, Foster Yarn, Inc., of Trenton, New Jersey, was incorporated in 1929 with a capitalization of $100,000.[1] The company made a variety of worsted knitting yarns and twists from 10-count to 30-count. The company also bought 300-denier rayon yarn, which it used in combination with yarns made from wool. The products were marketed direct. The company had 100 employees.

**5. Plant Layout and Power Application.** Steam to supply the company's heat, process, and power needs was generated at 115 pounds in an old boiler which was rapidly decreasing in efficiency. Power was supplied by a Corliss engine through a main drive shaft and take-off belts. A complicated and inefficient rope drive ran from the main drive shaft on the first floor to the scouring department, and belts led to main shafts on the

---

[1] Davison's *Textile Blue Book,* July, 1932.

second floor, from which there also were take-off belts.   Layout of equipment, together with shaft and belt drives, is shown for the first and second floors in Exhibits 1 and 3.

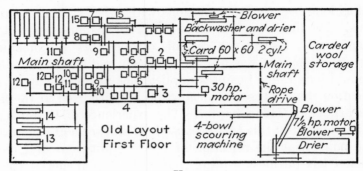

Key

1. Three single-head gill boxes, after backwasher.
2. Three single-head gill boxes, second process.
3. One punch box.
4. Three Noble combs, double dobber motion.
5. Three single-head gill boxes, first process after combing.
6. Three single-head open gill boxes, second process after combing.
7. Two double-head open gill boxes, third process after combing.
8. Two double-head open gill boxes, fourth process after combing.
9. Three 2-spindle open gill boxes, first process in drawing.
10. Two 4-spindle drawing boxes, second process in drawing.
11. Two 6-spindle drawing boxes, third process in drawing.
12. Four 10-spindle drawing boxes, fourth process in drawing.
13. Two 24-spindle reducers, fifth process in drawing.
14. Two 36-spindle reducers, sixth process in drawing.
15. Six 36-spindle finishers and two 100-spindle finishers.

EXHIBIT 1.   FOSTER YARN, INC.

**6. Objections to the Old Power Situation.**   Power-transmission maintenance costs were high.   Shaft bearings were not antifriction and therefore had to be lubricated at least once a week. The 3½-inch, 2-ply leather belts required frequent adjustment, and, in spite of every effort for proper maintenance, slippage occurred.   On damp days it was not uncommon to find variations of 15 to 20 revolutions per minute, which at the spindles resulted in discrepancies of 150 to 200 revolutions per minute. Variation in spindle speed was a serious matter, since uniform speeds were essential to high quality of output.   A soft yarn called for a certain spindle speed, while a hard yarn needed an equally definite though higher speed. Regulation of machine speeds was a matter constantly requiring the attention of foremen.

Whenever a change was made in the type of yarn being spun, a troublesome alteration in speed of drives was necessary. If a spinning frame had been running on 2-ply 20-count yarn and a change to 2-ply 16-count yarn was required, it was necessary

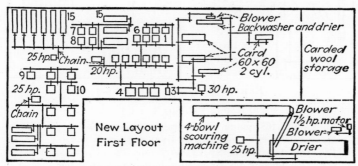

Note: The numbers in the Key to Exhibit 1 apply to Exhibit 2 except in the case of some of the regroupings of machines.

EXHIBIT 2. FOSTER YARN, INC.

to shut down all machines on the floor for a half hour while two maintenance men climbed up ladders, removed a heavy split pulley about 38 inches in diameter, and put on another that was equally heavy and hard to handle. With the exception of the particular frame whose speed was to be changed, the floor could then resume operation. On the one frame, however, change in pulley size necessitated change in the length of the 62-foot belt which connected the frame to the main shaft. Adjustment of this belt often took as much as an hour. Under these conditions seven or eight doffs [2] were considered a good day's output.

**7. Effects of Depression on Order Size and Frequency.** One effect of slackened business conditions throughout the industry was a great decrease in the average size of orders and an

[2] A doff is a complete replacement of full spindles on a frame with empty spindles, and necessitates adjustment of spindle speeds only when a change in type or size of yarn is made.

increase in the number of orders. It had become common for customers who formerly had ordered in 500-pound lots to reduce purchases to 50-pound lots. Decrease in total volume of

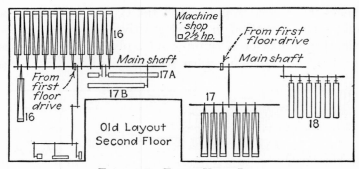

EXHIBIT 3. FOSTER YARN, INC.

Key to Exhibits 3 and 4

16. Twelve 168-spindle cap spinning frames, 3½-inch gauge.
17. Six 160-spindle cap twister frames, 3½-inch gauge.
17A. One 160-spindle cap twister frame, 3½-inch gauge.
17B. One 146-spindle cap twister frame, 4½-inch gauge.
18. Six 50-spool skein reels.

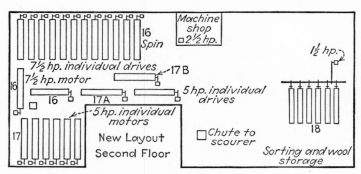

EXHIBIT 4. FOSTER YARN, INC.

orders and shrinkage in order size were critical problems for executives of Foster Yarn, Inc.

**8. Changes in Power Supply and Application.** Remedy for profit shrinkage was sought through reduction of production costs, and intensive consideration was given to all elements of expense. As a result of the study of power cost, the supply and application of power were completely changed at a cost of approximately $8,000. The first change was to stop producing power in favor of purchasing it from an outside producer. The steam-boiler equipment, although obsolete for power purposes, was still used effectively for supplying steam for processing and heating. The line-shaft drive layouts, shown in Exhibits 1 and 3, were scrapped, and in their places carefully considered combinations of group and individual motor drives were installed. Group drive was employed where the types of machinery were such that a number of machines could be operated economically as a group. In Exhibit 2, which shows the new first-floor layout, it will be noted that one 25-horsepower motor drives as a group the scourer, the drier, and the blower that conveys the wool from the scourer to the drier. The scourer and the drier were always operated at the same time, the one operation immediately following the other with the blower conveyor acting as the connecting link. This arrangement was much more economical than the complicated rope drive from the main shaft shown in Exhibit 1. As the individual machines making up this group were never operated singly, little would have been gained by equipping each machine with a motor of its own.

The equipment in the carding and drawing room suggested the arrangement into four groups, shown in Exhibit 2. A 30-horsepower motor drove the four cards and the backwasher. A 20-horsepower motor was used to operate 3 combs, 12 gill boxes, and the punch box. The drawing frames were segregated into two groups, each driven by a 25-horsepower motor.

Most of the second-floor equipment was individually motored, as shown in Exhibit 4. In the new layout there were 14 spinning frames, each of which was equipped with a 7½-horsepower motor. A sample frame had a 5-horsepower motor, and individual 5-horsepower motors drove the twisters. The six 50-spool skein reels were driven as a group, one 1½-horsepower motor being adequate for their operation.

In all cases, group line shafts were chain-driven rather than belt-driven. Motors were equipped with antifriction bearings. Those on the second floor were packed with waste that needed only three oilings a year. First-floor motors were controlled through manually operated compensators. The spinning frames had reduced-voltage primary-resistor control, and full-voltage push-button control was used on the twisters.

**9. Results of the Changes.** Change of speed on the twisters and spinning frames could be accomplished in a few minutes. It involved loosening the motor on its base, sliding the motor forward to release the multiple V-type drive belt, knocking the pulley from the tapered shaft of the motor, slipping on a new pulley of the proper size, replacing the drive belt, sliding back the motor to the point of proper belt tension, and tightening four bolts to hold the motor in proper position. Five to ten minutes was the time required.

The new layouts shown in Exhibit 2 and Exhibit 4 involved a total connected load of about 275 horsepower. With it 9 or 10 doffs per day were obtained. An annual power saving of $2,600 was effected, which, together with other savings, caused the vice-president of Foster Yarn, Inc., to make the statement, "We should not be in business today if we had not made the change."

**10. Summary and Conclusions.** It was not the power saving of $2,600 a year that enabled Foster Yarn, Inc., to stay in business. Far more important was the ability of the company to meet the changed demands made upon it. A period of business uncertainty affected the demand for yarns such as this company made. With the slackening in consumption came another change, namely, orders were smaller. Buyers were hesitant to stock yarns heavily and ordered in small amounts, reordering in small lots whenever demand seemed to justify it. Thus a manufacturer, to retain his share of the total demand, found it necessary to cater to market request for quick shipment of small orders. Price and quality were also of great importance for the manufacturer who was to retain his competitive status during the depression. Executives of Foster Yarn, Inc., were faced with the necessity of producing a high-quality product at low cost in such a way as to be able to make small shipments quickly and frequently.

*How the New Methods of Applying Power Were Superior to the Old.* The methods of applying power that had been in use were not well suited to the new requirements. It took a relatively long time to change speeds at the spindles when a different yarn construction was required. With the trend to small, frequent orders, these changes had to be made more often. Also it was necessary to shut down a large number of machines in order to make a change on one of them. This characteristic tended to waste both machine time and direct labor time.

By installing individual motor drives on each unit that required separate changes, it was possible to shut down one machine alone, and the cost of idle machines and men was nearly eliminated. The method of driving each machine also made it possible to change spindle speeds quickly and at little cost. In this way the characteristically high cost of producing in small lots to fill request orders was kept at a minimum, and the company placed itself in an advantageous position to cater to the new market requirements of quick delivery of small orders at low cost.

The use of individual motors connected to the spinning frames by multiple V-type belts improved the quality of the yarn by making it more uniform. The old driving method resulted in slippage, causing variation in spindle speeds of as much as 200 revolutions per minute. Much of the foremen's time was spent in attempting to keep equipment operating at proper speeds. In spite of all efforts, speeds had varied greatly. The new driving method eliminated this slippage. The foremen were thus relieved from constant watching for variation, and the product was much improved. This improvement in quality was of great importance to the company and, coupled with ability to deliver small orders quickly at low cost, explains in major part the ability of the company to meet the increasingly keen competition.

The equipment changes produced other economies. Maintenance costs were reduced. Less power was used, and power savings resulted.

*Individual Motor Drive versus Group Drive.* Obtaining the flexibility of individual motor drive is likely to be more costly in some respects than the use of one larger motor to drive several machines. The total horsepower of the several individual motors is usually greater than the horsepower of a single motor adequate to drive the same number of machines. This tends to increase both the cost of power equipment and the cost of power. Power rates charged by a central generating plant are determined in part by the total connected horsepower load of the customer. The utility company must be prepared to furnish power to meet the maximum connected load, and, therefore, the greater the aggregate horsepower of the motors operated by a manufacturer, the greater is that part of the rate which is based on total connected load.

The purchase price of motors per horsepower tends to be greater for small motors than for large. Also individual motor drives require more control devices and wiring, with their attendant costs. Maintenance costs tend to be greater per horsepower for a number of smaller motors with their starting equipment than for a single larger motor. It should also be mentioned that small motors are characteristically less efficient in the use of electricity than large motors.

It is obvious that from a business standpoint the use of individual motor drives as compared with group drives may well constitute a serious problem. The individual motor drive provides flexibility. When flexibility is needed, it will be well worth the greater installation and operation costs. When flexibility is not needed, group drive may well be superior in that its costs tend to be lower. The new layout of Foster Yarn, Inc., recognizes this situation and seems to meet it intelligently.

Situations of this sort are business situations and call for the thoughtful consideration of business executives. The need of flexibility to meet changing market conditions faced by Foster Yarn, Inc., is an excellent illustration of this. The executive need not be a power expert to discharge adequately his responsibility in this area. Technical services can always be purchased, and it is the function of the business executive to seek such service when it is needed and use it in a business way in the interest of profits.

## QUESTIONS

1. What were the major problems faced by the management of Foster Yarn, Inc.?

2. Why did the change in market conditions present a plant problem?

3. In what other respects was the old power installation unsatisfactory?

4. What was done to remedy these unsatisfactory conditions?

5. What were the advantages of the new type of power application?

6. Were there any disadvantages? If so, what were they?

7. Was the power problem of Foster Yarn, Inc., intelligently solved as a business problem? Explain.

8. Why is it not wise for a business executive to place the entire control of the plant power problem in the hands of the power engineer?

## DENNETT COMPANY

The Dennett Company, which made small machined parts for a variety of products, found that a combination of group and unit power drives was much more economical in both installation and operating costs than exclusive use of unit drives.

The Dennett Company carried on mass production of small, machined metal parts for a variety of products. It was one unit of a large number of plants operated by one company. After one of the other plants had been modernized and unit drives had been installed on each machine, the question arose of modernizing the Dennett Company plant, and the policy of adopting unit drives was advocated. In the Dennett Company plant, equipment was driven through long line shafts from large central power units. Engineering studies of the costs of installation and operation of the unit drives showed them to be uneconomical, however, and a combination of group and unit drives was installed in this plant. After several years of operation the management compiled data to determine the relative advantages of the plan adopted.

The following machines were employed in the plant:

21 automatic screw machines
 2 automatic turret forming machines
29 hand screw machines
 2 semiautomatic chucking machines
24 turret lathes
 1 special tapping machine
 1 burring machine
 1 chip separator
 1 blower
 9 grinders

Group drives were used on all machines except one large automatic screw machine, the burring machine, the chip separator, the blower, and six bench grinders, which were unit-driven because of infrequent use, large load, or location. Machines of one type were placed in two or more groups, permitting the complete shutdown of one or more of the groups if production decreased.

Motors ranged in size from 7½ horsepower to 25 horsepower and were operated at 1,150 revolutions per minute at full load. They were mounted at shaft ends and over aisles to permit easy maintenance and quick replacement of motors if necessary. Any motor could be changed in a half hour. Use of short drive shafts permitted this location on shaft ends. As the distance between shafts was small, short-center drives were employed, making offsetting shafts unnecessary. Shafts were mounted at right angles to sources of light, thus offering only the thickness of the belts instead of the width as an obstruction to the light. The quantity of natural light at the center of these departments varied between 20 and 22 foot-candles, according to readings of a foot-candle meter.[3]

The group drives employed nine shafts 60 feet long and three shafts 50 feet long. Shafts were all $1^{15}/_{16}$ inches in diameter and operated at speeds of from 202 to 375 revolutions per minute. Each shaft was provided with two couplings.

The building, which was of concrete, did not offer adequate support at the points where shaft hangers were necessary and therefore steel stringers were erected, which made a permanent installation needing no readjustments for alignment. Alterations in layout could be made easily.

The costs of installation and operation of group and unit drives for both the automatic and the hand screw machine departments as compared with costs if the same machines were operated exclusively by unit drives were summarized as shown in Exhibit 1.

The cost figures for operation under the unit drive were obtained as follows. Motor and controller costs were actual costs for a motor and controller on each machine, the sizes of motors

[3] The maximum foot-candles required for any type of operation listed is 20 in a table showing "Foot-Candles of Illumination Required for Good Lighting," *Management's Handbook,* L. P. Alford, editor, The Ronald Press Company, New York, 1924.

## EXHIBIT 1

### Dennett Company
### Costs of Two Types of Power Application
### Installation Costs

#### Automatic Screw Machine Department

| Combination Group and Unit Drive | | Unit Drive on Each Machine | |
|---|---|---|---|
| Motors and Control: | | Motors and Control: | |
| 1  20-hp............................ | $  286.74 | 1  15-hp........................ | $     251.10 |
| 3  15-hp............................ | 753.30 | 2  10-hp........................ | 432.54 |
| 1   5-hp............................ | 141.41 | 3   7½-hp...................... | 592.92 |
| 2   1-hp............................ | 143.40 | 5   5-hp........................ | 569.85 |
| 1    ½-hp......................... | 65.27 | 11   3-hp........................ | 1,047.64 |
| — | | 2   2-hp........................ | 167.80 |
| 8 | $1,390.12 | 3   1-hp........................ | 215.25 |
| | | 2    ½-hp...................... | 130.64 |
| | | — | |
| Wiring............................. | 1,235.00 | 29 | $3,407.74 |
| Line-shaft Installations Complete: | | Wiring............................. | 2,947.79 |
| 3 Group Drives and 5 Unit Drives... | 2,261.68 | Adapting Machines to Motor Drive: | |
| | | 29 Unit Drives................... | 11,598.00 |
| Total........................ | $4,886.80 | Total........................ | $17,953.53 |

#### Hand Screw Machine Department

| Combination Group and Unit Drive | | Unit Drive on Each Machine | |
|---|---|---|---|
| Motors and Control: | | Motors and Control: | |
| 1  25-hp........................ | $  316.71 | 2  5-hp......................... | $    227.94 |
| 1  15-hp........................ | 251.10 | 18  3-hp........................ | 1,714.32 |
| 2  10-hp........................ | 432.54 | 28  2-hp........................ | 2,349.20 |
| 1   7½-hp...................... | 197.64 | 8  1-hp........................ | 574.00 |
| 5    ½-hp...................... | 327.35 | 5  1-hp........................ | 326.35 |
| — | | 6   ¼-hp....................... | 174.60 |
| 10 | $ 1,525.34 | — | |
| | | 67 | $ 5,366.41 |
| Wiring............................. | 1,082.00 | Wiring............................. | 5,976.92 |
| Line-shaft Installations Complete: | | Adapting Machines to Motor Drive: | |
| 5 Group Drives and 5 Unit Drives.. | 5,002.45 | 67 Unit Drives................... | 13,675.00 |
| Total........................ | $ 7,609.79 | Total........................ | $25,018.33 |
| Total Cost of Group and Unit Drive | | Total Cost of Unit Drive Installation, | |
| Installation, Both Departments.... | $12,496.59 | Both Departments................ | $42,971.86 |

#### Annual Operating Costs

| Combination Group and Unit Drive | | Unit Drive | |
|---|---|---|---|
| Fixed Charges (15%)................ | $1,874.49 | Fixed Charges (15%)................ | $6,445.76 |
| Maintenance: | | Maintenance: | |
| 18 Motors, 12 Shafts.............. | 43.68 | 96 Motors, Belts, etc.............. | 1,080.00 |
| Power Cost: | | Power Cost: | |
| Annual Consumption | | Annual Consumption | |
| 60,579 kw-hr at $0.0223......... | 1,350.91 | 67,909 kw-hr at $0.0223 Plus | |
| | | Power Factor Charge........... | 1,886.15 |
| Total Operating Cost........... | $3,269.08 | Total Operating Cost........... | $9,411.91 |

being those recommended by the machine manufacturers for the particular operating conditions. When any doubt existed, the machine was tested and the motor size determined by the maximum load of the machine exclusive of moderate peaks of momentary duration. The figures for unit drive wiring costs were checked by actual costs in the plant. Actual installation and wiring costs were available for group-driven machines. Figures for line- and shaft-drive installation were computed with the actual equipment installed as a basis, since the drive installation costs were not separable from the machine installation costs in the plant records. The figures, however, were checked by the contractor who made the installation.

The higher wiring costs for the unit drive installations on any given group of machines were due largely to three factors: the greater number of motor circuits, control wirings, and motor settings; the larger copper and conduit sizes for circuit feeders and panels; and the corresponding increase in installation labor. For example, one group of machines was driven by a 25-horsepower, 3-phase, 440-volt motor and the installation costs were as follows:

| | |
|---|---:|
| Wire and Conduit Installed.............................. | $ 87.10 |
| Pro Rata Cost of Feeders, Panels, and Switchboard......... | 75.31 |
| Installation and Connection of Motor and Compensator...... | 35.00 |
| | **$197.41** |

To install a unit drive on each machine in that group would have required two 5-horsepower, eight 3-horsepower, and two 1-horsepower motors with the following installation costs:

| | |
|---|---:|
| Wire and Conduit Installed.............................. | $470.40 |
| Feeders and Panels and Pro Rata Cost of Switchboard...... | 333.32 |
| Installation and Connection of Motors and Controllers....... | 154.60 |
| | **$958.32** |

The cost of adapting the machines in the two departments for unit drive, as shown in Exhibit 1, page 350, was equal to the cost of labor and equipment necessary to fit each machine for a unit drive if purchased new without a motor. Such equipment included short-center drives, countershafts, and gear reduction units. The cost of adaptation, therefore, and the cost of installation of the combination group and unit drive were on a comparable base.

The total cost of motors, wiring, and installation for the existing combination group and unit drive for both departments amounted to $12,496.59, and that cost for unit drive installations was computed as $42,971.86.

Operating costs showed similar differences. Maintenance cost for group drive was the actual figure for maintenance in the plant during the third year of operation. The unit-drive maintenance charge was a conservative computation of the cost of inspecting, cleaning, and oiling the individual motors and drives once a week, which was considered necessary preventive maintenance on unit-drive installations in the plant. Maintenance cost included all minor repairs but not major repairs or replacements; such cost was included in fixed charges.

The power cost for the combination unit and group drives was $1,350.91 a year. The power factor [4] developed varied between 83 and 87 per cent and averaged slightly more than 85 per cent for a year. Power factor tests were made monthly.

The average weighted motor efficiency was 86.8 per cent. The efficiency of each motor was weighted for motor load to show the effect of each motor on the total consumption. As the total power consumption was affected by the efficiency of each motor, not only in proportion to its load, but also in proportion to its relative time in operation, the efficiency of each motor was again weighted for its work time in relation to the work time of the other motors.

To compute the power consumption of a complete unit-drive installation, the current annual consumption of the combination group and unit drive was taken as a basis and additions made for the differences in efficiency and power factor. The efficiency of each motor needed if unit drives were installed throughout was then taken from data on motor efficiencies furnished by the manufacturers, the average running load of each motor being

[4] See Appendix A.

taken into consideration. From this the weighted efficiency was found to be 74.3 per cent for the unit-drive installation.

The difference in motor efficiency between the two types of drives was 12.5 per cent. However, there was a line-shaft loss in the group-drive installation to be taken into consideration. Tests indicated that this loss amounted to 3.5 per cent, giving an over-all group-drive efficiency of 83.3 per cent. This still left a difference of 9 per cent between the efficiencies of the two drives, which added $163.46 to the basic power bill.

The power factor for individual motor drives, if used throughout, was likewise computed by considering the power factor of each motor and its effect on the total power factor. The resultant figure was 59 per cent as compared with 85 per cent for the combination unit- and group-drive arrangement. A power-factor charge, of course, would therefore be incurred, and a conservative rate was chosen as a basis for this charge, namely, 0.2455, which was a charge actually made for power factors between 55 and 60 per cent. This added $371.78 to the power bill. The total annual operating cost for a unit-drive installation was computed as $9,411.91, compared with $3,269.08 for the combination of group and unit drive.

The use of a few unit drives supplementing the group drives utilized all the unit-drive advantages wherever known in this plant, and the executive investigation definitely indicated that great economies were obtained over individual unit drives.

### Appendix A

#### Cost of Electric Power

Cost of electric power is subject to the three following influences: motor efficiency, load factor, and power factor.

When current is fed into an electric motor, the output of mechanical energy from the motor is somewhat less than the electrical energy input. The effectiveness of a motor in converting electrical energy into mechanical energy is called "motor efficiency." In motors of standard make, efficiency varies from 83 to 93 per cent. The higher figure is very good. Small motors tend to be less efficient than large motors. Since a company must pay for the energy consumed in driving the motor, just as it must pay for the energy furnished to equipment by the motor, the higher the motor efficiency, the lower the cost of power required to operate the machine driven by the motor.

When all the power development ability of a motor is being used in the operation of the machine or machines which it drives, it is said to be operating at full load. When the power used is less than the capacity of the motor, it is said to be underloaded. The ratio of the average power used over a period of time to the power producing capacity of the motor for that period of time is its load factor. High load factor tends to reduce power cost. When the full power producing ability of a motor is not used, the result is in effect idle equipment and excessive equipment investment cost, just as in the case of any piece of idle equipment. This excess equipment cost applies also to the generating equipment which feeds the motor. Generating capacity must be available to operate the motor at full load, and when the motor is underloaded generating capacity is standing idle. Power companies, therefore, commonly levy what is in effect an additional charge upon consumers whose load factor is unusually low. The higher the load factor of a plant, the lower the cost of power consumed.

Power factor is the third influence considered here and the most difficult of explanation. When alternating current is used to operate an induction motor, a certain amount of the current rushing back and forth on the line does no work. It is "wattless" current. It does not produce mechanical power. It does, however, tend to heat up the lines and the generating equipment. This reduces the limit of capacity of the generating equipment and distributing system. Power factor is the measure of this particular motor characteristic. It varies from unity downward with different types of motors. Power factor for a plant of from 85 to 70 per cent is common, although it is sometimes much less. If a plant has a poor power factor, the power generating company may assess an additional charge to compensate itself for the excess generating equipment necessary to produce the power required under conditions of poor power factor. If the power factor was nearer unity, the same amount of power could be produced with less investment in generating equipment.

To control power factor, management must be careful in its selection of motor equipment. Installation of the equipment is also important. Although power factor is an inherent characteristic of the motor, proper installation of types of equipment having high power factor on the same lines with equipment having low power factor tends to improve the over-all factor. Another consideration is the effect of load factor upon power factor and motor efficiency. Reduction in load tends to reduce both power factor and motor efficiency, thus indirectly causing an increase in power cost.

### QUESTIONS

1. From a business standpoint how does the Dennett Company situation differ from that of Foster Yarn, Inc.?

2. Why were some of the Dennett Company machines equipped with individual motors?

3. Why were machines of one type separated into two or more groups for purposes of group drive?

4. What consideration was given to lighting in placing machines and their driving mechanisms?

5. In the Dennett Company case, which involved the greater installation costs, group or unit drives?

6. Why was the one more costly than the other?

7. In the Dennett Company case, which involved greater operating costs, group or unit drives?

8. Why was the one more costly than the other?

9. Was the method of power application used in the Dennett Company case well suited to the company's needs? Explain.

10. When a utility company sells power to a manufacturer, what does it take into consideration in setting the rates to be charged?

# CHAPTER XV

## LABOR SUPPLY

### TUCKERMAN MACHINERY COMPANY

### 1. A·Manufacturer of Heavy Machine Tools Finds It Necessary to Increase the Supply of Workers for the Foundry.

For many years the Tuckerman Machinery Company had operated an apprentice school to provide it with the many trained workers constantly needed throughout its extensive plant. In the past an adequate number of the applicants for training had wished to prepare for jobs as foundry molders and coremakers. Recently the number of applicants for training for these jobs had become inadequate, and the company's personnel executives found it necessary to take active steps to supply the deficiency.

**2. Importance of Labor Supply.** No company can progress beyond the capacity and ability of its workers. Since the ascendancy of the machine in industry, management has too often lost perspective in this matter. This loss of balance in thinking is exemplified in the assumption that conflict between capital and labor is inevitable. The idea that the one can prosper only at the expense of the other gives inadequate attention to the truth that today neither can exist in the absence of the other. The productivity of the worker is largely influenced by the tools he uses. The productivity of the machine is dependent on the ability and willingness of the worker to utilize the machine. Trite though these observations are, they are important, for the emotional reactions of vested interests—both labor and capital—continually obscure the basic truth. There are not two sound points of view; a business succeeds to the ultimate only as both labor and machines are productive. Suitable labor supply is fully as important as adequate equipment and proper raw materials.

**3. Characteristics of Labor Supply.** The employer in ensuring himself of an adequate labor supply must recognize the importance of three aspects of the problem: the number of individuals available to the company, the physical skills of available workers, and their mental characteristics.

The number of employables is the factor that is most commonly considered. Knitting mills are sometimes deliberately established in a community where the chief industry is the production of cutlery. Why? The cutlery shops employ chiefly men. The result is a considerable number of unemployed women and girls in this community who would welcome an opportunity for factory employment. Knitting mills use much female labor, and the drift of these mills to the cutlery manufacturing community follows. The significance of number of employable workers is obvious.

**4. Selecting Workers.** Far too many jobs are filled on the basis of the applicant's being "a likely looking man." A young boy seeking factory employment for the first time had spent unsuccessfully many hours waiting at mill gates and in employment offices. Hot summer weather came on, and the youngster had his hair cut short and brushed it to a bristly pompadour. Two days later, he obtained an apprentice job in a department employing Polish grinders exclusively. Later the foreman said to him, "We have been needing a new hand for some time now. Yesterday, I saw you at the gate and I knew from the way you have your hair cut that you are a good Polish boy. That's what we need in here."

Procurement of industrial materials and supplies has been developed to the point where it is carried on with scientific care and exactness. The desirable characteristics of a material to be used for a specific purpose are painstakingly determined. If it is a metal that is needed, characteristics such as tensile strength, resistance to crushing, ductility, malleability, and elasticity are considered and the most suitable degree of each carefully determined. Detailed specifications for materials are prepared, and when purchased materials are received, they are tested and meticulously checked for these specified requirements. Management has found from experience that such care in the procurement of raw materials pays.

Workers vary in their individual characteristics just as greatly as materials do. Worker attributes which are comparable to raw materials characteristics include such variables as strength, quickness, finger dexterity, and a wide variety of acquired skills. In choosing workers, some companies have attempted to analyze the worker characteristics needed for each individual job and then to select workers possessing the desired attributes. As yet, our means for testing worker characteristics are limited and rather crude. This fact is probably chiefly responsible for failure of business executives to select workers with the same degree of care as is exercised in the selection of materials.

No purchasing agent will select steel bars because they are likely looking steel bars. A large portion of industrial workers are hired on just that basis, particularly where foremen select the men to be employed in their own departments. Under this method of hiring, religious and fraternal affiliation, family relations, social congeniality, and the like are the common determinants of selection. Such a basis for selection is better than none, but certainly the way a boy combs his hair bears little necessary relation to his adaptability to precision grinding and finishing in a manufacturing plant.

Labor differs from raw materials in a most important respect: attributes of labor are dynamic while characteristics of raw materials tend to be static. If carefully selected materials are properly stored, they are likely to be the same tomorrow as they are today. They will be just as strong, just as workable, just as useful for their predetermined purpose a week or a month from the time they were purchased as they were the day they arrived at the receiving dock. That is not true of labor. Worker characteristics are constantly changing. Furthermore, an accepted applicant for a job may be willing to exercise his best ability at the time he is hired, and yet a month later he may be in an entirely different frame of mind about using his abilities. Management must recognize this dynamic characteristic of labor, this tendency to change. Executives must accept as a major part of their function responsibility for directing change in workers. Properly discharged, this function will produce constant worker improvement: increased ability of workers, greater physical stamina, greater skill, better mental attitude, and improved mental stability. If management ignores this responsibility or, recognizing it, fails to discharge it skillfully, the result will be low worker productivity, worker unrest, high labor turnover, and perhaps worker antagonism and strikes.

**5. Securing Workers.** Existence of an adequate number of suitable workers in the vicinity does not in itself ensure an adequate work force. Workers must be attracted to the employ of the company. Various factors affect the willingness or desire of unemployed workers to get on the payroll of a specific company. The attitude of workers toward jobs offered is influenced by two types of consideration: conditions within the plant and outside conditions over which plant management has little or no control.

Companies quickly acquire reputations as being desirable or undesirable places to work. Liberal wages, steadiness of employment, good working conditions, and fair hours are typical of the internal influences which attract good workers to a manufacturing company. Whatever the company's policy in these respects, the community soon becomes aware of it, and thereby develops an outside influence which will be favorable or unfavorable as workers and the general public in the community appraise the company's personnel management.

Just as a definite opinion of an individual company is formed, so, too, public attitude toward types of work frequently develops. An industry may acquire the reputation of being exceptionally dangerous, or, over a period of time, of being nonseasonal in operation, thereby providing steady employment. Public opinion of this type will sometimes be a powerful force either for or against a specific company, even though that company may be an exception in its industry. However, it is sometimes possible for a company to capitalize on unfavorable working conditions in an industry by providing conditions which are relatively attractive in comparison with others in the same line of work, and thus secure the best workers of the type needed.

**6. The Tuckerman Machinery Company's Problem.** The Tuckerman Machinery Company, which manufactured machinery in a city of 175,000 population, employed approximately 5,000 workers. For 70 years, the company had conducted apprentice courses lasting for from 1½ to 4 years for the training of machinists, draftsmen, patternmakers, molders, and core-makers. Until recently the company had experienced no diffi-culty in recruiting boys to enter these courses. For the past year, however, few boys had made applications to enter the courses in molding and coremaking, which were given in the foundry. There were 100 boys from sixteen to twenty-one years of age taking the company's courses. Six were taking the course for molders; eight, for coremakers; five, for patternmakers; twenty, for draftsmen. Four were studying to be screw machine oper-ators, and fifty-seven to be machinists. Company executives deemed it advisable to increase the number of foundry appren-tices but had not succeeded in doing so.

**7. How the Company Obtained Skilled Workers.** The pur-pose of the company's apprentice courses was to educate young men in all phases of their chosen trades so that they could qualify with the company as skilled workers and as leaders of those who had not had the opportunity to obtain a varied training. The apprentices were trained to fill positions of responsibility and could look forward to promotions. In the past, the company's apprentices had been valuable additions to its force. Several of the department foremen and many of the section foremen were graduates of the apprentice courses. Responsible positions under the factory superintendent and in the drafting, engineering, and sales departments also were held by former apprentices. All graduates had attained a degree of skill for which there was a demand in other factories manufacturing machinery.

**8. The Apprentice Training Courses.** A grammar-school edu-cation was a prerequisite for all courses. For drafting, a boy was required to have, in addition, an education equivalent to com-pletion of the course in the local technical high school.

Each boy who desired to enter the plant of the Tuckerman Machinery Company and who had the required prerequisites was given a preliminary examination to test his knowledge of simple mathematics, including fractions, decimals, percentage, ratio and proportion, square root, and mensuration. If the results of the examination and the references he submitted were satisfactory, the company set a date on which the boy was to enter the course.

The first 12 weeks after a boy enrolled in a course constituted a trial period. If the boy's work was satisfactory at the end of the period, he signed a contract, in conjunction with his parents and an official of the company, indenturing him to the company for the specified term of his apprenticeship. When he signed the contract, the apprentice paid a fee as an evidence of good faith. He forfeited this fee if he did not fulfill his contractual obligations. At the time of graduation, the company paid each apprentice a bonus considerably in excess of the original fee.

Company officials believed that the formal agreement and the payment of a fee were necessary in order to discourage the enrollment of boys who would not complete the courses. A boy who lived at home could save enough of his earnings during the three months of the trial period to pay his fee when the contract was signed. The company permitted boys who were unable to make full payment at that time to pay in weekly instalments. The fee varied according to the length of the training period. The fee for machinists and patternmakers was $50 and the bonus paid them upon completion of the course was $150; the fee for draftsmen was $25 and the bonus $75; for molders, the fee was $25 and the bonus $100; for coremakers, the fee was $25 and the bonus $50. At the end of the trial period, machinists and molders had to buy tools which cost $13 and $19, respectively. The company furnished tools during the trial period. The company paid an additional "merit" wage to those apprentices whose ratings, based upon the quality of their work, their scholarship, and their deportment, was "excellent." Length of service and wage rates for the various courses are given in Exhibit 1, on page 362.

The boys were given a thorough training in all phases of their chosen trades. Machinist apprentices studied centering, lathe work, drilling both by the use of jigs and where laying out the work was required,[1] milling, fitting, assembling, screw cutting, repair work, screw machine operating, and toolmaking. Boys in the drafting course studied a variety of work which included the

[1] Drilling by the use of a jig involved setting up the machine according to the requirements of a blueprint. No measurements on the material were necessary to determine the place to be drilled. Where there was no provision for a jig on the machine, the operator had to determine the point to be drilled in the material from the dimensions specified in the blueprint.

**EXHIBIT 1**

Tuckerman Machinery Company

Lengths of Courses and Rates of Pay for Apprentices

| Apprentice Courses | Length, Years | Number of Periods | Length of Periods |
|---|---|---|---|
| Coremakers.................. | 1½ | 3 | 6 months |
| Draftsmen.................. | 2½ | 3 | 10 months |
| Machinists.................. | 4 | 4 | 1 year |
| Molders.................... | 3 | 3 | 1 year |
| Screw Machine Operators.... | 2 | 4 | 6 months |

| Apprentice Courses | Wage Rates per Hour | | | |
|---|---|---|---|---|
| | First Period | Second Period | Third Period | Fourth Period |
| Coremakers.................. | $0.60 | $0.65 | $0.75 | .... |
| Merit Wage.............. | 0.04 | 0.04 | 0.05 | .... |
| Draftsmen.................. | 0.50 | 0.55 | 0.65 | .... |
| Merit Wage.............. | 0.02 | 0.04 | 0.05 | .... |
| Machinists and Patternmakers | 0.55 | 0.60 | 0.70 | $0.75 |
| Merit Wage.............. | 0.02 | 0.04 | 0.05 | 0.05 |
| Molders.................... | 0.65 | 0.75 | 0.85 | .... |
| Merit Wage.............. | 0.04 | 0.04 | 0.05 | .... |
| Screw Machine Operators..... | 0.65 | 0.70 | 0.75 | 0.85 |

designing of parts for all machines manufactured by the company. Patternmakers, in addition to making forms from the specifications of the designing department, spent a portion of their training period in the foundry. Molding apprentices were given experience in floor molding, bench molding, coremaking, and cupola practice.[2] The work of coremakers, on both light and heavy cores, included trimming and baking. Screw machine

---

[2] The cupola is the shaft furnace in which pig iron is melted preparatory to casting. Pig iron, coke, and limestone are charged into the cupola near the top of its stack. The melted iron is drawn off at the base of the cupola.

operators were taught to be specialists at operating all types of screw machines.

There was classroom work in connection with all the courses. Instruction was given in machine shop mathematics, including linear and angular measurement; calculation for screw threads, gearing, feeds and speeds of machinery; and indexing. The drafting of jigs, fixtures, cams, and other mechanisms also was taught. Supplementary instruction through lectures by men outside the company's organization gave the apprentices a knowledge of subjects of general interest.

**9. The Shortage of Foundry Apprentices.** During the past year or two, the company had become aware of a shortage in foundry apprentices. This shortage continued. Most of the applicants did not want to enter the foundry course, and of those who did a majority quit within the first two weeks.

**10. Nature of Foundry Work.** All cast-iron parts for the machines manufactured by the company were cast in its foundry. The major operations in that department, which employed approximately 350 men, were molding, coremaking, melting, pouring, and cleaning.

Because of the nature of the operations, working conditions in the foundry were not so pleasant as in other departments of the plant. The work involved the handling of sand, bars of pig iron, iron scrap, coke, and limestone, and was so dirty that the workers made a complete change of outer garments in the morning before beginning work and at night before going home. Much of the work was heavy, particularly the carrying of flasks of sand from the molding bench to a point near the monorails. There was always danger of molten iron splashings. During the melting of metal, the furnace gave off obnoxious gases and smoke. The company, however, always had maintained as good working conditions as possible. A cement floor in all parts of the foundry eliminated dust to a large extent, and an adequate system of ventilation removed gases and smoke. Shower baths were provided for the employees.

**11. Executive Appraisal of the Situation.** Company officials had analyzed the dearth of foundry apprentices. The apprentice supervisor questioned all boys who were dissatisfied with the foundry courses. He learned that the boys considered the work too hard and dirty. Work in the other apprentice courses was cleaner and did not require the occasional heavy lifting that foundry work involved. There were no dust or fumes in the other departments where apprentices were trained. Other apprentices did not have to make a complete change of outer clothing; they merely put on overalls and jumpers over their street clothes.

Company executives believed, however, that foundry conditions in the industry as a whole, and not merely in their company, were keeping boys from choosing foundry work as a trade. A large number of foundries were built directly on a hard dirt floor, and many of them did not provide shower baths for the workers. Those conditions had become generally known, and boys preferred either white-collar jobs or apprenticeships in the machinist trades. The high wages in the building trades also appealed to boys just out of school. A boy could learn enough of the carpentry trade in six months to be in a position to earn $8 to $10 a day. With the abnormal activity in building, opportunities for jobs in that industry were fairly numerous.

It was the opinion of the factory superintendent that blame for lack of workers in the foundry industry could be placed on all companies which operated foundries with poor working conditions. He believed that better conditions throughout the industry would break down the antipathy to foundry work which boys just out of school felt. The National Metal Trades Association had succeeded in pointing out the trouble to foundries in the Milwaukee district, with the result that radical changes for the better had been made in working conditions there. The results were reflected in an immediate increase in the number of boys who took up foundry work as a trade.

Company executives considered that there were two methods of increasing the number of applicants for foundry training: paying higher wages or seeking to bring about general improvement in working conditions in the foundry industry.

**12. Summary and Conclusion.** *Origin of the Problem.* Throughout the life of the Tuckerman Machine Company, the city in which it was located had grown industrially. There had been a steady increase in the number and variety of opportunities in factory employment open to each succeeding generation. At the same time, the number of opportunities for nonindustrial employment had grown even more rapidly. As a result, industrial employers in the community had for years found it necessary to take active steps to obtain the skilled labor which local industry required. This was basically the origin of the shortage of foundry apprentices.

When the Tuckerman Machine Company needed additional employees, it had sought them in the local market. For years this source had failed to provide an adequate number of men of satisfactory skill. Particularly was there a lack of men who could eventually be promoted to supervisory positions. The remedy which the company had employed for many years was the apprentice training school.

The situation which the company now faced was simply the impact upon the training school itself of the very forces which had brought the school into existence. Potential applicants for foundry apprenticeship either were not having the opportunities in this field brought to their attention or felt that other employment offered more attractive opportunities.

*Why the Problem Became Acute.* As early as 1920, compulsory public education and a long-continued rise in the standard of living had focused the attention of young people almost universally on white-collar jobs. Physical labor under none too pleasant factory conditions was relatively unattractive. Many sons of skilled factory employees were urged by their parents to seek vocations of greater social prestige. Parents were complacent when a son or daughter accepted employment at relatively low wages if the job held forth a possible future of greater social acceptance. Clerical work often seemed preferable both to young people and to their parents. The insurance salesman and the bill collector held positions of esteem.

By this time the effects of immigration restriction were being realized by some manufacturers. No longer was there the lag of a generation between acceptance of physical labor, skilled and unskilled, and yearning for a white-collar job. The result was

the beginning of a vicious trend which is still persisting, labor
shortage in certain skilled crafts paralleled by unemployment.

The Tuckerman Machinery Company's apprentice school had
been helpful to it in meeting this change. The school had a
reputation for training excellent skilled workers. Its graduates
were in demand by many companies. Usually the Tuckerman
Machinery Company was able to retain its skilled apprentices,
who realized the opportunities for advancement to supervisory
jobs if they proved their ability as skilled workers. During the
training course, apprentices received relatively good wages, and
upon completion of their work they could make excellent earnings because their skill enabled them to command high rates and
to produce rapidly. Had it not been for its apprentice school,
this company would probably have felt the effects of changing
employment conditions more severely or earlier than it did.

*Why the First Apprentice Shortage Realized Was of Foundry
Applicants.* If the foregoing analysis is correct, the impact of
changed conditions on the apprentice school in the late 1940's is
readily understood. From the social viewpoint of the community, foundry work was the least attractive of any of the vocations in which training was offered. The work was heavy and
dirty. Only the physically strong were capable of it. The relatively higher wage paid during the foundry training period could
not combat community acceptance of the superiority of drafts-
manship as a vocation. It was not "smart" to be a foundry
worker. In social opinion, the draftsman was but one step removed from the engineer, who was looked up to as a professional
man. Foundries employed considerable common labor. Common labor was not in evidence in the drafting room. To work
in a foundry was to be known as an associate of common labor.
To work in a drafting room was to acquire a "position" rather
than to have a job.

The machinists and screw machine operatives were between
these two extremes. Their work was less arduous and dirty.
Many men of prominence in local plants had risen from these
positions. If one was going to work in a factory, these vocations
were more attractive than most. A first-class machinist could
always get a good job, and a reputation of being a skilled machin-

ist was worth having though difficult to get. Many a machinist was certain that he knew more and could do more than any engineer that ever came out of college. Many an older factory employee urged upon his son the security for the future enjoyed by a man skilled in the machinist's trade. And during and after the Second World War there was "good money" in it.

The shortage of foundry apprentices was the normal result of changed social conditions over which management of the Tuckerman Machine Company had little control. The problem of the company was to adapt itself to the new conditions. Good management makes such adjustments, expecting to be called upon to do so. Less able executives bemoan "the good old days" and berate the conditions which make for change.

*What the Management Should Do.* The suggestions for remedy considered by the management have merit. It is interesting that one considers change within the company while the other looks to improvement of external conditions. It is doubtful that either proposal alone would produce the desired result.

Increase in wages of foundry apprentices would make foundry apprenticeship more attractive. However, molders' wages were already the highest of the group, and there was nothing to show that the wage scale was the cause of the lack of interest. While higher wages for apprentice molders would tend to offset somewhat the adverse reaction toward foundry jobs, any reasonable increase could not be relied upon to bring a satisfactory number of applicants to the school.

Improvement in general foundry conditions would probably be more helpful. It would take time to bring about such improvement, and an even longer period would elapse before such improvement would influence general attitude toward foundry work sufficiently to overcome common aversion to it. It is also worth noting that if foundry conditions generally improved, the Tuckerman Machinery Company would lose any advantage it held in the past as a result of superior conditions in its own plant. A general improvement in foundry conditions is a desirable program as a long-run influence. While it could be expected to do but little for the Tuckerman Machinery Company for some time to come, the program should have been carried forward.

Two other possibilities deserve consideration. It is quite possible that the course of instruction offered to foundry apprentices could have been made more attractive. The case does not provide sufficient information to make decision in this matter possible. There are instances where change in methods of instruction and organization of materials have greatly improved the attitude of industrial apprentices toward their work. However, any such reorganization must not conceal the true nature of the work to be done, either during the training period or thereafter. Such deception is eventually fatal. There are many possibilities for honest improvement in teaching and instruction, and changes in instructing staff sometimes yield surprising results. The Tuckerman Machinery Company management should have investigated the matter fully.

The most promising partial solution to this company's problem would be a more careful selection and solicitation of candidates for foundry work. It is possible that the seemingly adverse features of the situation might be converted into assets. It should not be difficult to build up a reputation for foundry apprentices as being the physically superior group of the school, the "big boys," the "boys who can take it." Wrestling, boxing, or football might be employed to demonstrate this superiority. Such a program would require careful choice of apprentices for foundry work. A little money spent in adroit solicitation, perhaps through athletic organizations and clubs, should be effective. Once the foundry apprentice group had established a reputation for physical prowess, appeal and selection made on that basis would be very likely to produce desired results. If plant publicity were given to such a reputation, it would probably require a program carrying through into the foundry itself. Athletic superiority has more than once solved personnel problems for a factory. It might well do so in this case.

The importance of this suggestion lies in its remedial nature. It is an attempt to take conditions as they are and work with them, rather than to change conditions or fight them. The basis of the company's trouble was a social situation. The remedial means here suggested rely for effectiveness upon social reaction. Physical proficiency is desirable from a social point of view. A better selection of foundry apprentices in terms of characteristics which bring forth social approval might well do what no practical amount of financial compensation or improvement in working environment could accomplish. Such a program is suggested as being well worth consideration by executives of the Tuckerman Machinery Company.

The work force makes or breaks a manufacturing business. A company's work force must always be in process of replenishment, and, therefore, a continuous supply of suitable labor is imperative. Numbers of employables indicate little as to labor supply. No two workers are exactly alike, and different jobs call for different worker characteristics. Job analysis to determine just what sort of worker is needed is not easy. It is even more difficult to analyze the applicant to see if he meets the job requirements. Difficult as this task may be, the well-managed business undertakes it and in considerable degree meets with success.

The men on the job require just as much "handling" as the newcomers. Their physical capacities change, and, more important, their mental characteristics are highly dynamic. Thus maintenance of labor supply calls for two types of work: bringing the right men and women into the organization and then making and keeping them productive on the job. These two duties make up management's most difficult task—and probably the one which yields the greatest dividends in satisfaction when the desired results are attained.

### QUESTIONS

1. What was the problem faced by executives of the Tuckerman Machinery Company?

2. What steps were proposed to remedy this problem?

3. How do you explain the distribution of the 100 apprentices among the courses offered? Why was so small a group electing foundry training?

4. What was the basic cause of foundry apprentice shortage?

5. Should the Tuckerman Machinery Company have at-

tempted to improve its foundry labor supply by increasing wages?

6. Do you agree that it would be wise for company executives to work for improved conditions in foundries in the vicinity?

7. Would you expect a program designed to develop a reputation of physical superiority for the foundry group to be helpful?

8. Wherein is the personnel manager's job similar to that of the purchasing agent? Wherein are these jobs unlike?

9. Why is selection of workers more difficult than selection of materials?

10. What is the importance of the dynamic character of labor?

## ROGER BACON MILLS

The Roger Bacon Mills, located at Allston, Alabama, manufactured sheetings, drills, and flannels, classified as gray goods. The mills employed 400 people. The company found difficulty in obtaining operatives who would work regularly. Its labor turnover and absentee rates were excessive. The employees were not thrifty or foresighted and were not ambitious. The company had tried welfare work with questionable success, and the owners were debating whether to continue efforts to improve the caliber of the employees or to adopt a passive attitude, soliciting applicants whenever necessary from the surrounding countryside, keeping those who wished to stay, and regarding the overhead expenses involved as necessary and normal.

When the Roger Bacon Mills were established in 1902, no town of Allston was in existence. It was started by the mills. The town had grown to a total population of 2,500 persons. Approximately one-half of the town property had been erected on account of the mills. Allston was situated on two railroad lines, one of them a through line. The surrounding country was rough and primitive.

The operatives in the mill were recruited almost exclusively from surrounding hills and farms. The forefathers of these people were white farmers who owned no slaves. Those farmers could not compete with the wealthy, slave-owning planters in the growing of cotton and corn. Schools then were scarce and unpopular, and the poor farmer's children had little chance for education. Legally, the poor whites were free men, but actually they were little removed from slavery. The Civil War stripped them of their scant possessions and killed or maimed many of their best men. After the war they were in competition with emancipated slaves with low standards of living who also tried farming, and both white and Negro tenant farmers endured that form of economic serfdom known as the "single crop system" at the hands of the moneylenders.

The people that the Roger Bacon Mills employed came from shanties on farms and from shacks in the mountain wilderness. The trend of circumstances described had thrust them into a state of poverty and ignorance far below anything commensurate with their native abilities.

They had little ambition. On the other hand, they were not degraded, but independent, proud, and sensitive. The older generation as a class was unable to read or write; the younger generation had received some education as a result of the state compulsory education laws.

When these mountaineers or farmers came to the Roger Bacon Mills for employment, usually all the members of their families who were above sixteen entered the employment of the mill. Many of the older men were unable to adapt themselves to factory life. They quit mill employment and frequently remained at home, deriving their support from wives and children.

Agricultural life suited many of these people best. Every spring some of them returned to the farms to plant. If, at the end of six weeks, their crops appeared to be thriving, they stayed on the farm, but otherwise they returned to the mill. Such had been the situation for many years, and no remedy to check the shifting had been devised.

There was much movement of the labor supply between various companies' mills. Some of the workers drifted about in a casual way. They started without a destination from one town and settled more or less permanently wherever and whenever their funds were dissipated.

Lowland tenant farmers drifted to Allston from points 200 miles south of that place. Among Southern millowners a difference of opinion existed regarding the industrial qualities of the lowland tenant farmers as contrasted with those of the mountaineers. The lowland farmer was alleged by many to be less intelligent and less sturdy and industrious than the mountaineer. Few of the lowland farmers went to the mills, for farming was easier in those regions. An unquestioned difference existed between the workers in more recent mill towns such as Allston and those in older mill towns such as were found in the Carolinas and Georgia. In some of the older mill centers, three generations of workers had grown up about the mills, and the industrial qualities of the people in them were more satisfactory than the qualities of the mountaineer stock which the Roger Bacon Mills employed.

The situation in Allston was complicated by the presence of coal mines in the vicinity, in which men could earn from $10 to $12 a day. Although mining was open only to men, it drew some of the heads of families from Allston, and when they moved their families accompanied them. Employment in the coal mines was not steady in normal years, and men who left Allston for the mines frequently returned when their resources gave out in a period of idleness.

The houses built by the Roger Bacon Mills numbered 125. There was also a small hotel for men employed in the mill. Almost all the employees were accommodated in the mill properties. The total number of people living in those properties was 850. There were three types of dwellings, small bungalows of two and three rooms, two-story, two-family houses, and stucco bungalows of five rooms. All had electric lights, but only the third type had modern plumbing. The other types had water spigots in the yards, usually serving two adjoining houses. Employees were housed by the company at 50 cents per room per week, a rental that was 65 to 70 per cent less than the average charge imposed by private owners for houses in the town. The least satisfactory of the company's houses were far better than the huts from which many of the older workers came.

The Roger Bacon Mills had done some welfare work. A nursery was established for the children whose mothers worked in the mills. The company employed a nurse to look after the general health of the workers. A grammar school was erected by the company at a cost of $20,000, the teaching and maintenance cost being taken over by the county. Courses were given in home economics to girls. Many of the mill's employees had existed previously on fried food, the hog and hominy diet of the South, and new arrivals in Allston often appeared to be suffering from malnutrition. The company established a playground and supported baseball teams and a band. It remodeled a building into a motion-picture theater and provided it with a projector.

The employees supervised the running of the theater. A textile club was formed for boys working in the mills. The company started a small library, and during the first year 125 cards were issued to members of the mill force.

The mill organization consisted of a superintendent and seven department heads or overseers, one for each of the various processes, such as carding, spinning, weaving, and finishing. Under the overseers, and assisting them, were second hands. The superintendent ordinarily did not come into contact with the workers, since each overseer hired and disciplined employees in his department. The superintendent, however, had impressed upon the overseers the necessity for showing consideration to employees in view of their proud and sensitive spirit.

The first time the company encountered a labor shortage, it hired a labor agent who went into the surrounding districts and sent labor from farms and mountains to the mills. The next spring many employees left the mills, but, because of bad weather and a poor crop outlook, they returned after two months' absence. Then there was plenty of help and the labor agent was dismissed. The following year some workers again left for the farms, but, because of the mill's reduced operating schedule, there was no labor shortage at that time.

Another unsatisfactory trait of many of the company's employees was their unwillingness to work regularly. Operatives took time off for trivial reasons. Often no substitutes could be found and machinery was idle as a result. The company estimated that approximately 20 per cent of those on its payroll could have been released if the remaining persons worked regularly.

These unfavorable features of its labor supply were more than offset by the lower wages paid by the Roger Bacon Mills as contrasted with those paid by its Northern competitors. Twenty-five per cent of the final cost of cotton gray goods was labor cost. The lower wages paid Southern labor were explainable, in part at least, by the newer industrial development of that region and a consequently smaller demand for labor.

Along with the lack of industrial demand for labor was a condition of plentiful supply. If this labor had been willing to move outside the section, the situation would have tended to correct itself. Although the people moved about within the district, they lacked the resources and desire to venture into the North and West. Another fact having its influence upon labor supply was the tendency to large families. Six children was the average number, according to social workers with experience in Southern communities.

The individual wage paid to Southern millworkers was not an indication of possible family income, since several members of a family usually worked in the mills. A family consisting of a father, mother, and two children of working age could have earned $400 per month. This, however, was not a usual occurrence. The people did not earn to save but to satisfy immediate wants and an occasional extravagance. Their tendency toward intermittent work was evidence of a fixed standard of living, which, measured in terms of material goods, was confined to bare necessities. The cost of necessities was low. Perhaps 70 to 80 per cent of the workers lived in mill villages. Mill houses rented at approximately 50 cents per room per week, and that price generally included electricity and water. Coal was sold to mill labor at cost; its price ranged from $3.50 to $7 per ton, depending on mill location. Less clothing was purchased by Southern mill operatives than by those in the North. Frequently, there was opportunity to grow vegetables and pasture cattle in or near the villages.

Educational efforts toward raising the standard of living were limited to children under sixteen. It was almost impossible to change the views of the adult population, although occasionally a new article was added to the list of their customary expenditures after they had observed its utility. The parents in general were opposed to the education of their children beyond the grammar grades. They thought it best that children then should go to work in the mills. On the other hand, the mills, because of Federal legislation and experience with juveniles, had curtailed employment of children.

Only a small percentage of the total children enrolled in public schools graduated from the high schools. The figure was about one-fourth the comparable percentage for the total United States.

The reasons assigned were incapacity, lack of ambition, lack of encouragement, and financial necessity. The last was a rare reason. The teaching staff in some of the mill towns was poorly paid and not held in esteem.

Welfare work of Southern mills was criticized as paternalistic. Employees said that they preferred to have the money which was spent for it put in their pay envelopes. Few prized the facilities furnished them under welfare programs. The mill managements conducted this work because they believed it essential to maintain the health and morale of the mill community. Diets and modes of life feasible on the isolated farms from which many employees came were impossible in towns and under confining conditions of work. Another aspect of the welfare program was that it exercised a mildly selective influence. Persons drawn by these facilities were more regular employees and were likely to advance in their standards of living.

A further consideration was that Southern mills in general had more modern equipment than Northern mills. This was true of the Roger Bacon Mills. Good equipment was a positive factor in the morale of mill help, since it caused fewer irritations; yet many operatives had no comparative experience with poor equipment, and, on that account, this factor was less important. The new equipment of Southern mills entailed heavy overhead charges and rendered it essential that machinery should not be idle on account of labor absenteeism or turnover.

In some ways the Southern cotton-mill workers were superior to those in the North. Southern millworkers were English-speaking almost without exception, and hence there was no language or racial barrier between them and their overseers. Moreover, Southern workers were not organized in labor unions as completely as they were in New England. Since workers were not divided along racial lines in the mills, there was not the group solidarity and jealousy that often occasioned difficulty in Northern mills. At work, the Southern operative was satisfactory in ability and willingness, but his pace was likely to be slower than that of the Northern textile worker. To what extent climate was responsible was an unsettled question, but those interested agreed that it was an active factor.

As stated, the Roger Bacon Mills management was undecided whether to take positive steps to improve the industrial qualities of its employees or to pursue a passive policy. The executives realized that they were dealing with intangible forces operating over long periods, and that any program they might endorse had possibilities of unforeseen complications in later years. It was probable that improved standards of living would be accompanied by demands for higher wages and perhaps bring about unrest of a sort quite different from that which had thus far characterized the population. However, the greatly increased activity of the CIO and the AFL might easily bring about the same result anyway.

The company decided not to attempt to mold the industrial qualities of the people directly, for it did not wish to assume responsibility for the results. It decided to continue its modest program of welfare work, concentrating chiefly upon educational efforts. The specific fields of endeavor were domestic science, personal hygiene, and character building.

Was the decision of the management sound?

## Problem 35

### ALBATROSS FOOD COMPANY

The Albatross Food Company had gone through a period of great expansion, during which it established a large number of retail food stores in certain parts of the country. In the opinion of the management, this growth had reached a point where further rapid increase in the number of unit stores was not likely to occur. During this period of development, opportunities for promotion to store managerships had been numerous, but, with the completion of the expansion program, chances for such advancement were limited to the natural turnover in the stores already established. Executives of the company believed that this change in the rate of advancement might have far-reaching consequences, and, in order to be prepared for such a contingency, they ordered a survey of the entire problem of personnel administration as it related to their various unit stores. This survey convinced the officials that the existing personnel policy of the company was inadequate.

The Albatross Food Company began business as a small manufacturing and selling organization.  After a number of years of restricted operation, the company entered upon an extensive developmental program which included the establishment of a large number of retail food stores in certain predetermined districts.

During this period of growth, company executives devoted practically all their time and energy to such problems as extension of activities into new cities, selection and acquiring of store sites, development of company brands, effective purchasing in large quantities, extensive advertising, establishment of effective retail prices, and financial programs.  They gave little attention to problems of company personnel.  There was a ruling that no one could become a store manager until he was at least twenty-five years old.  In general, their policy was to hire clerks who were relatively mature.  Men in the middle twenties were preferred.  They seldom hired a man under twenty-four, and the average age of clerks was thirty-five years.  One reason why the executives had adopted this policy was that such a course would make possible the rapid development of store managers and men for the more responsible supervisory positions, for whom there was such great demand during the period of expansion that the executives often promoted clerks to store managerships after a period of only 12 or 14 weeks of service.  Clerks worked on an average of 52 hours a week.

Wages paid to clerks approximated $35 a week, which was on a par with the rates competing stores were paying.  Store managers received a regular weekly wage plus a commission on sales, the total amounting to about $65 a week.  Store managers were transferred from one place to another as need arose.  District supervisors were selected from the store manager group.  District supervisors were paid a salary of approximately $85 a week.  A district included approximately 12 stores.

The expansion program of the company proved sound.  The volume of business transacted increased rapidly, and soon the Albatross Food Company was generally recognized as an example of successful expansion.  Company officials themselves felt well satisfied.  They had laid out an aggressive program covering a period of years, and at the end of that time the territories in which the company had successfully established itself were even more extensive than had been originally contemplated. The executives were convinced, however, that there were no particular advantages to be gained from a further rapid increase in the number of unit stores. Rather, they felt that from then on their time and thought should go into the work of effectively solidifying their position in the territories in which they were already established.

As officials scrutinized their organization to see wherein it could be improved, they were repeatedly confronted by evidence that the personnel in their stores was not of the high quality they desired. The executives were disturbed by this situation and began an investigation of personnel conditions in their stores. This survey showed that the rate of turnover among their clerks was excessive, often reaching 70 per cent a year. Complaints from customers charged clerks with carelessness, inattention, and dishonesty. Shortages in store accounts was an outstanding cause of dismissal. A check of past records of clerks showed that a typical employee had held four or five jobs before entering the employ of the Albatross Food Company. The investigation also showed that many times during the period of rapid growth the company had been unable to find efficient clerks in its own stores to promote to store managerships, and as a result had been forced to go elsewhere to get the necessary personnel. Officials were convinced that the company could improve its contact with the consumer public through the development of a better type of clerk.

In describing the kind of person that the Albatross Food Company wished to hire, one of the officials said: "We want a clerk who can meet the public in an agreeable manner and who, at the same time, is active and businesslike. He must be able to add a column of figures quickly and accurately. I believe that a knowledge of foodstuffs on the part of each clerk is highly desirable. He, of course, must be honest with both the public and the company, and should convey to the customer an impression of real loyalty to the company. We wish that loyalty to be genuine."

It was obvious that there was a serious discrepancy between what the Albatross executive wanted in the matter of store personnel and what the company actually had as shown in the survey.

The company was also disturbed by the fact that the type of clerks which it was then hiring would not make efficient store managers in the future. Furthermore, a common practice among the managers was to keep good clerks in their stores as long as possible for purely selfish reasons instead of recommending them for promotion. Thus, the task of ferreting out the better clerks for positions as managers fell largely on the shoulders of the district supervisors. For selfish reasons, also, each district supervisor was anxious to keep in his territory all his first-class store managers.

In discussing the problems which confronted the company, a chief official expressed his belief that in the future the company should select its personnel from recent graduates of vocational high-school courses. He pointed out that such boys had had the necessary training in arithmetic and that for one reason or another they were the type of boys who expected to spend their lives in vocational pursuits. He added that the vocational graduates usually came from families where the father was a mechanic or factory worker whose wages averaged from $50 to $65 a week when he was employed.

The same official believed also that the company should institute training courses for all new clerks. The first part of the course should be formal instruction in foodstuffs. The second should be a probationary training in a demonstration store where the chief aim should be to teach the boy how to meet the public effectively. This training should extend over a period of two years. The official believed that under such a program, a graduate from a vocational high school course could look forward to becoming a store manager within a period of approximately five years.

To what extent, if at all, would the proposed change in the source of labor supply solve the problem of the Albatross Food Company?

# CHAPTER XVI

# JOB STANDARDS AND WAGE PAYMENT METHODS

## HALLERTON MACHINERY COMPANY

### 1. An Experience in Incentive Wage Payment.

The Hallerton Machinery Company was confronted with an increasing cost of production resulting principally from rising hourly wage rates. In an attempt to increase worker productivity, the company changed the method of wage payment for some jobs to piece rates set from past performance records. Many workers were dissatisfied with these rates, and production costs continued to rise. The management decided that a revision of the wage system was necessary. In the case of certain turret lathe operations a satisfactory solution was found in the adoption of a modified Halsey premium plan of wage payment.

### 2. The Need for Incentives in Securing Worker Productivity.
In the preceding chapter it was pointed out that the work force is the most highly dynamic element of the production process. Regardless of how carefully a worker is chosen and how well he is suited to a particular job, his continued productivity can be ensured only by sustained constructive treatment. It is a function of management to make certain that the worker has full opportunity for exercising his abilities on the job and to stimulate the worker to a full utilization of his capacity. If this is not done and management rests on the assumption that, having been properly chosen and placed in the organization, the worker will automatically produce as a properly adjusted machine produces, the outcome will not be satisfactory to either management or worker.

### 3. Incentive Wage Devices.
For many years factory workers were paid on a time basis, either by the month, the week, the day, or the hour. The assumption underlying this method of wage payment is that the employee places his time at the disposal of his employer and it is the responsibility of the latter to see

that the former is kept busy. The time basis of payment is still in use in many places and for certain types of jobs probably always will be used.

In more recent years there has been a general recognition on the part of production managers that time wages have certain serious limitations. All workers are not equally productive. Some have less physical and mental capacity for work than others, and they do not all possess the same desire to work. Under such circumstances it does not seem fair that the pay of the more efficient and more ambitious workers should be the same as that of the less efficient and the less ambitious. To meet this situation, the piece-rate system of wage payment was devised. Under the piece-rate plan, a base rate is set for performing a given task, for example, workers assembling carburetors in a factory making automobile parts may be paid 50 cents for each carburetor assembled. A slow worker may assemble only 16 carburetors a day. His wage would accordingly be $8. A medium worker, assembling 24 carburetors, would receive $12, and a very superior workman, completing 32, would receive $16. Each is paid according to his productivity. This is the thought underlying piece-rate payment.

In the past 35 years there has been a rapid development of modified piece-rate plans. These plans include three provisions: (1) that a normal daily output for the average worker is established; (2) that the worker is guaranteed a stipulated payment whether or not he attains this normal output; (3) that if a superior workman exceeds the task set as normal, he receives a bonus in proportion to his productivity in excess of normal production. The purpose behind all incentive plans is to get the worker to produce as large a daily output as possible. The employer is naturally much interested in high productivity of his workers, for it means that his machines are being used continuously and that his raw materials inventories are passing through the factory rapidly. Lack of capacity operation for machines and slow-moving raw materials have spelled bankruptcy for many a plant. The energetic production manager, therefore, does everything in his power to secure full worker productivity. A common device is the use of incentive wage plans.

**4. The Labor Group of the Hallerton Machinery Company.** The employees of the Hallerton Machinery Company, which made machine parts for the automobile industry, were recruited locally. The community was highly industrialized, and, while the labor supply was large, the demand for labor was also great, and under ordinary conditions demand exceeded supply. The Hallerton Machinery Company employed unskilled, semiskilled, skilled, and some highly skilled workers. Because of competition of other factories for workers, it had been unable to get a selected group of employees, even though it had an efficient employment department. Consequently, a cross section in any one of its production departments would have shown some poor workers, some medium, and some superior.

**5. Wage Conditions.** In the early years of its existence, workers of the Hallerton Machinery Company were paid hourly wages. Confronted with rising wage rates, company executives concluded that steps must be taken to increase worker output. As a result many operations were placed on a piece-rate basis.

**6. How the Piece Rates Were Set.** These piece rates were based on records of past performance supplemented by the experience of the foremen. The records consisted of departmental cost cards for each product, and showed the unit labor costs by products for each department. From these records were calculated the times taken by workers in the past to do each job. These records showed that the time taken for any one task varied greatly. The foreman's experience was very helpful in determining from these variations how much time was to be allowed in the future for the performance of the task.

Foremen were also helpful in setting a rate to be paid for each completed task. The cost cards showed the hourly rates men had been receiving on that job. Each past hourly rate was scrutinized to determine whether it seemed to be in line with the type of work and the so-called "going rate" for that class of work in the community. If it was not, it was revised, and the revised rate was used in calculating the piece rate.

If from a study of the records it was decided that the average worker would do a certain job in 20 minutes, the question then arose as to how much he should be paid for that job. If $1.05

was considered a proper hourly rate for that work, the piece rate for the 20-minute job would be one-third of the hourly rate, in this case 35 cents. This method of setting piece rates was simple, inexpensive, and quick. It was the method followed in setting all piece rates by the Hallerton Machinery Company.

**7. Results of Use of Piece Rates.** In use, these piece rates proved unsatisfactory. Some rates were set too low and some too high. As a result there was growing dissatisfaction with them on the part of both workers and management. When the rates had been set too low, workers were inclined to accuse the company of exploitation. When rates had been set too high, the management was inclined to hold the workers responsible for the increased costs of production which continued to develop in certain departments of the plant. Finally, conditions reached a point where the general manager decided to revise the whole wage payment structure. An industrial engineer was put in charge of the work of drawing up a new wage system. With the help of assistants, he at once began making time and motion studies to be used as the basis of new job standards.

**8. How the New Job Standards Were Set.** Much preliminary work was necessary to ensure reasonable accuracy of the time studies. First, the work in process was divided in such a way that each machine always received the same kind of material. Next, a study was made of all shafting, the feeds and speeds of the different machines, the tool holders, toolboxes, and all other equipment used on the automatic machines. Tools were tested in order to determine the best materials to be used in them and the correct methods of sharpening. After standardizing the entire equipment according to the tests which had been made, each operation was studied, the simplest, most advantageous methods of work performance were determined, the correct feeds and speeds were recorded, and the proper tools were designated.

When these preliminary details had been completed, workers were taught the best, least fatiguing, and most rapid method of performing each operation. This included instruction in the correct use of the equipment and drill in the exact motions to be employed. Finally, time studies were made of each operation as it was performed by skilled mechanics. Several studies were made of each operation, and observations were taken at various hours throughout the work day. From the data thus compiled, a standard performance time was calculated. This standard time was then increased by a carefully considered allowance for fatigue, relief periods, and interruptions not under the control of the operative. The result was a job performance time which could be safely used as a basis for a wage rate.

During these studies, effort was made to secure the cooperation of the workers being timed. Employees throughout the plant understood that the objectives were the determination of the best way of doing jobs and the setting of a standard of accomplishment that would be fair to the average worker in the company's employ. While jobs were being studied and work standards were being set, no attempt was made to set up either wage payment methods or wage rates. Both the engineers and the management preferred to treat wages as a separate problem. The objective of the job analyses was determination of work methods and fixing of accomplishment standards. This isolation of the wage problem from job analysis was sound. All too frequently the two problems are treated together and thereby confused. When that is done, no clear picture of either problem is obtained, and the results often are unsatisfactory. It is far better to study work methods and to fix job standards without considering wage methods or rates. If these are considered later as a separate problem, better results are usually obtained.

In setting work methods and performance standards, the character of the work force is importance. Whether the best or average workers are studied, the results will always be applied to the work group which the company actually employs or can hire. To set standards on any other assumption is a mistake.

**9. Choice of Wage Payment Method.** After the job studies had been completed, the question arose as to what method of wage payment should be used. One of the first jobs considered was that of performing certain turret lathe operations on cast-iron clutch spring sleeves used in automobiles. The industrial engineer favored the Taylor differential plan.[1] He said that he

---

[1] For descriptions and comparisons of various wage payment plans, see *Cost and Production Handbook,* Sec. 12, The Ronald Press Company, New York, 1940.

had had remarkable success with this system. He thought that it was well suited to the particular turret lathe job, which was simple in nature and required only dexterity and watchfulness on the part of the worker. Turret lathe operatives in the past had been completing an average of 25 sleeve castings per hour, for which they had been paid 4.5 cents per piece. The job studies showed that this output was low, that with a little training and stimulus the average worker could easily produce 38 pieces per hour, and that a superior workman should produce between 45 and 50. Therefore, the engineer proposed that standard production be set at 38 pieces per hour as shown by the job studies, that provision be made to train all workers in the more efficient methods, and that two piece rates be established, a low rate to be applied to all workers who did not attain standard, *i.e.,* 38 pieces per hour, and a high rate to be paid to all workers who attained or exceeded standard. The low rate would, he pointed out, penalize the slow, inefficient worker. As a result, one of two things would happen: either he would increase his output so as to earn the higher rate or he would become discouraged and quit the employ of the company. The engineer believed that either of these alternatives was preferable to present conditions. The high rate would act as a great stimulus, since workers who exceeded the standard would receive the high rate for all pieces produced. Thus, if a worker attained standard, *i.e.,* if he produced 38 pieces per hour, he would receive the high rate for all 38 pieces.

The general manager of the Hallerton Machinery Company did not agree that the Taylor differential system was best suited to turret lathe operations. He pointed out that the plan placed so great an emphasis upon the superior workman that its adoption might result in a serious drop in earnings for many of the workers and that general dissatisfaction might become so widespread as to jeopardize the whole plan of wage revision. He also emphasized the fact that since competition for first-class workers was so strong in the community, he had no reason to believe that the Hallerton Machinery Company could supply itself almost exclusively with superior workmen.

The production manager suggested as an alternative the adoption of a modification of the Halsey premium plan of wage pay-

ment.  He had had experience with this system before coming
to the Hallerton Machinery Company and had found it satisfactory.  Under the Halsey premium plan, the production standard, or task, was set on the basis of performance as shown from
past records.  If a worker completed an operation in less than the
standard time allowed, one-half the time so saved would be
credited to him for a bonus.

The objection to the installation of the Halsey plan in this
particular instance was that time and motion studies had already
shown that past records of performance were no indication of
what workers could do.  Consequently, it would not be advisable
to use them as a basis for payment.

After considerable discussion, it was finally decided to adopt
a plan which was a combination of the Taylor differential and the
Halsey premium plans.  Turret lathe operatives were guaranteed
a base rate of 90 cents an hour for this operation, irrespective of
the number of pieces produced.  The production of 38 pieces per
hour as determined by the time study was recognized as the
standard task.  If a worker exceeded standard, *i.e.*, if he completed 38 pieces in less than one hour, he was paid for 50 per cent
of the time so saved as a bonus for superior productivity.  If a
very superior worker completed 38 pieces in 40 minutes he would
save 20 minutes on the task.  For producing the 38 pieces in 40
minutes he would receive 60 cents ($^{40}/_{60}$ of 90 cents) plus 15 cents
($\frac{1}{2}$ of $^{20}/_{60}$ of 90 cents) or a total of 75 cents.  This worker's earnings on this job would thus be at the rate of $1.12$\frac{1}{2}$ an hour.

At the same time the company would benefit.  If the worker
produced 38 pieces in one hour he would receive 90 cents for the
work and the labor cost per piece to the company would be 2.37
cents (90 divided by 38).  If, however, the worker produced the
38 pieces in 40 minutes the labor cost per piece to the company
would be 2 cents per piece (75 divided by 38), a saving of over
$\frac{1}{3}$ cent per piece.  Under this method of wage payment the company always saved one-half of the dollar value of the time saved
by the worker.  If a worker failed to meet the standard output,
the labor cost was high.

**10. Summary and Conclusions.** *Importance of Accurate Data.*
The modified Halsey plan appears to have been a common-sense

manner of paying turret lathe operatives for the task in question. The evidence seems clear that the original piece rates did not act as an incentive to high output, largely because of inadequate methods employed in fixing rates. For this state of affairs the management, not the workers, was primarily to blame.

The case shows the need of accurate data on specific production operations before a wage system is devised. The fact that a modified Halsey premium plan appeared to suit the needs of these turret lathe operatives should not be taken as evidence that such a plan should have been used throughout the whole factory. A company frequently finds it necessary to employ more than one wage payment method in order to meet particular conditions in various parts of the factory. Such procedure, however, is not without its drawbacks. Several plans of wage payment, when used simultaneously, may increase the difficulties of administration. The amount of paper work in the form of records, production orders, job tickets, and payroll computations may become complicated. Workers are likely to be dissatisfied if they are unable easily to compare their own wages with those received by their companions and friends. A clear understanding of the wage method on the part of the workers is very important.

*Use of Incentive Wages.* Incentive wages are a basic concept of scientific management. Each year sees additions to the long list of wage devices already in use. Some of these plans have been prepared to meet particular situations and some are of more general application. Space does not permit a description of these plans in detail. Much has been written concerning them, and information regarding specific systems is easily obtainable. Exhibit 1, on page 389, presents in tabular form a comparison of important characteristics of the more commonly used plans. This table was compiled by the National Metal Trades Association for use of its members.

*Group Bonus Plans.* The fundamental idea underlying a group bonus is that when all members of a given group cooperate as a unit, the total productivity of the group is greater than when each employee works individually. It is basic to this idea that the members of the group be able to assist each other.

## EXHIBIT 1

### Characteristics of Wage Plans

| Wage Plan Analysis | Straight Time (Hourly) | Production Bonus | Task and Bonus (Gantt)(Diemer)(Baum)(Multiple Time)(Standard Time) | Ordinary Piecework (Contract) | Piecework with Guaranteed Day Rate (Manchester)(100% Premium)(Standard Hour) | Differential and Multiple Piecework (Taylor)(Merrick) | Premium (Halsey)(50-50)(Rowan) | Empirical Formula Premium (Barth) | Supervisory Element (Bedaux Point)(Haynes Manit) | Efficiency Scale (Emerson)(Knoeppel)(Bigelow)(Wennerlund) | Miscellaneous (Ficker Machine)(Individual Group)(Bigelow Waste)(Lichtner Quality)(Economy)(Parkhurst) |
|---|---|---|---|---|---|---|---|---|---|---|---|
| Standard Determination | None | Past performance | Should be accurate | Must be accurate | Should be accurate | Must be accurate | Past performance | Past performance | Must be accurate | Must be accurate | Must be accurate |
| Task Level | None | Low | Varies | Medium | Medium | High | Low | None | Medium | High | Varies |
| Incentive | Poor | Fair | Good | Excellent | Excellent | Greatest | Fair | Fair | Good | Good | Fair |
| Guaranteed Day Rate | Yes | Yes | Yes | No | Yes | No | Yes | No | Yes | Yes | Generally |
| Favorable to New Employees | Yes | Usually | Yes | No | Yes | No | Yes | Very | Yes | Yes | Usually |
| Employee Understanding | Easy | Easy | Hard | Easy | Easy | Hard | Easy (Rowan very difficult) | Extremely difficult | Hard | Hard | Extremely difficult. Some almost impossible |
| Payroll Computation | Simplest | Simple | Very complex | Simple | Simple | Very complex | Involved | Very complex | Involved | Very complex | Very complex |
| Supervisory and Indirect Labor Participation | No | Possibly | Only in groups | Only in groups | Only in groups | Only in groups | No (Halsey only in groups) | No | Yes | Usually | Possibly |
| Applicable to Groups | Yes | Yes frequently | Possibly | Yes | Yes frequently | Yes occasionally | Yes occasionally | No | Yes frequently | Yes frequently | Yes |

Cigar-making machine operatives are frequently paid on this basis. It requires three girls to operate one machine. If they work as a team, rather than as individuals, the hourly output of the machine is greater than if they do not help each other. The group is paid a rate for each cigar made, this amount being divided among the members of the team on a predetermined basis. The speed of the machine, in terms of cigars made, is dependent on the operatives. The raw material, tobacco, is never absolutely uniform, and the tasks of the operatives require somewhat different abilities. As three girls work together on one of these machines, they gradually come to know each other's abilities and soon have shifted the jobs among the three so that each is assigned the work she does best. Then the nature of the operations is such that the girls can help each other. Particularly is this possible when a nonuniform supply of wrapper comes to the machine.

The desirability of getting teamwork on this job is shown by the falling off in output when, for any reason, the regular routine of a group is upset. If one of the regular members of a group is unable to work, the introduction of a new girl into the group invariably results in lowered output. The girls object strenuously when a group is disturbed. This is because they are paid as a group for the number of good cigars produced, and when a group is disrupted, production falls off regardless of the effort of the new team and earnings drop.

Situations such as the foregoing satisfy the basic requirements for successful group payment.

Group bonuses are also sometimes paid workers on assembly lines. Frequently the management motive here is only partly to secure teamwork. There is usually little opportunity for workers to help each other when workers on the line are paced by the movement of a conveyor. Jobs are set so that each worker has about all he can do to perform his task before the conveyor takes the work on to the next operation. Still, in such circumstances there is occasional opportunity for one worker to help another temporarily, and as the earnings of the group are dependent on the rate of performance of the slowest operation on the line, the incentive to teamwork does exist even though the opportunity for it is not great.

The more dominant motive for group payment under such circumstances is ease of setting output standards. The work is evenly divided among all workers on the line, and instead of setting a task standard for each worker and computing each worker's earnings separately it is only necessary to fix the standard for the group as a whole. This is less costly than the setting of individual standards and also requires much less clerical work in keeping track of workers' earnings.

Workers are less likely to approve of group payment for long assembly lines than they are for small compact teamwork situations. The workers do not know all members of the group well. Each man is likely to feel that he contributes more to the earnings pool than his associates. Constant change in group make-up is unavoidable, and, when the day's output is low, discontent and grumbling are sure to follow.

Adverse worker reaction is responsible in considerable degree for the rather general abandonment of group bonus payment by automobile manufacturers. It has been found that hourly wages and machine pacing of workers tend to result in equal output with less worker dissatisfaction.

Sometimes group payment produces unexpected but desirable results. Rubber overshoes are usually made (assembled) by a group of 12 to 18 girls and men working on a production line basis. These lines have mechanical conveying of the work in process and the pace of the slowest worker determines the rate of output of the group as a whole. The group of workers is paid a predetermined sum for each shoe made. At the end of the day the total earned by the group is divided among the members of the group by a previously set ratio. If for any reason the line is shut down temporarily, each worker receives an hourly base rate for the amount of the down time. This hourly rate is less than the average hourly earnings when the line is in operation. With this method of payment it was always necessary for the line superintendent to keep an accurate record of all down time. Occasionally workers complained that they did not receive full time credit when a line was down. To eliminate this cause of dissatisfaction, the management installed a large electric time-recording clock at the head of each line where it could be plainly seen by the workers. The electric switch that started and stopped the conveyor line also controlled the action of the clock. When the switch was thrown to stop the line, that action automatically started the clock which then ran until the switch was set to the position that started up the line. When the line started, the clock stopped. Thus at the end of each day the clock automatically registered the amount of time the line had been shut down during the day and there could be no question as to the amount of hourly base pay each worker should receive because of line-down time.

The installation of the clocks effectively stopped worker complaints that they did not get all the down-time pay to which they were entitled. It also had another totally unexpected result. The difference between hourly base rates of pay and average earnings when the line was in operation was substantial. The workers soon came to regard the running clock as a source of loss to them. Whenever the line shut down, the workers became "clock-watchers," and unless operation was resumed quickly they would complain directly to the supervisor and urge him to get the line started again as rapidly as possible. These groups became very effective in putting pressure on supervision to maintain continuous operation of the lines. From a management point of view, this of course was very desirable, for the payment of base rates to a group of workers when a line was down was a direct loss to the business.

The group bonus is a wage specifically designed to foster cooperative effort on the part of a group of workers. Obviously, it is applicable only when conditions are such that cooperation is possible. When the opportunity for group activity is lacking, for any reason, there is little to be gained by the use of this device. Group bonuses have been used rather indiscriminately, and naturally many failures have resulted. When conditions are suitable, intelligent application of the group bonus will yield most satisfactory results as an incentive to increased productivity.

*Essentials of Successful Wage Plans.* Enough has been said to illustrate the fact that there are certain prerequisites to the successful operation of modern wage incentives.  Three conditions should be particularly noted.  First, the incentive itself must be suited to the job and its requirements.  Nothing is gained by using an incentive device to induce workers to attempt the impossible, nor is an incentive wage valuable except as it increases the productivity of the recipient.  This means that before a wage incentive plan is established, very careful study should be given to the problem of what constitutes a normal task and the various details which surround the performance of the job in question.  Second, the adoption of an incentive plan should mean that previous arrangements have been made to provide a steady flow of raw materials to each worker in just the quantity and at just the times needed.  It assumes that machines are kept in first-class condition so as to run at maximum speed.  There is nothing that will strike fire with the average worker more quickly than to be stimulated by the possibilities of high earnings by means of a bonus, only to find that such premiums are beyond practical realization because of conditions over which he has no control.  Third, experience has shown that if means are adopted to spur the worker to maximum productivity, the management must provide sufficient inspection service to care for any possible increase in defective work.  It is only natural that when operatives are highly stimulated to increase production, quality may suffer somewhat.  The modern production manager realizes this situation and makes provision for it.  In some of the more modern plants this is accomplished by means of incentives for quality.  More will be said on this subject under Quality Control, Chap. XXIII.

*Conclusions as to Incentives.*  Much has been written on wage incentives and much still remains to be learned concerning them.  The following statement, however, can be vouchsafed: if the production manager understands that high wages can mean low labor costs, if he is willing that labor retain a reasonable share of the increased productivity above a normal task, then there can be no possible objection to the use of wage incentives. When, however, these devices are used—as they sometimes are—to speed up the worker without commensurate remuneration to him, they are merely instruments of labor exploitation and do not deserve the support of socially minded citizens. If wage incentive devices are used intelligently and honestly, they will result in high wages to the worker, low cost to the management, and low prices to the consumer. If they do not result in this threefold benefit, careful investigation will inevitably reveal serious managerial malad-justment somewhere along the line.

*Union Attitude Toward Incentive Wages.* Today one fre-quently hears the statement that labor unions object to and successfully resist the use of wage incentives. This statement is a half-truth. Some unions definitely forbid and prevent the use of incentive wages. Other unions are equally insistent on the use of incentives. Currently there seems to be a slow trend toward increase in the use of incentive wage methods in unionized plants. No one will object more quickly than a union to a poorly designed incentive plan or to poorly set incentives. A number of unions today have their own well-trained time-study men. In an increasing number of plants, company and union technicians jointly set job time standards.

### QUESTIONS

1. Why is management interested in having workers produce at maximum output?

2. What is meant by incentive plans of wage payment?

3. What are the objectives of such incentives?

4. Describe production conditions in the turret lathe depart-ment of the Hallerton Machinery Company.

5. Compare past records with job study as means of setting job standards.

6. Why is it important that job standard determination be separated from wage rate fixing?

7. Explain the Taylor differential system of wage payment.

8. Explain the Halsey premium system of wage payment.

9. Why did the general manager believe that neither of these systems was best suited to the turret lathe operations on spring clutch sleeves in his plant?

10. How did a combination of these two plans tend to solve the problem?

**11.** What are the advantages and disadvantages of group payment plans? Under what circumstances is their use likely to prove successful?

**12.** What are the essentials necessary to the successful operation of wage incentive plans?

## L. S. STARRETT COMPANY

The L. S. Starrett Company manufactured an extensive line of machinists' precision tools. Micrometer calipers, which constituted the most important division of this line, were produced in a wide variety of frame styles, but with similarly constructed measuring heads. The accuracy of the measuring head, and hence of the tool itself, depended on the skill with which its spindle screw was finished. The finishing operation on spindle screws was done on a piecework basis of wage payment. This practice was questioned by the company's sales manager.

The L. S. Starrett Company of Athol, Massachusetts, was established in 1880 to manufacture combination squares. These tools combined the functions of a machinists' square, a level, and a measuring scale. Success was almost immediate, and profits of the company permitted rapid expansion. Other high-grade precision tools were added to the line as circumstances permitted until the company was said to be the largest manufacturer of machinists' precision tools in the world. Its line included many sizes and styles of micrometer, vernier, and spring calipers, combination squares, dividers, speed indicators, steel rules, machinists' levels, steel tapes, protractors, thickness gauges, screw-pitch gauges, steel scales, and hack-saw blades. These tools were well and favorably known for their high quality and accuracy.

The outside micrometer caliper, as shown in Exhibit 1, consisted of a C-shaped frame ($A$) carrying a hardened steel anvil ($B$) at one end, and a measuring head at the other. Measuring heads were similar and of the same range (1 inch) for all sizes, but the frames and anvils varied with each capacity. The principal parts of the measuring head were a spindle ($C$), a sleeve ($D$), and a thimble ($E$). The spindle was a steel rod about 2½ inches long and ¼ inch in diameter. It was hardened, ground, and polished for about half its length, and threaded with a 40-pitch screw (40 threads to the inch) for the remainder of its length. The sleeve was a tube of sufficient bore to accommodate the spindle. One end of the sleeve bore was smooth and the other was threaded to fit the spindle screw. The smooth bore end was fastened to the frame opposite the anvil. The thimble was a tube closed at one end and fitted over the sleeve. When the measuring head was assembled, the plain portion of the spindle passed through the end of the frame and into the sleeve. The spindle screw was threaded through the outer end of the sleeve and fastened to the inside of the thimble. The outside of

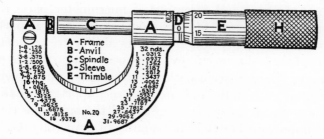

EXHIBIT 1.  L. S. STARRETT COMPANY.  MICROMETER CALIPER.

the sleeve was graduated for a distance of 1 inch into 40 equal parts. These graduations extended along a line drawn parallel to the axis of the head. The other circumference of the open end of the thimble was graduated into 25 equal parts. The whole head was assembled so that when the end of the spindle came into contact with the anvil, the zero graduation on the thimble would coincide with the axial line on the sleeve at its first graduation. One turn of the thimble would advance it and its attached spindle $\frac{1}{40}$ inch (0.025 inch) or one graduation on the sleeve. Since the thimble was graduated into 25 parts, one part or $\frac{1}{25}$ of a turn would advance the thimble and spindle $\frac{1}{25}$ of $\frac{1}{40}$ inch or 0.001 inch in relation to the sleeve and anvil.

To a great extent the success of the company resulted from the unusual intelligence and ability of its employees. A large percentage of these workers were exceptionally skillful mechanics. In addition, the nature of the products was such that long experience was required for the satisfactory performance of many of the "key" operations. Much care was given to the selection of new workers. Many of the company operatives had been born in the vicinity of Athol, and others had been attracted there by the reputation of the company. The local supply of workers possessing the requisite degree of skill and experience was limited, and the company had found it difficult to secure satisfactory new workers for key operations.

The outside micrometer caliper was the best known item in the company's line. It was a tool for making accurate linear measurements, and was manufactured in several styles and in sizes from ½ inch to 24 inches in capacity.

The manufacture and assembly of micrometer parts required an unusually high degree of mechanical skill. A large part of the success of the company was due to its ability to produce a micrometer of superior accuracy. Concentricity of the spindle, sleeve, and thimble; accuracy of graduations; and precision of contact between spindle and anvil were important quality factors, but company executives considered the spindle screw to be the most important factor in the quality of a micrometer. It had to run smoothly through the nut, its finish had to be excellent, and its diameter and pitch had to be as accurate as possible.

Micrometer spindle screws were roughed out on an automatic screw machine, and finished in two operations on a specially designed screw-cutting lathe. The machinists assigned to the finishing operation were men of long experience and recognized outstanding ability. Even skilled toolmakers required practice before they could produce micrometer screws acceptable to the company's inspectors.

The method of wage payment for workers finishing micrometer screws had been the subject of considerable discussion by the executives of the company. Originally these workers had been paid a straight hourly rate. Later a piecework rate for the job had been put into effect. The piecework rate was based on past production records. It took into consideration average earnings and average production of workers involved. Workers understood, however, that in accordance with company practice, piece rates thus established were only tentative. If experience proved them to be too low, they would be raised, and if too high, they would be cut.

Workers were not credited with finished work until it had been passed by inspectors. Defective screws had to be repaired without additional pay to the worker. This latter practice had a tendency to promote friction between inspectors and workers. The practice of paying for micrometer screw finishing on a piecework basis was questioned by the sales manager.

Should the finishing of micrometer screws have been paid for on a piecework basis?

## Problem 37

### BARBOUR STOCKWELL COMPANY

The Barbour Stockwell Company received an order from a well-known automobile manufacturer to make 10,000 steel pins.[2] The company had made similar pins on several occasions, but always in small quantity. As a general rule, workers were paid day wages. Company executives believed, however, that production costs for 10,000 pins could be lowered by establishing piecework rates as a basis of wage payment. Accordingly, they requested the shop superintendent to estimate such rates for the job in question. He was to base the piece rates upon the production costs of previous orders for pins.

The Barbour Stockwell Company operated a large iron foundry, a forge shop, a pattern and woodworking shop, and a well-equipped machine shop. Although the company had been

EXHIBIT 1. BARBOUR STOCKWELL COMPANY. DESIGN OF ROUND PIN.

formed originally to manufacture street railway equipment, such as frogs and switches, managing executives had, over a period of years, extended activities until they had established an enviable reputation for designing and building special-purpose machinery, both hand-operated and automatic. The company made a spe-

[2] See Exhibit 1.

cialty of producing machine parts, stampings, and iron castings for other manufacturers and was prepared to furnish engineering advice, to design machines and parts, and to supply patterns and models. It also stood ready to supply experienced crews of workmen for repairs on a wide variety of mechanical and electrical equipment.

Special machinery was frequently built on the basis of cost of material plus a flat hourly rate for direct labor. The labor rate, in such cases, was set sufficiently high to include burden and profit. Machines on which the company had had previous experience, machine parts, stampings, and castings were usually manufactured at a contract price agreed upon in advance. Prices were estimated by men of long experience from their knowledge of the materials, direct labor, and plant burden involved.

Workers on machine parts were usually paid straight hourly rates. This method was used because the quantity of pieces involved was usually small. Whenever the quantity was sufficiently large, however, the management often inaugurated piecework rates for specific tasks. Company executives believed that this policy was particularly desirable in the case of their company because of the type of worker employed. A wide variety of products required skilled workmen sufficiently versatile to operate any standard machine tool and to assemble and adjust intricate mechanisms. The primary requisite demanded of such operatives was excellence of work rather than speed. For the most part they were inexperienced on routine production jobs where speed and manual coordination were required. The management decided, therefore, that, whenever these men were required to do any considerable amount of work wherein speed and manual coordination were primary considerations, they should be paid on a wage basis which placed particular emphasis upon speed.

The Barbour Stockwell Company received an order from a well-known automobile manufacturer for 10,000 round steel pins as shown in Exhibit 1. Each pin was to have a total over-all length of 3½ inches. The shank, which was to be 3 inches long and ½ inch in diameter, was to have a ½-inch head, 1 inch in diameter. Such work was ordinarily produced on a turret lathe.

In this case, the automobile company had specified that the pins should have center holes in each end and that the shank should be concentric with these holes to 0.002 inch. With such specifications, it was necessary to turn the pins on an engine lathe at considerably more expense.

The company had made pins of similar character several times before, but always in small quantities. Competition for the new order had been keen, and the management had been forced to reduce its initial price considerably. As a result of an existing business depression, the working force of the company had been considerably reduced and only skilled mechanics remained. Since circumstances surrounding the making of the 10,000 pins seemed to warrant it, company executives instructed the shop superintendent to establish piecework rates on operations where they seemed practical.

On examining the drawings, the superintendent found that the pin could be made from cold-rolled steel bar stock of 1-inch diameter. This steel presented a polished surface which made additional finishing of the head at A (Exhibit 1) unnecessary. The initial operation was limited to cutting bar stock to correct lengths for the pins. The work could be done on a cutting-off machine by a circular metal saw. Several bars were placed in the machine at the same time, and sufficient stock for one pin was cut from each bar at one setting of the machine. The cutting-off machine was easy to set and required about 20 minutes to cut off sufficient stock for 10 pins. A boy or the foreman could tend the machine during spare time. Consequently, the shop superintendent decided that there was no particular advantage in applying piece rates to the initial operations. The second operation called for drilling and countersinking the ends of each piece in order to provide centers for turning on a lathe. This operation also was very simple and fast. A boy employed at part time could easily produce enough to supply several lathe operatives. There appeared to be no substantial savings in applying piece rates to this task. The superintendent did believe, however, that piece rates were adaptable to the lathe work.[3] This task consisted of three cuts, two roughing and one finishing, on the shank

[3] See "Lathes" and "Machine Tools" in the *Encyclopaedia Britannica*.

*B;* a squaring cut on the head at *C,* and a chamfer at *D.*[4] A lathe operative would turn the shank *B* to within about 0.02 inch of finished size by the two roughing cuts. He would then change tools and square the head at *C.* The finishing lathe operation required another change of tools and consisted of making the finishing cut on the shank *B.* Lastly, the operative cut a chamfer at *D* with a file. Each of the three lathe operations would be performed on several hundred pieces before a change in tools was made. The chamfering operation would be done at the same time as the finishing cut on the shank.

Reference to the records showed the superintendent that the lathe operation on five previous orders had been performed by five different men. The production record and hourly rate of each man is shown in Exhibit 2. All these men had left the employ of the company, but the superintendent remembered them. Johnson was an expert diemaker and toolmaker; Riley was a good machinist, efficient on production lathe work; Smith was a worker of little skill and small intelligence, usually acting as a helper; Walsh and Thomas were high-class all-round machinists who usually acted as assembly men.

**EXHIBIT 2**

Barbour Stockwell Company

Wage Rates and Production Records

| Employee | Hourly Wage Rate | Number of Pieces | Total Hours Required |
|---|---|---|---|
| Johnson.................. | $1.85 | 815 | 135.83 |
| Riley..................... | 1.20 | 685 | 85.63 |
| Smith.................... | .80 | 1,100 | 220.00 |
| Walsh.................... | 1.25 | 550 | 78.71 |
| Thomas.................. | 1.35 | 110 | 12.22 |

With this information before him the superintendent computed the number of pieces per hour and the cost per piece for each of

[4] A chamfer is a narrow bevel at the intersection of two surfaces. Its purpose is to remove rough or sharp edges and in the case of pins to provide a slight taper for ease in assembling.

the five men. The results of his computation are shown in Exhibit 3.

**EXHIBIT 3**

Barbour Stockwell Company

Calculation of Unit Labor Costs

| Employee | Hourly Wage Rate | Pieces per Hour | Cost per Piece |
|----------|------------------|-----------------|----------------|
| Johnson................. | $1.85 | 6 | 0.308 |
| Riley.................... | 1.20 | 8 | 0.150 |
| Smith................... | .80 | 5 | 0.160 |
| Walsh................... | 1.25 | 7 | 0.178 |
| Thomas................. | 1.35 | 9 | 0.150 |

The contract called for delivery of the entire order in six weeks. To accomplish this, the superintendent would have to provide six men. He had available two production machinists and four all-round machinists who usually worked on machine assembly and intricate repairs. The task still remaining was to set a piece rate for the six workers.

**QUESTIONS**

1. What should the piece rate have been?
2. Should the job have been put on a piece rate?
3. Should past records have been made the basis for rate setting if a piece rate was to be used on this job?

**Problem 38**

**AUCKWAY PRODUCTS COMPANY**

The Auckway Products Company employed a large number of men and women. Some of these workers were paid by the day or hour; others received straight piece rates; and others received bonus payments based on standard tasks. The engineer in charge of wage systems for the plant recommended the installation of a group bonus wage plan for workers in the automatic screw machine department.

The Auckway Products Company was a well-known maker of typewriters and calculators. Most of its products were assembled from a large number of small finshed parts. Sometimes there were as many as 12,000 of these in one machine as well as a limited number of heavier parts. Between 7,000 and 8,000 men and women were employed throughout the plant. These workers were paid by a variety of methods: day and hourly wages, piece rates, and incentive bonuses. Employees in the automatic screw machine department were paid straight piece rates.

Screws and similar small parts were important items for the Auckway Products Company. During the course of a year, they used millions of these small pieces in a large number of varying sizes and shapes. The making of such parts was not, however, an intricate process requiring the time of skilled mechanics. Automatic screw machines turned out such items in bewildering volume.

In the screw machine department of the Auckway Products Company, automatic machines were arranged in banks. One operative tended four machines. His task was to set the machines for the desired type of product and to keep the magazine of each machine filled with bar steel or brass. He also had to control the correct flow of water and oil. In case of minor troubles, he had to remedy the defect. Bar stock was automatically fed from the magazine into the machine, which performed all the necessary operations for making the part automatically. Intelligent supervision of the machine was necessary, however, at all times, and it was highly undesirable to have a machine idle because the magazine was empty or the machine out of adjustment.

The engineer in charge of installing wage systems believed that productivity in the automatic screw machine department could be further increased by the use of a group bonus in addition to the piece rates in force, and he recommended that such an installation be made.

## QUESTIONS

1. Just how did the engineer expect a group bonus to result in increased productivity in the automatic screw machine department?

2. Do you think the recommendation was sound?

3. Explain how a worker benefits under a group bonus plan.

4. Under what conditions is a group bonus superior to individual piece rates?

### Problem 39

## CUTLER AND CUTLER, INC.

Cutler and Cutler, Inc., had been paying overtime bonus checks to its employees at Christmas time. After the company was merged with a group of companies producing similar and allied products, the management of Cutler and Cutler, Inc., considered the desirability of continuing the Christmas bonus.

Cutler and Cutler, Inc., of Portland, Oregon, manufactured a complete line of packing house equipment for the handling of apples, pears, and similar fruits. Its products were recognized as being of outstanding excellence throughout the fruit-growing districts of the Pacific Northwest. Equipment manufactured by the company was also much used in other apple-growing regions of the United States and in the citrus fruit districts of the South. A relatively small portion of its output was exported.

The demand for the company's principal products came almost entirely in the months of July, August, September, and October. Its production was organized to meet this seasonal demand. A crew consisting of its most skilled workers was maintained permanently. The proportionate size of this regular force had been gradually increased as the management had by various means somewhat relieved the highly seasonal nature of its market. The permanent crew was supplemented in periods of high production by temporary workers. These workmen knew that their jobs were of short duration, but because of good working conditions, excellent wages, and the fair treatment received, they were glad to work for Cutler and Cutler, Inc. Each year, a large number of the temporary workers were men who had been similarly employed by the company in past years. Whenever additions were made to the permanent work force, selection was made from the temporary employee group. All employees of the company were native Americans, highly intelligent, and possessed of the considerable degree of education typical of Pacific Coast labor. The plant had always been operated on an open-shop basis.

All workers in the company's plant were paid hourly wages. During periods of rush production many employees worked overtime, which they were paid for at one and one-half times the regular rate. If a workman did not wish to work overtime, he was not urged to do so. There was no discrimination between those who were willing to work overtime and those who were not.

For several years the company had given its permanent employees bonus checks at Christmas time. The amount of the check depended on the wages received during the preceding year, the amount of overtime worked, and the profits earned by the company. The overtime factor was weighted heavily in computing the bonus, and the men were given to understand that the bonus was additional compensation for long hours of overtime work. The men were likewise repeatedly told that the payment of a bonus depended entirely on the ability of the company to earn a profit and that when profits were not realized there would be no bonus checks.

Bonus checks had been paid for several years. The last bonus payment was the largest. At that time, a permanent employee who had worked 2,639 hours during the year, 320 hours of which were overtime, at the regular hourly rate of 90 cents, would have received a bonus check of $93.93. If this man had worked no overtime, his bonus check would have amounted to $51.

The method of computing the bonus had been carefully explained to the men each year. A sum of money was set aside from profits at the end of the fiscal year. This sum was divided into two equal parts. One-half was divided among the permanent workers in proportion to the number of hours worked (overtime excluded) and the hourly rate of pay received. The other half was divided among those permanent workers who had worked overtime in proportion to the number of overtime hours worked and the hourly rate of pay received.  The sum set aside for this purpose was practically the same for each of the three years when bonuses had been paid.  The last bonus payment was a surprise to the men because they had somehow come to believe that profits for that year would be low if not non-existent.

Since its organization, Cutler and Cutler, Inc., had always been owned and managed by two brothers.  The company had been successful from the start and had enjoyed a steady growth.  The owner-managers had always known the employees personally and had had daily contact with them throughout the plant.  Superintendents and foremen had worked their way up through the organization and were personally familiar with the policies and aims of the management.

Cutler and Cutler, Inc., joined in a merger consisting of six companies manufacturing products that were similar or allied to those of Cutler and Cutler, Inc.  The merged companies and their products were as follows:

| Name | Location | Products |
| --- | --- | --- |
| John Bean Manufacturing Co. | San Jose, California | Orchard sprayers |
|  | Lansing, Michigan | Sprayers |
| Anderson-Barngrover........ | San Jose, California | Canning machinery |
| Sprague—Cells Corp......... | Hoopton, Illinois | Canning machinery |
|  | Buffalo, New York | Canning machinery |
| Citrus Machinery Co........ | Dunedin, Florida | Orange-packing equipment |
|  | Riverside, California | Orange-packing equipment |
|  | Anaheim, California | Orange-packing equipment |
| Cutler and Cutler, Inc........ | Portland, Oregon | Packing-house equipment |
|  | Toppenish, Washington | Packing-house equipment |

Following the merger, Cutler and Cutler, Inc., retained a large portion of its autonomy as far as operating management was concerned.  The Cutler brothers remained in charge and made frequent periodic reports of operations to the board of directors of the merged companies.  One of the brothers was a member of that board, which held monthly meetings at San Jose, California.

The merger proceedings were viewed with curiosity and some concern by the employees and sales organization of Cutler and Cutler, Inc. The general reaction seemed to be a feeling of uncertainty as to the future. In the past the men had felt that they were working for the Cutler brothers personally. With the coming of the merger they wondered if they had become employees of a large corporation with far less personal interest in the individual worker. There was no outstanding manifestation of change in employee attitude. The only evidence of change was in little things such as carelessness in the use and preservation of small tools. The company purchasing agent had reported a noticeable increase in expenditures for such items.

In August of the year in which the merger was effected, the company payroll included 50 permanent and 100 temporary workers. At that time the management was considering the advisability of continuing the bonus check practice as a means of labor motivation.

Should the bonus have been continued?

## Problem 40

### CORPORAL MOTOR CAR COMPANY (A)

The Corporal Motor Car Company of Denver, Colorado, was equipped to do complete automobile repair and service work in addition to handling the sale of new and used cars. In June, 1948, the service division was handling between 65 and 75 cars per day that were in the shop less than 24 hours. There were also 20 to 30 cars in the shop at all times for major repair work that lasted from two days to six months. The amount of repair work was subject to considerable random daily variation in volume and some seasonal variation with the summer being the busiest season. The charges to the customers on every repair job were divided into labor, parts, and supplies, such as gas, oil, and accessories. The service division billed labor charges of $10,000 to $12,000 per month.

The entire service and repair organization was under the direction of the service division manager, Mr. Currier.  The service division employed approximately thirty people in the following jobs: five service salesmen, eleven general utility mechanics, one radio repairman, two grease-stand operators, one washstand operator, three body repairmen, four painters, one automatic-clutch repair specialist, one control-tower operator, and one car jockey.  The general utility mechanics were available to do any type of repair or service work not handled by one of the specialists listed above.  One of the body repairmen and one of the painters were designated as lead men in their respective departments.

When a customer first entered the garage, he was met by one of the service salesmen.  The service salesmen had the responsibility of maintaining satisfactory customer relations.  These men had the duty of discussing the customer's needs with him and giving the customer a definite delivery promise time.  The service salesmen arrived at a proper delivery promise time by consulting with the control-tower operator.

The control-tower operator had his office in an elevated centrally located booth in the shop.  He maintained a master daily control sheet listing all the pending repair and service jobs.  From the information on this master daily control sheet and on the basis of his own experience the tower operator set delivery promise times for service salesmen.  Once delivery promises were made, it was the responsibility of the tower operator to see that the promises were fulfilled.  In order to accomplish this, the tower operator handled the work scheduling and instructed the mechanics as to which cars they were to work on and when they were to do them.  The control-tower operator was assisted in his work by a two-way communication system connected with 15 different speakers on the garage floor and by a general public address system.

The service salesmen entered the customer's delivery promise time as supplied by the tower operator on an invoice form.  They also entered information as to the nature of the repair work to be done.  The invoice form was filled out in triplicate and served as a complete record of the repair job.  The service salesmen forwarded the first two copies of the invoice form to the control tower to supply the information for entries on the master daily control sheet. From the control tower these first two copies were sent to the parts room and eventually to the cashier's desk to serve as a customer billing. The stiff third copy of the invoice form was attached by the service salesmen to the automobile to be repaired. This third copy served as an explanation to the mechanics of the nature of the repair work to be performed. When any mechanic finished working on any car, he glued a time ticket on the back of the third copy of the invoice form. The time ticket indicated the standard labor charge for the job performed, the date, and the number of the mechanic doing the work. The mechanics retained a copy of these time tickets and regularly turned them in to the service division office as a record from which wage payments were to be computed.

Since 1935 the service division had used a "flat-rate" system of paying its employees and in 1948 was paying all its employees on this basis with the exception of the service salesmen, the washstand operator, the control-tower operator, and the car jockey. The flat-rate system served as a means for both making labor charges to the customer and paying wages to the mechanic. Under this system the customer was billed a standard labor charge based on the standard time in hours required for performing the specified repair work, multiplied by $2.50, the standard labor rate per hour. The mechanics performing the work received 40 per cent of the labor charge as their wage.

The standard time required to perform all types of repair work, with the exception of body repair and paint work, on all car models was obtained originally from a standard rate book. This rate book was supplied by the manufacturer of the car for which the Corporal Motor Car Company had a sales dealership but covered practically all other makes as well. The last book listing standard times had been issued by the automobile manufacturer in 1942. Since that time the Corporal Motor Car Company had been unable to increase the basic labor charge of $2.50 per hour. The company had resorted to various devices for increasing the earnings of its mechanics in order to hold them during the war period. The principal device used was the increase of the standard time allowed for performing the different repair jobs. All the standard times in use in 1948 were higher than specified in the 1942 rate book as a result of the gradual increasing of these rates by the management over the intervening years. For example, the standard allowed time for performing a certain overhaul job on rear shock absorbers had been increased from 1.1 hours in the 1942 rate book to 2 hours, the rate used in 1948. There was some justification of these rate increases on the basis that during the war the average age of the cars being repaired was increasing and as a direct result repair work became more difficult. However, the chief reason for the rate increases was to enable the mechanics to increase their earnings. As an additional incentive to its mechanics, the management during the war guaranteed a minimum income of $55 a week to its service employees who were being paid on a flat-rate basis. This guaranteed minimum income was discontinued at the end of 1946. In 1948 the Corporal Motor Car Company was anticipating raising its basic labor charge rate from $2.50 per hour to $3 per hour.

During 1948 the weekly income of the service division mechanics had been ranging from $50 to $100 a week. The mechanics were able to earn this money during a 44-hour work week in which Mr. Currier estimated the mechanics spent on the average three-fourths of their time actually doing repair work. The variation in weekly income was a result of variation in the nature of the work being done by the mechanics and the amount of work in the shop. The general utility mechanic's average weekly income was about $65 per week. The body repair man's average income was around $100 a week. These weekly income figures may be compared with weekly incomes of $55 to $60 being paid to mechanics working on straight hourly wages in the same area.

It was common knowledge in the service division that certain repair jobs were "tough" and certain ones "easy" as regards the ability of the mechanic to better the standard time. It was one of the duties of the control-tower operator to see that no mechanic was assigned an excessive number of "tough" repair jobs. The control-tower operator had developed considerable skill in making equitable work assignments to the various mechanics. Mr. Currier had received from the mechanics very few complaints of discrimination in this regard.

Mr. Currier followed a policy of avoiding as much as possible the increasing of his service division staff. All the mechanics knew that the hiring of an extra mechanic meant that the available repair jobs and the income therefrom would have to be divided among a larger group, and they expressed their disapproval of any additions to the group. Mr. Currier hired new personnel only when it became evident over a period of time that it was impossible for the staff to handle all the available work.

There were two checks made upon the quality of the repair work done by the garage mechanics. Before any car was returned to the customer, the service salesman, who handled the original order, had the responsibility of checking the car over to make sure that the customer's wishes had been fulfilled. The customer himself provided the second check on the repair-work quality, since most customers did not hesitate to bring back cars with faulty performance. Every mechanic was required to "rework" his own faulty repair jobs without additional compensation. Excessive complaints about the quality of the repair work of any one mechanic came to the attention of Mr. Currier.

Mr. Currier felt that the flat-rate system of wage payment had proved to be highly satisfactory over the years. He brought out the fact that the Corporal garage mechanics had developed especially fast methods of handling repair work. He reported that one of his mechanics had replaced an entire automobile body frame in 12 hours when the standard time for the job was 22 hours. He stated that all the mechanics privately had purchased special tools to assist them in performing their jobs rapidly. Many of the mechanics had invested as much as $200 in these special tools. Most of the service division staff had been with the company for many years, and very few employees had left the organization voluntarily.

Be prepared to discuss the advantages and disadvantages of the wage payment method employed by the Corporal Motor Car Company:

1. To the workers
2. To the management
3. To the customers

# CHAPTER XVII

## WAGE DETERMINATION

### THE BRIGHTVALE COMPANY

## 1. An Example of Union-Management Cooperation in Setting Wage Rates.

The Brightvale Company made valves and allied fittings for the plumbing trade. A few months after the company signed a contract with a CIO affiliated union a large number of wage grievances were brought to the attention of the management by union representatives. Study of these complaints indicated that the company's wage scale needed thorough revision and the management arranged with the union to study all jobs and to set new wage rates wherever the study indicated that change was needed.

## 2. Nature of Wage Determination.

There is nothing remotely resembling a formula that will tell how much a worker should receive for the performance of a specific task or for working for a specific period such as an hour or a day. It is possible to indicate rather exactly what influences must be taken into consideration in setting a wage rate whether it be a rate per unit of output such as a piece rate or a unit of time such as an hourly rate.[1] The quantitative expression of the values of these influences cannot be determined with anything like mathematical, engineering, or scientific exactness. In every case a substantial element of human judgment is required.

There are three kinds of major considerations that are important in setting a piece rate. The three factors that are important piece-rate ingredients are the time required to do the task; the job content, the things required of the worker in the performance of the task; and a host of related influences, most of them external to the job itself. These latter include such common-

[1] For the purposes of this discussion, the piece rate will be used as typical of productivity rates and the hourly rate as representative of time rates.

place notions as the supply of and demand for workers capable of performing the work, organized pressures such as state and Federal laws, union demands and regulations, company wage policies, changes in the cost of living, current profits of industry, and the like.

**3. Time as a Wage Element.** The time actually being required to do a task can often be measured with considerable accuracy. To determine how much time it should take to do the job is a quite different problem that calls for the best of human judgment. Judgment considerations of major influence include the following: the skill of the worker observed doing the task relative to other workers of more or less ability who may do the job, the speed at which the man was working at the time he was observed, the effects of fatigue both physical and mental on the worker's production proficiency, the extent to which workers will be interrupted in the performance of the task, the need for and the results of worker training in a relatively easier way of doing the work, and the desire or lack of desire of the observed worker to attain a reasonable rate of output. None of these things can be measured exactly. However, careful adjustment of observed times, if all necessary modifications are considered, can give a reasonably reliable figure for the time it normally should take to do a task.

**4. Job Content as a Wage Factor.** Clearly, jobs differ greatly from one another in the ability required to perform them. This difference will be very influential in determining how much should be paid for the performance of the task. Analysis of the work involved in setting up and adjusting a screw machine so that it will turn out hundreds or thousands of duplicate pieces automatically will show that it is a vastly different task from the job of keeping the machine supplied with the necessary raw material and removing the finished parts that result from operation. The former is a highly skilled task that can be performed well only by a man who has had years of training and experience. The latter job calls for almost no training and can be performed by any reasonably strong person after a few minutes of instruction. Clearly the nature of the setup job is such that we should expect to pay a relatively high hourly rate for it in contrast to the hourly rate of the unskilled "operator" of the machine after it has been set up.

Job content, the nature of a job, can be accurately determined by an experienced analytical observer and can be set down in writing. To evaluate the relative "worth" of the content of two or more jobs cannot be done with an accuracy as great as is possible in determining the time it should take to do the job. Skill required to do a specific job, responsibility inherent in the job, physical drain of the job, and other common job characteristics are so intangible as to be difficult of measurement. However, methodical attempts at job content analysis usually will give more satisfactory comparative results than will reliance on general information or the foreman's offhand knowledge of the job. Such systematic analysis of job content requirements has become common in industry and is useful just so long as it is recognized that no index of relative job content can be determined with complete scientific accuracy.

**5. Related Influences, the Third Type of Wage Factor.** The third type of wage consideration, related influences, is even less subject to measurement than is the time required to do the job or the nature of the job itself. The so-called "going rate" in the community is commonly taken as an index of the impact of supply and demand on each other. The validity of this assumption can be challenged but inasmuch as the going rate concept is a useful one we will not concern ourselves with the question of whether it is an accurate measure of supply-and-demand influences. The going rate itself is not easy to determine. But again let us accept the notion that often a representative figure is obtainable.

Such influences as minimum wage laws are more readily determinable. Union pressures and cost of living influences are matters of negotiation. Company wage policy as a wage determinant influence is a problem of definition and interpretation. When a company executive explains that his concern has a policy of paying the going rate or better, it is necessary to convert this generalization to something much more specific. Other influences resemble more or less closely some one of the foregoing. It is obvious that matters such as these are important considerations when it comes to fixing a wage rate. It is also clear that they do not lend themselves readily to measurement. In many cases quantitative expression is even more difficult than would appear on the surface.

This third class of wage determinant can be the most difficult of all when it comes to taking executive action. To understand and properly attend to these influences requires much thought and discrimination. Here they are treated only in superficial fashion, the objective being to make clear the nature of the problem of setting wage rates.

To summarize, a piece rate is an expression of a three-part complex: time, job content, and related influence. None of these is completely subject to objective measurement. Systematic analysis pointed toward measurement is beneficial and should be a procedure of more common practice than is now prevalent.

**6. Comparison of the Hourly and Piece-rate Problems.** The setting of an hourly rate involves two of the three types of influence just summarized. The time factor is omitted as the basic assumption of the hourly rate is that management assumes the responsibility for the worker's proper use of his time while he is on the job. Thus the hourly rate is the result of combining job content considerations with all the related influences of the third class.

Actually an acceptable piece rate assumes the predetermination of an hourly rate for the task. In part there is a mathematical relationship between the two. Assume that a job content analysis and appraisal of all related factors have resulted in an hourly rate of 90 cents for a specific job. Assume also that time study of the job shows that a normal output for the job is 30 pieces. On this job the wage payment per piece should be 3 cents (90 divided by 30). This relationship is sound and basically it holds. Not infrequently, however, certain other considerations enter the picture. Situations such as the guarantee to the worker of a minimum hourly take-home pay and the desire to make the piece rate serve as an incentive to a high rate of output frequently will cause departure from the simple mathematical relationship of the time standard to the basic hourly rate as it was just illustrated. Whatever the practice in relating the standard time for the job to the hourly base rate the function of each is the same. Time standards are units of time; time study in itself never produces dollar values. Job content when combined with related influences will produce a dollar value per hour or other time unit. To get dollar values per piece produced or operation completed necessitates relating the two: the standard time per piece and the dollar value per unit of time.

**7. Magnitude of The Brightvale Company Undertaking.** When executives of The Brightvale Company agreed with union representatives to a complete overhauling of the wage rates paid for the 400 or more jobs performed by its workers, they recognized that they were undertaking no small task. They realized that a result satisfactory to workers and management alike would require restudying most jobs to set new time standards, analyzing all jobs and evaluating their content in terms of a common standard, and finally negotiating with the union the base rates for each job studied. Demand for the company's products was at an all-time high point, and the executives were devoting their entire energies to increasing production to meet this demand. The proposed study would call for steady work by a group of capable technicians for at least 12 months. The company had a small efficient time-study department but had no experience in formal job rating. It was decided that in the light of these considerations it would be desirable to employ a firm of management consultants to do the work and to this the union agreed.

**8. Company-union Relationships.** Many of the company's 1,200 employees were either highly skilled or semiskilled. They included foundry workers, machine shop workers, assemblers, and maintenance workers. Although the company's experience with a union was brief, its relations with the workers and their union representatives thus far had been excellent. This friendly relationship was the result of a constructive attitude taken by the company executives. While the plant manager had regretted that the union had established itself in the company, he accepted the situation and made every effort to work with it. For months he had been devoting a large portion of his time to training his foremen and supervisors in ways of working with the union. He was sure that good union-management relations could be had if his foremen and supervisors understood the importance of day-to-day working together and knew how to conduct themselves to this end in their daily operating contacts with the workmen and their representatives. That he had made good progress with this program was shown by the way in which the union shop stewards were bringing wage inequalities to the attention of the foremen. The union stewards were aggressive in this work and were insistent that management take action. In every instance, however, they had gone to the appropriate foreman rather than directly to the plant manager and had shown understanding of the management's problem.

**9. The Management's Approach to the Wage Grievance Problem.** When investigation of the cases of improper wage rates began to indicate that the company's wage structure as a whole was at fault, the management called in the union representatives and explained the situation frankly. After several meetings the union agreed to a long-range program of complete resetting of standards and rates and in return were assured by the management that the union would be represented throughout the entire process.

Shortly thereafter the local president of the union gave the production manager the names of three of the company's employees with the request that they represent the union in the development and carrying out of the program. All three men had been employed by the company for some time and were known by the management as good reliable workers. One of these men worked in the foundry, one in the machine shop, and one in the assembly division. The management accepted the union's request that the machine shop representative should give his full time to the wage program and that the others should be available whenever required, particularly whenever work was being carried on in either of the departments they represented.

The company then assigned its chief industrial engineer to be responsible for the carrying out of the program. The chief engineer immediately requested the union committee to arrange to have two union representatives assigned to the time-study department for training in time and motion study work at the company's expense. This was done. The management then asked the three-man union committee to work with it in the selection of an engineering firm to carry out the work.

After considerable negotiation the union and the management selected the White Management Consultants for the job and in the fall of 1948 a "task force" consisting of the three union representatives, two men from the consulting firm, and the company's chief industrial engineer went to work.

At the start it was agreed that the program would cover three things: setting of time standards for all jobs in the plant; evaluation of all jobs in terms of their content; setting new piece rates for all jobs on piece rates and new hourly rates for all other jobs. It was agreed that the new job standards would be set by company time-study engineers and the newly trained union time-study men working jointly under the supervision of one of the industrial consultants. The other industrial consultant was to head a group consisting of the union representative of the machine shop and either the foundry or assembly division representative plus two men assigned from the company's industrial engineering department. This group would analyze all jobs and evaluate them, using a procedure that the management consulting firm recommended as having produced satisfactory results for a number of its clients.

Both of the industrial consultants were to be responsible to the company's industrial engineer who had been given responsibility for the entire program. This individual was to be responsible for combining the results of all studies and together with the plant manager for the negotiation with another committee from the union of new piece or hourly rates on all jobs.

The management believed that bringing the union so completely into the picture throughout the study would tend to make for union acceptance of the resulting changes. The union was confident that by being so represented it could protect the interests of its members throughout. The White consulting firm had been selected from several applicants because it had a record of successful experience in cooperative union-management working out of such programs. Both the union committee and the management were impressed by the consultant's statement that his concern would be unwilling to accept the assignment on any other basis.

**10. Progress of the Time-study Program.** From the beginning the study progressed satisfactorily. At first the work of the time-study group was slow. There was some disagreement between the union and the management time-study men as to suitable allowances for rest, interruption, worker speed, worker proficiency, and the like. However, the consultant in charge of the work insisted that the time-study men work out these differences themselves. They soon learned that by consulting with the workers on the job and the foreman in charge they could work out mutually satisfactory standards. This result was due in part to the fact that the time-study men did not concern themselves with wage rates; their responsibility ended once they obtained union and management acceptance of a standard time for the performance of a task. The time-study men worked in pairs, a union man and a company man. As soon as they agreed on a standard for a job, they reported the standard time for the task to the company's chief industrial engineer. He submitted the standard to the plant manager and to the union president. Usually after going over the work of the time-study men these three men would officially accept the standard. Occasionally it was necessary to bring in the two men who had set the standard for an explanation when the new standard differed radically from the one it was to replace. By getting official acceptance of a new standard as soon as it was worked out both the management and the union early gained confidence in the program. This served to speed up the progress of the work.

**11. The Work of the Job Rating Group.** The steps followed by the job evaluation group consisted of the following:

1. Getting a written description of every job in the plant.
2. Rating each job according to the procedure provided by the consulting firm.
3. Ranking the jobs as a check against the second step.
4. Plotting the jobs on a scatter chart and drawing a wage curve.

**12. Job Descriptions.** Each job description was prepared by a union representative and a company man working together.

They observed the job carefully: what the worker did; what tools and machines he used; what accuracy the work called for; the worker's responsibility for materials and for any helpers he directed; his responsibility for the safety of himself, his helpers, and for any others; the conditions under which the job was performed, such as temperature, dirt, fumes, etc. They talked with the worker and his foreman to learn to what extent the job involved planning by the worker, how much physical effort was involved, how constantly physical and mental effort had to be applied in performing the work.

From the information thus obtained the investigators wrote a description of the job. They were careful to make it cover all aspects of the task, to make it clear and as simple as possible. As soon as a job description was written, the investigators submitted it to the worker or workers who performed the task. If they approved the description, they signed their names to it. If they suggested changes, the description was rewritten until everyone concerned approved. This procedure was followed for all jobs in the plant.

**13. Results of Writing Job Descriptions.** The job descriptions were completed in about three months. One result was the reduction of the number of jobs from 412 to 260. Many jobs were duplicated in different parts of the plant. In the past this duplication had not been recognized although the management knew that some duplication existed. Each of the 412 tasks had been treated as a different job and wage rates had been set on each. These rates were not always the same. When the job descriptions revealed that actually there were only 260 different jobs, one cause of unsatisfactory wage rates at once became apparent. Both the union and the management were satisfied that one major source of past troubles was already located.

**14. Rating the Jobs from the Job Descriptions.** The next task undertaken by the job evaluation group was to rate the jobs using the written job descriptions as a basis. Six job characteristics (factors) were used in rating each job. Following is a list of these factors and the maximum values allowable for each.

Skill—Dexterity—Experience Required.............. 300
Responsibility Involved........................... 200
Practical Knowledge Required...................... 80
Mental Effort.................................... 100
Physical Effort................................... 60
Working Conditions............................... 60

The job evaluation group first rated each of the 260 jobs for the relative skill, dexterity, and experience required for satisfactory performance on the job. The highest rating given any job for this factor was 300 and the lowest was 60. The group then rated the 260 jobs for responsibility involved in the performance of the job. Here the highest rating was 200 and the lowest 20. In like manner the 260 jobs were successively rated for each of the remaining four factors. The rating group worked together in making these ratings. Occasional disagreements were settled by observing the job again and talking the problem out with the workers and the foremen. The next step was to total the six factor values for each job. This resulted in a total rating for the highest rated job of 510 points and a rating for the lowest rated job of 205 points. The total number of different ratings given the 260 jobs was 64.

**15. Checking the Results of Job Rating.** To get an over-all check on these ratings, the group arranged the 260 jobs in a rank list from highest rating to lowest rating. Examination of this rank list revealed three jobs that seemed to be out of line on the basis of the ratings. These jobs were restudied starting afresh with the preparation of new job descriptions and rerating of the jobs on the basis of the new descriptions. It was found that one of the original job descriptions was faulty and that when this job was evaluated on the basis of the corrected description it fell into its proper place in the rank list. No errors could be found in the descriptions or evaluations of the other two jobs and the group concluded that the original ratings were correct and should stand.

**16. Converting the Point Ratings to Dollar Values.** The union and the management had agreed that after the job ratings had been established they were to be converted to dollar values according to the procedure that had been used in the past by the consultants. Six jobs that rated from low to high in the rating scale were selected as the basis for setting a wage curve. These were jobs on which everyone agreed that the present hourly or base rates were correct. This conclusion was checked carefully by going to a number of other employers in the area and obtaining the rates they were paying for jobs which investigation

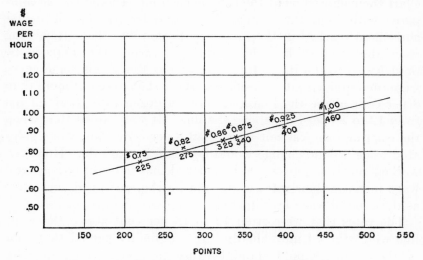

EXHIBIT 1. THE BRIGHTVALE COMPANY. WAGE CURVE.

showed to be similar to the six jobs as they were performed at The Brightvale Company plant. These rates were further checked by comparing them with rates paid for the same jobs by competitors of The Brightvale Company that were located in other though similar industrial areas. The dollar rates for the six base jobs were established in this way. The point and dollar values of the six jobs were then plotted on a chart with the result shown in Exhibit 1.

It was found that a straight line could be drawn that would pass through four of the six plotted points and that the other two points were practically on this line. It was agreed that this line was to be the wage curve for establishing rates for all 260 jobs. Theoretically the hourly or base rate for every job could be determined by tracing the point value of the job up to the wage line and reading the dollar value of that point in the line from the wage scale at the left.

**17. Negotiating the Wage Rates.** Originally it had been agreed that the dollar rates for all jobs were to be negotiated. In preparing for this negotiation a chart was made up similar to that in Exhibit 1 on which were plotted all 260 jobs. This chart then showed what the rate on each job "should be" as compared with what the company was actually paying. The first agreement reached in the wage negotiation was that all existing rates that were below the evaluated wage curve were to be brought up to the line. Rates that were above this wage curve were then divided into two classes: those that were not more than 8 per cent above the line and about a dozen rates that ranged from 12 to 18 per cent above the line. It was agreed that when the existing rate was not more than 8 per cent above the evaluated wage line no change would be made in the rate. However, workers on these jobs would be notified that in event of a general wage increase their rates would not be changed until such time as the general wage level increased by more than 8 per cent.

The rates that were from 12 to 18 per cent above the wage line were studied individually. It was finally agreed that four of these rates should stand because they conformed to rates then being paid generally in the community for similar work. No such justification was found for the other rates in this group, and after long and somewhat heated discussion it was agreed that these rates should be reduced to a figure 8 per cent above the rate as shown by the evaluated wage curve and should remain at that point until such time as general wage increases exceeded 8 per cent.

**18. Future Rate Changes.** It was further agreed that in the future there would be no individual rate changes except as (1) the job content changed and (2) the management requested the union to allow an individual rate increase when there was no change in the job content. This latter provision was requested by the management to allow it to meet possible competition for workers under unusual community conditions of supply and demand. Apart from these two exceptions all future wage changes were limited to general wage level changes to be negotiated by the union and the management according to the provisions of the union contract. Four weeks of negotiation were required to work out the foregoing negotiation after the job ratings were completed.

**19. Setting New Piece Rates.** New piece rates for jobs on piece rate were to be set from the hourly rate. The number of pieces per hour as established by the new time studies would be divided into the new hourly rates to get the dollar value per piece produced. This meant that for piecework jobs the evaluated hourly rate would serve as the base rate.

**20. Results of the Program.** The wage program was completed in 14 months. Both workers and management were satisfied that much had been accomplished. Systematic consideration had shown at what points rates were out of line with what they should be, and a regularized basis for dealing with future problems of the sort had been established. Management believed that the program had been well worth the cost. The immediate impact on the company's payroll was an increase of about 2.6 per cent. The management believed that this increase in cost was fully offset by the relief it gave management by freeing it from constant attention to wage grievances. It further believed that the experience of working cooperatively with the union on so knotty a problem had increased the understanding by each party of the other's problems and had advanced union-management relations very substantially. The experience convinced the company executives that good continuing relations with the union were possible, provided that management would take the initiative in developing and furthering the relationship. The president of the local union stated that in his opinion the experience was most valuable in consolidating the position of the union and in developing confidence on the part of union members in management and in their own leaders.

**21. Summary and Conclusions.** *Operating Problems as the Basis for Union-management Cooperation.* Little need be said in appraisal of the experience of The Brightvale Company in handling its wage problem. That experience speaks for itself. In union-management relations there is no more pervasive or important problem than that of wage rates. The case demonstrates that a union and a management can work together to the benefit of both.  It is clear that good results depend on the willingness of management to accept the responsibility for such cooperation and the ability of the business executives to provide leadership.  The only thing in the way of a procedural pattern that can be deduced from this experience is the wisdom of bringing the union into the action pattern completely.  By so doing from the start, understanding is developed by both parties and acceptance of change becomes much easier.

It should not be inferred from the description given here of this company's experience that no difficulties were incurred.  Disagreements were frequent but the individuals involved soon learned to respect the opinions of all concerned and an open-minded give and take developed.  At no time did the cooperative procedure threaten to break down.  Much of the credit for this goes to company and union leaders alike.  Not all business executives would have had the patience shown by The Brightvale Company men.  Not all union leaders have either the wisdom or the ability necessary to handle their own constituencies under like conditions.  Slowly both labor and management in this country are learning how to work together and there is no basic reason why the industrial game cannot be played successfully under today's rules.

*Job Evaluation as a Management Technique.*  Just a word about the job rating procedure described in this case.  Job evaluation is a most misunderstood technique.  Rating reveals little except relative job content as it exists in a given plant.  Like time study it never provides a wage rate or a dollar value for a job.  Frequently management expects it to do so and when undertaken with this expectancy it inevitably fails.  Job content is one of two factors in the setting of hourly rates and one of three factors in the setting of piece rates or other types of productivity rates.  Time study can help to determine how long it should take to do a given job.  Job analysis is a useful way of determining job content and of comparing several jobs as to what is involved in their performance.  Neither time study nor job evaluation results in a dollar value.  The third class of influence, that which includes such external factors as the going rate in the community and organized pressures such as union demands is the third essential element in rate setting. When the nature of the wage-setting process is understood and the limitations of contributing techniques are realized, the systematic "scientific" approach to a problem can give results much superior to reliance on such standbys as know-how, tradition, and straight pressure "bargaining." Intelligent negotiation becomes possible.

## QUESTIONS

1. What is the difference between a piece rate and an hourly rate?

2. What types of factors must be taken into consideration in setting an hourly rate?

3. What types of factors must be taken into consideration in setting a piece rate?

4. What does time study contribute to the setting of a wage rate?

5. What does job evaluation, systematic job rating, contribute to the setting of a wage rate?

6. How are piece rates and hourly rates related?

7. What are some of the considerations, other than time and job content, that are important in setting a wage rate? Why are they so very important?

8. If time study and job analysis are employed in setting a wage rate, why and how does negotiation become a step in wage rate setting?

9. The work of the job evaluation group of The Brightvale Company was divided into four steps. What were these steps? What purpose did each step serve?

10. Why was each job description signed by the workers and the foreman concerned?

11. What gains resulted from writing the job descriptions?

12. What were the six factors used in rating the jobs? Why were they given different maximum point values?

13. How were the job ratings checked?

14. How were job point values converted to dollar values? Why was it necessary to negotiate a reconciliation of the wage

rates as given by the evaluation curve with the rates actually paid by the company?

15. Were the results of the wage negotiation sound?

16. How did the job evaluation procedure aid in the wage rate negotiations?

17. Why was the management willing to have its payroll increased 2.6 per cent?

18. What function is job evaluation designed to perform as a management technique?

19. Why do operating problems provide an excellent opportunity for developing good union-management relations?

20. Why did the executives of The Brightvale Company believe that it is management's responsibility to take the lead in furthering good union-management relations? Is this conclusion reasonable?

## Problem 41

## FORBERG MANUFACTURING COMPANY [2]

The time-study department of the Forberg Manufacturing Company, manufacturers of valves and fittings for plumbing-heating purposes, had prepared time studies and set piecework rates on most production jobs performed in the Forberg plant. By 1946, many of the time studies for jobs performed on standard valves and fittings had been in existence for almost 20 years. Most of the work in the plant was paid for on a piecework basis. The average plant-wide hourly base rate was $1.13½. The average worker on a piecework basis received approximately 120 per cent of his hourly base rate for piecework. Time studies on "fin grinding" and "snagging" of standard valves and fittings had been in use at the Forberg plant since the late 1920's. These particular time studies resulted in the setting of standards that allowed fin grinders and snaggers, in spite of the fact that they were considered relatively unskilled laborers, to receive weekly take-home pay amounting to considerably more than the average plant worker's take-home pay. This condition was called to the attention of Mr. M. M. Palmer, assistant to the works manager, by the head of the time-study department shortly after Mr. Palmer started working at the Forberg plant in early 1946.

The Forberg company had built up a good name in the valve and fittings trade. It concentrated on the production of valves with pipe sizes ranging from ⅛ inch to 3 inches in diameter. In 1946, the company employed approximately 500 production workers and operated on a 40-hour work week.

In June, 1946, Mr. Palmer received a summary of the piecework hours and wages paid to the fin grinders and snaggers during May, 1946 (Exhibit 1). This summary was prepared by the head of the time-study department for Mr. Palmer's use. During the month of May, wages for the two fin grinders totaled more than $300 each, while wages for the ten snaggers averaged almost $250 each; five of the snaggers received more than $275 each. These figures were compared with a monthly plant average amounting to approximately $210 per production worker in May, 1946. On

[2] Copyright, 1948, by The President and Fellows of Harvard College.

**EXHIBIT**

Summary of Piecework Hours and Wages

May, 1946

| Employee and No. | Operation | Wed. 1 | Thur. 2 | Fri. 3 | Mon. 6 | Tues. 7 | Wed. 8 | Thur. 9 | Fri. 10 | Mon. 13 | Tues. 14 | Wed. 15 |
|---|---|---|---|---|---|---|---|---|---|---|---|---|
| Fin grinder 410 | Piecework hours | 7.5* | 7.4 | 6.2 | 6.3 | 7.7 | 5.7 | 7.1 | 4.5 | 6.8 | 5.8† | 0 |
|  | Wages, dollars | 14.15* | 15.55 | 16.35 | 16.01 | 15.59 | 16.74 | 15.87 | 12.62 | 17.11 | 14.97 | Abs. |
| Fin grinder 411 | Piecework hours | 7.7 | 6.2 | 4.9 | 5.1 | 7.0 | 7.5 | 6.4 | 6.5 | 0 | 6.6 | 6.7 |
|  | Wages, dollars | 11.10 | 15.80 | 12.85 | 11.72 | 16.73 | 17.97 | 15.32 | 15.36 | Abs. | 12.08 | 16.00 |
| Snagger 412 | Piecework hours | 6.1 | 6.9 | 7.7 | 7.1 | 7.3 | 7.7 | 7.0 | 7.7 | 7.7 | 7.7 | 7.7 |
|  | Wages, dollars | 13.92 | 12.58 | 12.44 | 14.19 | 12.67 | 13.43 | 13.71 | 12.81 | 12.19 | 13.61 | 13.09 |
| Snagger 413 | Piecework hours | 4.2 | DW† | 3.6 | DW | DW | DW | DW | 1.6 | 1.5 | 4.7 | 1.1† |
|  | Wages, dollars | 11.58 | 7.85 | 8.71 | 7.48 | 7.48 | 7.48 | 7.48 | 7.23 | 8.70 | 11.24 | 11.29 |
| Snagger 414 | Piecework hours | 3.6 | 7.7 | 7.7 | 7.7 | 7.7 | 7.7 | 7.3 | 7.4 | 7.7 | 7.7 | 7.7 |
|  | Wages, dollars | 10.65 | 11.41 | 11.67 | 11.16 | 13.11 | 10.09 | 12.97 | 10.92 | 12.39 | 11.89 | 9.53 |
| Snagger 415 | Piecework hours | 6.7 | 6.6 | 7.7 | 7.7 | 4.8 | 6.2 | 6.3 | 7.7 | 7.7 | 7.7 | 7.7 |
|  | Wages, dollars | 11.81 | 12.87 | 11.39 | 12.81 | 12.48 | 12.78 | 11.94 | 15.08 | 12.67 | 13.51 | 12.81 |
| Snagger 416 | Piecework hours | DW† | 6.9 | DW† | DW† | DW† | DW | 2.6† | DW† | 4.1† | 1.8† | DW† |
|  | Wages, dollars | 9.79 | 10.96 | 9.78 | 9.79 | 9.79 | 7.48 | 10.65 | 9.79 | 8.75 | 9.75 | 9.79 |
| Snagger 417 | Piecework hours | 2.5† | 7.7 | 7.7 | 7.7 | 6.7 | 2.7† | 7.0 | 7.7 | 0‡ | 0‡ | 0‡ |
|  | Wages, dollars | 9.65 | 12.26 | 11.42 | 11.63 | 11.61 | 9.88 | 10.89 | 11.24 | Abs. | Abs. | Abs. |
| Snagger 418 | Piecework hours | 5.7 | 3.7 | 7.7 | 7.7 | 6.1 | 5.3 | 7.7 | 7.7 | 7.7 | 7.7 | 7.7 |
|  | Wages, dollars | 13.11 | 11.75 | 14.55 | 15.88 | 11.13 | 12.75 | 15.88 | 15.71 | 16.31 | 14.48 | 15.32 |
| Snagger 419 | Piecework hours | 5.6† | 3.7 | 7.7 | 7.7 | 4.8 | 5.4† | 7.2 | 7.7 | 7.7 | 7.7 | 6.3† |
|  | Wages, dollars | 15.79 | 12.52 | 17.17 | 15.31 | 12.73 | 16.83 | 17.72 | 16.59 | 13.45 | 18.53 | 16.18 |
| Snagger 420 | Piecework hours | 4.6 | DW† | DW† | 3.7 | DW | DW | DW | DW | DW | DW | 0 |
|  | Wages, dollars | 9.74 | 7.68 | 8.54 | 10.00 | 7.16 | 7.16 | 7.16 | 7.16 | 7.16 | 7.16 | Abs. |
| Snagger 421 | Piecework hours | 4.5† | 3.1 | 6.1 | 6.6 | DW | DW | 6.9 | 4.4† | 2.4† | 7.7 | 4.5† |
|  | Wages, dollars | 15.00 | 11.29 | 16.08 | 12.87 | 7.48 | 7.48 | 13.51 | 14.53 | 13.19 | 14.97 | 15.00 |

* Example showing method of figuring daily wage (Employee 410):

   7.5 Piecework Hours (Rate × Number of Pieces) = $13.68
   .5 Daywork Hours × $.935 (Daywork Rate)     =   .47
      (including .3 hour cleanup and .2 hour day-
      work)

8.0 Hours            Total Wage for May 1 = $14.15

† Indicates man was on retainer during a portion of the day when he was not on piecework or straight daywork.

1

## Paid to Fin Grinders and Snaggers

(A Typical Month)

| Thur. 16 | Fri. 17 | Mon. 20 | Tues. 21 | Wed. 22 | Thur. 23 | Fri. 24 | Mon. 27 | Tues. 28 | Wed. 29 | Fri. 31 | Total Piece-work Hours | Total Wages for May 1946 | Number Days Absent in May |
|---|---|---|---|---|---|---|---|---|---|---|---|---|---|
| 6.7<br>16.27 | 5.3<br>15.00 | 5.3<br>14.43 | 7.1<br>17.33 | 4.9†<br>17.44 | 4.7<br>12.57 | 7.1<br>15.71 | 6.0<br>14.19 | 5.6†<br>14.74 | 5.7†<br>17.00 | 7.3<br>14.39 | 130.7 | $ 324.03 | 1 |
| 6.3<br>14.53 | 4.9<br>12.71 | 7.5<br>15.23 | 6.5<br>16.06 | 7.0<br>14.95 | 6.5<br>14.81 | 6.9<br>15.51 | 6.9<br>14.67 | 6.6<br>15.80 | 6.7<br>16.95 | 6.7<br>14.51 | 137.1 | 310.66 | 1 |
| 7.7<br>11.94 | 7.4<br>12.97 | 7.7<br>11.73 | 7.1<br>12.60 | 6.6†<br>13.62 | 7.7<br>11.42 | 7.7<br>13.59 | 7.7<br>11.40 | 7.7<br>13.51 | 7.7<br>13.95 | 6.4<br>11.22 | 162.0 | 282.64 | 0 |
| 2.5†<br>10.77 | 1.1†<br>10.09 | 4.9†<br>11.76 | 3.3†<br>9.33 | 5.3<br>11.33 | DW†<br>7.85 | 1.9†<br>8.19 | 2.3†<br>10.73 | 4.8†<br>11.53 | 2.0†<br>9.15 | DW†<br>10.62 | 44.8 | 207.87 | 0 |
| 6.1<br>8.32 | 7.7<br>9.77 | 7.7<br>10.80 | 6.3<br>10.33 | 7.7<br>11.04 | 7.7<br>9.05 | 7.7<br>12.55 | 6.7<br>10.23 | 6.3†<br>10.86 | 7.7<br>11.08 | 6.2†<br>11.84 | 157.7 | 241.66 | 0 |
| 7.7<br>12.86 | 7.7<br>11.99 | 7.7<br>11.70 | 7.7<br>13.11 | 7.7<br>12.89 | 7.7<br>12.70 | 7.7<br>12.84 | 7.7<br>11.19 | 7.7<br>14.16 | 7.7<br>12.40 | 6.8<br>12.96 | 160.6 | 278.95 | 0 |
| DW†<br>9.79 | DW†<br>9.27 | 1.8†<br>9.39 | DW†<br>9.79 | DW†<br>9.79 | DW†<br>8.58 | 1.8†<br>9.51 | DW†<br>9.79 | DW†<br>9.79 | DW†<br>9.79 | 4.2†<br>8.69 | 23.2 | 210.50 | 0 |
| 0‡<br>Abs. | 0‡<br>Abs. | 7.4<br>10.50 | 6.1†<br>10.36 | 7.7<br>9.85 | 7.7<br>11.44 | 7.1<br>11.17 | 7.1<br>12.27 | 7.7<br>10.41 | 7.7<br>11.17 | 7.4†<br>12.90 | 115.6 | 188.65 | 5 |
| 7.7<br>15.91 | 5.1<br>11.03 | 7.6<br>14.87 | 6.9†<br>14.38 | 5.9<br>12.00 | 7.7<br>14.68 | 5.4†<br>12.56 | 0<br>Abs. | 7.7<br>15.18 | 7.7<br>13.53 | 7.7<br>14.47 | 144.1 | 295.48 | 1 |
| 7.7<br>14.08 | 7.7<br>16.75 | 7.7<br>13.11 | 7.3<br>17.03 | 4.4†<br>13.44 | 7.7<br>16.60 | 7.2<br>15.70 | 7.7<br>12.47 | 0<br>Abs. | 0<br>Abs. | 7.7<br>11.58 | 136.6 | 303.58 | 2 |
| DW<br>7.16 | 3.0<br>8.80 | 1.0<br>7.88 | DW<br>7.16 | DW<br>7.16 | 4.9<br>9.61 | DW<br>7.16 | 2.7<br>9.70 | 5.4<br>10.62 | 5.3<br>11.99 | 0<br>Abs. | 30.6 | 166.16 | 2 |
| 6.1†<br>13.40 | 7.5<br>13.91 | 7.7<br>14.48 | 7.3†<br>13.99 | 3.3†<br>13.96 | 4.6†<br>18.11 | 5.4†<br>15.00 | 5.1<br>15.01 | 7.7<br>11.88 | 6.8†<br>17.09 | 6.4<br>11.55 | 114.1 | 299.78 | 0 |
| | | | | | | | | | | | 1,357.1 | $3,109.96 | 12 |

Retainers were paid for certain special jobs performed on a daywork basis but requiring some special work.

A retainer generally amounted to payment of an hourly rate somewhat above the worker's base hourly rate.

‡ Vacation.

Note: .3 hour per day per employee was allowed for cleanup in the fin-grinding and snagging department and was paid for on a daywork basis regardless of whether employee was working on a piece-work basis or on daywork basis.

an hourly "daywork" basis, however, the top rate for fin grinders and snaggers was 93½ cents as compared with the average rate of $1.13½ for all production workers.  Thus, even though fin grinders and snaggers were, according to the management, properly classified well below the plant average on an hourly rate basis, nevertheless, their average take-home pay was well above the plant average take-home pay.

In 1940, the Forberg workers had chosen the United Steel Workers of America (CIO) as their bargaining agent, no union having existed in the Forberg plant prior to that time.  Relationships between the local union and the Forberg management were considered by the management to be good.  A section of the union-company contract covered changes in standards or in rates.  It stated, "Whenever a job has been time studied and there is no change in the method or procedure of performing the job, the rates established will not be changed except in those cases where there is a change in the general wage structure of the plant."  Previous to 1940, company action regarding changes of standards or rates was governed by substantially the same policy. Hence, the time standards set for fin grinding and snagging of standard valves and fittings, although they were farther out of line than any other time standards in the plant, had never been changed.

Pay for all work performed by fin grinders and snaggers was not on a piecework basis.  As a general rule, unusual and infrequent jobs were not time studied.  Also, new jobs were not time studied until the usual production "short runs" were completed.  A retainer was paid to a worker who performed a special job on a daywork basis; this arrangement generally amounted to payment of an hourly rate somewhat above the worker's base hourly rate.  Moreover, all daywork performed by fin grinders and snaggers did not consist of fin grinding or snagging operations.  Thus, occasionally an employee might be asked by the foreman to clean an area or run an errand, for which he would be paid at his base hourly rate.  The foreman over the grinding department determined the allocation of work.  He attempted to rotate work among the employees; but generally the most difficult and lowest paying work was performed by the man with the least seniority. By the summer of 1946, all the fin grinders and snaggers had been working on their jobs for at least three years.

Fin grinding and snagging were two different grinding operations. The wage scales for the operations, however, were identical, ranging from 83½ cents to 93½ cents per hour. Also, both operations were performed on small, ordinary belt-driven grinding machines. Fin grinding was accomplished by using a narrow grinding wheel approximately ¼ inch wide; its purpose was to remove the "fin" left on valve-part castings or fitting castings at the location where pattern blocks joined together during the molding operations. The operator removed the fin by simply pressing the casting against the grinding wheel, following the contour of the casting. Little skill was required for such an operation. Snagging was accomplished by using a grinding wheel approximately 1½ to 2 inches wide; its purpose was to remove the "snag" or projection left on the "gate" or open ends of valve-part castings or fitting castings after molding operations. The operator removed the snag by simply pressing the casting against the grinding wheel, removing somewhat heavier metal than was removed by fin grinding. The snagging work was slightly heavier than the work performed by the fin grinders.

The amount of fin grinding and snagging on individual valve-part castings or fitting castings varied considerably. Sometimes castings required no fin grinding or snagging; it was the duty of the inspector in the grinding department prior to the fin grinding and snagging operations to segregate these castings from the castings requiring fin grinding and snagging. A fin grinder and snagger received credit for all valve parts and fittings that he handled, regardless of the amount of work actually required for each valve part or fitting. Theoretically, the time standards took variations in the amount of fin grinding and snagging into account by averaging out the variations.

Mr. Palmer stated that the company desired to pay employees in accordance with their abilities and efforts; therefore, from the company standpoint, the situation regarding pay for fin grinders and snaggers was considered highly unfair. Furthermore, excess labor costs resulting from such a situation had to be compensated for by reduced costs in some other area in order to maintain the profit margin desired by the company. Prices on valves and fittings were determined largely by competitive factors.

It was common knowledge among all employees that the fin grinders and snaggers received very high pay, even though the work did not require a great deal of skill or effort. Rates and amounts of pay were discussed freely among the employees. The attitude of the other employees toward the unbalanced situation and toward the fin grinders and snaggers seemed to be one of slight resentment. Other employees did not ordinarily begrudge a fellow worker's receiving good pay; they shrugged the situation off generally with a remark such as "What a hungry . . . that fellow is!" and wished perhaps that they were in the shoes of the fin grinders or snaggers.

What action should Mr. Palmer take?

### Problem 42

### TAVA SHOE COMPANY [3]

The Tava Shoe Company manufactured men's high-quality shoes that retailed from $9 to $15 a pair. The company operated as a union shop. Over a 47-year period it had experienced no serious labor troubles. The company made a final change in the "cleaning" operation whereby one man was able to do with a machine the work formerly done by three men by hand. Originally all the work had been done by hand, but in the previous year a process was developed which allowed two-thirds of the work to be done by machine. In 1946 a final change was made which enabled the machine to do the complete cleaning process. The final method had proved very satisfactory in operation, but the management had difficulty in reaching an agreement with the union concerning the piece rate to be paid the machine operative.

The Tava Shoe Company's plant was located in a small New England town in which the company was the only large employer. The Tava Shoe Company had been incorporated in 1875, and since that time had continuously maintained friendly relations with the townspeople, most of whom had worked in the company's plant during some part of their lives. Normally the company employed 450 workers. Late in 1947 the company was operating at about 60 per cent of its capacity and was employing about 300 workers.

In 1897 an affiliate of the American Federation of Labor, the Boot and Shoe Workers Union, had organized a union in the company's plant. The company operated for 40 years as a union shop under a contract with this union which called for conciliation and arbitration if differences could not be settled in conferences between the management and labor. The plant was closed to nonunion labor. Until 1944 the Boot and Shoe Workers Union had maintained its position unchallenged. But in the following two years the union had lost members, and there had developed a so-called "district union" which had acquired most of the former members of the Boot and Shoe Workers Union. This district union had no national affiliation and its members were workers of shoe companies within, roughly, a 20-mile radius of the Tava Shoe Company's plant. The management believed that a few of the Tava company workers still retained membership in the old union.

The operating officials of the district union were elected by the workers of the plants which it represented in the district. These officials bargained directly with the managements of these plants on such matters as hours of work, wages, and working conditions.

The union officials appointed a chief steward for each plant to act as the official representative of the union at his plant. The chief steward was in each case an employee of the company at which he was the union representative. The function of the chief steward was to meet with dissatisfied workers, to act as their representative in discussing with the management any grievances that arose, to be the official bargaining agent in cases involving working conditions, and to report to the union officials. The chief steward, however, was not the bargaining agent for the union with the management on questions of wages and rates. On those matters the union officials themselves negotiated directly with the management of the plant. The district union paid the chief steward $1 for each hour that he spent on union duties when he would otherwise have been at his regular employment.

In each room or department in a plant the workers elected one of their number to act as room steward. It was the duty of the room steward to represent his fellow employees of the department in their relations with the chief steward. Room stewards served without additional compensation.

Whereas the Tava Shoe Company had dealt with only one representative of the Boot and Shoe Workers Union, it now became necessary for the management to come in contact not only with the officials of the district union but also with the chief steward and room stewards in its own plant. The company, however, as had been its custom, made every effort to cooperate with whatever union organization the men desired. Whenever a difference arose, the management attempted to make its position so sound that the union would perforce agree. As one company executive stated, before the management insisted upon its way, it made every effort to be absolutely sure that there was no possible chance that it could be mistaken. It disliked being forced to come out openly against a union claim or stand; it preferred, if possible, to attain its end through its knowledge of human nature in general and of shoe workers in particular.

An example of the method employed by the management occurred when the men in one department had elected by popular vote a room steward whom the management came to consider unsatisfactory. The management believed that not only had this man shown himself to be undesirable from the company's standpoint but also he had given insufficient attention to the task of attending to the interests of his fellow employees. Nevertheless, the management had not openly opposed him but had permitted the situation to develop until it became unsatisfactory to the workers. Then one day when the general manager was passing through that department, he saw the room steward attempting to get a drink of water at the bubbler fountain. The general manager noticed that little or no water came forth. Upon investigation he found that the pipe was so old that it restricted a free flow of water. He thereupon called the room steward and, in a tone of voice audible to all the workers in the room, blamed him for failure to see to the comfort of his fellow workers. The general manager stated at that time that the room steward knew very well that the management was dissatisfied with such a situation and wished to have unsatisfactory working conditions reported to it at once. The general manager then hastened to have new pipes installed. The management later said that this incident was only one example of this man's failure to do an adequate job as the elected representative of his fellow employees. Shortly thereafter the workers gradually lost faith in the room steward and elected another man to this post.

When the established method of cleaning and finishing the manufactured shoes was changed, the management encountered a problem in setting piece rates which would be satisfactory to the union. Under the old method the work had been done in three operations. First, a man took a pair of shoes from a wheel-truck rack, examined them for blemishes, rubbed off with a brush stray bits of leather and any dust and dirt that might be on the shoes, and returned the shoes to the rack. Second, the worker applied a liquid cleaner which removed stains or other superficial blemishes. Third, the clean shoes were brushed and burnished. These operations might be done by three different workers under conditions of capacity production, but usually the work was done by a single hand "treer," a skilled workman.

Treeing had formerly been a highly skilled and important function in the manufacture of shoes. A treer examined the manufactured shoe while it was on the last, checked it for its fit and shape, trimmed off any rough edges that remained from cutting, examined the lining, and applied filler and surfacing material to the leather. After this treeing operation, the shoe was ready for cleaning and polishing. Technological developments and improved methods of cutting, fitting, and assembling the shoe had, however, simplified the treer's job and made it less important. Modern leathers were ready for cleaning and polishing without the application of fillers and surfacing materials. Cutting and assembly blemishes were rare.

By 1946 the three operations involved in finishing shoes could have been done almost wholly by unskilled workers if the union would have permitted it. The union, however, insisted that the first of the three operations outlined above must be done by treers, although under conditions of capacity production the final two operations might be done by unskilled workers.

The new machine which the Tava Shoe Company had finally developed performed all three operations and did them, the management stated, more satisfactorily than hand labor. The machine had been manufactured for the Tava Shoe Company by the company from which it regularly leased much of its equipment. The Tava Shoe Company had sold to this company the rights to manufacture and sell the new machine. It was expected that this company would build and lease a large number of these machines in the near future.

The new machine consisted of a rapidly rotating friction brush onto which a fine nozzle sprayed a volatile cleaning fluid. All that the operative had to do was pick up a shoe, step on the pedal which controlled the spray mechanism on the machine, and hold the shoe against the burnishing brush. The brush deposited the proper amount of cleaner on the shoe, imparted the desired surface finish, cleaned the shoe thoroughly, and removed any excess dust and bits of leather that had accumulated from handling during the preceding hundred or more operations.

The machine was almost foolproof. If the heel of a shoe was thrust against the brush first, the burnishing brush would be rotating against the grain of the leather and would roughen the surface. The natural, easiest way of holding a shoe, however, was by the heel. So held, the shoe was almost sure to be thrust against the burnishing brush so the toe met the brush first; and the brush would properly burnish the shoe with the grain of the leather. Furthermore, it was not possible for the worker to hurt the shoe by applying an excessive amount of the liquid cleaner. Should he keep his foot on the control pedal too long, the heat generated by the rotating brush would sufficiently accelerate evaporation so that no damage would be done to the shoe.

The management believed that the job of operating the finishing machine was essentially unskilled, but acceded to the union's demand that the machine be operated by a skilled worker who had formerly been a treer. The management had the machine installed and began operation, paying the operative the union day rate. Throughout 1947 the management attempted to place this man on a piece rate. The management stated that time and motion studies showed clearly that it would be possible to turn out 900 pairs of shoes a day on this machine without undue strain upon the worker. Although the management had no doubts about the accuracy of the studies, it was willing to base a piece rate upon a production standard of 600 pairs a day. Piece rates throughout the Tava plant were so set that a man who produced up to the established normal production would receive 15 per cent more than the accepted day rate, under which a worker earned $50 for a 40-hour week. The operative of the finishing machine reported to the shop steward that this operation was difficult and claimed that it was hard to produce 250 to 300 pairs a day. This operative happened to be room steward in this department, which employed about 20 workers. The management was convinced that the operative was soldiering on the job and could see no reason for production so much below the estimated normal, unless it be narrow selfishness and personal bias on the part of the operative.

At the rate at which this man was working, it was uneconomical to route all types of leather shoes over the machine. It was cheaper to use the old hand method on most shoes. Therefore, only certain types of leather which required abnormal amounts of cleaning and treatment were being cleaned and finished by machine.

The union had supported the employee in his contention, and the management had been unable to change the union's stand. Analysis of the operation, based on time and motion study, had not been convincing evidence to the union. Recognizing the difficulty of the problem, the general manager in December, 1947, was seeking some means of showing the union the fallacy of the worker's reasoning; he was convinced that, if he could accomplish his purpose, the union would be ready to accept the piece rates proposed by the management.

What do you think the general manager should do?

# CHAPTER XVIII

## PERSONNEL ORGANIZATION

### JUTE BAG COMPANY

## 1. Need for Personnel Organization.

The Jute Bag Company, a well-known producer of bags and bagging, was experiencing difficulties with its personnel. Labor productivity was declining, and an increasing feeling of hostility between workers and management was evident. The company had never established a separate organization for handling personnel activities. One of the vice-presidents recommended the adoption of a personnel program which was identical with one in operation in a well-known textile mill. The question was before the executives of the company for final decision.

## 2. Scope of Personnel Activities.
Many managements do not confine their personnel activities to the establishment of employment departments and the inauguration of scientific wage systems. They go much further, and spend a great deal of effort and money in inaugurating policies and devices which, they believe, will result in keeping working conditions in the factory as satisfactory as possible. Ill health, for example, is the great enemy of the working force; consequently, many concerns employ full-time doctors and nurses to look after the health of their workers and to maintain healthful working conditions. Sometimes dentists and other specialists, such as psychiatrists, are members of the health corps. Periodic physical examinations of workers are rather common practice in factories, and if tasks must be performed under particularly unfavorable conditions, special appliances, such as gas masks, goggles, special kinds of shoes, clothing, and equipment, are furnished to workers. Safe work places are regarded as a basic condition of employment. This has been particularly true since the general adoption of state workmen's compensation laws. Many companies have elaborate safety programs in which workers are taught the need

of caution. Dangerous equipment is guarded, and safety codes are established which must be respected by both supervisors and employees.

Cafeterias are maintained where workers may obtain clean, wholesome food at cost. Heat, light, noise, dust, and dirt receive constant attention to the end that conditions of work may be made as agreeable as possible. Machines are kept clean and in good running order. Some managers even go to the extent of painting machines in colors so that the machine will contrast with the material to be worked on. Experience with machine painting has shown that in many instances quality and quantity of output have been distinctly improved. Provision for athletic facilities, educational programs, paid vacations, and vacation camps are commonplace devices for arousing worker loyalty to the company. Means are provided for handling worker grievances and discussing in a fair and friendly manner problems of mutual interest to workers and management. Some plants have had extensive programs of employee stock ownership so devised that the permanent employee may purchase stock at less than current market price and pay for it over a period of years in small monthly instalments. The worker thus, to a limited extent, becomes a "partner in the business." Security against unemployment has been provided in some cases by guaranty of a given number of weeks' pay each year. Some firms make it a practice, if it becomes necessary to dismiss regular employees because of installation of labor saving machinery or closing down the work of a department, to pay dismissal wages to the employees thus let out. Such remuneration helps to tide over the period of readjustment incident to finding a new job. The number of devices used in modern personnel departments is legion, and space does not permit even an enumeration of them.

Such activities cost money. Companies carry them on because their executives believe them profitable. They believe that worker productivity is increased, and when that happens raw materials move through the plant more rapidly and capital is turned over more quickly.

Organizations for carrying on personnel activities vary greatly. Sometimes health work is set up as a separate unit. Sometimes it is a branch of a department which looks after safety. In other cases it may be but one of several diverse activities under the control of one supervisor. There may be a general educational director, or training activities may be subdivided according to departments. Sometimes personnel control is decentralized and made the responsibility of all operating foremen. In other cases all personnel activities are brought together in one department and a personnel director is put in charge.

**3. Personnel Activities of the Jute Bag Company.** For more than half a century the Jute Bag Company manufactured bagging in the little town of Brighton, in a Middle Atlantic state. The village of Brighton was located some 20 miles from a large industrial center. The mill was the only manufacturing concern in the town.

At the time the plant had been established there was no town of Brighton. It had grown up around the mill, and most of the buildings, both public and private, had been built by the Jute Bag Company. More than 90 per cent of the 3,500 employees lived in company-owned houses. The public school buildings had been built by the company and later deeded to the village. The company had also erected most of the store buildings. Likewise, over a period of years, it had built a clubhouse, a restaurant, a gymnasium, and a moving-picture theater. It owned and supervised a large park and an athletic field.

**4. Labor Supply.** Workers for the plant were secured from the large industrial center 20 miles distant. The Jute Bag Company maintained an employment agent in that city. Originally, employees were native Americans, with Pennsylvania Dutch stock predominating. After 1895 Scotch and Irish immigrants flocked to the mill. By 1910 most of these had been replaced by workers coming from central and eastern Europe. Currently a large majority of the employees were Poles who could neither read nor write the English language. Extensive use of interpreters was necessary.

**5. Supervisors.** Foremanship positions were held almost entirely by workers of Scotch extraction. These men, for the most part, had been trained in Scotland and, while they were excellent workers, their ideas of mill routine were the same ones they had held in Scotland 25 years previously. As a class, the supervisors were conscientious and determined, but they regarded with open distrust such innovations as the use of a stop watch, time and motion studies, and so-called scientific methods of wage payment.

**6. Decline in Productivity.** The management of the Jute Bag Company was acutely aware that productivity in the mill was gradually falling. Quality, which was a consideration of some importance, was becoming more difficult to control. An investigation of conditions showed that a wide gap existed between workers and foremen. The Scotch overseers appeared to be fair and just to the workers, but they had no great respect for the Polish employees and found it exceedingly difficult to work with them by means of interpreters. Much of the actual supervision consisted of illustrating to employees by means of personal example just how a given task should be performed, and of punishment for minor infractions of working rules.

The workers had developed a pronounced antagonism to the management and appeared to be working for the Jute Bag Company only because they did not know how to get a job outside of Brighton. There was some evidence that employees were being exploited by their interpreters. Workers appeared to stand in great fear of what an interpreter might tell the foreman. There was no company loyalty or *esprit de corps*. Outwardly, things were calm, although supervisors occasionally received unsigned threatening letters, and there was growing talk of the possibility of forming a local "Red" organization. The management regarded the whole situation with growing uneasiness.

**7. A Ready-made Personnel Program.** One of the vice-presidents of the Jute Bag Company made a trip to New England, during which he visited a large textile plant. He was very much interested to find that within the past year this company had centralized its extensive personnel activities in one department. The man in charge of this work occupied an important executive position in the company organization and enjoyed the title of assistant to the president in charge of personnel.

The textile mill, though employing foreigners, did not have the same nationality problem as did the Jute Bag Company. Interpreters were unnecessary. The foremen, moreover, were all American-born and were much in advance of the Scotch overseers as far as breadth of vision was concerned. An employment department had been in successful operation for 10 years. Although some of the foremen had balked at these innovations at first, they had long since become used to them. These and similar devices were regarded by them in the same light as the cards and the spinning machines—all a part of the game.

The vice-president of the Jute Bag Company was enthusiastic over what he saw in this textile mill. The workers were bright and alert and could easily explain the details of their jobs. To the vice-president they appeared to be fairly bubbling over with loyalty to their company. The executive returned to Brighton thoroughly convinced that a solution to the problem facing the Jute Bag Company lay in the adoption of a plan similar to the one in force in the textile mill.

At first other officers of the Jute Bag Company were little impressed with what the vice-president had seen, but the more he talked the more sympathetic they became, and it was finally voted to secure a detailed copy of the personnel program used in the New England plant.

A study of the plan thus obtained showed that personnel work in the New England mill was organized into 11 divisional activities: employment, health, safety, sanitation, recreation, employee representation, education, systems of wage payment, stock ownership, pensions, and miscellaneous. Some idea of the extent to which details of various activities had been worked out can be seen from the following summary of the employment division.

The functions of the employment department are as follows:

1. To maintain an adequate labor supply for all production, mechanical, and outside departments.

2. To adjust the labor supply within the organization by means of transfers.

3. To adjust disputes between workers and overseers when called upon to do so.

4. To terminate the employment relation between an employee and the company after investigation has assured the employment manager that such action is to the best interests of the company.

5. To maintain adequate records for all individuals who have sought or entered into employment relations with the company.

6. To summarize available statistics so as to show tendencies in the supply and permanency of labor in the production, mechanical, and outside departments of the company.

7. To cooperate with all departments in all matters where any questions of labor supply or maintenance are involved.

Each of these details was further subdivided. For example, instructions relative to the task of "Hiring" covered several printed pages and explained clearly and in careful detail just how this function was to be carried out.

A study of the details of the personnel program convinced executives of the Jute Bag Company that these activities had been worked out and correlated very effectively. There seemed to be little doubt about the efficiency of the plan as applied in the textile mill. Some of the officials, however, were not certain that such a program was best suited to the needs of the Jute Bag Company, and they asked that more time be allowed for study of the whole matter.

**8. Summary and Conclusions.** *Need of Further Study.* No one can examine the situations in the bag mill and the textile plant without being convinced of the need of further study on the part of officials of the Jute Bag Company. A fundamental consideration underlying any plan of personnel organization is that the activities in question should be suited to the individual needs of the company installing them. In fact, there is no justification for setting up personnel activities except in terms of specific requirements.

Even a casual survey shows that the situation in the bag plant differed basically from that found in the textile mill. The difficulties in the former plant arose in part from the fact that foremen were nonprogressive. They distrusted innovations of all kinds. They did not sense the spirit of scientific management as found in many American factories today. A real loss of contact between management and workers had taken place. Such contact was not easy to reestablish because of language barriers and racial jealousies which made it very difficult to develop and maintain a friendly, cooperative group consciousness on the part of the working force.

In the textile mill the situation was quite the reverse. Language barriers and racial jealousies, if they had ever existed, had been broken down. The worker group was animated by a spirit of loyalty and friendliness to the management. Overseers were alert and willing to adopt the most modern means for increasing productivity. The scope of the personnel activities which had been developed at the textile mill is to be taken as evidence of the extent to which the management had put its house in order before consolidating all personnel activities under one executive. Devices for personnel control can be used successfully only when they harmonize with production conditions in the plant.

There is no reason to believe, for example, that the adoption of the textile mill plan by the Jute Bag Company would in any way make its foremen more progressive, reestablish a real contact between workers and management, or in any other way motivate the workers to increased productivity. Executives of the Jute Bag Company must work out their problem along lines peculiar to their situation. They cannot secure a ready-made plan and expect it to work. Standardization in managerial control has not developed to that extent, and there are no present indications that it will soon do so.

*Solution of Jute Bag Company Problems.* It appears that a common-sense analysis of the problems faced by the Jute Bag Company would lead to the conclusion that the first thing needed was provision for foremanship training. This program should not be primarily for the Scotch overseers, for they are, except in isolated cases, beyond the reach of any training course. It should be used for the development of the more promising Polish workers, looking forward to the day when such employees can assume foremanship responsibility. The other pressing need is for an Americanization program for the workers. The English language and an understanding of the ideals underlying American institutions should be stressed. The present language barrier is serious, and an appreciation of American institutions is indispensable if the company wishes to forestall the development of ideas harmful to those institutions.

It is very doubtful whether much else in the way of a personnel program, except possibly organizing recreational work, would be of immediate service to this company. As, however, a group of Polish foremen are trained in more modern methods of process and personnel control and as workers learn to understand the English language and gain some appreciation of American economic, political, and social institutions, ways will be opened for an enlargement of personnel activities. Devices such as the installing of scientific methods of performing tasks, incentive methods of wage payment, and plans for worker representation normally follow in the development of a comprehensive program. Such plans cannot, however, be safely injected into the situation until a firm foundation has been built.

*Summary.* A system of personnel control is only one factor in scientific management. If personnel work is to develop successfully, it must maintain a very close relationship with other managerial developments in the factory. Personnel devices should be installed and used only when they perform definite functions. The ill-advised attempts of companies to gain wholesale benefits by establishing complete, ready-made personnel departments usually result disastrously both to the treasury of the company and to the very cause they are supposed to advance. The reason for failure is that the personnel devices have not been sufficiently correlated with the operating program as it is carried on from day to day.

Personnel work is very necessary. It is hard to overestimate its importance in any scheme of scientific management. Personnel devices must, however, be used with discretion. In and of themselves, they neither advance the cause of management nor further the welfare of employees. When, however, they are used intelligently and in conjunction with other sound production devices, they are very powerful aids making for effective management. The question of whether a personnel program should assume one specific form or another, whether it should be centralized or decentralized, is of secondary importance. Substance and not form should be the controlling factor in establishing any personnel policy. If the substance of a given program is sound, the particular form that it should assume can easily be worked out over any reasonable period of time.

## QUESTIONS

1. Enumerate some of the activities carried on by personnel organizations.

2. What was included in the New England textile company's plan of personnel organization?

3. What were the outstanding labor problems facing the Jute Bag Company?

4. In just what ways would the adoption of the plan used by the textile company tend to solve the problems faced by the Jute Bag Company?

5. What do you think would be the proper procedure for the Jute Bag Company to follow respecting a personnel organization?

6. What is the justification of including Americanization as a part of the personnel work of the Jute Bag Company?

7. Why do you suppose the text says that "personnel devices should be installed and used only when they perform definite functions"?

## ARNO ANNELLO, MACHINIST

The standards department of the Schoonway Machine Company recommended that Arno Annello, who operated a battery of automatic gear-
cutting machines, be discharged for failure to attain required minimum
production as set by the standards department. The foreman in whose
department Annello was employed objected to the recommendation. The
matter was placed before the production manager for final decision.

Arno Annello came to this country from Finland. He had
received the equivalent of a grade-school education in his native
land but had practically no knowledge of the English language.
He secured a job as a floor cleaner in the Schoonway plant. He
showed himself to be industrious and thorough, and the foreman
of the milling and gear-cutting department became interested in
him. One day he suggested to one of Annello's friends that the
floor sweeper should apply for a better job. When Annello heard
this, he signified his desire to become an operative of the
automatic sharpening machines. These machines were used to
sharpen the teeth of cutters after the cutters were otherwise
finished. They were automatic in operation, and with proper
setup there was very little danger of spoiling the work. The
foreman or an experienced assistant personally supervised each
setup. The operative inserted and removed the work, started
and stopped the machines, and dressed the emery wheels when
necessary. He operated from four to eight machines, depending
on the character of the work.

When a vacancy occurred in the department, the foreman decided to give Annello a chance, and obtained his transfer (on trial)
from the cleaning department. Over a period of several months,
Annello, with the assistance of the foreman, became proficient in
operating the machines, and he was given a permanent job. For
the next two years Annello showed steady improvement. He
became known in the department as a first-class operative of

automatic cutter-sharpening machines and finally developed into a skilled machine setter. While he improved as a machinist, Annello showed no aptitude in mastering the English language, and any extended or involved conversation had to be handled through an interpreter. The foreman, however, believed that Annello had the makings of a first-class machinist and was willing to put up with this inconvenience.

The company decided to install a new battery of gear-cutting machines for milling the teeth in cutters, and the foreman was confronted with the task of getting additional operatives to run these machines. The work of operating the automatic gear-cutting machines required considerably more skill than was necessary to run automatic cutter-sharpening machines. The machine attendant had to set up the indexing mechanism for the cutter blank, set the tooth-milling cutter at the correct distance off the center line of the blank, see that the cutter was properly sharpened, and set the machine for the correct stroke. The machine fed and indexed automatically, but considerable care was necessary on the part of the operative to keep the indexing at exactly the proper adjustment. The foreman approached Annello with the suggestion that he prepare himself to work on the new machines. Annello was highly pleased and put in all his spare time trying to familiarize himself with the work. He succeeded so well that by the time the machines were finally installed the foreman felt that Annello was sufficiently qualified and gave him a place on the new battery. Here Annello worked along with the other workmen, all of whom had been trained at one time or another by the foreman. He appeared to do average work and was well liked by the other men.

The standards department of the Schoonway Machine Company decided to institute a series of studies relative to the operations of gear-cutting machines for milling teeth in cutters. After the routine research had been made, the standards engineers announced the minimum amount of output which a worker must attain in order to be considered efficient. No bonus could be earned until this standard was exceeded.

During the period in which the studies were made, Annello was nervous. He appeared unable to keep his machine in proper adjustment. The pieces which he turned out were inferior in quality, and the total number gradually fell below the point at which the minimum standard was finally set. Engineers from the standards department, knowing that Annello was a protégé of the foreman, sought to ascertain the cause of his trouble, but he was unable to make an intelligible explanation. They warned him of the seriousness of the situation. For several days there was no change. Then, at the suggestion of the foreman, time-study men retimed Annello, in an endeavor to find the cause of his failure. His showing was worse than ever. The engineers began to question whether or not he had the native ability to do the work. The head of the standards department expressed that doubt to the foreman. The foreman insisted that Annello was a first-class workman. The standards department believed that the foreman was prejudiced because he did not object when they suggested that Joseph Smith be discharged. Smith had been employed on the new battery for about the same length of time as Annello and his output was not so low.

With their watches concealed in their pockets so as not to arouse Annello's suspicion, the time-study men clocked him for a third time. Still he showed no improvement. After that, the standards department became insistent that Annello be discharged. The foreman was obdurate, and the standards department appealed to the production manager for a final decision. The latter listened to the recommendations of the standards department and to the objections which the foreman raised, and then made a ruling that at the end of one week the standards department was to make another clocking of Annello's work. If it still was unsatisfactory, the foreman was to be given an additional week in which he could take any measures he chose in attempting to bring the machinist's work up to standard. If he failed to do this within the allotted period, Annello was to be fired for inability to attain the minimum standard.

At the end of the first week the new timings were made. Annello showed no improvement. When the foreman received this information, he went to Annello accompanied by a friend of the latter's, who acted as interpreter. The foreman told the machinist that his work was coming along well and that he had no need to fear the time-study men, that they would bother him no more. He said he would see to it personally that nothing happened to Annello and that as long as he tried his best he always could have a job with the Schoonway Machine Company. Annello thanked the foreman profusely and said that he always tried to do his best. The next morning he appeared at work smiling and happy. His output for the day was just at the minimum standard, but the quality was excellent. The next day his output increased. At the end of the week he was earning a good bonus. Six months later the standards department, as well as the foreman, rated him as the best worker on the automatic gear-cutting machines.

## QUESTIONS

1. Was the foreman justified in taking the action described in this case?

2. What do you think of the quality of personnel management of this company?

3. What is the foreman's function with respect to personnel management?

# CHAPTER XIX

## JOB SECURITY

### PROCTER & GAMBLE COMPANY

**1. A Large Company Manufacturing Soaps and Allied Products Adds Job Security to Its Personnel Program.**

In 1923, after two years of preparatory work, the Procter & Gamble Company announced to the workers in its soap plants that henceforth they could be assured of at least 48 weeks of work or 48 weeks' pay each year.

**2. What the Worker Wants.** A preceding chapter contains a discussion of the relative merits of various wage plans as methods of compensating industrial workers for effort expended. Usually workers are more interested in the amount they can earn on a job than in anything else the employer has to offer. Workers frequently make the statement that they "want it in the pay envelope."

Nevertheless, a worker in choosing between two employment opportunities considers a variety of things in addition to the rate of pay. Working conditions, physical risks, periodic bonuses, hours of work, steadiness of employment, duration of the job, holidays and vacations, and a fairly long list of other considerations sometimes makes one job more attractive than another.

Second only to rate of pay in general interest is assurance of employment. Is the business seasonal so that periodic layoffs are to be expected? Does the business feel the effects of general depression quickly and severely? Does this particular employer do all he can to keep his men continuously at work? When layoff becomes necessary, what plan does the management follow in selecting workers to be laid off first? Questions such as these are of great moment to the worker. Fortunate indeed is that employer whose business permits his providing steady employment for his work force.  Other things being equal, steady employment will attract the best of the available workers and frequently, because of high annual earnings, will tend to keep wage rates at a somewhat lower level.

In periods following business depression, workers tend to have more interest in employment security than they do during boom times.  When people are out of work and jobs are scarce, the worker who is relatively sure of a job is envied.  When jobs are plentiful, workers often quit their employment voluntarily to take other jobs which seem to offer more.  While it seems easy for some workers to forget the strain and actual suffering of workless weeks, that is not universally true.  Many workers, particularly men with family responsibilities, prize the assurance of steady employment and will make great effort to get on and stay on the payroll of a company that has a reputation for offering steady work.

**3. Difficulties of Providing Steady Employment.**  It is difficult for most manufacturing companies to provide steady employment for its entire work force.  Few manufacturers enjoy a steady volume of sales.  Seasonal and cyclical variation in volume of demand are common.  Some businesses experience periodic interruptions as the result of product model change. Radio and automobile manufacturers are well-known illustrations of this type.

Seasonal demand variation may often be more easily dealt with than cyclical swings.  When a company makes standard products, seasonal highs and lows in demand may be ironed out by manufacturing for stock during dull periods.  Even when this does not entail the risk of product change, the carrying of inventories may be so costly as to preclude this policy.  Another means sometimes employed to meet regularly recurring production ups and downs is product diversification.  If a company can use one plant and work force to make two seasonal products that have offsetting demand fluctuations, it is almost as well off as if it did not suffer from seasonal market variation.

Manufacture for stock ordinarily will not serve to iron out cyclical variations in demand.  Occasionally a company producing a raw material that has a relatively stable demand will be financially able to keep on producing as demand falls. It takes large amounts of working capital to do this, and the length of the depression period is usually so long as to make such a policy extremely hazardous.

During the last 20 years, various companies have tried many schemes to alleviate the effects of business swings on output. No solution of universal applicability has been found. Most companies find it necessary to curtail and expand manufacturing operations to correspond roughly with changes in demand. Few companies are in such a position that their executives can say to their employees, "We can give you steady work."

**4. Experience of the Procter & Gamble Company.** In 1920 the Procter & Gamble Company, maker of soap and cooking products, decided to work out a plan of guaranteed employment for all workers who had been with the company for a period of six months and had become profit sharers. This guaranty provided for at least 48 weeks of work each year or 48 weeks of pay. After two years of investigation and preparatory work and a year of constructive development, a plan was put into operation in November, 1923.

**5. History of the Company.** The Procter & Gamble Company was started as a partnership in 1837 by two young men, William Procter and James Gamble. Both had been trained in England, Procter in the candle business and Gamble in the heavy chemical industry. At the time the partnership was established, Cincinnati was the greatest hog market in the country. The partners located a plant near the stockyards to produce lard, lard oils, and candles. For many years soapmaking was regarded as a subsidiary enterprise, and only in comparatively late years had the company developed cooking products based on vegetable oils. By 1929, however, these two latter lines had become of prime importance, many minor lines had been added, and lard production had been discontinued. The total annual sales approximated $200,000,000. The controlling ownership and actual management of the business were in the hands of the direct descendants of the founders.

Three groups of products were manufactured: soaps, vegetable-oil cooking compounds, and a miscellaneous group of related products. All were produced in standard qualities and sizes by mass production methods. Chief among the soaps were Ivory soap and chips, Chipso flakes, and P. & G. White Naphtha soap. The company was engaged in putting into distribution two new articles, Camay, a high-grade toilet soap, and Chipso granules for dishes.

In the field of oil products for cooking, the company manufactured Crisco in cans for retail and in bulk for the baking trade, Flakewhite, and Puritan Oil. These were made from vegetable oils, cottonseed being the most common base.

The company also marketed large amounts of glycerin and glycerin products, stearic acid, winter oil, and intermediary products such as coconut oil, cottonseed meal, cottonseed lint, and copra meal and cake. Ivo, a glycerin antifreeze mixture, was developed, also.

**6. The Soap Manufacturing Industry.** In recent years, soap manufacture in the United States had become well established. Small unit producers, for the most part, had either merged with large concerns or passed out of existence. While the industry was still highly competitive among large-scale producers, the situation was characterized by a large, steady market which was well correlated with increasing standards of living. The competitors of the Procter & Gamble Company, like that company itself, had strong financial backing. Moreover, modern soap production had become so technically complex, required such a vast outlay of capital in the form of building, equipment, and process development, and rested so firmly on the national and international development of certain brands and trade-marks, that the field was almost closed to the small, inexperienced producer. Big producers, however, waged continuous battle for the supremacy of given trade-marks or brands and new processes.

**7. The Edible Oil Industry.** The production of edible oils was not comparable with that of soap. Lard continued to be an outstanding competitor of such oils, and the amount of lard on the market at a given time was not correlated with the demand for it. Rather, it was closely related to the number of hogs killed during a given period, and the killing of hogs was of itself an item which varied with seasonal and other fluctuations which were beyond the control of even the meat packers. The price of corn might, for example, influence the rate of hog killing. The price of corn, in turn, was influenced by crop conditions.

Furthermore, the field of edible oil production taken by itself represented no such stability as was found in soapmaking. Oils with a cottonseed base competed freely with those of coconut and corn bases. The cost of an oil with a cottonseed base was closely related to the abundance of cottonseed, but the amount and price of seed at a given time was influenced by many factors far removed from the consumption of cottonseed oil itself. Moreover, the whole field was still new. Competition had not yet been stabilized as among a few large units. New processes and products were continually being developed. Neither demand nor processes showed a constancy comparable with that found in soapmaking. At the same time, Procter & Gamble Company had become well established in oil production and had obtained national distribution of products.

**8. Character of the Work Force.** Procter & Gamble Company employed over 5,000 workers, of whom about 12 per cent were women. Over 90 per cent of the employees were native or naturalized Americans. The labor supply of the main plant at Ivorydale came from the Mill Creek Valley district near Cincinnati.

Workers could be divided into four groups: (1) 150 research chemists at Ivorydale engaged in studying new processes and products and in perfecting old methods and products; (2) women workers who tended automatic machinery and did other work not too heavy, too disagreeable, or too technical; (3) men workers engaged in a variety of tasks such as unloading raw materials (*e.g.,* coal and copra); tending kettles, retorts, presses, mills, and furnace equipment; watching machines; or packing, handling, and shipping; (4) office force. Except for research, there was relatively little highly skilled work. Mechanical contrivances did much of the heavy work which formerly characterized soapmaking. Wages paid and hours worked in the Procter & Gamble Company were somewhat more favorable to the workers than the wages and hours of their local competitors.

**9. The Company's Labor Policy.** Following a strike which occurred in the 1880's, the Procter & Gamble management began a consistent policy of improving labor conditions. In 1886, the company inaugurated a profit-sharing plan, which was modified from time to time. Any employee whose wages were below $2,000 a year might become a profit sharer after six months' employment with the company. The profit-sharing plan provided for the purchase of common stock at market value to the amount of the employee's annual salary. On this stock, the worker received the ordinary dividends and, in addition, a profit-sharing dividend which began at 10 per cent of his wages and increased to 20 per cent with length of service at the rate of 1 per cent per annum. In addition to profit sharing, the company had developed and installed well-organized pension and benefit plans, an employees' conference committee plan, and a suggestion system. The guaranty of employment was its latest major undertaking in the field of personnel relations. This guaranty promised to all participants in the company's profit-sharing plan "full-time pay for full-time work for not less than 48 weeks in each calendar year, less only time lost by reason of the customary holiday closings, or through fires, flood, strike or other extreme emergency." In making this guaranty, the company held the right to transfer any employee to work other than his regular job. The company also reserved the full right to discharge, and to amend or terminate the guaranty after six months' notice.

**10. Origin and Development of the Guaranteed Employment Plan.** The situation which gave rise to the plan and the necessary changes in production and selling programs were set forth in the following company memorandum:

Prior to 1920 it was accepted as a necessary evil that there must be fluctuations in our sales, and with them all the difficulties attendant upon manufacturing. In that year, Mr. Procter, president of the Procter & Gamble Company, suggested that a study be made of our method of selling, with the object of effecting more stabilized production, and in consequence a condition which would permit of regularized employment.

The results of this study brought out the fact that while output fluctuated widely by months, our yearly sales varied only to the extent that might be expected and fairly predicted by the normal growth of the country's consumption of our products. The problem, then, to spread the production of the year evenly over 12 months, was clearly defined as one, primarily, of distribution and sales policies.

In the period preceding 1920 all our products were sold exclusively to jobbers, and a review of the buying practices of these distributors indicated that their purchasing policies were based largely upon market conditions and firmly entrenched buying habits. Heavy buying occurred in the fall and early spring. Frequently these orders covered their needs for months to come. Our factories operated at capacity, enrollment increased, and our people were required to work overtime. After a period of full production, orders began to fall off, and the jobbers' stocks were more than adequate to meet their normal sales' needs. Our production then continued until our depleted stocks were again replenished, when curtailment of output and reduction in enrollment of necessity followed.

During these periods of feast and famine in our factories, the actual consumption of soap continued on a uniform basis. The people use about the same amount of soap the year around, and the slight fluctuation in the retail price does not materially affect the consumer's demand. It was evident that we were manufacturing for speculation and not to meet actual consumption. It was also quite apparent that, among other things, the buying of the jobber was and probably always would be a widely fluctuating thing, dependent on market conditions and well-established buying habits. It was at this time that our plan of selling was changed, and broadened to include the retailer.

The new policy of selling made it necessary to augment our sales force very largely. Where we had been dealing with a comparatively small number of jobbers, the new plan required that we establish relations with hundreds of retailers for every account represented by a jobber in the past. The country was divided into districts, each to be covered by a complete sales unit. Warehouses were erected or acquired, and a tentative schedule of production and distribution, based upon our knowledge of consumption and experience of yearly production in the past was initiated.

The sales division met each obstacle, and after approximately five years, more than 75 per cent of our sales are made direct to the retailer, and shipped to him to meet his normal needs, making it possible for us to estimate very closely our sales department's demands for a period of one year.

The question of stabilizing our production was primarily a sales problem— about the methods employed by the sales department, and the coordination of its activities with those of the manufacturing department.

The first step necessary was to estimate the sales for the coming year. Approximate figures were supplied by the sales supervisors, each of whom is in charge of a group of 10 to 15 salesmen, covering a territory representing roughly a population of 200,000. These estimates were tabulated by the various district sales managers, and forwarded to the general sales department at Cincinnati, where they were reviewed, revised when necessary, and definite quotas prepared for each division of the sales department. The sales department agreed to stand by its estimate and to dispose of the products in a steady flow throughout the year. The sales figures were then translated into a production schedule by the manufacturing department, covering the year's activities in the various plants.

Supplementing the quota laid down at the beginning of each year by the sales department, very close contact is maintained between the manufacturing and the buying and sales divisions, and on the twentieth of each month a revised production schedule is worked out, determining the various brands and sizes that will be required during the following month (the previous estimates were only of totals, not of brands and sizes). You will understand that the purpose of these meetings is only to correct minor discrepancies in the production and distribution schedule. As a whole, production based upon the yearly estimate is maintained, even when it becomes necessary for some of the finished products to enter the warehouses for a time, or when the sales exceed the production for the month.

This change in sales policy was made effective in 1921, and given a thorough trial for two years, before any definite employment policy was announced. In August of 1923, however, the experiment had proved so generally satisfactory to the management, the sales department, the manufacturing department, the trade, and the worker, that our employment guaranty was announced, assuring every employee who was a profit-sharing stockholder not less than 48 weeks' work each year.

During the five years of the new sales policy, in only one year did the actual sales and estimate fail of tally within a reasonable figure. In this particular year, the sales exceeded the estimate.

The terms of sale for soap shipments were changed. Previously, orders were shipped as fast as they could be filled. Since the change in policy, only noncancellable orders are accepted, for delivery at the regular rate which experience has shown the buyer will sell the goods. The buyer is not billed until the goods are shipped. The arrangement amounts to selling on contract for weekly or monthly delivery. The policy is combined with extensive warehouse facilities throughout the country, from which all shipments are made.

By January, 1928, guaranteed employment had been extended to the workers at the company plants at Ivorydale, near Cincinnati, Ohio; Port Ivory, on Staten Island, New York; and Kansas City, Kansas. In 1929, the management extended the plan to two newly acquired plants.

**11. Summary and Conclusions.** *Why Procter & Gamble Company Executives Believed Guaranteed Employment Sound for That Company.* There are several reasons why Procter & Gamble Company executives might well believe guaranty of employment to be sound for that company. The extensive changes in marketing methods had resulted in exceptional stability of demand on production facilities. Soap was a consumer's good that was not greatly subject to seasonal shifts in demand. Cyclical changes would have some effect on soap consumption but much less than on most commodities. The change in marketing method had brought the plants and the markets closer in the sense that production could be paced more nearly by actual consumption. There was good reason to believe that in the future production would be relatively stable.

The company was still subject to variations in volume that might result from shifts in the competitive balance. However, competition would be mostly within the soap industry. Procter & Gamble Company was firmly established in the field, and the company had long been an aggressive leader in developing the product and in meeting selling competition. The industry was well organized in the sense that competition had become stabilized, and new units in the industry were unlikely to upset the situation. Competitively the company seemed exceptionally stable.

Guaranty of employment fitted in well with the company's personnel policy and program. The management had long believed in a "fair deal" for its workers. Employees were relatively free from financial worry. They had confidence in the company and had been taught to believe that the management would always promote employee well-being without the necessity of active effort on the part of workers beyond the doing of their daily jobs. They were a loyal group. Employment assurance would tend to follow out the company policy of fostering this loyalty and would be further assurance to the workers that they could rely upon the management to provide for workers' interests.

The company already had a varied program of employee motivation devices. Wages were high and working conditions good. Stock ownership and profit-sharing plans, a pension plan, a plan of sickness, accident, and death benefits, a suggestion system, and a conference plan had all been in operation for a long time. Employees were fully familiar with these devices, and might well be expected to look upon guaranty of jobs as a fitting complement to other benefits.

Most of Procter & Gamble Company employees were of the type which might well be expected to prize employment security. The worker characteristic most important to this company was reliability. The whole personnel program seems to be such as to attract and hold workers who had a well-developed sense of responsibility. Such workers are likely to respond well to job security. Family pressure is a very important influence in this respect. Again, employment guaranty fitted the case.

Certainly, if industrial job guaranty can ever rest on firm foundations, this company seems to be on solid ground in providing economic security for its workers. The nature of the product, the company's marketing organization, the character of the workers, the personnel policy and program, and conditions in the industry all look propitious. Procter & Gamble Company executives had much indeed to justify their beliefs and actions.

*Should the Company Have Guaranteed Its Workers Jobs?* To question a program of such seeming soundness as the one here under discussion may seem foolhardy. However, there are questionable aspects of the situation which justify raising the issue.

Just what did the employees gain from the guaranty? A feeling of confidence, no more, no less. From the changes that made the guaranty possible they gained much. These changes stabilized employment for them to the extent that it did away with the necessity of frequent periodic layoff. If the company had created a situation which provided steady work, what need was there for guaranteeing employment? The workers in Procter & Gamble Company vegetable-oil plants and cottonseed-oil mills were the ones who most needed employment guaranty. Because steady work was not available for these people, work could not be guaranteed to them. Thus it seems that the less a company is able to ensure its workers constant employment, the more those workers need a guaranty of earning security, while employees of a company that can guarantee jobs have much less need for job ensurance.

*Worker Reaction to Job Assurance.* It has already been pointed out that the formal announcement of the guaranty following employment stabilization would give the workers a feeling of security. That is true, but it does not follow that the announcement of this guaranty was necessary to gain this end. Had the company, upon completion of the developmental and trial period, simply told its employees what it had done to promote continuous employment for them, worker reaction would probably have been the same. It is quite possible that the feeling of satisfaction in security would have resulted if no announcement had been made. Is it not safe to conclude that shortly the employees themselves would have discovered their changed status? Frequently what employees discover and conclude for themselves is far more effective in shaping their reactions than pronouncements of management.

*Risks of the Guaranty.* The company took some risk in making its guaranty. By changing distribution policies and methods, company executives had made it possible to stabilize the rate of production throughout the year. Seasonal layoff of workers was thereby avoided, and the risks involved in promising workers steady employment were not great so far as seasonal variation in rate of operation was concerned. However, demand for soap and soap products is not completely free from the influence of general business conditions. Particularly is this true in periods of protracted depression when there is much unemployment. The company plan reserved the right to discontinue the guaranty on six months' notice. This would go far to protect the company financially. It offered no protection against adverse worker reaction if it should ever be necessary for the company to suspend the plan during a period when its benefits would be most needed by the workers. This is a serious risk.

*Company Gains from the Plan.* It seems likely that the gains from the plan were worth the risks. Favorable worker reaction coupled with rather widespread public approval of the action may well have improved the company's competitive position. It did not injure labor to announce the guaranty, and the stabilization of operations which preceded the guaranty was of great benefit to the workers. The risk of having to suspend the plan was real but seems somewhat remote. As most business innovations are accompanied by some degree of risk, it would seem that the program as a whole was wise.

*General Applicability of the Plan.* There is little in this situation which holds forth much promise to labor generally.  Few companies are in a position to stabilize operation to the extent or in the way that Procter & Gamble Company did.  Industry is constantly changing, is essentially unstable.  To stabilize the position of any one factor in the situation, when the situation itself is essentially unstable, is very difficult.  There is probably little hope for general development along the lines followed by Procter & Gamble Company.

*Solution of the Periodic Unemployment Problem.*  The alleviation of unemployment risks must come about in some other way.  The Social Security Act of 1935 is probably the type of approach that is much more likely to produce the desired results than dependence on the ability and effort of the individual employer.  In its present form this program may not be perfect, but it is a move in the right direction and experience will provide a basis for improvement.

Federal action overcomes one of the greatest objections to individual state programs.  If the cost of unemployment compensation falls more heavily on the industry of one state than it does upon competing units in another state, the more heavily burdened units are at a competitive disadvantage.  The Social Security Act of 1935 makes it possible for the states to formulate their own programs.  Because its tax provisions apply to manufacturers in all states alike, it is possible for a state to set up an unemployment compensation program without necessarily thereby putting employers within the state at a competitive disadvantage.  That this is an important consideration is shown by the general similarity of the state plans which have been set up following the passage of the Federal act.

*Industry-wide Security Measures.*  A most recent attempt to provide additional security for workers is the Health and Welfare Fund of the United Mine Workers.  During 1946 the mine operators who had contracts with the UMW paid 5 cents for each ton of coal mined into a fund to be administered for the benefit of the coal miners by a board of three trustees: one for the union, one for the operators, and one neutral.  The total paid into that fund during 1946 was reported to be $26,-

000,000.[1]   Under the 1947 contract with the operators, the assessment was increased to 10 cents a ton with a reported total contribution of $39,000,000.   The union stated in June, 1948, that 146,980 persons were receiving aid from the Miners' Fund, that the average total benefit was $530 with average monthly payments of $61.   Over 60 per cent of the grants from the fund were of 12 months' duration.   The breadth of the aid from this fund is shown by Mr. Lewis's statement that practically every family in the mining industry was related to some one of the 146,980 recipients of aid from the fund, either by blood or by marriage.

It should be observed that this worker security measure was not paid for by the mine operators but by the consuming public, which was immediately assessed the cost increase.   It should be likewise pointed out that the consuming public had no voice in the creation of or determination of the conditions of this arrangement.   In this respect the whole matter was vastly different from the Social Security Act of 1935 and the associated state programs.   Also it should be realized that in its incidence on the consuming public this method of financing social security most nearly resembles a sales tax and in this respect again differs radically from most approaches to the problem of worker security.

Whether or not the fund tax on output is an economical method of meeting the requirements of the situation is not easy to judge, but from the standpoint of the public one cannot help but question the desirability of this method if it were applied to industry in general, or as it is being employed in this industry in particular.

Obviously, the best way to ensure financial security to industrial workers is to provide them with steady work.   Unfortunately, the very nature of competitive industry precludes this. Some employers can provide continuous jobs for their workers; many employers cannot.   If that be true, some other solution must be sought.   One doubts if that devised by Mr. Lewis and the UMW is the best.

[1] *The New York Times,* June 7, 1948.

## QUESTIONS

1. How would you characterize the relationship that existed between Procter & Gamble Company management and employees?

2. Describe the company's personnel program.

3. Would you expect guaranteed employment to be effective in attracting desirable employees to the Procter & Gamble Company?

4. Would it serve this company as an incentive to secure worker productivity?

5. Was the Procter & Gamble Company in a sound position to guarantee its workers employment?

6. What, if any, objections are there to the company's action?

7. Should the company have made the guaranty it did?

8. If you were in charge of one of the company's plants making cooking compounds from vegetable oils, would you seek to have the guaranty extended to your plant?

9. How generally applicable is the Procter & Gamble Company plan throughout industry? Explain.

10. What is the workers' interest in job security?

## Problem 44

## STUDEBAKER CORPORATION

The Studebaker Corporation, South Bend, Indiana, manufactured automobiles. Like others of that industry, the company experienced wide seasonal and annual variations in the demand for its product. Fluctuation in market demand was reflected in comparable variation in volume of output, which in turn was responsible for several of the major production problems faced by the management. The labor requirements of the company varied from month to month and year to year with a resulting increase in labor turnover and decrease in labor efficiency. The company developed a plan which it believed would improve this admittedly undesirable labor situation.

The Studebaker Corporation was one of the oldest manufacturers of automobiles in the United States. It produced a complete line of cars ranging in price from $1,450 to $2,595 at the factory. The company also produced trucks, busses, and funeral cars. The products of the Studebaker Corporation had long enjoyed an excellent reputation for quality.

An established policy of the Studebaker Corporation was the production in its own plants of practically all parts entering into its product. Its foundry, machine shop, motor, body, chassis, and assembly divisions at South Bend were well equipped and efficient. Like other producers, the company purchased such accessories as tires, carburetors, and electrical and lubricating equipment from established parts producers. The ability of the automotive parts industry to produce quality products at low cost had caused the Studebaker Corporation to depart in a few instances from its established policy of producing all parts in its own plants. Examples of parts purchased outside were wheels and frames. These were obtained from well-known producers specializing in these lines and were considered the equal in quality of similar parts produced in Studebaker shops. Such purchases were, however, exceptions rather than the rule, since the company desired to maintain the policy under which it had established a reputation as "The Great Independent."

The labor policies of the Studebaker Corporation were as modern as its plants and equipment. The flyleaf of its "Factory Rules and Regulations" carried the following statement of its policies.

The continuous growth of Studebaker business during the seventy-eight years of its existence has been due solely to the fact that Studebaker products have met the requirements of the customer. Our employees should always remember this basic fact and realize at all times that the continued prosperity of the business and their own daily welfare depend on Studebaker products being correctly designed, honestly manufactured, and fairly sold in the markets of the world.

Studebaker ensures every employee fair wages, reasonable hours of employment, safe and healthful working conditions and an opportunity to progress within the organization if he shows better than average ability, industry and ambition.

In the organization of the Studebaker Corporation responsibility for all matters of acquiring and maintaining its labor force was centralized in a personnel department which was known as the Cooperative Department. In addition to the responsibility of hiring, transfer, firing, wages, safety, health, and recreation, this department had organized and was maintaining a group of "Cooperative Plans" which included the following:

Suggestion plan
Stock purchase plan
Service medal plan
Pension plan
Group insurance plan

The suggestion plan had been in operation for five years. It provided a routine whereby any employee might suggest ways and means of improvement in product, production process or equipment, waste elimination or utilization, and cost reduction. Cash awards were made for all suggestions found worthy of adoption.

The stock purchase plan was designed to aid employees of the company in the purchase of shares of Studebaker Corporation stock.

In 1923, the management began the practice of giving service medals to all employees who had been in the continuous service of the company for five, ten, fifteen, and twenty or more years. By January 1, 1930, 9,940 five-year, 2,367 ten-year, 675 fifteen-year, and 409 twenty-year medals had been awarded.

The pension plan was designed to apply to any employee who at the age of sixty-five years, having been in the continuous service of the company for 20 or more years, and whose earnings for the preceding five years had not averaged more than $3,000 per year, wished to be retired from the service of the company on a pension. The pension would consist of an amount equal to 25 per cent of his average annual earnings for the five years preceding retirement with a minimum of $30 per month.

The group insurance plan enabled employees to obtain at a low cost insurance policies incorporating death benefit, permanent total disability benefit, accidental dismemberment and loss of sight benefits, accident and sickness benefits. During a three-year period, claims totaling $1,347,995 were paid on policies in force. Of this amount, $646,512 was for 7,998 sickness and accident claims and $701,483 covered 409 life insurance claims.

The management considered the Cooperative Plans to be of mutual benefit to the employees and to the company. Annual expenditures by the corporation in connection with these plans exceeded $2,000,000. The management believed this cost justified in view of the increased labor efficiency and productivity that resulted from a stabilized labor group.

None of these plans, however, relieved the company of one serious problem which had long been an outstanding characteristic of the automobile industry. Market demand had a distinct seasonal variation which it had been found impossible to eliminate. Total annual sales of the industry and of individual producers varied greatly from year to year. The experience of the Studebaker Corporation had been no exception to the general rule. This fluctuation in market demand, together with rapid technical development of the product, a dominating style factor, and high-pressure selling, had made it impossible for the manufacturer to lay out a uniform production schedule. It was necessary, therefore, to employ some production plan which would take into account the frequent fluctuations.  Short-time fore-casting of market demand was common practice in the industry, and production schedules were constantly revised in terms of these market forecasts.

The fluctuating operation schedule gave rise to many produc-tion problems.  Not the least of these was the maintenance of an adequate supply of trained labor.  When production schedules mounted, large numbers of additional workers were required. When schedules fell off, retention of the peak work force was impossible.  Plants could not be operated at capacity; shorter work weeks were the rule, and many employees were temporarily or permanently dismissed.

The Studebaker Cooperative Department had found transfer somewhat effective in reducing this labor turnover.  Not all departments experienced maximum and minimum labor require-ments at exactly the same time.  It had been found possible to shift men temporarily from one department to another and thus reduce both layoffs and hirings.  In furtherance of this policy the company urged its employees to become efficient in several differ-ent types of work.  Complete personnel records facilitated such interdepartmental shifts.

Departmental transfers could not, however, go far toward overcoming the extreme fluctuations in labor needs that were commonly experienced by the company.  The need for some effec-tive means of stabilizing labor requirements was keenly felt by both the company and the workers.  Practically all direct labor in the various plants was paid on some form of piece-rate basis. When the shops were operating at normal capacity, workers earned excellent wages.  If curtailed schedules called for short-shift operation, workers' earnings were less, and when curtail-ment of production involved layoffs, complete cessation of earn-ings became critical with many employees.

The Cooperative Department presented to the plant super-intendents and foremen a plan which the department believed would go far toward remedying the existing situation.  Super-intendents and foremen were asked to study the plan carefully, discuss it thoroughly, and then express an opinion as to its effec-tiveness and suitability to the conditions of the Studebaker plants. As presented to this group, the essentials of the proposed plan were as follows.

In the past, full advantage had not been taken of the fact that men were willing to accommodate themselves to the conditions inherent in the business. Theretofore it had been considered desirable to keep the working hours per day and the working days per week within comparatively narrow bounds of variation, making it necessary to lay off men in large numbers in time of low production and to employ additional men in large numbers in time of heavy production. Company officials believed that men would be willing to work more than normal hours at some periods to offset thereby the less than normal hours available in other periods. The company wished to give them the opportunity to make unusually large earnings at certain times to offset the unusually small earnings which must be faced at other times.

At the time of the proposal, there were approximately 5,000 productive employees in the Studebaker plants. About 139 productive hours were expended on each car produced. If the plants had operated 8 hours per day for 12 days in a month (an average of 3 days per week), this force of 5,000 productive men would have built and would have been paid for approximately 3,450 cars. If these men had worked 25 days in a month (an average of 6 days per week, including Saturday as a full day), 12 hours per day instead of 8, they would have produced 10,800 cars instead of 3,450 and they themselves would have had the larger earnings, practically three times as great, which would have come from the larger production. If, however, in a month when production schedules called for 10,800 cars, the men had worked 6 days per week, 9 hours a day with Saturday afternoons off, they would have produced only about 7,000 cars instead of the 10,800 called for by the production schedule. It would then have been necessary to employ about 3,000 additional men to get the required production, and the increase in the monthly payroll, which would have represented this additional 3,800 cars, would have gone to the new men employed—to the temporary men rather than the 5,000 regular producers.

Under the new plan as proposed by the Cooperative Department, the 10,800 cars would have been built by the 5,000 regular workers. The department believed that the employees and the company would both profit thereby. To ensure the success of the plan, the company would agree to observe the following rules:

1. No additional permanent workers would be added to the existing working force.

2. In event of a production emergency or increase in schedule, the hours and days of work would be increased.

3. All approved labor requisitions would be filled by loaning and transferring of workers.

4. Workers would be loaned on requisition only from one department to another for a period of two weeks.

5. If and when the hours and days were increased to the maximum, and it should become necessary to add to the existing force, foremen would be permitted to requisition additional temporary workers.

6. When temporary workers were added to a department, all their records and payrolls would be marked with a symbol indicating that they were T men.

7. T workers would be permitted to work only so long as the department was operating the maximum number of hours and days.

8. In event of reduction in schedule making necessary a reduction of work force, T workers would be laid off first.

## QUESTIONS

1. Should the Studebaker Corporation have adopted the plan proposed by its Cooperative Department?

2. How generally applicable is this plan throughout industry?

3. What would be the effect of a general adoption of this plan?

### Problem 45

## JONES CONSTRUCTION COMPANY

The Jones Construction Company erected office buildings, factories, and houses, and did other construction work on the Atlantic seacoast, in the Middle West, and in the Central South. During a period of high activity in the industry the personnel manager of the company found that labor turnover was increasing rapidly and sought means of effecting its reduction.

The company had first employed a personnel manager at a time when labor turnover was high, and the company had been experiencing difficulty in obtaining satisfactory workers. The manager made a preliminary investigation of the method of employing workers and the causes of the existing labor turnover. He found that when the company contracted to construct a mill in a Southern state, it sent to the location its engineers, efficiency men, and minor executives. The skilled workers, such as mechanics, carpenters, and steel workers, and unskilled labor were recruited locally or from the nearest city or other available source. In recruiting these workers for each new job it was, of course, impossible for the superintendent to know who would make good foremen and subforemen and which of the workers were the most efficient. Naturally, in handling so many employees, two to four weeks elapsed before a superintendent could determine the efficiency of each new man employed.

As a result of his investigations, the employment manager decided to try to build up a permanent skeleton personnel of both skilled and unskilled laborers. By keeping for each employee a complete record covering the type of work he did, his ability, his personality, whether he was married or single, and his willingness to go from one part of the country to another in order to work for the company, the employment manager was able to sort out the type of worker he wanted. Six years of effort along this line had provided an experienced nucleus for any work the company might undertake. One of the main reasons for the employment manager's success in holding these men was that he gave them continuous employment and always paid them the rate of wages paid in the city in which the home office was situated. As it happened, this rate was as high as that paid in any part of the United States during that period.

The unskilled laborers on his permanent list, assuming that the company had work for them the entire year, received $2,600, and skilled carpenters received $4,800.

The unskilled workers consisted chiefly of Italians who, as a class, were said to send approximately two-thirds of their wages back to Italy. The other third of their wages appeared to be more than sufficient to provide them with room and board on jobs where the company did not supply these and also give them spending money enough to meet their requirements.

The personnel manager, in going over his card list of unskilled laborers, found that in a large majority of cases he had the same workers with whom he had started six years earlier and that most of these workers had earned the maximum amounts per annum as stated above. He noticed, however, that many of the Italians had recently stopped working and that the labor turnover had started to increase. He immediately investigated this and found from his talks with the Italians that after earning $2,000 a year they did not see any reason why they should continue to work, and, furthermore, that they now for the first time were having a chance to have a vacation and to enjoy themselves. They had no idea of working for any other company but merely believed that they were earning enough money without working continuously. In fact, one Italian when questioned why he was not working said, "Why is it necessary for me to work? I will earn this year over $2,000. This is more money than I ever earned before. I am sending $800 back to Italy, which is more than the folks have ever received, and at the present rate of exchange, it amounts to an awful lot of money for them. That leaves me $1,200, which is more than I want to live on and I don't see why I can't take a vacation and enjoy myself."

What should the personnel manager have done to induce these men to go back to work?

# PART III

## CONTROL OF THE PRODUCTION PROCESS

# CHAPTER XX

# PRODUCT DEVELOPMENT AND INTRODUCTION

## WESTERN ELECTRIC COMPANY, INC.

### 1. An Electrical Equipment Manufacturing Company Prepares to Produce a New Product.

Engineering work involved in preparing for the manufacture of a new product was part of the work of the planning departments in the plants of Western Electric Company, Inc. This work included setting up various operating standards essential for economical production and for control of the manufacturing process, and also improving on the original designs furnished by other departments. This preproduction planning was considered of great importance because, in the words of a company executive, "the ability of a manufacturing institution to produce a quality product, at a proper price, within a predetermined interval, is only equal to its ability to do a satisfactory engineering job in the first place." For production of the telephone handset, the planning department was able to effect many savings.

**2. Preparing for Production.** Between the origin of the idea of a new product and the actual manufacture of the product a vast amount of design, planning, and preparation must take place. The product must be designed, tested out, redesigned, and retested—sometimes a lengthy and costly process. When a satisfactory design has been evolved, the methods of manufacture must be planned in detail. When these plans are satisfactorily completed, the requisite facilities for production must be provided. These, of course, include equipment and tools, raw materials, and workers.

**3. Designing the Product.** The design of a new product must be carried out from three points of view, which we shall call functional design, market design, and production design.

Functional design has to do with the performance of the product in use. If one were to design a new lawn mower, he would surely make certain that it would cut grass. He would so design it that it would cut evenly and cleanly, and would endeavor to have it cut everything in its path. The design should be such that the mower could be pushed easily. The less effort required to operate the mower, the better. Another aspect of design would be durability. The mower should continue to function well for a long time, to stay sharp, and to push easily. There are other matters of design having to do with the functioning of the new mower which would probably be considered; these might include provision for lubrication, amount of noise made by the mower when operated, and similar characteristics of the machine. Since functional design has to do with performance in use, it is obviously of primary importance in planning a new product.

It is not enough that a product do well the work for which it is intended. In addition it must appeal to people who might be interested in buying it; it must incite consumer demand. Much of the "streamlining" that has recently been done on many products is in the interest of market appeal. Streamlining a lawn mower does not improve its ability to cut grass. Recently "de luxe streamlined" lawn mowers have come on the market; they have a more attractive appearance than the orthodox models. At least one manufacturer of lawn mowers included in a recent line several models featuring "centralized lubrication." These mowers had but one point to be oiled; pipes and ducts carried the oil from the central reservoir to the various friction points of the mower. It is doubtful if centralized lubrication improves lawn mowers functionally, nor does it seem probable that convenience in use is increased. Nevertheless "centralized lubrication" may be an important feature if it increases the competitive appeal of this manufacturer's products. Designing products to increase their buyer appeal apart from superior functioning of the product is familiar practice and an important requisite of the well-designed product.

Excellent functional and market design are of no greater importance than design in terms of production cost. The idea that a better mouse trap will cause a path to be beaten to your factory door is good only if you can make that mouse trap at a cost low enough to permit an attractive purchase price. Cost of production is greatly influenced by product design. It usually costs less to punch holes than it does to drill them. Thus good design from a production standpoint will, if possible, permit the punching of such holes as are required. Also, the fewer holes needed, the lower will be the cost of making holes. Few products designed in terms of function and market appeal are suitable for profitable production until they have been thoroughly redesigned in terms of manufacturing ease. Changes in design to simplify processing must not sacrifice excellence of functional and market design. Occasionally some compromise between the three is necessary, but design excellence aims at a maximum of all: functional perfection, consumer appeal, and low cost of manufacture. It is the combination of the three that puts design on a business basis.

**4. Planning Production.** Once satisfactory design has been achieved, it is necessary to plan the methods of production. Product specifications must be restated as manufacturing specifications, processing methods must be determined, and control methods and standards must be worked out. In the case of our lawn mower, sharpness, ease of operation, durability, and appeal to the eye must all be translated into material specifications, exact shapes, definite tolerances of parts, fit, color, and color combination specifications—a thousand concrete, exact standards. These are necessary if the design of the sample that has been approved is to be repeated without deviation in the product eventually shipped to market.

These manufacturing specifications form the basis for process planning. Detailed methods to be followed in manufacture must be predetermined. Operations, specifications, sequence of operations, assembly ways and means must be worked out. When properly done, this planning leaves little to chance, and actual manufacturing costs will closely approach estimated costs.

This realization of anticipated results will obtain only if control for that purpose is provided. Inspection must start with materials and carry through to finished product. Worker productivity must be provided for. Interruptions to smooth flow of work in process must be guarded against. Everyone from the purchasing agent's clerk to the chief engineer is affected, and

the correlation of the effort of all as control factors must be ensured by careful preplanning of control functions.

**5. Providing Production Facilities.** As plans for production
mature, the actual provision of production facilities will get
under way. These facilities include plant space, equipment and
tools, suitable workers and supervisors, and the specified materials. The ability to acquire these and the cost of acquiring
them, of course, will have been under consideration during various stages of design and planning. The actual acquisition of
facilities takes time and should begin as early as the definiteness
of plans permits. It takes time to build equipment; it takes time
to prepare raw materials and process purchased parts; it takes
time to train workers and supervisors.

At this stage the time element frequently becomes very important. Usually a company does not have unlimited time in which
to bring out new products. Competitors may have sensed the
need or opportunity for the new introduction. To keep ahead of
competition, or even to keep up with it, is important. If too
much time is consumed in getting new products into the market,
some of the gain from them may be lost. One of the most common criticisms of the production organization voiced by the sales
department refers to the length of time required to get a new
product into production so that they can have it to sell.

Too much hurry in starting manufacture is as bad as slowness.
Preplanning makes for profits: it ensures low costs, satisfactory
quality, ability to make quick delivery promises, and then keep
them. These are all-important to the success of a new product.
Of equal importance is the placing of the item in the market at
the most advantageous time from the standpoint of securing sales
volume.

Product planning and introduction are problems of great business importance to the manufacturer. Frequently the time factor
is the essence of success. The magnitude of the problem grows
out of the great amount of detail involved and the necessity of
correlating these details. The introduction of new automobile
models each year is, in many respects, a marvelous human
achievement. Fortunate indeed is the manufacturer who must
face this problem rarely or has ample time to carry the planning

through without rush when new products are introduced. The experience which follows is unusual in this respect; the market situation makes possible a thorough, unhurried performance of the various activities and functions inherent in the introduction of new products.

**6. Planning Production of a New Product at the Western Electric Company, Inc., Plants.** When the development of a new piece of apparatus at Western Electric Company, Inc., had progressed to the point where executives contemplated its manufacture, the planning organization was furnished with a model or preliminary drawing of the apparatus and specifications covering its electrical and mechanical functions, the materials to be used, tolerances, quantities likely to be manufactured, etc. The planning engineers did not originate or design new products; their work included the following nine functions:

1. Studying the original design from a manufacturing standpoint and preparing a cost estimate
2. Preparing manufacturing drawings
3. Determining the kind and quantity of raw materials required
4. Planning the manufacturing process
5. Designing and providing required tools
6. Providing the proper machinery
7. Prescribing the grades of labor to be used
8. Establishing time or output standards
9. Prescribing the wage payment plan

**7. Make-up of the Department Personnel.** At the Hawthorne plant of Western Electric Company, Inc., the planning department included more than 1,000 people, of whom more than 700 were engineers, mechanical designers, drafstmen, and supervisors over engineering work. The personnel was required to possess a combination of practical knowledge gained from training in factory and machine shop with theoretical knowledge acquired in college. Work was functionalized according to the various types of engineering involved. There were mechanical engineering specialists on screw machine, milling, drilling, and pressing operations; specialists in each branch of tool design; specialists on metal-finishing operations; industrial engineers specializing on methods of wage payment and allied activities; both electrical and mechanical engineering specialists on apparatus design and production; etc.

**8. An Example of the Department's Work.** When the design of the telephone handset had been developed by the Bell Telephone Laboratories to the point where the Western Electric Company, Inc., executives considered it advisable to proceed with production, designs and specifications for the instrument were turned over to the planning department, which was responsible for taking the remaining steps necessary to put the set into production. Since the functional and market design work had already been carried out, the first step was study of design to detect any features inconsistent with efficient manufacturing processes, and suggestion of remedies if weaknesses were found. This careful scrutiny was the work of engineers specializing in design and production of the type of apparatus to which the telephone handset belonged.

By training and experience, these men were especially fitted to discern changes or modifications in design which would facilitate production and ensure low costs. An important consideration in this study was interchangeability of parts. Tolerances had to be controlled to permit parts to be assembled interchangeably without sacrificing quality, and clearances were made large enough to permit assembly without trying or fitting. The greater the possible clearance between companion parts, the lower was the cost to manufacture. The effect of the design of parts upon the cost and life of tools was also studied in the interest of achieving design which would permit use of rugged tools and thereby eliminate interruption in production because of tool breakage or adjustment.

**9. Illustrations of Improvement in Production Design.** An example of results obtained from such design study in the interest of manufacturing economy was a change made in parts of the cradle support for the handset mounting. In the design as originally submitted to the planning department, the screw bushing was specified to have a 32-pitch thread at the top, necessitating threading the entire length of the cradle stud and requiring about 28 turns in assembly. Engineers in the planning department after obtaining design approval from the Bell Telephone

Laboratories, changed this thread design to 24-pitch and moved it to the bottom of the bushing.  As a result of this change, only $\frac{9}{16}$ inch of the cradle stud needed to be threaded and the turns in assembling were reduced to about 15.   In addition, it was easier to produce the coarse thread on the aluminum-silicon die casting from which this cradle was made, and, to a large extent, the hazard of stripping in assembly was eliminated.

Another instance of design improvement was the redesigning of the plunger rod in the cradle, which operated the contacts in the base of the handset mounting.  For bearing purposes, this rod had a shoulder on it near the cast head.   The plunger stem was only $\frac{1}{4}$ inch in diameter, but according to the original plans it was necessary to make the part from $\frac{3}{8}$-inch rod in order to provide for the shoulder.   Manufacture required a deep cut on a screw machine, which, besides producing considerable scrap, was a slow operation, especially since the rod was made of bronze. After having been cut, the rod had to be buffed to eliminate toolmarks and prevent sticking or sluggish action when the handset was lifted.   This part was redesigned, the proposed bearing shoulder on the turned rod being replaced by a close-fitting sleeve. The change made it possible to use $\frac{1}{4}$-inch bronze rod, which could be purchased commercially with a satisfactory finish so that the only manufacturing operation necessary was to cut the rod to proper length.   The sleeve was simple to make and its manufacture did not cost so much as turning a shoulder on $\frac{3}{8}$-inch rod.

**10. Preliminary Cost Estimates.**  When design had been thoroughly studied to ensure economy in manufacturing, the planning engineers prepared a preliminary cost estimate, the purpose of which was to aid executives in deciding whether the proposed apparatus was practical from the standpoint of the relation of costs to expected demand.   In preparing the cost estimate, the planning engineers specified the operations to be performed on each part, the types of machines on which the parts would be run, and the anticipated hourly outputs.   They then applied the standard burden and labor rates to these figures.   The weight of material was determined and unit raw material costs applied, which gave an approximate material cost for each part.   The costs of all the parts were then added to the assembly and inspection costs to make up the total estimated cost of the set. These estimates were scrutinized by other engineering specialists on telephone apparatus to make sure that they were not inconsistent with the cost of similar apparatus already in production.

**11. Setting Standards and Specifications.** After approval by these specialists and final authorization for manufacture by executives, the planning department made the manufacturing drawings. In addition to detailed drawings of each part, the engineers made a stock list of the kinds and quantities of the various parts required and drawings showing how the various parts were to be assembled. They also prepared manufacturing specifications covering mechanical and electrical requirements which the apparatus had been designed to meet. Further measures to ensure economical manufacture often were incorporated when these drawings were made, for example, at this stage in the development of the handset, savings were effected by changing dimensions of holes to permit them to be punched instead of drilled.

**12. Manufacturing Facilities and Procedures.** After the drawings were completed, final specifications were made for the kind and quantity of raw materials to be used. The actual operations of manufacture, assembly, and testing were defined, and tools, gauges, machines, and other equipment decided on. In the selection of raw materials, consideration was given to the nature of the operations to be performed on them and the most advantageous sizes and quantities of materials to purchase.

Four main considerations were involved in determining the best manufacturing procedure. The first was the quantity of parts to be made and its effect on the grade of tools and equipment to be specified, and the possibility of using laborsaving devices, automatic machinery, and special raw materials. The second was the quality of parts and its effect on the quality of tools and rate of machine operation. The third was the expected permanency of demand and its relation to the economy of establishing most efficient methods at the start. The fourth was the safety of employees as it related to use of machines and tools, installation of proper ventilating equipment, and sometimes even wearing apparel.

The company maintained a perpetual inventory of machinery available for production and similar information for floor space and bench equipment. The planning department made use of this information when assigning machines for the manufacture of a new product. If machines of new design were required, they were ordered from a large machine-building organization under the supervision of Western Electric Company, Inc. A large part of the company's production, however, was turned out on purchased machinery of standard type.

The company usually designed and built most of its tools. The tool-designing unit was a large group in the planning department, and the company toolrooms were equipped for large-scale production. Much had been done in standardizing designs, and the company maintained stocks of standard tool parts, making repairs possible with little delay and cost. Standard parts were used also in new tools, which often were a combination of standard parts and special new parts.

**13. Testing Original Plans.** Since production generally was started on a smaller scale than was needed to fill later demand, the planning engineers had an opportunity to test their original plans in operation, to study the most economical processes and tools to use when production increased, and to improve on their original designs. When first put into production, the bakelite parts of the telephone handset, such as the handle and the outer cases for the receiver and transmitter, were molded on gas-heated five-platen presses. Single-compartment hand-operated molding dies were subsequently used, and, as the demand increased, production was further facilitated and cost reduced by use of presses in which the dies were steam-heated and water-cooled, and which opened automatically. As a further improvement, the development engineers on plastic molding developed a 250-ton press especially suited to the large-quantity production of these parts. Advantage was taken of the shape of some of the bakelite parts to design combination dies which produced two parts simultaneously, one lying within the other in the die.

**14. Planning for Labor.** In the planning functions dealing with labor, use was made of job analyses, which the company's industrial engineers had prepared for every operation in the com-

pany's plants.  Each of the thousands of manufacturing operations carried on had been analyzed and graded, and a symbol for
it had been established.  Each symbol represented a range of
hourly pay rates, the minimum of which was the base rate.  Every
factor of each operation had been analyzed and evaluated from
the standpoint of the operative and the company.  Consideration
had been given to the personnel requirements of the job, such as
strength, skill, experience, alertness, nimbleness, responsibility,
and accuracy, and such conditions as the monotony, strain, humidity, temperature, fumes, dirt, and hazards associated with
the job.  Consideration also had been given to the local supply of
the particular kind of labor required, to local living conditions,
and, for a class of work entirely new in the territory, to the rates
required to attract at least a nucleus of trained personnel from
elsewhere.  At different plants, a given symbol carried a slightly
different range of rates, fitting into the wage level of the territory.
Final establishment of symbols was authorized by the vice-president in charge of manufacture.

Labor grades were used by the employment departments in
hiring help, by the foremen as a guide in classifying the personnel
of their organizations and in revising rates of pay, and by the
planning departments in estimating labor costs of new products
and in furnishing the base rates for the determination of incentive rates and control of costs.  When the first labor grades were
being set, every new job rate was compared with the corresponding rates of other companies, but later comparisons were mostly
internal with only occasional outside checks, and it was usually
found that even when new products were added the operations
involved had already been graded.  Records of labor turnover
were classified to aid in reconsidering wage scales and making
revision necessary to meet fluctuations of the labor market and
thus ensure an unbroken supply of labor of each class.

For the manufacture of the telephone handset, it was not necessary to set up new labor grades for each machine operation,
since most of the parts were manufactured with standard equipment for which grades were available.  Assembly of the apparatus, however, presented a large variety of labor requirements for
which the planning department had to provide new grades.

The step following establishment of the new labor grades was to set up "time standards," or the standards of output which should be obtained by the average operative when a reasonable amount of effort was expended. Instead of making time studies of each operation, it was the practice of the industrial engineers of the planning department to make fundamental time and motion studies of the human and mechanical elements involved in each general class of work. For example, studies were made of drill-press work in general to determine what the constant and variable elements of such operations were, considering such factors as feeds, speeds, depth and diameter of holes, kinds of material, and weights and sizes of parts. Basic curves and charts were then developed in accordance with set formulas, which were used to establish piece rates or other incentives on any variety of parts within the range of work to which the standard was applicable. To obtain final rates there remained only a mathematical calculation, which often could be made by a technical clerk. Engineers could set final base rates for operations that had been analyzed without ever seeing the particular operation performed. Standards were being set to cover the entire range of the company's operations in manufacture and assembly of apparatus and equipment.

In manufacture of the telephone handset, the time standards were used as a basis of establishing incentive rates and standard costs and also in connection with figuring manufacturing capacity and calculating savings involved in cost reduction and manufacturing development studies.

**15. Determining Wage Payment Methods.** Following establishment of the appropriate labor grades and output standards, the final task of the planning engineers was to decide on the methods of wage payment most suitable for the operations. Setting incentives was complex because of the diversity of jobs performed. Experience of the company had shown that not all classes of labor worked to best advantage under one method of incentive wage payment. The planning department constantly reviewed and improved on existing methods, keeping in touch with developments throughout the country and abroad. The company used individual and gang piecework, calculated weekly, biweekly, or monthly; individual and gang premium; and several special incentive plans which were being tried experimentally. Incentive plans were applied to practically all routine and repetitive work in the manufacturing departments, and engineers were working on incentive plans for jobs that always had been on a time or salary basis.

**16. Summary and Conclusions.** In Western Electric Company, Inc., the organization for putting new products into production was more elaborate than is often found in industry. Also the detail of preplanning was more thorough than for most companies. Nevertheless, this large organization was probably well worth the cost. It prevented serious mistakes. It enabled management to plan operations in general far ahead. It tended to ensure profits. The time required for the making of such thorough studies would not be available to companies whose market and competitive situations place a premium on quick action. Where speed is important, less preparatory work will be possible although the scope of the preparatory work will be much the same. Design will cover product function, market appeal, and production cost. In addition to product design, manufacturing specifications and standards of some degree of exactness must be set. The process of manufacture must be planned at least in its broad outlines, and provision for checking results must be supplied. Finally, production cannot get under way until the necessary facilities—plant and equipment, tools, materials, and labor —are at hand. Even the smallest business must go through this procedure when bringing out a new product. The more nearly the new item resembles an old one, the less difficult, expensive, and time consuming the preparatory work will be. The more radical the innovation and the more pressing the need for getting it on the market quickly, the more difficult will be the task and the more uncertain will be the results.

*Preplanning and Personnel Control.* The carrying through of product and production planning into the area of personnel control, as was described in the case of Western Electric Company, Inc., is rather unusual. More often this work is done in a separate personnel department. The Western Electric procedure is subject to some risk. There is danger that the personnel work may become mechanical, too much an engineering type of treatment. This, of course, is contrary to the thesis developed in this text that the most important characteristics of the worker are his reasoning ability and emotional reactions. These characteristics are difficult to blend with slide rule and "log" table methods. Attempts at personnel control as an exact engineering science seldom have developed fully the potentialities of a work force. Planning department control of job standards, worker selection, wage payment methods, and wage rates need not necessarily become mechanical. There is danger that it may do so. Any such development should be very carefully guarded against.

Removal of job and wage control from the personnel department might adversely affect the ability of that department to function well in creating and maintaining labor relations. Many difficult problems in personnel relations have their beginnings in job and wage situations. To isolate control of these matters from personnel management would seem to make personnel relations difficult. Success of any one company in keeping these problems separate is not conclusive proof of the desirability of so doing. The wisdom of such separation as a usual practice is doubtful. It carries too many possibilities of trouble.

*Product Improvement.* Product development and new product planning are often the lifeblood of a business. The producer of games and toys is engaged in a business of that type. Some manufacturers are in an entirely different position, not so dependent on continually having new things to offer the buying public. The producer of Portland cement is an illustration of this situation. However, every manufacturer should continuously seek product improvements. It is commonly assumed that this need is the result of constant consumer demand for better things. This is true in part only. It must be remembered that consumer desires and demands are shaped very largely by those who cater to them. A manufacturer will find it fully as important to consider constantly what his competitor may be about to offer the consumer as to consider what the consumer might rationally be expected to want. Too little attention is sometimes given the competitor and too great reliance placed on the consumer as guides to product improvement, development, and change.

## QUESTIONS

**1.** Describe and explain the personnel employed in the product planning department of Western Electric Company, Inc.

**2.** Why was the product planning department of this company able in large part to ignore functional and market aspects of product design? What attention was given to these aspects of design?

**3.** What was the first step taken by the department when a new product was to be considered? What was the objective?

**4.** Cite some examples of design improvement in the case of the telephone handset.

**5.** What was the purpose of the preliminary cost estimates which followed initial consideration of product design?

**6.** What were the purposes of each of the functions 2 to 9 of the product planning department as listed on page 481 of the Western Electric Company, Inc., case?

**7.** Why does performance of these functions follow the sequence given in the case?

**8.** What are the advantages and disadvantages of placing control of job standards, worker requirements, wage payment methods, and wage rates in the hands of the product planning department, as described in the Western Electric Company, Inc., case?

**9.** Are the product planning policy and procedures of this company well suited to its needs?

**10.** Would other companies find these methods suitable for their purposes?

## Problem 46

### CUTLER COMPANY

The first product of the Cutler Company was a machine which graded apples for size and facilitated grading them for quality. The company had been established for 10 years. During that time its business had grown steadily until it had the reputation of being the foremost producer of fruit packing house equipment. A variety of attachments had been devised and produced which adapted the fruit grader to special situations. An example was a special type of bin system to be used when the graded fruit was to be barreled rather than packed in boxes. The increase in variety of output had adversely affected production costs. To reduce costs and still satisfy market demand for variation in capacity and type of product, company engineers redesigned the chief product of the company.

The Cutler Company was organized by two brothers who came to the Pacific Northwest and engaged in fruit raising. Both men were trained in eastern engineering schools and early saw the possibility of utilizing mechanical equipment in the preparation of fruit for market. They devised a machine which sorted apples into the various sizes used in packing. The machine sized accurately. Each apple was weighed mechanically and automatically deposited in a bin according to its size. The weighing scales were provided with a simple adjustment device which made the machine adaptable to any variety of apple regardless of the size range.

The complete machine was made up of three essential units. The first of these was the sorting table. Fruit from the orchard was deposited upon the padded end of this table (see Exhibit 1, page 492). At the side of the table sat or stood the sorters. Northwest apples were sorted into four quality grades: extra fancy, fancy, choice, and cookers. Only the first three grades were packed. The cooker grade was used by canneries or in vinegar making. Quality was largely a matter of color, surface blemish, worm stings, and shape. Quality grading could not be accomplished mechanically. However, the sorting table of the Cutler grader was designed to facilitate it. Extending lengthwise of the table and passing in front of the sorters was a series of rollers and canvas conveyor belts. The rollers were wound spirally with sash cord, the windings being spaced about 2 inches apart. These rollers revolved slowly in the same direction. A slight incline of the padded portion of the table upon which the fruit was first placed caused the fruit to move slowly forward until it came in contact with the spiral rolls. The movement of

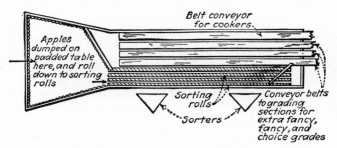

EXHIBIT 1.   CUTLER COMPANY.   SORTING TABLE OF FRUIT GRADER.

the rolls caused the fruit to revolve slowly and at the same time progress forward along the rolls and past the sorters. The turning motion imparted to the apples by the rolls enabled a sorter to see all parts of the apple without picking it up. As the fruit passed them, the sorters allowed the grade which was predominant to remain on the revolving rolls, from which it was automatically transferred to a belt leading to the sizing sections. The other fruit was taken from the rolls and placed according to grade upon belts which conveyed it to the sizing machine, except in the case of the cookers. The belt upon which the cookers were placed did not go to a sizing section but to containers, from which the apples were removed for storage or shipment to cannery or vinegar mill.

The second unit of the grader was the sizing unit. It consisted of a series of scales, a device for loading apples into the scales, and the driving mechanism of the entire machine. The apples were conveyed to the scale loader by the canvas belts from the sorting table. The scales were attached to an endless chain which passed along the length of the sizing section over a series of bins. The scale loader was timed with the scale chain so that as empty scales passed in front of it the loading device deposited one apple in each scale. As the scale chain passed over the bins, a tripping device was actuated wherever the apple in the scale was heavier than the counterweight of the bin over which it was passing. The counterweights were so arranged that the heaviest apples were deposited in the first bin and the lightest in the last bin at the end of the sizing section. The action of sizing was entirely automatic, and the device was very accurate in operation.

The third unit of the machine was the bin system. This was made up in two sections, one for each side of the sizing section. The drop of the apples from the weighing scales to the bins was checked by a series of webbing baffles. The bins in which the fruit was deposited had canvas bottoms, which prevented bruising of the fruit. These bins were hinged at one end and supported on spiral springs at the other. As the bins filled up, the weight of the fruit compressed the springs, and as the canvas bottom settled down, more space was available in the bin. The bins were made in sections separate from the sizing section and were bolted to the latter when the machine was erected in a packing house. The three units, the sorting table, the sizing section, and the bin system, constituted a complete machine. Each of the units was completely assembled at the shop and was shipped with simple instructions which enabled the packer to erect the machine in his warehouse. Exhibit 2 shows the relation of the three units to each other in the assembled machine.

A machine made up of a sorting table, a sizing section, and a bin system composed of two sections would size but one quality grade at a time. The grades not being sized were run into containers and sized later. If more than one quality grade were to be sized at one time, additional sizing sections were needed, one for each additional grade to be run. If more than one sizing section were used, corresponding bin sections were required. Only one sorting table was used regardless of the size of the machine.

The additional sizing sections differed from the one described in that they did not contain a loading device and power unit. One loading device would care for two sizing sections, and, by variation of the motor size, a single driving mechanism would operate from one to four sizing sections, the maximum number used. When more than two sizing sections were used, two loading devices were required. It was therefore necessary to manufacture four types of sizing sections: one mounting both loading

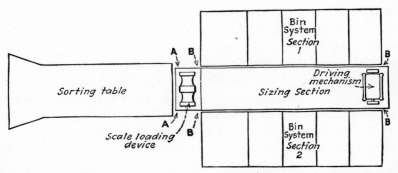

EXHIBIT 2. CUTLER COMPANY. DIAGRAM TO SHOW ERECTION OF FRUIT GRADER.

and driving devices, one carrying only the loading device, one carrying only a driving mechanism, and one which had neither a driving nor a loading device. Bin sections were built in four models to correspond to the four types of sizing sections. Exhibit 3 is illustrative of a four-section grader, the large type used in

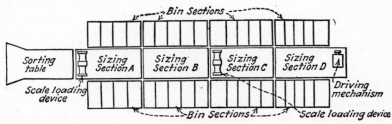

EXHIBIT 3. CUTLER COMPANY. FOUR-SECTION FRUIT GRADER.

central and cooperative packing houses. In such a machine, three types of sizing sections with their corresponding bin sections were used. These types were all different from the single-section type illustrated in the last diagram. Sizing sections A and C were similar in that they each carried a scale loading device. Section $B$ had neither loading nor power equipment. Section $D$ carried the driving mechanism.

In order to be able to furnish all sizes of grading machines for large as well as small packing establishments, it was necessary to manufacture four distinct types of sizing sections, four types of bin sections, and two types of sorting tables. The two types of sorting tables were necessary because a table large enough to provide space for the number of sorters required to keep a four-section sizing machine running at capacity would be much too large for a single-section machine.

Many of the individual machine parts were common to all sizes of graders. An example was the weighing scales, which were interchangeable as among all machines. However, a large number of the parts could be used only in a machine of given size.

The grader was completely redesigned to bring about a much higher degree of standardization. None of the basic principles of the machine was altered, but the division of the machine into units was completely changed. The starting point in this standardization was the sizing section. The section used in the single sizing section type of machine was reworked into three separate sections. The scale loading device was removed from the sizing section and built up as a complete section in itself. The same thing was done with the power unit. It was then possible to design a sizing section which would be standard for all machines. With a standard sizing section, the bin system could be standardized so that but one type of bin section was produced. The redesigned machine with a capacity for sizing one quality grade of fruit was composed of five units instead of the three used in the old models. Exhibit 4 shows the units which made up the new single-section machine and can be compared with the figure used to illustrate the old single-section type (Exhibit 2).

Any type of machine could be assembled from the standard units used in the single-section machine. To add grade capacity, it was only necessary to add standard sections. Machines of various capacities required standard units as follows:

Machine to size 1 grade:
    1 sorting table (small)
    1 scale loading unit

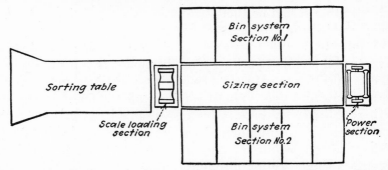

EXHIBIT 4. CUTLER COMPANY. FRUIT GRADER ASSEMBLED FROM STANDARD SECTIONS.

   1 sizing section
   1 power section
   1 bin system composed of 2 standard sections
Machine to size 2 grades:
   1 sorting table (small)
   1 scale loading unit
   2 sizing sections
   1 power section
   1 bin system composed of 4 standard sections
Machine to size 3 grades:
   1 sorting table (large)
   2 scale loading units
   3 sizing sections
   1 power section
   1 bin system composed of 6 standard sections
Machine to size 3 grades with extra hourly capacity:
   1 sorting table (large)
   2 scale loading units
   4 sizing sections
   1 power section
   1 bin system composed of 8 standard sections

The difference in hourly capacity of the machines made it necessary to produce two sizes of sorting tables. However, most of the component parts for the table were standard for both sizes. This was particularly true of metal parts.

The standardized grader presented many manufacturing advantages over the old type. The total number of different parts was greatly reduced, and the standard parts could be produced in much greater quantity. The business was very seasonal in its nature and fluctuated greatly from year to year. Under such circumstances, standardization was of substantial value in planning the year's production. Crating materials could be standardized and cut in quantity. Inventory control was simplified, as was production control. The standardized machine offered advantages from the standpoint of the user. A grower whose immediate need was for a small machine could purchase the type of grader needed and, as his output increased, could add standard sections to his small machine and increase its capacity proportionately without completely scrapping the grader first purchased.

The changes in design presented certain immediate problems. There were several hundred Cutler graders of the older types in use. The company's policy stressed the importance of servicing its product. It was necessary to provide repair parts and sections for expansion for all these machines. Eventually the standard machine would replace the older machines in the growers' hands. In the meantime, putting the standard machine on the market added to the inventory of repair parts which it was necessary to carry. Most of the parts in the standardized machine were interchangeable with the older machines. However, standardization involved certain parts changes and certain parts additions.

In its attempts to relieve the extreme seasonal situation in the industry, the company had made vigorous efforts to market its products in districts outside the Northwest boxed apple area.[1] However, it wished to confine itself to the production of packing house equipment. An increasing amount of its product was sold to eastern apple producers, foreign apple growers, California citrus fruit producers, and Texas tomato growers. Most of the machines sold outside of the Northwest were equipped with special devices which adapted sorting and sizing functions to the products of the locality. The bin system was the point of most frequent change. Alterations in the sorting table were sometimes necessary. This expansion program was opposed to standardization. The company was convinced of the advantages of both

---

[1] Company officials were convinced that production must be confined to products which could be marketed through the existing sales organization or a simple enlargement of this organization.

situations. However, expansion into specialized fields seemed to set very definite limits to the standardization program, and standardization might limit the ability of the company to serve specialized users.

What advantages and disadvantages resulted from redesigning the apple grading machine?

## Problem 47

### YORK-JACKSON COMPANY

The York-Jackson Company manufactured machine tools, such as light lathes, small milling machines, and shapers. To meet increasing competition, the company was redesigning many of the parts of these machines to make them easier and therefore cheaper to produce. One such part was a stopblock which was standard on all shapers. This block was made in three sizes.

The stopblock was a rectangular cast-iron block 3 inches long and 2 inches wide at the base. On its top was a raised bar that ran lengthwise of the block. This raised bar was ½ inch high. The stopblock was made in three sizes, which were specified as ¾ inch, 1 inch, and 1¼ inches. These dimensions referred to the width of the raised bar that ran lengthwise of the block. The three sizes of stopblock were exactly alike except for the width of this bar. Exhibit 1 is a sketch of the stopblock and a shop drawing of the design.

In the past the stopblock had been made by casting an iron block 2 inches wide, 3 inches long, and 2 inches high. All three sizes were made from the same size casting. The first machining operation was to make the bottom surface of the block flat. This was done by putting the block in a milling machine and passing it slowly beneath a rotating cutting wheel. Usually 20 blocks of one size were made at one time, and the first operation was performed on 20 castings before any other work was done on the block. The need for performing this operation is shown in the front view of the shop drawing of the part, Exhibit 1. The $f$ mark on the bottom line calls for machining that surface.

The next operation was to machine the top.[2]  This also was done on a milling machine.  Three cutting wheels were mounted side by side in the milling machine.  Two of these cutters were the same size.  The other cutter was 1 inch less in diameter and

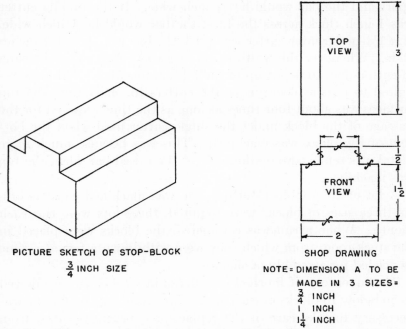

PICTURE  SKETCH  OF  STOP-BLOCK

$\frac{3}{4}$ INCH  SIZE

SHOP  DRAWING

NOTE= DIMENSION  A  TO  BE
MADE  IN  3  SIZES=
$\frac{3}{4}$  INCH
1  INCH
$1\frac{1}{4}$  INCH

EXHIBIT 1.  YORK-JACKSON COMPANY.  PICTURE SKETCH AND SHOP DRAWING OF STOPBLOCK.

was exactly the width of the bar to be cut on the top, either ¾ inch, 1 inch, or 1¼ inches.  The three cutting wheels were mounted side by side in the milling machine with the smaller diameter wheel in the middle.  It took about 20 minutes to mount the cutting wheels in the machine and to adjust them to make the proper cut.  After the milling machine was set up, a cast block with its machined base down was passed under the revolving cutters.  The two outside cutters removed the proper amount of metal on each side of the top of the block and left the

[2] See finish marks on top surfaces in front view of shop drawing, Exhibit 1.

raised bar. The third cutter, the one of smaller diameter which had been mounted between the two larger cutters, machined off the top of the raised bar. The width of the bar depended on the width of the smaller cutter in the middle. If the smaller cutter was ¾ inch thick across the face, the side cutters would be ¾ inch apart and the bar would be ¾ inch wide. If the middle cutter was 1 inch thick across the face, the bar would be 1 inch wide. If a 1¼-inch center cutter was used, the bar would be 1¼ inches wide. Whenever the width of the bar was changed, a new gang of cutters had to be set up in the milling machine. The time required to pass a block under the cutters for machining the top surfaces was about four times as long as the time required for the passage of the block under the single cutter used when the bottom of the block was machined. This was because much more metal was removed on either side of the raised bar when the top was machined.

A lot of 20 stopblocks of one size was machined each month. As three sizes of blocks were required, three lots were run each month. When a run was completed, the blocks were placed in the stock room from which they were withdrawn a few at a time as needed for assembly of shapers.

The inventory of finished stopblocks in stock was not allowed to go below 10 blocks of each size. This minimum inventory was necessary to take care of the replacement orders received from customers who had previously purchased shapers. The raised bar on the stopblock wore in use, and periodically stopblocks had to be replaced.

The company's design engineer proposed that the stopblocks be made differently. He suggested that the part consist of a rectangular cast-iron block 2 inches by 3 inches by 1½ inches high with the top and bottom machined flat. Two threaded holes would be made in the top of the block. The raised bar would be made separately and would be cut from 10-foot strips of cold-rolled steel bar stock which would be purchased ½ inch thick and in three widths: ¾ inch, 1 inch, and 1¼ inches. The raised bar would be made by cutting off 3-inch lengths of bar stock of the proper width and drilling two holes in each 3-inch piece.

These holes would correspond with the holes drilled in the cast-iron block.  The steel strip would be assembled to the cast-iron

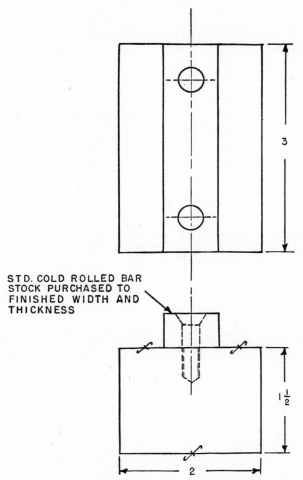

STD. COLD ROLLED BAR
STOCK PURCHASED TO
FINISHED WIDTH AND
THICKNESS

EXHIBIT 2.  YORK-JACKSON COMPANY.  SHOP DRAWING OF REDESIGNED STOPBLOCK.

block by means of two flathead screws.  No additional machining would be required on the raised bar as the size and finish of cold-rolled bar stock would be adequate for the proposed use.  Exhibit 2 is the shop drawing of the redesigned bar.

## QUESTIONS

1. What are the advantages and disadvantages of the proposed new design?

2. Do you think the new design should be adopted to replace the old one?

# CHAPTER XXI

# PLANNING AND SCHEDULING

## BELMONT JEWELRY COMPANY (A)

**1. A Department Manager Installs Records as a Basis of Production Control.**

Production in the pin and coat-of-arms department of the Belmont Jewelry Company had been lagging behind schedule. A new superintendent was obtained for the department, and the president of the company made him responsible for improving conditions in the department. The superintendent requested that he be permitted to install records as the first step in a system of production control.

**2. Management, the Fourth Factor of Production.** To the three factors of production, land, labor, and capital, the economists add a fourth, the enterpriser. Essentially, his function is that of control of the other factors. He decides what to make and when and where to make it. He brings together in a plant suitable raw materials, labor, and machinery. He decides how much of the product selected is to be made at one time and how it is to be made and then organizes and controls the process of its manufacture. Such is the occupation of the manager in the field of production.

**3. Planning and Scheduling, a Management Problem.** The factory manager's task is of two parts, planning the work and then controlling its execution. For convenience, planning may be subdivided into two divisions. The first includes problems of what to make, how to make it, when to make it, and how much to make at one time. This division is commonly spoken of as master planning or frequently merely as planning. The second part, scheduling, includes the assignment of work to departments, the designation of equipment and men for specific tasks, correlation of the various steps in the processing of parts, and regulating the assembly of parts into finished product. Master planning and scheduling together have as their function the getting of a product into production and follow-up throughout the process.

**4. Other Problems of Control.** Planning and scheduling are responsible for but a part of the manager's troubles. There are raw materials to be supplied and controlled. The entire producing personnel requires supervision. Machines and equipment must be serviced and kept in repair. A dependable source of power must be ensured at all times. Plant conditions such as light, heat, ventilation, and sanitation need continuous control. Quality is always important and is frequently a source of much trouble. These and many other problems constantly call for supervision if waste is to be controlled. And, finally, through all, and usually above all, costs demand unceasing supervision.

**5. Magnitude of the Planning and Scheduling Functions.** The present chapter will confine itself to planning and scheduling. A very simple illustration will serve to demonstrate something of the magnitude of these tasks.

A child's toy, a miniature vacuum carpet cleaner, was sold in a department store for 25 cents. It is likely that the store paid the manufacturer from 5 cents to 10 cents less. In appearance, the toy was a faithful reproduction of one of the best known, nationally advertised cleaners. It was about one-quarter the size of the original, was substantially built, and attractively finished.

Analysis of the toy revealed the following parts:

Parts stamped and drawn from sheet metal:
    1 motor housing
    1 fork for attaching handle
    1 upper part of cleaner housing
    1 lower part of cleaner housing
Wood parts—turned:
    1 handle
    2 wood wheels, one at each end of cleaner brush
    1 double wood wheel at rear of carriage
Cloth parts:
    1 dust bag
    1 elastic strap for attaching bag to handle
Other parts:
    1 round wire brush

1 pin to form axle for rear wheel
1 screw hook for attaching cleaner bag strap to handle

This made a total of 13 parts, the production of which involved various processes.

The sheet-metal parts were first stamped out on a press using dies especially made for the purpose. Different sets of dies were required for each of the four parts. After these blanks had been stamped out, they were drawn and pressed into required shape by means of another set of specially designed tools on presses. The shaped parts were then finished by either dipping or spray-painting, probably the former. The motor housing was finished in black, the three other sheet-metal parts in silver gray. The production of each of these parts thus called for at least three operations, a total of 12 operations for the production of this first group of parts.

The handle was turned on a lathe, sanded, and dipped. The wood wheels at the ends of the brush were probably made by turning a rod of the desired diameter and then cutting it into the required segments to form the wheels. Holes were made in the centers, and the wheels were then dipped to give them a black finish. Two of these wheels were required for each toy. The rear wheel was similar except that it was larger and had a groove cut about its circumference midway between the sides. The production of these wood parts probably involved 16 operations for each cleaner.

The manufacture of the dust bag involved cutting two pieces of cloth to proper shape, hemming one end of each, sewing the two pieces together along their other edges, turning the resulting bag inside out, and stamping the name of the cleaner on one side of the bag. At the closed end of the dust bag an elastic loop was sewn. From five to eight operations were involved in the production of this part.

The three other parts may have been made by the toy manufacturer but more likely were purchased from concerns which specialized in the type of part required.

Assembly of the 13 parts needed for each toy was probably accomplished in about 12 operations. The motor housing was attached to the upper part of the cleaner housing by inserting lugs on the motor housing through slots in the cleaner housing and then bending the lugs over.  The rear wheel was attached to the lower housing by placing the wheel between the two rear supports, slipping the pin through the holes, and pressing a head on the unheaded end of the pin.  A wheel was next slipped over the projecting axle wire at each end of the round brush, and the three parts thus assembled were snapped into place in holes provided in the sides of the lower part of the cleaner housing.  The upper and lower cleaner housing subassemblies were then put together and fastened in place by bending lugs after they had been inserted in corresponding slots.  The dust bag could then be attached to the cleaner by slipping the open end over the projecting ring at the rear of the housing assembly and flanging this ring to hold the bag in place.  The wooden handle was fastened to the handle fork by closing tight in a press, or with a hand tool, a metal band designed to hold the handle in place.  The fork could then be snapped into place on the cleaner housing and the elastic band caught over the hook, which previously had been screwed into the handle, and the toy was completely assembled.  The entire assembly operation involved not less than a dozen separate steps, and the production of parts and assembly probably required from 40 to 50 operations.

Controlling the production of 35,000 to 50,000 units of this simple toy in lots economical in size, yet satisfactory for delivery needs, required planning of tools, supplying of raw materials and parts purchased outside, scheduling of parts production of a half million pieces, each requiring several operations for its production, and assembly of these parts by means of 12 different operations into finished product.  It is likely that the total cost for raw materials, purchased parts, labor, and factory burden did not exceed 12 cents per finished toy.  Quite possibly it was less than that.

In the meantime this same plant was probably producing dozens of other more or less unlike products, each presenting its own numerous problems of production control.

Manufacturing plants do not operate themselves.  From the time the production of some certain article is proposed to the time it is on the shipping dock, constant supervision calling for the making of scores of decisions is involved. The problem of scheduling the production of a toy vacuum cleaner is a simple one as compared with the scheduling job required to make a real electric cleaner with its stamping, drawing, casting, forging, machining, finishing, polishing, and winding, and much more intricate raw materials and assembly problems. The household vacuum cleaner is likewise a simple product as compared with an automobile, a steam locomotive, a 50-story office building, or a battleship.

Complex as the planning and scheduling jobs seem to be, in the case of repetitive production they can usually be reduced to a few fundamental steps which permit operations to proceed in orderly fashion to the accomplishment of definitely predetermined results. The following experience of the Belmont Jewelry Company is more or less typical of process control problems and their solution.

**6. Nature of the Business.** The Belmont Jewelry Company specialized in the manufacture of fraternity and sorority pins and badges, all kinds of jewelry with college and fraternity seals, stationery and calling cards, and dies for coats of arms. The business, by its nature, was highly seasonal, the heaviest sales being made just prior to the holiday season, the fraternity pledging, and college graduation periods. All production was for order, and the orders were usually small. This meant that great confusion was experienced in various departments during peak periods because of the multiplicity of small orders. There were approximately 20 firms operating in the industry, so that competition was unusually keen and prices varied from time to time.

**7. The Lack of Records.** Although the company was 15 years old, little had been done in the way of records, but the president had justified the situation on the ground that rapid growth of the company had necessitated centering attention on problems of actual production. In spite of the fact that the records were meager, it was obvious that the company was profitable and that its business was continuing to grow.

**8. New Department Manager Wishes to Install a System of Production Records.** Recently in the pin and coat-of-arms department, which was one of the six production departments, there had been much confusion, and production had been retarded. Two men of equal rank had been trying to operate the department, and, because of conflicting ideas, production activities were muddled. The president of the company, to iron out the difficulties, hired a new man, with considerable experience in similar businesses, to take charge of the department. The first request of the new department manager was for the records of the past performance of the department so that he might see where mistakes had been made and plan a campaign of reorganization. The president explained that the records desired had never been kept because the various executives and department managers had concentrated their attention upon solving production difficulties. The new department head was under the impression that one of the causes of the confusion in the pin and coat-of-arms department was the lack of records and that he could not iron out his difficulties if he did not have records. Although the president was anxious to "straighten out the production problems first," he said that the new manager was to be responsible for the department to which he was assigned and that it was up to him to get results. To accomplish this end the new manager could do anything he liked.

**9. A Temporary System Is Devised and Tried Out.** Realizing that he had nothing to go on and that he would have to build from the ground up, the new department head worked out a simple system of production control which was to serve temporarily until experience could be made the basis for a permanent organization.

The manager knew that the largest item of raw materials was gold (sheets and wire). Occasionally pins and badges were ornamented with small jewels, but for the bulk of the output gold was the only raw material of importance that needed control, and to that extent the situation was relatively simple.

The multiplicity of small orders, however, presented a more difficult situation. The work was all by special order, and it was imperative that delivery promises be kept. It therefore seemed necessary that control devices regulate the putting of each order into process at a time such as to ensure its completion on schedule, and that continual follow-up of each order during the manufacturing process be provided. At the same time the system for control had to be most simple, since otherwise its cost would be entirely out of proportion to the savings effected.

The extent to which the temporary method devised by the manager conformed to these requirements while serving its purpose can best be shown by explaining the system as it was in operation. The following is a description of a typical order from the time it was received in the general office to its completion for shipment.

**10. How the System Operated.** On April 16, the sales office had received an order for 40 class pins similar in design to an order made up the previous year (design number 6130) except that the enamel specified in the new order was to be blue whereas that of the previous year had been red. Also, the engraved numeral on the pin was to be '48 instead of '47. Delivery had been promised for May 18.

As the design and specifications for the pin were already in the company's file and last year's dies were stored, it was only necessary to make the changes in specifications noted and the order was ready for issuance to the pin department, where it was to be made up. From the recorded experience of the previous year the production order clerk in the plant manager's office knew that nine days would be sufficient time for the processing of the order. Wishing to provide a certain margin for delays, the clerk on May 2 issued to the pin department production order number 742 covering this job. The production order gave all information necessary to enable the pin department superintendent to make up the order. The production order was accompanied by a copy of the design drawing and corrected specifications for the pin.[1]

Because work in his department was pressing, the superintendent did not put order number 742 into production until May 6. At that time, his assistant made out a job ticket [2] covering the work (see Exhibit 1, page 510). This ticket was the record upon which all process control was based. The assistant knew from experience the amount of gold required for the job and made out a

---

[1] The procedure outlined in this paragraph had been followed by the company for some time, and the new department manager saw no reason for changing it.

[2] The portions of the job ticket filled in by the superintendent's assistant at that time are indicated in the form in Exhibit 1.

requisition on the storeskeeper for it.  He then detached coupon
1 from the job ticket and filed it for his future reference.   He

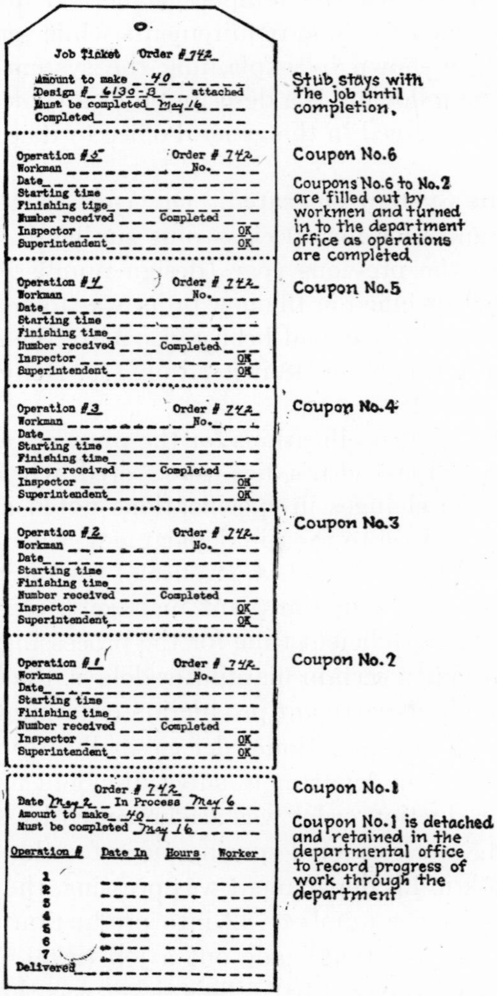

EXHIBIT 1.  BELMONT JEWELRY COMPANY.  JOB TICKET AS MADE OUT BY THE
SUPERINTENDENT'S ASSISTANT.

clipped together the balance of the job ticket, the design drawing
and specifications, and the materials requisition and gave them to
John Sawyer, the workman who was to perform the first operation on the order.  Sawyer had just returned an order upon which

he had completed his operation; therefore the new job was issued to him with instructions to start work at once.

Before beginning work, Sawyer obtained the necessary raw materials, and entered his name and number, the date, and the time of starting the work on coupon 2 of the job ticket. When he had completed the operation some hours later, he entered the finishing time on coupon 2, and called an inspector. The inspector checked the quality of the work, entered the number of good units upon which that operation was O.K., and signed his name on the coupon.

Had any of the work been improperly done or had an insufficient number of pieces (as called for on the job ticket) been made up, the inspector would have required that Sawyer rectify the error before the inspector approved the job by signing coupon 2.

Upon completion of the work, Sawyer took it and all records covering it to the department supervisor's assistant and received another job. The clerk initialed the coupon covering operation 1 (coupon 2) for the superintendent, detached it, and dispatched the job to the workman who was to perform the second operation as soon as that workman was available. From the information on coupon 2, the clerk entered the date completed, the number of labor hours applied, and the workman's number opposite the proper operation number on coupon 1, which was always retained in his file.

This procedure was followed for all five operations necessary to complete the job. Throughout the process, the job ticket remained with the worked material. Each time an operation was completed, the proper operation coupon, completely filled out and signed, was detached and made the basis of entry on coupon 1. Upon completion of the order, the date of completion was entered on both coupon 1 and the job ticket stub. The finished order, with the job ticket stub still attached, was sent to the shipping room, and the production order clerk in the plant manager's office was notified.

**11. Summary and Conclusions.** *Results of the Temporary System.* By means of the temporary procedure here outlined, the work of the department was greatly improved. The confusion of the past was eliminated; work was put into process in orderly manner and completed on time. Delivery dates were met, and the president was well satisfied with the work of the new department manager. The cost of the system was relatively small. The cost of forms was limited to the job tickets, and clerical work required only a portion of the time of the department clerk. It was estimated that the additional clerical work equaled not more than half the time saved for the department workmen, since they no longer had to wait for work assignment upon the completion of one job before beginning another.

*Improvements Resulting from Experience.* As the system was used, certain improvements were effected. It was found advisable to relieve the workmen of the task of filling in the operation coupons. This work could be done more quickly and accurately by the department clerk at the time the jobs were issued and returned. Later the several operation coupons were consolidated into one coupon which retained the same information given on the several coupons. Individual coupons had been forwarded by the department clerk to the accounting department, where they had been used with the time-clock cards for payroll make-up. A simple uniform system of daily departmental labor reports had been put in force for the entire plant. After that the separate coupons were unnecessary, and when the next lot of job tickets was ordered from the printer all operation coupons were printed as one consolidated coupon.

At that time one other change was made, two more items of information being added to the job ticket stub. They were the time of beginning the first operation and total time required for processing. After a completed order was invoiced and shipped, the job ticket stub was forwarded to the production order clerk in the plant manager's office. The additional information included on the stub made it possible for him to use it as the basis for determining the length of time required for the production of future similar orders. The efficiency of his planning was thereby increased.

*Reasons for Success of the System.* The satisfactory operation of the plan seems to have been due essentially to the fact that it was devised by a man thoroughly familiar with the particular problems it was designed to control. In other words, the system was built up specifically to fit the particular conditions of operation, and no attempt had been made to adapt some preconceived method of control.  For example, the small physical size of each job made it easy for the workman to transport the job itself to and from the clerk's office between each operation.  By so doing, the use of more or less complicated systems of move orders and work assignment was made unnecessary.

Simplicity seems to have been the keynote of the whole plan. There was no attempt to provide a routine of paper work to control occasional departures from usual practice.  The handling of such situations was left entirely to the personal attention of the department superintendent or his clerk.  The relatively small size of the department made this entirely practical and much more advisable than any paper-work system designed to cover departures from usual routine.

The suitability of the system and its simplicity largely accounted for its success as a device for regularizing operations. These characteristics were likewise responsible for the low cost of its installation and maintenance.

## QUESTIONS

1. What, in your opinion, had been the trouble in the pin and coat-of-arms department of the Belmont Jewelry Company?

2. What seems to have been the reason for failure to get out production in time to meet promised delivery dates?

3. Describe the control system temporarily installed by the new department manager.  Be prepared to explain the purpose and importance of all records and procedures involved.

4. Explain the results of the installation of the temporary system.

5. What changes were made in the system? Why was each made?

6. What justification is there for the conclusion that the success of the system was due in considerable measure to its simplicity?

7. Why was it possible to have a system simple yet effective?

8. In general, what are the practical requirements of a system to control production scheduling successfully?

## Problem 48

### BENNING ELECTRIC COMPANY

Benning Electric Company officials had devised a simple method of controlling volume of raw materials supplies and work in process. Control was facilitated by means of two simple graphs.

The Benning Electric Company manufactured five standard electric products: toasters, irons, radiators, ranges, and pads. The company manufactured these products for stock in accordance with schedules set by the general manager. The schedules specified the total number of each kind of product to be made by a certain date. For example, the schedule for toasters which was delivered to the factory superintendent on January 1 called for a total of 30,000 toasters to be made by July 1. Revisions were made in the schedules whenever warranted by business conditions; in practice, the schedules for each product were changed or extended two or three times a year.

The company controlled manufacturing operations by means of two sets of graphs: one set to control raw materials supplies, and one to control work in process, illustrated here by Exhibits 1 and 2, respectively. A raw materials graph and a production graph were prepared for each of the five products.

The raw materials needed for the manufacture of a particular product were listed on the left-hand side of a sheet of coordinate paper. Across the top of the sheet were listed the days of the month and the quantities of the product scheduled to be completed on those days. Whenever any raw material was received, a horizontal line was drawn on the graph opposite the name of that raw material, the length of the line showing the quantity received in terms of finished product. Thus, in Exhibit 1 the line after "Nichrome Wire" does not indicate that 1,600 feet of wire had been received, but that enough had been received to make 1,600 toasters. The total length of the line shows, in terms of finished product, the wire received since the beginning of the schedule. By referring to the date over the end of the line, and

514

the current date, the executives could see how many days the supply of that raw material was behind or ahead of the schedule.

The total number of items listed on these raw materials graphs was about 300. The graphs were given to the planning supervisor, who, acting upon information drawn from them, made a

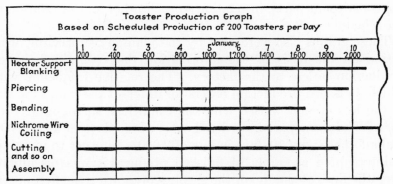

EXHIBIT 1. BENNING ELECTRIC COMPANY. TYPE OF GRAPH USED TO CONTROL SUPPLIES OF RAW MATERIALS.

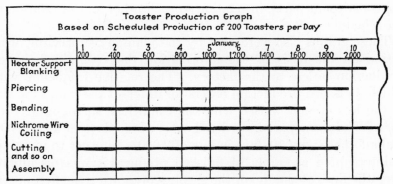

EXHIBIT 2. BENNING ELECTRIC COMPANY. TYPE OF GRAPH USED TO CONTROL WORK IN PROCESS.

report each month to the purchasing agent showing the requirements of each item for the month to follow. This report served as a purchase requisition.

Coordinate paper was used also for the five production graphs. On the left-hand side of each of these graphs were listed the operations necessary to the production of the constituent parts of the product, i.e., the most important or key operations. The number of these varied for the different products from 15 to 75. The last operation listed on each graph was the assembling of the product.

Across the top of each sheet were listed the days of the month, with the corresponding number of units of product to be completed on each date according to the schedule. From daily reports showing the number of parts finished, lines were drawn opposite each operation listed, so that the total length of the line for any operation showed the number of units on which that operation had been performed since the beginning of the schedule. All operations performed were expressed in terms of finished product, regardless of the number of pieces required per unit of product. Consequently, the lengths of the different lines could be compared directly. Thus, if a certain operation was completed on 500 sides, of which there were two for each toaster, the line for that operation would be drawn to represent 250 units, or enough sides to make 250 toasters. The relation of scheduled production to actual production was apparent from a comparison of the date over the end of the assembly line and the current date. The lengths of the other lines showed the quantitative status of the constituent parts, in relation to each other and in relation to the schedule.

These graphs also were kept by the planning supervisor, who, acting on the basis of the information they contained, issued production orders to the factory. The relative frequency with which he issued production orders for different parts and the size of the lots ordered varied with the conditions surrounding each part. Thus, one part he ordered every three days in lots of 600, and another every 10 days in lots of 2,000. In order to maintain uninterrupted assembly of finished product, it was his aim to keep the lines at the top of the sheet, representing the first operations, longer than the lower lines. If a perfect balance was maintained, the lines on the production graphs would look like this:

When the planning supervisor issued a production order, a light cross was made on the proper graph opposite the item affected at the point to which the line would reach when the order was completed. Thus, on the production graph in Exhibit 2, if a production order for enough heater supports for 300 additional toasters was issued, a cross would be made opposite the words "Heater Support" under the figure 2,300.

## QUESTIONS

1. What records were maintained to control manufacturing operations of the Benning Electric Company?

2. Describe the method used to control raw materials inventories and purchases.

3. How would you go about it to supply the information needed to maintain this graph?

4. Describe the method used to control work in process.

5. Would this method be satisfactory as a process control method for the Belmont Jewelry Company? Explain.

6. Were the raw materials and process control methods of the Benning Electric Company suitable and adequate for that company's needs?

### Problem 49

### EASTERN TEXTILE EQUIPMENT COMPANY

In a large machinery manufacturing company, the considerable amount of paper work and number of telephone conversations regarding process control required of foremen seemed to indicate that some revision of the system was desirable. To relieve foremen of this work and allow them to devote more of their time and energy to other duties, the head of the planning department requested that he be allowed to place representatives of his office in the various production departments throughout the plant.

The Eastern Textile Equipment Company, manufacturer of machine parts and textile machinery, employed approximately 1,500 men. The execution of work in this company's factory was in accordance with the Taylor system of scientific management. Work was planned completely before a single move was made.

A route sheet showing the names and order of all the operations which were to be performed was made out, and instruction cards were clearly written for each operation. Requisition on the stores department, showing the kind and quality of materials and where they were to be moved, and lists of proper tools for doing the work were made for each operation. The best method and apparatus for performing each operation had been previously determined by the company and were a part of the written instructions.

Thus, the order and assignment of all work, or routing as it was called, was conducted by a central planning or routing department. Likewise, the control of all operations in the plant and of the progress and order of the work was centralized.

In operating under this system of management, a certain amount of paper work was required for the routing of materials or of work and for reports of progress from the manufacturing departments to the planning room. For example, the order of work for each machine was scheduled by tags placed on a bulletin board in the manufacturing departments, and as each operation was started it was necessary to notify the planning department, or as materials were moved from operation to operation it was essential for someone to sign the move card. This paper work had been handled by the foremen, and it had been customary for the clerks in the planning room to call foremen on the telephone, asking whether certain material had arrived, or when a certain operation was started, and so forth. A messenger service had been developed for carrying the reports between the planning department and the manufacturing departments. Nevertheless, it had been found that the foremen were required to spend a considerable portion of their time either handling paper work or answering questions. The head of the planning department had suggested that he be allowed to place in each manufacturing department a representative of his department to handle all the paper work and to answer the telephone calls from his department to the manufacturing departments.

## QUESTIONS

1. What are the advantages and disadvantages of the type of management specialization shown in this case?

2. Under what conditions is this type of organization most likely to be successful?

3. Should the request of the head of the planning department be granted?

4. Should the planning room representative be directly responsible to the foreman of the manufacturing department or to the head of the planning department?

### Problem 50

### CORPORAL MOTOR CAR COMPANY (B)

In October, 1945, the Corporal Motor Car Company installed a control tower to handle all scheduling of its automobile repair work. After a year and a half's experience with the control tower in operation, the management of the garage was satisfied with the results of the installation and felt that it had contributed a great deal to the effectiveness of the repair-work scheduling.

The Corporal Motor Car Company was located in Cambridge, Massachusetts, and combined a new car sales dealership with its automobile repair service. Exhibit 1 shows the floor plan of the garage. In June, 1947, the service division was usually handling between 65 and 75 cars per day that were in the shop less than 24 hours. In addition there were 20 to 30 cars in the shop at all times for major repair work that lasted from two days to six months. The amount of repair work was subject to considerable random daily variation in volume and some seasonal variation, with the summer being the busiest season. The charges to the customers on every repair job were divided into labor, parts, and supplies, such as gas, oil, and accessories. The service division billed labor charges of $10,000 to $12,000 a month.

The service division employed about 30 people in the following categories: five service salesmen, eleven general utility mechanics,[3] one radio repairman, two grease-stand operators, one washstand operator, three body repairmen, four painters, one automatic clutch repair specialist, one control-tower operator, and one car jockey. One of the body repairmen and one of the painters were designated as lead men in their respective shops.

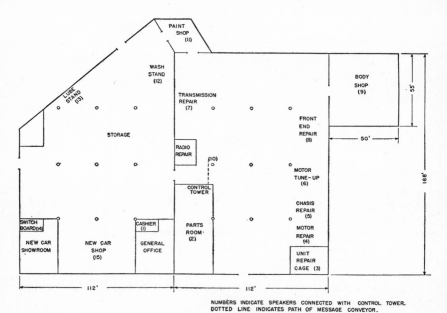

NUMBERS INDICATE SPEAKERS CONNECTED WITH CONTROL TOWER.
DOTTED LINE INDICATES PATH OF MESSAGE CONVEYOR.

EXHIBIT 1.  CORPORAL MOTOR CAR COMPANY (B).  DIAGRAM OF GARAGE LAYOUT.

Each service job on any model of automobile had been assigned a standard labor charge. The mechanics performing a specific service job were paid 40 per cent of the standard labor charge. The service salesmen were paid a straight salary. In addition to this salary, each service salesman also received a bonus of 5 per cent of the labor charges on all service sales they wrote up over and above $3,000 per month.

Prior to the installation of centralized scheduling in the control tower all scheduling and delivery time promises were made

---

[3] Each of these general utility mechanics normally did only one or two kinds of repair work but any of them could be shifted to other kinds of repair work in an emergency.

by the five service salesmen. These men had the job of meeting the customer, discussing his needs with him, and writing up the customer's order on the invoice form (Exhibit 2). The service salesmen used their judgment of the work load of the shop in making delivery time promises to the customers. It was then the

| | | | DATE 6/9/47 | | | |
|---|---|---|---|---|---|---|
| NAME M. D. Burkhardt | | | PHONE BUS. | | | |
| ADDRESS 427 Ivy Road | | | PHONE RES. | | | |
| CITY Boston, Massachusetts | | | MODEL 76-46 TYPE Club Coupe | | | |
| PROMISED Order Written By: | | | SERIAL NO. ENGINE NO. | | | |
| REMARKS | | | LICENSE NO. 621147 MILEAGE | | | |

| | OPERATION NO. | DESCRIPTION OF WORK | CHARGE FOR | | AMOUNT |
|---|---|---|---|---|---|
| | | | LABOR | MAT. | |
| INVOICE | | Adjust Steering Apparatus | . | | |
| | | Align Wheels | | | |
| | | Lube | | | |
| | | | | | |
| | | | | | |
| | | | | | |

| FOREMAN'S O.K. | ESTIMATES FOR LABOR ONLY—MATERIAL ADDITIONAL | TOTAL LABOR ONLY | | |
|---|---|---|---|---|
| | | TOTAL PARTS | | |
| | It is understood that this Company assumes no responsibility for loss or damage by theft or fire to vehicles placed with them for storage, sale or repair. | TOTAL ACCESSORIES | | |
| | | TOTAL GAS-OIL-GREASE | | |
| CASH ☐ | | TOTAL SUB-LET REPAIRS | | |
| CREDIT ☐ | | TOTAL AMOUNT | | |
| | CEILING HOURLY RATE $ 2.50 | | | |
| | THIS WORK AUTHORIZED BY | | | |

EXHIBIT 2. CORPORAL MOTOR CAR COMPANY (B). INVOICE FORM.

responsibility of the service salesmen to see that these promises were carried out and that good service and proper attention were given to the customers' automobiles. In order to do this, the service salesmen personally contacted the shop mechanics and arranged with them to have the needed repair work done. Although the service salesmen consistently tried to have the work completed on time, there were many cases in which the delivery promises they had made were not kept. It was chiefly to eliminate these troubles that the service division introduced the control-tower system.

The control tower was constructed in a central location in the shop and elevated above the floor level to facilitate vision and eliminate any interruptions in the work of the tower operator. The control room was enclosed on two sides with glass panels. An electric intercommunication system was installed that enabled the tower operator to carry on a two-way conversation with anyone at the different speakers on the floor of the shop (Exhibit 1); a general public address system was also part of this equipment. A panel of control lights was installed on the outside of the tower; there was a red light, a green light, and a yellow light for each major department in the shop. There was also a message conveyor or shuttle similar to those used in department stores that carried invoice forms from the shop floor into the control tower.

Under the new scheduling procedure a service salesman met the customer as usual and discussed his repair and service needs. Before the service salesman made a delivery time promise to the customer, he referred to the control-tower light panel. A green light under any department indicated that the department concerned was not busy and was ready immediately to start work on any job. A yellow light indicated that the department was temporarily busy and the service salesman could call the control tower to find out when the department would be free to work on his customer's car. A red light meant that the department concerned was busy with jobs for the remainder of the day and that the service salesman would have to check with the tower to find out when the department's facilities would become available. With the help of this information the service salesman determined when the shop would be able to start work on the various jobs that needed to be done on his customer's car. The service salesman then drew on his own experience to determine how long his customer's job would take once repair work was started on it. On the basis of these calculations, the service salesman made a delivery promise to his customer. This delivery promise time was entered on the invoice form (Exhibit 2) along with the details of work to be done.

The invoice form was made out by the service salesmen in triplicate and Exhibit 3 is a diagram of the movement of these copies through the shop. As is indicated on the diagram, the first two copies were forwarded by the service salesmen to the control tower. The stiff third copy was attached to the automobile to be repaired in order to supply the necessary information to the mechanics. The control tower entered the information from copies one and two of the invoice onto the master daily control sheet (Exhibit 4).

The jobs to be done were entered on the control sheet in the order in which they first were received at the tower, and this

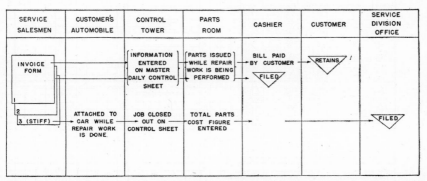

EXHIBIT 3. CORPORAL MOTOR CAR COMPANY (B). DIAGRAM TO SHOW MOVEMENT OF INVOICE FORM THROUGH THE SHOP.

sequence established the priority order by which each job was given access to the available shop facilities. Once the job order was entered on the master daily control sheet, it was the responsibility of the control-tower operator to meet the promised delivery time. He had complete charge of routing the cars around the shop. If the control-tower operator perceived that it was impossible to meet a promised delivery time, it was his responsibility to see that the customer was informed of the delay and given a new delivery promise time. The whole emphasis of the new system was on moving the cars out of the shop as quickly as possible.

When the invoice had been booked on the master daily control sheet, the control-tower operator dropped the first two copies of the invoice form down a chute into the parts room. These copies were held in the parts room while the work was being performed on the car, and a record was kept on these forms of any parts which were issued to the mechanics for use in connection with the repair job. Each service division employee informed the control tower by telephone as soon as he finished working on any car. When the work on any car was finished, the last mechanic work-

| OWNER | LICENSE NO. | MODEL | INVOICE ORDER NO. | SERVICE SALESMEN INITIALS | PROMISE DATE | WASH | SIMONIZE | GAS | HOUR PROMISE * | | LUBE | SEAT COVERS | TIRES | AIR CLEANER | FLUSH MOTOR | FLUSH RADIATOR | TUNE CHOKE | TAPPETS | CLEAN CARBON | VALVES GRIND | MOTOR SUPPORT | HEAVY |
|---|---|---|---|---|---|---|---|---|---|---|---|---|---|---|---|---|---|---|---|---|---|---|
| | | | | | | | | | | MOTOR | | | | | | | | | | | | |
| STANDARD TIME FOR PERFORMANCE OF WORK IN HOURS | | | | | | .5 | 25T. | | | | .5 | | | | | | | | 6. | | | |
| DOLAN T. | 145327 | 9/76 | 31975 | N | 4/9 | | | 1 | 5 | ⊕ | | | | | | | | | | | |
| SIDD H. | 1649 | 49/50 | 31052 | N | 4/9 | | | 2 | 4 | | | | | | | | | | | | |
| MULCHANEY | 62491 | 46/75 | 31053 | N | 4/9 | | | 3 | | 45 | | | | | | | | | | ② | |
| KRAWCHER | 224778 | 14/f | 31054 | N | 4/9 | | | 4 | | 45 | | | | | | | | | | | |
| PLATT CONST. | 64/322 | 8/7L | 31035 | G | 4/9 | | | 5 | | ⊕ | | | | | | | | 36 | | | |
| O'HARE | 278144 | 9/74 | 31979 | R | 4/9 | | | 6 | 12 | 46 | | | | | | | | | | | |
| LYNN UMBRELLA | 633601 | 4/74 | 31006 | N | 4/9 | | | 7 | | ⊕ | | | | | | | | | | | |
| REVITA | 844732 | 2/66 | 31057 | N | 4/9 | | | 8 | | ⊕ | | | | | | | | | | 67 | |
| POWERS H. | 47320 | 4/80 | 31018 | N | 4/9 | | | 9 | | | | | | | | | | | | | |
| REGAN | 746210 | 4/74 | 31037 | G | 4/9 | | | 0 | | | | | | | | | | | | | |
| | | | | | | | | | | | | | | | | | | | | | |
| HORAN | 264119 | 44/76 | 31019 | G | 4/9 | | | 1 | 12 | | | | | | | | | 36 | | | |
| ALASTROM | 236203 | 4/f | 31020 | G | 4/9 | | | 2 | 5 | | | | | | | | | | | | |
| ELDER | 97425 | 9/66 | 31067 | N | 4/9 | | | 3 | 4 | 46 | | | | | | | | | | | |
| BURKHARDT | 621147 | 4/74 | 30166 | R | 4/9 | | | 4 | | O | | | | | | | | | | | |
| | | | | | | | | 5 | | | | | | | | | | | | | |
| | | | | | | | | 6 | | | | | | | | | | | | | |
| | | | | | | | | 7 | | | | | | | | | | | | | |
| | | | | | | | | 8 | | | | | | | | | | | | | |
| | | | | | | | | 9 | | | | | | | | | | | | | |
| | | | | | | | | 0 | | | | | | | | | | | | | |
| | | | | | | | | 1 | | | | | | | | | | | | | |
| | | | | | | | | 2 | | | | | | | | | | | | | |
| | | | | | | | | 3 | | | | | | | | | | | | | |
| | | | | | | | | 4 | | | | | | | | | | | | | |
| | | | | | | | | 5 | | | | | | | | | | | | | |
| | | | | | | | | 6 | | | | | | | | | | | | | |
| | | | | | | | | 7 | | | | | | | | | | | | | |

EXHIBIT 4. CORPORAL MOTOR CAR COMPANY (B).

ing on the car forwarded the stiff third copy of the invoice to the control tower by means of the message conveyor. The tower operator indicated on his master control sheet that the job was finished and sent the third copy on to the parts room. Upon receipt of this copy, the parts room entered the total cost of all parts issued on each copy of the invoice and sent all three copies to the cashier's desk. When the customer picked up his car and paid for the work at the cashier's desk, he was given the second copy of the invoice for his personal records. The first copy was filed in the central company office and the third copy was sent to the service division for filing.

The control-tower operator made out a separate master control sheet for major repair jobs that would be in the shop for more than 24 hours. He usually fitted this work into the daily schedule during slack hours of the day.

| BRAKES | | | | FRONT END | | | | UNIT REPAIR | | | | | | ELECTRICAL | | | CLUTCH AXLE TRANSMISSION | | | | | STRAIGHTEN FRAME | EXHAUST PIPE | TAIL PIPE | MUFFLER | TIGHTEN RATTLES | INSPECTION | BODY | SHEET METAL | PAINT | TRIM | THERMOSTAT | HOSE | ANTI FREEZE | WINDSHIELD WIPER | RADIATOR | TOW CAR | GLASS REPLACEMENT | MISCELLANEOUS |
| MINOR MAJOR ADJUST | BLEED | CABLES | RELINE | ADJUST STEERING | ALIGN | OVERHAUL STEERING | BALANCE WHEELS | STARTER | GENERATOR | DISTRIBUTOR | CARBURETOR | FUEL PUMP | WATER PUMP | ELECTRICAL | HORN WIRE | RADIO | ADJUST CLUTCH | OVERHAUL CLUTCH | OVERHAUL TRANSMISSION | HYDRAMATIC ADJUST | REPAIR AXLE | | | | | | | | | | | | | | | | | | | |
|---|---|---|---|---|---|---|---|---|---|---|---|---|---|---|---|---|---|---|---|---|---|---|---|---|---|---|---|---|---|---|---|---|---|---|---|---|---|---|---|
| 5/3 | | | | 2.7 | 1.2 | 11 | | 6 | EST | EST | 1.3 | 1.5 | 1.4 | | | | EST | 2.6 | 2.9 | 11. | 3.0 | | | | | 1.5 | | | | | | | | | | | | | |

WORK TO BE DONE

(2) NUMBER OF MECHANIC PERFORMING WORK

WORK IN PROGRESS (IN HOUR PROMISE COLUMN)

WORK FINISHED (IN HOUR PROMISE COLUMN)

* A BLANK IN THE "HOUR PROMISE" COLUMN INDICATES THAT THE CAR WOULD BE PICKED UP AFTER THE CLOSE OF THE WORKING DAY.

SERVICE CONTROL SHEET FOR JUNE 9, 1947.

## QUESTIONS

1. At 10:15 A.M. on June 9, 1947, Mr. Burkhardt brought his motorcar into the Corporal Motor Car Company for a lubrication job and to get the steering apparatus adjusted and the wheels aligned. Mr. Burkhardt desired the return of his motorcar at the earliest possible time. Mr. Ryan, one of the service salesmen, wrote up the order (Exhibit 2) and checked with the control tower before setting a delivery promise time. The yellow light was burning on the control panel under the steering department so Mr. Ryan called Mr. Henry, the control-tower operator, to

find out when Mr. Burkhardt's service work could be started. Exhibit 4 shows the condition of the control sheet when Mr. Henry received Mr. Ryan's call. Operator 20 was the only mechanic who did steering adjustments and wheel alignment work and he had started work at 8:00 A.M. on Mr. Dolan's car. Operator 20 normally took a half hour for lunch. What time should Mr. Henry give as the time when the work could be started on the steering apparatus and the wheels of Mr. Burkhardt's car? What delivery promise time should Mr. Ryan give Mr. Burkhardt?

2. Evaluate the production control procedures of the Corporal Motor Car Company.

# CHAPTER XXII

# RAW MATERIALS INVENTORY CONTROL

## EMPIRE COMPANY

### 1. A Company Considers Reorganizing Its Inventory Control Routine.

The Empire Company manufactured surgical supplies. Materials used were segregated into three groups under the captions unclassified stores, classified stores, and raw materials.

A continuous, or perpetual, inventory of classified stores was maintained. In the past the book inventory record of each item had been checked by physical count whenever the tag record at the bin was full and a new tag was required. Consideration was given the desirability of making physical checks at more frequent intervals.

### 2. Importance of Raw Materials Inventory Control.
Most manufacturing operations require raw materials or purchased parts for processing. The problem of supplying such necessities has been treated in Chaps. X and XI. Acquiring title to or physical possession of raw materials and purchased parts is only the first step in ensuring their presence when needed in processing. The control of parts and raw materials after they have arrived at the plant receiving dock is essentially a matter of factory housekeeping. It is an important problem, however, and its solution is essential if process flow is to be uninterrupted, preplanned results are to be accomplished, waste is to be kept at a minimum, and costs of production are to be controlled.

### 3. Purchasing Policy of the Empire Company.
The Empire Company manufactured gauze and absorbent cotton products for surgical use. The products were marketed through wholesale medical supply houses and directly to hospitals and to the medical services of the government. The company employed 250 persons. Supplies and raw materials inventories were divided into three types: unclassified stores, classified stores, and raw

materials.  The unclassified stores, such as lumber for minor repairs and articles of office equipment, were not carried in stock regularly, but were purchased from time to time as the need arose.  Classified stores were those articles regularly carried in stock to be used for recurring manufacturing and administrative purposes.  Raw materials included raw cotton and gray cloth. These two items were purchased speculatively by a purchasing agent who based his forecasts on estimates of consumption, future orders, and market conditions.  Classified and unclassified stores were purchased by the routine purchasing agent.

Replenishment of classified stores was controlled by the stores ledger clerk in the planning department.  The stores ledger record consisted of a file of cards, one card for each item of stores. These cards provided the information which formed the basis of classified stores control.  The card showed the clerk what should be purchased, how much should be purchased, and when requisitions should be made.  The actual purchasing was done by the routine purchasing agent upon requisition from the stores ledger clerk in the planning department.

**4. The Classified Stores Ledger.**  The form in Exhibit 1 illustrates the stores ledger card used by the Empire Company. The information on this card was of three types: general information, record of consumption, and inventory details.  At the top of the sheet were spaces for general information of importance for control purposes: the name of the item, its classification symbol, its location in the storeroom, description of the item, order point, and amount to order.

**5. Determining the Order Point.**  The order point was the figure below which the amount on hand, as indicated on the card, should not go without a requisition for additional purchase being sent to the purchasing department.  This point was fixed by the head of the planning department.  In setting it, he considered such matters as average monthly consumption, time required to purchase and obtain delivery, and the most economical size of purchase order.  Once the order point had been fixed, it was entered in the proper space on the card.  The order point was reset whenever changes in any of the controlling factors made alteration advisable.  Each day the stores ledger clerk went over

## EXHIBIT 1

Empire Company
Balance-of-stores Sheet

Name_____ Symbol_____ Location_____

Description_____

Order Point_____ Amount to Order_____

**Average Monthly Consumption**

| Months | | | | | | | | | | | | | | | | | | | | | | | |
|---|---|---|---|---|---|---|---|---|---|---|---|---|---|---|---|---|---|---|---|---|---|---|---|
| Consumption | | | | | | | | | | | | | | | | | | | | | | | |
| 12-month Average | | | | | | | | | | | | | | | | | | | | | | | |

| Receipts | Issued | On Order | | | Balance on Hand |
|---|---|---|---|---|---|
| | | No. | Date | Am't | |
| | | | | | |

the cards in the file to make entries on them. Whenever a card showed that the amount of an item on hand was down to the pre-determined order point, he made out a requisition for the amount shown on the card as "Amount to Order" and forwarded it to the purchasing department.

Fixing of the order point and amount to order was facilitated by the record of monthly consumption shown in the second division of the card. There each month's consumption in physical units was recorded and beneath it was entered the average of the past 12 months' consumption. Increase or decrease in the trend of this average was useful in making revisions of the amount to order and the order point.

**6. Balance-of-stores Sheet—a Perpetual Inventory.** The clerk obtained the monthly consumption from the third division of the balance-of-stores card. There were four major headings: Receipts, Issued, On Order, and Balance on Hand. In the Receipts column were entered the physical amounts of all in-shipments of the item when they were received in the storeroom. The Issued column contained a record of all amounts of the item issued to the processing departments. Items were issued upon requisitions signed by departmental foremen. The Balance on Hand column at all times showed the existing excess of receipts over disbursements of the item. It was always possible to know the amount of an item on hand by referring to the proper ledger card and noting the last entry in the Balance on Hand column. Whenever stores were received or issued, the amounts were recorded in the Receipts or Issued columns and the proper addition or deduction was made in the Balance on Hand column. The stores ledger thus always contained complete, up-to-date information relative to the classified stores inventory. The value of the classified stores inventory could be quickly obtained by taking the physical balance on hand from the balance column of each card, pricing it, and totaling the valuations thus obtained. The stores ledger itself did not contain any monetary figures.

The On Order columns were not an indispensable part of the balance-of-stores sheet. However, they provided valuable information. Whenever the stores ledger clerk found that the balance in the Balance on Hand column was down to, or below, the order point and therefore issued a requisition to the purchasing department, he entered the number of the requisition, the date, and the amount of the requisition in the proper On Order columns. This made it possible for him to determine at any time, not only the volume of an item on hand, but also the amount that could be expected to be on hand in the near future, and the approximate date when an in-shipment would arrive. When a shipment came into the storeroom, the stores ledger clerk made the proper entry in the Receipts and Balance on Hand columns and then, in the same space in which he had noted the date of requisitioning that in-shipment, he wrote the date on which the shipment had been received. The head of the planning department had found this information of value in revising order points and amounts to order.

**7. Raw Materials Control Routine.** Purchase requisitions for classified stores originated in the planning department as a routine matter. These requisitions were authorized by the head of the planning department, and then they were sent to the purchasing department. Each such requisition had to be approved by the works manager, after which a purchase order was made out in quadruplicate. The original was sent to the vendor. The second copy was sent to the planning department as a notification that the requisition had been approved and the order placed. The third copy went to the receiving clerk in the storeroom. He used it as a basis of checking the order and its invoice when the stores arrived. The fourth copy was retained in the purchasing department, where it was used to follow up the order and see that delivery was made on schedule.

When classified stores were received in the storeroom, a careful inspection was made for quantity and quality. Accepted stores were then placed in stock, each item of stores having its own bin in a definite location in the storeroom. On each bin was a tag. The tag gave the description, symbol, and location of the stores item contained in the bin. There were also three columns similar to the Receipts, Issued, and Balance on Hand columns of the balance-of-stores sheets in the stores ledger. Whenever additional items were placed in the bin, the amount was entered in the Receipts column on the bin tag and the amount in the Balance on Hand column on the tag was increased proportionately.

At the time he placed in-shipments in stock, the receiving clerk in the storeroom made out a notification of stores received and sent it, together with his copy of the purchase order, to the classified stores ledger clerk in the planning department. The ledger clerk made the proper entries on the balance-of-stores sheets and forwarded the papers received from the receiving clerk to the accounting department for cost accounting and administrative purposes.

In the storeroom, classified stores were issued only on the authority of factory department heads or their representatives, such authorization being made in the form of a signed stores issue slip. When stores were issued, the receiver signed for their receipt on the slip. After the issue of stores had been recorded on the proper bin tags, the stores issue slip carrying the storeskeeper's signature was sent to the stores ledger clerk in the planning department. There it formed the basis of making withdrawal entries on the proper balance-of-stores sheets, after which it was forwarded to the accounting department.

Whenever stores that had been issued were returned to the storeroom, entries were made on the bin tag and a stores credit slip was made out and forwarded through the regular channels.

**8. Function of the Bin Tags.** The routine here described was built around two records: the bin tag and the balance-of-stores sheet. The bin tags provided the storeskeeper with the information he required to carry out his function. The storeskeeper signed for all stores received and was held personally responsible for them until they were checked out of the storeroom on authorized stores issue slips. The storeskeeper's responsibility covered a great number of items of large aggregate value. Dozens of storeroom transactions were effected every day. It was essential, therefore, that he have an orderly record of all that went on. The bin tags constituted that record.

**9. Function of the Balance-of-stores Sheets.** A detailed knowledge of the condition of the classified stores inventory was essential to the planning department if it was to discharge its function. The balance-of-stores sheets which made up the classified stores ledger provided this detailed information at all times.

The routine whereby these records, the balance-of-stores sheets and the bin tags, were maintained was essential to the orderly control of classified materials.

**10. Checking the Book Inventory.** If no errors were made in the carrying out of the routine just described, the balance on the bin tag for store SES2D would exactly agree with the balance as shown on the balance-of-stores sheet for SES2D, and likewise this figure would accurately represent the number of pieces actually in the bin. The reliability of a continuous inventory record depends on the extent to which the inventory shown on the balance-of-stores sheets represents exactly what is on hand in the stock room.

It is practically impossible to eliminate all inventory discrepancies. To keep errors at a minimum it is necessary to make periodic checks. The number of pieces in a bin are counted and results compared with the balance shown on the bin tag. In the past this had been done in the storeroom of the Empire Company whenever an entry, made as the result of an addition to or withdrawal from the bin, filled the last space on the bin tag. If there was any discrepancy, it was noted on the bin tag and either a stores received or stores issue slip was made out for the amount long or short. This slip was signed by the storeskeeper and forwarded with the completed bin tag to the planning department. The head of the planning department then authorized a similar adjustment to be made in the classified stores ledger.

In the storeroom a new bin tag was made out with the corrected balance brought forward from the old bin tag. In this way the perpetual book inventory was checked by physical count.

**11. Proposed Changes—Advantages and Disadvantages.** It had been proposed by the head of the planning department that the old bin tag be forwarded to the balance clerk, a physical count taken, and a new bin tag made out each time a new lot of a store was received. This, he pointed out, would reduce the chance of error between the quantity of the supply recorded on the balance-of-stores sheet and the actual quantity in the bin. The size of readjustments in the records would be minimized, because physical inventory, if taken each time a shipment of supplies was received, would be more frequent, and any necessary adjustment would be made immediately.  The number of adjustment entries might increase somewhat, but the greater accuracy growing out of more frequent check would be of sufficient advantage to justify the increased work, particularly since no additional clerks would be required to carry out the plan.

On the other hand, the planning and purchasing departments had been troubled only slightly by the occasional discrepancies which had occurred between the actual inventories in stock and the records of them on the balance-of-stores sheets.  Both the chief storeskeeper and the planning department head thought that such errors as had occurred were caused by occasional rush conditions which made for carelessness.  Only rarely, when serious or repeated discrepancies were found, had attempts been made to place responsibility.

Approximately 2,400 bin tags per year were used for 1,200 items, and it was estimated that about 5,000 additional tags per year would be required under the proposed plan.  Supplies were received every two months on an average, whereas receipts and issues for a period varying from six months to two years in length could be entered on one tag.  The practice of checking a bin when the tag was full had resulted in checking those items in active use more frequently than those with slower turnover. This was recognized as desirable.  A change to checking each time stores were received would have the effect of making a checkup of all items more frequent.

As a result of study of the proposal of the planning department head, the chief storeskeeper suggested that a change be made along somewhat different lines.  He asked that each morning the planning department send to the stores department a list of 20 or 25 items to be inventoried and bin tags checked during that day.  He believed that this would afford a better check of the book inventory.  In making up the daily check lists, the planning department clerk could see to it that all items were checked at regular intervals, that items most subject to error were checked most frequently, and that the total inventory was checked at least once in each 60- to 90-day period.

This method would regularize the volume of physical inventory work required in the storeroom.  Checking inventory when bin tags were full might cause inconvenience if a large number of tags should happen to be completed in one day. Furthermore, checking from a list would be more convenient, since the work could be done when storeroom clerks were not otherwise occupied. This method would also have a greater tendency to discourage any pilfering. Although the chief storeskeeper did not believe this to be a problem with the Empire Company, he recognized it as a matter of common consideration in stores control.

**12. Summary and Conclusions.** The planning department head studied the chief storeskeeper's plan and came to the conclusion that it was fully as satisfactory as his own as far as providing accuracy in the classified stores record was concerned and that it had certain additional advantages. The work required to make up check lists could be handled by the present staff in his department, and he recognized the desirability of regularizing the volume of adjustment work in his department as well as inventory taking in the stores department. The two departmental heads drew up a recommendation in report form and submitted it to the works manager.

The works manager studied the report in detail and notified the department heads concerned to put the recommendations into effect. The works manager recognized the desirability of accuracy in the book inventory. The Empire Company had installed the perpetual inventory method some years before and had experienced considerable difficulty in bringing its accuracy up to a point where it could be depended on. At the end of the first year of its use, an over-all physical inventory of stores had shown that the book inventory had many glaring errors. However, upon the advice of outside auditors the company had retained the perpetual inventory system and had found that experience in its use had improved it constantly. At the time of the case here discussed, improvement in the book inventory had been such that no over-all physical inventory had been taken for two years. Outside auditors periodically employed by the company and income tax officials were willing to accept as accurate the inventory figure obtained from the classified stores ledger.

The works manager recognized the importance of meticulous, systematic control of stores within the plant. Processes could not flow smoothly or preplanned results be obtained unless stores of the proper quality and in required amounts were on hand in the various manufacturing departments at the time they were required for processing. Inasmuch as the proposal to regularize physical checking of the classified inventory records used in the planning department tended to improve production control by reducing the amount of discrepancies between book balances and physical count, the works manager looked with favor upon the plan. The increased accuracy of cost records, operating statements, and balance sheets he considered additional advantages. Finally, the possibility of accomplishing the change without substantial increase in costs of control caused him to order the new plan into operation.

## QUESTIONS

1. Explain the procedure for determining when, for what, and for how much purchase requisitions for classified stores should be issued.

2. When a purchase order was written in the purchasing department, three copies were made. The original was sent to the vendor; one copy was sent to the requisitioner; one copy was sent to the receiving clerk in the stores department; and the third copy was retained in the purchasing department. What use was made of each of these copies?

3. Upon receipt of a shipment of stores in the storeroom, the receiving clerk, having checked the shipment for quality and quantity, filled out a notification of materials received and sent it together with his copy of the purchase order to the balance-of-stores clerk in the planning department. Why was this done?

4. The chief storeroom clerk was responsible for all materials and stores received by the receiving clerk until such time as they were issued to operating department heads upon proper requisition and written receipt obtained therefor. The bin tag was the device used in the storeroom to facilitate the discharge of this responsibility. Explain its use and value.

5. In the planning department, the balance-of-stores ledger duplicated the information found on the bin tags. Was this duplication necessary or desirable? Explain.

6. What would be the advantages and disadvantages of taking an inventory and forwarding the bin tag every time a new shipment of a store was placed in the bin?

7. What are the advantages and disadvantages of the plan proposed by the head storeskeeper?

8. Do you think the action taken by the works manager of the Empire Company was sound?

9. The balance-of-stores clerk forwarded all stores issue slips and materials received slips to the accounting department after they had been recorded in the planning department. Why was this done?

10. What are the advantages of a systematic control of raw materials such as that used by the Empire Company? What dangers must be safeguarded against in such a scheme?

11. The purchasing policies of the Empire Company differed for speculative raw materials, unclassified stores, and classified stores. Why?

12. What was the responsibility of the purchasing department for raw materials and classified stores purchases?

13. Authorizations for classified raw materials purchases originated in the planning department. Explain the reason for this procedure.

14. The planning department of the Empire Company issued work orders to the various production departments as authorizations of work to be done. The production department heads thereupon made out requisitions for the necessary raw materials. When these requisitions were presented to the storeskeeper, the raw materials were issued, and the department head signed a receipt for them. Would it not have been better for the planning department to issue the materials requisitions?

15. Under what circumstances does systemization of raw materials control tend to break down entirely from the standpoint of effective maintenance of raw materials supply?

## KNIGHT AUTOMATIC COMPANY

The Knight Automatic Company manufactured machine tools. A considerable number of parts used in the product were not made in the company's own works. Inventory of parts purchased was controlled by a perpetual inventory ledger.

Machine tools manufactured by the Knight Automatic Company were assembled from three types of parts: standard parts made by the company; standard parts purchased from parts makers; and special parts made by the company to comply with special requirements of the individual customer. Standard parts were made in lots of economical size and placed in stock. Purchased parts were bought at intervals sufficient to meet the assembly needs of the company and carried in stock. Special parts were made up to the customer's specifications after an order had been accepted. No assembly operations were carried on until orders were received. Each order was assembled separately.

When an order was accepted, the planning department prepared a parts list and notified the storeroom of standard parts quantities required for that order and the dates upon which they would be needed. One division of the storeroom was called the "bank." As soon as a parts list covering an order was received in the storeroom, the parts called for were removed from the stock bins to the bank. There parts for one order were placed together in a rack and held for requisition by the assembly division.

As soon as the production of special parts required for an order was well under way, the planning department issued an assembly order to the "erection" division. This assembly order was accompanied by a copy of the bill of materials originally sent to the storeroom. The copy served as a requisition from the erection department on the storeroom and was the authority upon which

EXHIBIT 1

Knight Automatic Company
Purchased Parts Ledger

Name_____  Number_____

Pattern Number_____  Used on Types_____

Specification Number_____  Location_____

Maximum_____ Minimum_____ Order Quantity_____

| Ordered | | | Received | | | Applied | | | Issued | | | In Stores | |
|---|---|---|---|---|---|---|---|---|---|---|---|---|---|
| Purchase Order No. | Date | No. Pieces | No. Due | Purchase Order No. | Date | No. Pieces | Works Order No. | Date Required | No. Pieces | Works Order No. | Date | No. Pieces | No. Pieces Unapplied | No. Pieces Actual |

parts segregated in the bank for that order were removed to the erection floor.

Both standard manufactured parts and purchased parts were controlled by means of perpetual inventory ledgers. Exhibit 1 shows the form of the Purchased Parts Ledger sheet.

## QUESTIONS

1. Explain the nature, purpose, and value of each item of information shown in Exhibit 1.

2. Was this record suitable and adequate to the needs of the Knight Automatic Company?

### Problem 52

### BELMONT JEWELRY COMPANY (B)

The Belmont Jewelry Company manufactured class and fraternity jewelry. Much of its product was made to special designs or specifications submitted by purchasers. A new department superintendent had improved process control in the pin and coat-of-arms department. He suggested that a systematic control of raw materials be devised and installed.[1]

A check of the raw materials used by the Belmont Jewelry Company revealed that about 300 items (sizes and colors included) were carried in stock. None of these items was bulky, and a considerable number of them had a high unit value. Flat gold, gold wire, and small precious stones for jeweling pins and rings were examples.

Orders from salesmen were received in the general office. From these orders an assistant to the plant manager made up production orders, which were issued to the superintendents of the six production departments. These men planned the work within their own departments and requisitioned the materials needed.

Materials were in charge of a storeskeeper in the plant manager's office. Most of the purchasing was done by the president of the company. Theoretically he bought on a routine basis from

---

[1] See Chap. XXI for detailed description of control methods in the pin and coat-of-arms department of this company.

information as to stocks on hand furnished him by the stores-keeper. Occasionally, however, he learned of "buys" in certain of the materials commonly used by the company and took advantage of them regardless of the amount in stock.

Prepare a plan of materials control suited to the needs of the Belmont Jewelry Company.

# CHAPTER XXIII

## QUALITY CONTROL

### INDIA TIRE & RUBBER COMPANY

### 1. A Company Improves Quality and Increases Profits.

The India Tire & Rubber Company was experiencing severe competition, decreased demand for its products, low earnings, and pressing bank loans. Consideration was given to lowering the quality of the product as a means of effecting a reduction in price and thereby increasing sales volume and profits. After a thorough study of the factors involved in such a change of policy, the plan was rejected. The president decided that maintenance of high quality was essential to the company's future success and that it was possible to maintain quality and at the same time reduce costs of output. A comprehensive plan for securing these results was worked out. It included improvements in processes, careful control of capital expenditures, payment of bonuses for quality maintenance, and shortening of work shifts. As a result of these measures, quality control was secured and costs were lowered to such an extent that sales volume was more than doubled, profits were increased, and the bank loans were retired.

**2. Importance of Quality Control.** The need for creating and attaining definite standards of quality in products manufactured is self-evident. National advertising of branded goods has, of course, tended to intensify this need. Reputation for uniformity and dependability of quality of output is in many cases one of the most important assets a concern can have. Appreciation of the value of such good will has caused many manufacturers to build up quality reputations and then to guard them jealously.

**3. Essentials to Quality Control.** Effective quality control has three essentials: definite fixing of responsibility for quality of output, clear-cut standards to be used in measuring quality, and an inescapable routine to ensure uniform application of standards of measurement. Unless some one person or group of persons is specifically charged with responsibility for quality control, everybody's business becomes nobody's business and quality suffers. Unless definite quality standards are carefully worked out and formulated, measurement of quality becomes a matter of human judgment, and again quality is sure to suffer.

The "matching" of piston and connecting-rod assemblies in high-class motor production is a good example of this principle. If a gasoline motor is to run smoothly, it is necessary that the weights of reciprocating parts balance as closely as possible. It is common practice, therefore, after pistons and connecting rods have been assembled, to sort them as they come from their assembly lines on the basis of weight. It would be a tremendous task, however, to sort out for one motor eight such assemblies having exactly the same weight. In practice, these assemblies are sorted into classes, all assemblies within a class having approximately the same weight. Thus, solution of the problem of just what assemblies are to be included in a class will have to be left to the judgment of the "matcher" unless definite limits for each class are worked out and established as standards. With such standards, matching requires little or no judgment on the part of the worker. All that is needed is close attention to the weighing scale and care in placing the weighed parts in the proper class bin as predetermined by the standard matching scale. Often, to decrease the possibility of error, the weighing scale, instead of being calibrated in usual avoirdupois units, is marked off in divisions corresponding to the standard matching scale. The fixing of such standards and their use as a basis for balancing an automobile motor ensure much higher quality than would result from leaving matching to the judgment of the operative.

Quality standards are of little avail unless they are consistently applied. To assure such application, it is important that a routine making for their utilization be employed. Here, again, the production of automobile motors furnishes us with an illustration. After motors are assembled, they are often set up on "blocks" in the factory and run to check their performance before they are mounted in the chassis. Such testing goes a long way to assure quality in motor operation. Some companies so test every motor produced, and, to make certain that every motor goes through the test, the motor assembly line empties into the block testing room. The testers in this division are then required to chart a full report of each motor's performance, and the report, bearing the number of the motor tested, is attached to the motor as a basis for future reference of the inspector who finally releases the motor for chassis assembly.

Such a testing procedure is costly, and some manufacturers might feel that the accuracy of motor assembly was sufficient to render block testing of every motor unnecessary. In such a case, block testing would probably be done on a sampling basis. Only occasionally motors would be taken from the assembly line at the block testing division. Such a sampling test would be expected to have two results: enough motors would be tested to measure the general quality of the assembly work, and the tests would also serve as an incentive to accurate performance on the part of assembly men. To assure the efficiency of sample testing it is necessary, however, to provide a definite frequency with which tests are to be made. The absence of such a routine would lower materially the beneficial results of the testing procedure.

**4. Cost of Quality Control.** This last example illustrates the importance of the cost aspect of quality control. Ordinarily it is not difficult to make sure that a minimum of defective finished product leaves the plant. Sufficient application of rigid standards will ordinarily bring about such a result. The cost of attaining such quality may, however, be entirely out of proportion to the value obtained. Inspection in the production of a $10,000 automobile should be a very different procedure from inspection of a $1,500 car. Certainly a company making $10,000 automobiles should block test every motor and should probably test each motor on the road by installing it in a test chassis and driving it under severe operating conditions before it is placed in its own chassis. Such a road test would call for an expenditure unwarranted in the case of the $1,500 car, and sample block tests should assure quality commensurate with the quality expected of a finished product of that class.

Degree of quality desired or needed is always a question for consideration. It is not good policy to say that the goal to strive for always should be the highest quality. It is much better to determine carefully just what quality requirements are feasible in terms of cost of production, the use to which the product is to be put, and price in a competitive market. Upon the basis of such conclusions quality standards should be set.

The following is a graphic example of the results of lack of proper consideration of quality requirements. The superintendent of a shop doing a high grade of job machine work was asked by a business acquaintance to make a flat cast-iron plate 3 feet square. The buyer said he did not care much how thick the plate was, ½ inch to 1 inch would be all right, but that he did want the plate flat. The shop superintendent asked how flat the plate should be and his friend said he wanted it "absolutely flat." The superintendent said he would do his best. , About 10 days later the plate was finished and the buyer called at the shop with a truck for it. He looked at the plate and said that it seemed "fine" and wanted to know the bill. The amount was a trifle less than $200. Astonishment does not fully describe the buyer's reaction, nor protest adequately characterize his reply.

As a matter of fact, everyone was at fault in this incident. The buyer wanted a metal plate on which to place a stove in his warehouse office. The floor was irregular and he had experienced difficulty in leveling up the stove. To his mind a flat surface would remedy the trouble and a cast metal plate, flat on top, seemed the obvious answer.

When, however, he told his friend that he wanted an "absolutely flat" plate, his statement, from the standpoint of quality, had a meaning to the superintendent which the speaker little guessed. Actually, absolute flatness is most difficult, if not impossible, to attain. To the shop superintendent, flatness was a matter of relative degree, and absolute flatness represented a condition attainable only by means of scientific methods and utmost skill in workmanship. The shop superintendent had done his best and with excellent equipment and skillful personnel had turned out a job of which he was justly proud. The $200 charge was modest considering the work involved in the job and represented little profit to the shop. When he was informed, however, that his friend wished the plate as the base for a warehouse stove, his shock was no less great and his language no less picturesque than that of his friend.

The whole ridiculous situation grew out of failure to determine just what degree of quality, in this case flatness, was desired in terms of the use to which the product was to be put, and then neglect to set a standard of quality commensurate with the degree called for. While this incident is an exaggerated example of the importance of setting quality standards in terms of purpose of the product, cost to produce, and market price, it does involve principles of quality control common to most manufacturing situations.

**5. The Constructive Attitude toward Quality Control.** Analysis of the degree of quality desired is important because high quality means high cost. One of the best methods of keeping down the cost of quality is to be found in what might well be termed a constructive policy concerning quality control. Inspection of materials, parts, and finished product will prevent putting defective products upon the market. Only in an indirect way, however, will it prevent the performance of defective work. It is like locking the garage after the car has been stolen. It is much better policy to make the theft impossible. An understanding of just what is involved in constructive or preventive quality control can be had from a study of the case here considered.

**6. A Company Undertakes Quality Improvement.** The India Tire & Rubber Company of Akron, Ohio, employed about 400 workmen in the manufacture of tires and other rubber products. The president of the company had had experience as a factory worker, a salesman, and a reorganizer of industrial concerns. When earnings of the company showed signs of becoming seriously low, this executive sought a solution in keeping with the company's responsibility to its employees and its stockholders. While lowering the quality of the company's products would have been an easy way of reducing prices to meet competition, he concluded that a sounder means of building up a permanent demand was to maintain quality or, if possible, improve it, and seek to lower operating costs.

**7. The Executive Bonus System.** One of the first measures undertaken in the president's program of quality control was the institution of a system of bonuses for the attainment of quality production. The bonus system was designed to apply to practically every worker and supervisor in the plant.

Fourteen supervisors were included as eligible for bonus earnings: the plant engineer, assistant superintendent, draftsman, time-study man, chief chemist, assistant chemist, chief mechanic, general factory foreman, mill-room foreman, tube-room foreman, two foremen in charge of the plant's tire-building divisions, foreman of the air-bag department, and foreman of the wrapping room. The management ranked these men according to its opinion of the relative importance of what they would be able to contribute toward the lowering of operating costs, basing judgment on long experience and taking into account both the capacities of the individuals and the nature of the work for which they were responsible. The plant engineer was judged the most valuable man in the group because he had the greatest opportunity to improve mechanical equipment and thereby increase output per worker. He, therefore, was allotted 1,000 points, the highest point rating. A total of 10,000 points was divided among the 14 members of this group.

If experience with the plan showed the management that a supervisor had increased his value to the company, his point assignment was to be increased to reflect this value, and the total number of points assigned to the group would be increased by the same amount. This prevented the success of one individual from lowering the point rating of the other supervisors in the group. Likewise, the point rating of any future additional members of the supervisory group eligible for bonus would be added to the total number of points assigned to the group.

The point ratings were used in the computation of each supervisor's bonus earnings. Each day a standard budget was established for the day's production in terms of perfect tires finished. The daily budget figure varied with changes in size and types of tires needed and total demand. If the actual production of a department was greater than the standard, the department supervisor earned a bonus. If department output was less than standard, no bonus was paid. For example, if the day's budgeted production was 5,000 tires and only 4,850 were cleared through the wrapping room, the foreman of the wrapping room made no bonus, although the foremen of those departments which had exceeded the standard for that day did receive bonuses. If, however, the wrapping room cleared 5,100 tires on that day, the foreman of that department earned a bonus because he had exceeded his budget standard. Thus, the bonus of a departmental supervisor was dependent on his ability to exceed the budgeted daily volume of perfect tires in his own department. Supervisors whose work was not limited to one department received bonus payments in proportion to the extent that the plant as a whole produced more than the budget standard of finished tires for the day.

The amount of daily bonus earned by a supervisor depended on two things: the amount of production of his department in excess of the day's budget, and his point rating as a member of the supervisory group. Thus, the plant engineer, who had the highest point rating, received a greater bonus payment for exceeding the daily budget by 5 per cent than did the foreman of the wrapping room. The management considered that the responsibility of the plant engineer for quality production throughout the plant as a whole was greater than that of the wrapping room foreman in his one department. Therefore, the bonus reward to the plant engineer was greater for the same amount of excess production.

Production figures for all departments were posted daily, and supervisors could tell at once whether they had earned a bonus and the amounts of such earnings. Supervisors met at least once a month and discussed methods of increasing quality production by means of better process or mechanical control.

The bonus for executives focused attention of all supervisors on the new program. As rewards were calculated on volume of output, it might be said that the bonus was paid for quantity of output rather than quality. True, quantity was the basis of calculation but it was quantity of tires of standard quality. Also, the basis for computing individual point ratings was relative responsibility for quality of output. The form of this bonus puts the emphasis on quality without setting up a tendency to sacrifice quantity in the interest of quality.

Basically, it should not be necessary to offer bonuses to executives in order to stimulate them to their best effort. Furthermore, executive bonuses often tend to injure teamwork, which is of great importance at the executive level. In the case of the India Tire & Rubber Company, the bonus for executives was probably not only desirable but also fundamental to the success of the company's program. The business faced an emergency. Quality was to be the answer to that emergency. The bonus for executives kept that emergency need clearly before every member of the organization each day. It should have had the desired effect.

The executive bonus should have been looked upon as a temporary measure, to be discontinued as soon as possible. This should have been made clear to all involved at the time the plan was started. If continued indefinitely, the bonus could be expected to lose its effectiveness and quite possibly to start development of undesirable executive tendencies.

**8. Workmen's Bonuses.** The application of the quality bonus plan to workmen may be illustrated by the methods used with the tire builders. These men had been paid on a piecework basis with a guaranteed minimum daily rate. The quality bonus plan called for the payment of an additional sum for sustained output of perfect tires. A standard daily output was established, and whenever a tire builder's daily output for a period of 25 consecutive days averaged standard or better, he was given as extra compensation a bonus of 5 per cent of his regular earnings for the period. If he maintained this rate of perfect ouput for the following 25-day period, his bonus rate for the second period was increased to 7½ per cent. For a third consecutive 25-day period, the rate was raised to 10 per cent, at which point it was maintained as long as he continued to attain standard quality production and was not insubordinate.

A cumulative bonus of this type either is powerful as an incentive or is entirely ineffective. The guaranteed minimum daily rate would probably tend to make the new quality bonus effective, provided the guaranty was set reasonably high. The tire builders might be expected to take the attitude that they had much to gain and nothing to lose. However, the cumulative aspect of the plan placed a great premium on continued accomplishment of the standard and yielded a very substantial reward. A worker who did not earn a bonus might be disgruntled. Such an effect would be very undesirable. In this case, it is probable that the minimum guaranty would serve to prevent any great amount of such adverse reaction. As an incentive to high quality of output without sacrifice of volume, the bonus to tire builders should have been effective.

**9. The Calendar Department Bonus.** In the calendar department, the quality bonus took a different form. Because of conditions over which the workers had little or no control, a certain amount of defective output was bound to occur for which the workers could not fairly be held responsible. Slight variations in fabric and compound, weather conditions, and conditions within the plant sometimes were of sufficient influence to cause defective output. It was, therefore, necessary to make provision for these factors, and the management set up a standard waste allowance of $2\frac{1}{2}$ per cent of the total weight of the fabric going through the department. Care on the part of workmen in threading fabric into calendars and attention to details of operation enabled them to reduce somewhat the amount of poor quality output. Whenever waste in the department was by such means kept below the standard allowance, credit for the amount thus saved was divided between the employees and the management according to an established scale. This device served to keep the quality of workmanship in this department at a high level.

**10. Inspection and Inspection Incentives.** As a result of the utilization of these incentive devices, the management of the India Tire & Rubber Company was able to depend in large measure on the employees to maintain quality output. However, in order to make the incentives effective in this respect, as well as to provide a check on results obtained, systems of departmental and finished product inspection were maintained. Only first-grade men were employed as departmental inspectors. They were paid relatively high day wages and, in addition, a bonus of 10 cents for each defective piece or part found. The quality bonus idea was thus extended even to the point where it acted as a check on itself. In addition to departmental inspections, an exhaustive inspection of a sample of the week's output was made weekly by the following group of men: the general tire superintendent, the chemist, the superintendent of the wrapping department, and the man in charge of construction and design. Fifty tires that were ready for shipment were taken from stock, the packages broken open, wrappings torn off, and the tires minutely examined, even to such details as labels, striping, and medallions. In this way careful check was maintained on quality, and the results obtained from the use of quality incentives were known. In the opinion of the company executives the effectiveness of the quality control devices applied to workers and supervisors made it practical to depend in large measure on the workers themselves to secure high-grade output.

**11. Cost Reduction.** In addition to the bonus plans adopted, other means important in keeping down costs in the India Tire & Rubber Company plant were devised by the production manager and plant engineer. Tasks were made easier as the result of changes in production methods. Typical of such efforts was the development of a mechanical device for breaking open tire molds. This task had been done by hand, and when so performed the work was arduous. The mechanical mold opener eliminated the strenuous physical exertion and, in addition to reducing materially the fatiguing effect of the work, speeded up the operation. The result was greater output per worker and better output as well, with the reduction of carelessness caused by fatigue. Other improvements in process had similar results. In addition, careful attention to causes of accidents and process interruption resulted in changes which reduced such costly occurrences to the minimum.

Savings in operating costs were obtained by installing insulation which reduced steam losses and increased the efficiency of vulcanizing equipment. By careful attention to motors and electrical devices, the plant engineer raised the power factor to 98 per cent. He also made it possible to decrease coal consumption from 29 tons per 24 hours to 21 tons in spite of the fact that production and steam demand doubled. As a result of these improvements, his own bonus was increased, and in many instances workmen were enabled to increase their bonuses as well.

**12. Effect of Shortened Workday on Quality and Cost.** In the summer, a change was made in hours of labor for the men employed in the vulcanizing department, commonly called the "pit." In this department the atmosphere was hot and humid. Furthermore, the work called for a considerable degree of skill. Tire demand was heaviest in the summer, and 24-hour operation seven days in the week was usual. Three eight-hour shifts had been employed and the results obtained had not been satisfactory from the standpoint of either quantity or quality of output. The substitution of four six-hour shifts was therefore tried, with the following results:

1. The number of workers employed in the department was increased 33⅓ per cent.
2. Output was brought up to budget standard, many days showing a perfect score of quality output. At no time did failure to make standard exceed 5 per cent, an output much better than had usually been attained with the three eight-hour shifts.
3. Absences, which had previously been a frequently disturbing factor, were almost eliminated.
4. Labor cost per unit vulcanized declined 8.2 per cent.

The reduction in labor cost was computed from figures for two months during which conditions were identical, with the exception that in one month three eight-hour shifts were employed while in the other four six-hour shifts were employed.

Results from the improvements described above had not been sufficient to enable the company to operate profitably, and workers were given a 20 per cent reduction in pay. At that time they were told that the wage cut would be temporary if the organization was able to make itself profitable during the following six months. Six months later sales had increased so greatly that it was necessary to increase the working force, and certain departments were put on a seven-day week. Soon the improvement had become so great that the promised return to the original wage rates was made, and some 400 factory and 50 office workers benefited from the increase.

In the meantime, the experiment with six-hour shifts in the vulcanizing department had been carefully watched. The results obtained in both busy seasons and slack seasons were so favorable that it was decided to extend the four-shift system to other departments of the plant. This was done, and within three months practically the entire plant was on a six-hour-day basis. It was expected that the plan would be further extended to include the salaried personnel.

The direct savings as a result of the extension of the four-shift plan were less easy to compute exactly than those which had been obtained in the vulcanizing department because of the difficulty of finding exactly comparable periods on the eight-hour and six-hour bases. The management stated, however, that the savings were at least equal to those secured in the first instance. No change in wage rates was made when the six-hour shift was installed.

The satisfaction of the management with the six-hour shift plan is explained in the following statement of one of the company's executives.

We have found that four six-hour shifts not only enable us to employ 33⅓ per cent additional men, thus giving more men employment, but that the change from three eight-hour shifts to four six-hour shifts per day enables individual workers to perform their tasks better. The six-hour day, coupled with the high rates paid in our factory, enable our employees who are working six hours a day to earn within 7 per cent as much as the highest paid worker did when working eight hours per day.

Then, too, there are many sociological benefits derived from the six-hour day.

1. It provides more spare time each day which the worker can use for recreation or private hobbies of whatever sort.

2. It most likely will lengthen the years of industrial life of the worker in that he seldom reaches the point of fatigue and thus he will wear out more slowly than in the past.

3. Monotony, which is a heavy accusation hurled at modern specialized industry, is relieved after only six hours, and then the worker may in other private spare-time efforts vary his activities sufficiently to avoid any unhealthy mental attitude that might come from too much of one thing.

4. Employment of more men is of course obvious, in that four shifts are employed instead of three. Almost any social calamity can conceivably develop from large-scale unemployment, which can be substantially bettered by shortened working hours for an increased number of workers.

To the employer, benefits in the form of better workmanship, better attendance, and better health of workers should result from shortened working periods. These advantages should be sufficient to provide the increased hourly wage rates that a shop would usually be obliged to set up if a six-hour day became standard. India's existing liberal wage rates have taken abundant care of the shrinkage in hours. In addition India realizes a steady flow of perfectly made merchandise from this plan. India can thus operate continuously seven days per week, through the hot peak season, even with its heavier tire sizes, and by so doing have its employees healthier and happier, and meet its heavy sales demand.

As a result of the measures described in the case, the India Tire & Rubber Company was able to control the quality of its product and, while so doing, lowered costs to such an extent that sales volume more than doubled, profits were increased substantially, and bank loans were retired.

**13.** **Summary and Conclusions.** *The Advantages of a Quality Program.* The comprehensiveness of the action taken by the management of the India Tire & Rubber Company to secure high quality of output is the outstanding feature of this case. Practically all companies employ some device or devices to ensure the desired quality of product. Few companies employ so complete and carefully integrated a quality program as that described in this chapter. It is important to realize how universally the contributors to the production process can influence quality of output. Proper raw materials are obviously essential. This case shows that plant equipment and working conditions are of equal importance. It is also clear that good workmanship can be secured at low cost and without sacrifice of volume if suitable incentives are used. The results of directed effort and coordination on the part of all members of the supervisory force are demonstrated. The company had a program that covered practically every element of production that could influence quality. From first to last, this integrated program was constructive in its aims and devices. That is why company management found its efforts in behalf of high quality so effective in reestablishing profits.

*Inspection and Disciplinary Action.* Inspection is the most common method of assuring quality of workmanship. The usual means of making inspection effective is disciplinary action in the form of reprimand, reduction in pay, layoff, or, in serious cases, discharge. Such disciplinary action is expected to have a corrective effect upon the workman involved and upon his fellow workers as well.

*The Importance of the Foreman.* The effectiveness of disciplinary action for control of quality depends largely on the skill with which the situation is handled. Usually this is a matter of foremanship. An intelligent foreman can often make disciplinary action constructive. Such results are, however, all too uncommon. Unintelligent disciplining of a work force destroys shop morale and precludes any beneficial results from the action taken.

*Preventive Quality Control.* Recently, preventive measures have tended to take the place of remedial efforts in quality control. Executives who advocate preventive measures believe that creating within the work force a desire to do good work and providing the means and methods for doing work well are much more profitable than prescribing punishment after unsatisfactory work has been turned out. Such executives insist that workers be provided with the best of working conditions, that they have the proper tools always in proper condition, and that they be thoroughly trained in the most efficient methods of task accomplishment.

Creating conditions favorable to excellent workmanship is the first step; the second is providing positive incentive in the form of a reward for making the most of good working opportunities. The quality bonus is a typical incentive. Such bonuses have been worked out and found successful in a variety of circumstances. Occasionally they have been tried without the preparatory conditioning of workplace, tools, and methods, and under such circumstances have usually failed. Intelligently devised, and applied under suitable conditions, quality incentives have proved themselves profitable, time and time again.

## QUESTIONS

1. What was the basic problem of the India Tire & Rubber Company?

2. What policy did company executives adopt in solving that problem?

3. Describe the bonus plan the company devised for its executives. What were the advantages and disadvantages of that plan?

4. What do you think of the idea that executive bonuses are desirable only under exceptional circumstances?

5. Describe the quality bonus system for tire builders. What were its points of strength and weakness?

6. Be prepared to describe and discuss any other quality incentives described in the case.

7. What were the advantages and disadvantages of the shortened workday in the vulcanizing department?

8. Do you think the shortened work shift had equal merit in other parts of the plant?

9. How did the short workday make for better quality in the India Tire & Rubber Company plant?

10. How generally applicable is the six-hour workday in industry?

11. Describe the various other means employed by this company to improve quality and decrease cost.

12. Explain the constructive, or preventive, concept of quality control. Is it better than other approaches to the problem? If so, how?

## ROBINSON ELECTRICAL COMPANY

The volume, variety, and technical nature of the products of the Robinson Electrical Company and the desire of the management to retain the good will of its customers required effective organization of the large corps of trained inspectors. The chief duties of the inspectors were considered to be protection of the customers' interests, maintenance of the company's standards, and preservation of its reputation with a minimum of delays in production. Inspection could be organized as part of the production department, as part of the engineering department, or as a separate organization of the same importance as the other departments and responsible directly to the management.

The organization of the inspectors of the Robinson Electrical Company as part of the production department tended to sacrifice quality for quantity. This tendency was enhanced by the system of manufacturing to schedule in order to make deliveries on the dates quoted to customers. It was believed that although a customer wished delivery on the date specified, he would prefer to wait rather than to receive goods which were mechanically imperfect. Delays often were prevented, however, by diverting materials from other orders or other products. This solution of the difficulty would be strongly urged upon the inspectors if they were a part of the production department, with an attendant failure to eliminate defective work at its source.

The organization of the inspectors under the engineering department placed all the emphasis on quality. The aim of designing engineers was to specify the best materials available; they changed their specifications only when convinced that production was more practicable with other materials. If the inspectors were a part of the engineering force, therefore, smooth production according to schedule was likely to be sacrificed.

A separate inspection department provided a more impartial body to consider cases, but it was often dependent on production and engineering for information leading to decisions. It relieved the management from coordinating the opposing views, but it became one more factor in any serious discussion that required settlement by the management.

The decision was made in favor of an inspection department, according to the following notice:

### INSPECTION DEPARTMENT AND ITS DUTIES

The status of the inspection department is to protect our customers' interests, to maintain the Robinson standard, and preserve its reputation. Therefore it is not connected in any way with the manufacturing element and is considered a separate organization, as much as the engineering department, coming directly under the manager and his personal supervision.

It is expected, however, that the inspectors will make every effort to co-operate with the factory in getting out production and to eliminate any unnecessary holdups. All instructions to the inspectors will be given through the Chief Inspector's office.

The above has the approval of the management.

(Signed) ———————————————

Chief Inspector

### QUESTIONS

1. What were said to be the chief duties of the inspectors of the Robinson Electrical Company?

2. What three methods of organizing inspection were considered?

3. Why did the management finally decide to organize a separate inspection department?

4. In view of your consideration of the India Tire & Rubber Company case, what would you say was the weakness of the plan adopted by the Robinson Electrical Company?

5. What should be the function of inspection in a production program?

### Problem 54

### MILES SHOE COMPANY

The Miles Shoe Company paid practically all its labor on a straight piece-rate basis. It was proposed that the cutting of leather uppers be put on the basis of a piece rate with bonus to encourage better utilization of raw material.

The plant manager of the Miles Shoe Company, which manufactured soft-soled slippers, was reorganizing certain of the shop departments in anticipation of an increased volume of business during the approaching busy season. For the past two years there had been a steady market shift from felt to leather in medium-grade slippers such as those produced by the Miles Shoe Company. This shift was largely responsible for the critical consideration that was being given the cutting department of the plant.

In this department the cutting of leather uppers was an operation requiring both dexterity and judgment on the part of the worker. As compared with the wages paid, the raw material involved represented a much greater cost. No two hides were exactly alike in size, shape, or quality. The problem in cutting was to utilize every available inch of the hide without including imperfections. Carelessness in the cutting operation could entirely absorb the margin between cost of production and selling price of this grade of slipper.

The cutting operation was performed in two ways, by hand with patterns or on clicking machines with dies. The choice of method depended on the volume of the particular slipper pattern being made. When a sufficient number was to be produced to warrant the investment, dies were purchased and the uppers cut on the clicking machines. When only a small lot of the particular slipper was made, it did not pay to purchase dies and the leather was cut by hand from patterns.

Regardless of the process chosen, the cutters were paid piece rates. The rate for cutting a given pattern was, of course, greater when the operation was performed by hand than when it was done on a machine. These rates had been established with reference to past experience in the Miles plant and wages commonly received on similar operations in other plants in the vicinity. No attempt had been made to fix the rates scientifically by means of time or motion studies. Both workmen and management were satisfied with the existing rates.

The cutting room foreman was responsible for the quality of finished parts produced in his department. An over-all inspection was made of the finished product just prior to packing for shipment. Very few of the company's slippers were returned to it as defective, nor was any considerable volume of imperfect product returned to the workrooms as a result of final inspection. The cutting room foreman was also responsible for proper utilization of raw materials. He made frequent inspection of the scrap that accumulated at the machines and benches and was thus able to note the amount of waste of each workman. During the busy season of the previous year, the duties of the foreman had been so arduous as to compel him to work overtime regularly.

On the basis of past experience, the Miles Shoe Company had established standard costs for each style and size of slipper produced. Thus, when a cutter was assigned a job, he was issued the standard quantity of raw material which the costs sheets showed would be needed. Sometimes he was unable to get the required job out of the standard issue; occasionally there was raw material left over after the lot was cut. The cutting room records charged the standard amount of raw material to the job when it was issued. Any excess or shortage was recorded after the lot had been cut. This raw material saving or shortage was due to two things: the ability and care of the cutter and the degree of uniformity in quality of the leather. Careful inspection and sorting of the hides led the cutting room foreman to believe that the workman was the more important factor of the two.

It had been suggested to the plant manager that raw material would be better utilized if, in addition to the piece rate paid them, the cutters received a bonus based on the amount of raw material saved from the standard amounts issued. It was pointed out that in the present wage system there was no constructive incentive to economical utilization of raw material.

The management decided not to install a bonus. Executives thought that the plant was too small for such a policy. As the volume of work increased, an assistant would be given the cutting room foreman to relieve him of some of his routine duties, such as assignment of work to individual workmen.

Was this the best way of meeting this company's problem?

## Problem 55

## GILLIS & ECKART MANUFACTURING COMPANY

The demand for the products of the Gillis & Eckart Manufacturing Company had become greater than the potential capacity of the plant. The pressure of work and the haste of the employees in order to earn higher wages had resulted in an increase of defective work. The management wished to reduce the amount of spoilage but to maintain the total output.

The products of the Gillis & Eckart Manufacturing Company were tubular and slotted rivets, shoe hooks, and riveting machines. The company manufactured 300 sizes and kinds of rivets. Shoe hooks were made in a single style, which was produced in five finishes. The company manufactured one basic type of riveting machine, although minor changes might be made in some of its specifications.

The fabricating processes of the slotted and tubular rivets were as follows:

Slotted:
    Blank—round wire fed to machine, cut to proper length, and headed
    Remove oil
    Split shanks
    Clean and grind off burrs
    Sort

Tubular:
    Blank—same as slotted
    Center shank
    Trim heads
    Remove oil—same as slotted
    Burr shank to proper depth and diameter
    Clean and grind off burrs—same as slotted
    Sort—same as slotted

The sorting and testing were done by automatic machines for rivets manufactured in large quantities and by hand for those produced in small lots. Before the machines could be used with safety, it was necessary to inspect the rivets in order to eliminate scraps of metal, wire, and badly spoiled products. If the finish was to be brass, aluminum, or nickel, the rivets were immersed in tanks filled with the proper solution; the plating was done by electrolysis.  If the rivets were to be japanned or varnished, they were rotated in a small can which contained the appropriate coating.  After the finish had been applied, the rivets were sorted again to eliminate grit and metal scraps and then packed.

Shoe hooks passed through a similar routine.  Blanks were made from flat wire on a special machine; and, instead of being bored or slotted, the blanks were bent over to form the hook.  The testing and finishing processes for shoe hooks were the same as those for rivets.

A large number of operations were required in making, finishing, and assembling the parts of the riveting machines.  The workers who performed these tasks also did many repair and machine jobs.  The men who manufactured riveting machines were paid time wages.

The rivets were blanked, bent, bored, and sorted by mechanical means.  Each workman operated from two to six machines.  It was his duty to maintain the supply of oil, to replenish the wire, and to eliminate metal, chips, grit, or similar material which would clog the machines.  The machines had been operated productively on the average about 60 per cent of the time.  Since the machines were automatic, the quantity of output depended on the continued operation of the machine.  The workers were paid a bonus when the machines under their control were utilized more than 65 per cent of their maximum potential capacity.  For each 1 per cent increase over 65 per cent utilization the employee received a 1 per cent increase in his wage.  For all other operations, where the quantity of output did not depend on the continued operation of automatic machines, the employees were paid piece rates.  The output of the best workers in the plant had been used as the basis for setting the piece rates.

In order to earn the bonus, the men operated the machines at too high a speed.  As a result, there were many breakdowns and much damaged material.  In the departments in which employees received a piece wage, the same situation occurred.  Sorters and inspectors, who were paid piece rates, performed their tasks in a slipshod manner; they not only passed defective work because of haste but they also failed to eliminate all dirt, grit, and pieces of metal. Failure to remove such foreign matter had caused the destruction of numerous parts of the automatic inspection machine.

What steps should the management take?

# CHAPTER XXIV

## COST CONTROL

### BELMONT JEWELRY COMPANY (C)

**1. A Department Executive Proposes to Elaborate a Production Control System to Include Costs.**

The president of the Belmont Jewelry Company had employed a new superintendent for the pin and coat-of-arms department of his company. Production in that department had been lagging behind schedule, and it was the task of the new superintendent to straighten out that situation. He did so, and at the end of the first year of his service to the company the department was working smoothly.

Before coming to the Belmont Jewelry Company the superintendent had worked for several years for a company which depended in large measure on production and cost records as aids in the formulation of managerial policy and as means of measuring results. In straightening out the affairs of the pin and coat-of-arms department of the Belmont Jewelry Company the superintendent had devised a simple system of production control. This system had been improved during the year in which it had been in effect. The superintendent had found it of great value to him and wished to elaborate these records somewhat to include information as to the costs of carrying on the work of the department.

**2. The Objective of Management—Profits.** It is frequently said that the objective of management is the making of profit. If by that is meant the ensuring of future profits as well as the gaining of immediate returns, most of us will agree. At least it is true that the modern method of measuring success or failure of a business is by means of profit or loss resulting from operations.

**3. Records of Business Progress—the Balance Sheet.** The two records most commonly used to tell the story of success or failure in the management of a business are the balance sheet and profit and loss statement. We shall consider the balance sheet first.

In many ways a balance sheet may be compared with a single

exposure cut from a motion-picture film. The motion-picture film is a series of "stills," each successive exposure differing from the preceding one very slightly. If a person cuts one such exposure from a strip of film, he will have a picture of conditions in the screen story just at the instant of time when the exposure was made.

In this respect the single exposure from the film is like the balance sheet. That record, if properly prepared, will show just what were the conditions of the business it represents at the time the statement was made. It will show a value in dollars for the plant and for its equipment. It will tell the amount of goods manufactured which had not been sold and which were, therefore, on hand. It will give the value of the raw materials owned and the value of products then in process of making but not completed. These and many other values to which the business held title will be shown under the caption "Assets."[1] The balance sheet will also show what the business owed, its liabilities,[2] and will give some indication as to the time when those obligations had to be met. In addition, the claim of the proprietors (owners of the business) upon the asset values as shown is set forth as the proprietorship[3] interest of the business.

In other words, the balance sheet represents a picture of the business at an instant of time just as the single still cut from the motion-picture film shows conditions in the screen story at the moment the exposure is made. The still shows, perhaps, the exterior of a beautiful city residence, a powerful roadster standing before it, with a marvelous young lady seated at the wheel. One window of the beautiful building is open and from it protrudes the foot and leg of a man. Thus we have a picture of conditions exactly as they were at that instant of time.

**4. The Comparison of Balance Sheets.** Another single exposure taken from the same film at a point 50 feet beyond the first cutting will show a different condition which is the result of the happenings portrayed in the 50 feet of film separating the two cuttings. In some degree a study of the two separated ex-

---

[1] An asset may be defined as something which a business owns.

[2] A liability may be defined as an amount which a business owes.

[3] Proprietorship may be defined as the excess of asset values over liabilities.

posures will tell what has been going on, but only in a very general way. To know exactly what has happened to bring about the differences between the two single exposures it would be necessary to consult the intervening film.

Let us measure off some 50 feet of the film from which the exposure already described was taken and select another cut at random. The scene is changed; it is a busy city street. However, our powerful roadster is still there, and we recognize the same marvelous lady, who now seems to be driving the powerful roadster at terrific speed inasmuch as her hat is gone and her curls are streaming out with the wind. There is a new element in the picture, however. A well-dressed man sits beside the marvelous young lady, but he has on a soft black hat, pulled well down over his eyes, and we can tell little about him.

However, by having the two exposures we now know more than we did when we had but one. Apparently, the marvelous lady was waiting for the mysterious man whose leg we saw thrust out the window in the first picture. It seems fair to assume that at that time he was coming out rather than going in, and now they appear in a hurry to get away from the beautiful building. We cannot be exactly sure about all these things, but they seem (in the light of our past motion-picture experience) to be rather fair assumptions.

Just as the two exposures cut from the film tend to explain each other, so two balance sheets tell much more than one. It has become recognized as good practice to set up balance sheets of a business at regular intervals, usually of one year, and to compare them for information useful to the managers. Comparison shows increases or decreases in various items from which many valuable inferences may be drawn.

Frequently, however, the causes and significance of these changes are not clear. Just as in our motion-picture exposure comparison we cannot tell whether the marvelous young lady is hurrying the young man away from his irate father, whether they are simply going to meet a train, or whether, having accomplished a successful jewel robbery, they are on their way to dispose of the loot, so we cannot be entirely sure of the inferences we draw in the comparison of two balance sheets. In the case of the motion picture, we wish we could see the 50 feet of film intervening between our two exposures, for that would probably tell us much as to what has occurred and, more important still, why. In the case of our business investigation, we need more knowledge of what has taken place during the year which has elapsed between our two balance sheets.

**5. The Operating Statement.** The need for information supplementary to the balance sheets has resulted in the second commonly used business record, the profit and loss, or operating, statement. The purpose of this statement is to tell what business has been done during a period and to give the income therefrom in comparison with the costs of carrying on that business. These costs are set forth in more or less detail, the detailed statements usually being made up exclusively for the use of the executives of the company. Such statements, as they are concerned with production, are essentially annual or semiannual summaries of total cost of direct labor employed, total cost of raw materials used up during the period, and totals of factory expense items, such as taxes, repairs, indirect labor, heat, light, power, shop superintendence, insurance, and depreciation. The data included in the profit and loss statement are most informative to anyone attempting to understand and evaluate the cross sections of the business shown in balance sheets, and for that purpose the operating statement is an eminently suitable summary of what has taken place.

**6. Inadequacy of the Operating Statement.** The shop executive or foreman finds the usual operating, or manufacturing, statement of rather less value than does the general executive. For shop purposes, such statements are lacking in two respects. In the first place, the information cannot practically be made currently available. Annual and semiannual statements are the rule. Occasionally, a company compiles this information as frequently as once a month. Even in such cases the information has limited usefulness for the operating executive. It is not properly classified or sufficiently detailed for his purposes. For example, it is most rare for such statements to show costs by products or types of products. Such a classification is most essential for production control, and, what is more, product costs should, in most cases, be subdivided by operating departments. Lack of timeliness and lack of properly classified detail make the ordinary manufacturing statement of relatively little value to the production executive.

**7. Importance of Detailed Current Costs.** Detailed current information on costs is of major importance in production control. Such information serves two purposes: it provides, in part, the basis for policy formulation; and, equally important, it helps the executive to measure the effects of actions taken as a result of policies adopted. When sensibly undertaken, the compilation of cost data is neither excessively difficult nor expensive, and as a usual thing the values gained from a properly devised method far exceed the costs of collection.

**8. Accuracy of Cost Data.** One matter of policy as regards the compilation and use of cost data should be stressed at this point. It may seem an exaggeration to say that in practically all cases it is humanly impossible to determine *exactly* what it has cost a company to produce a product. The statement is nevertheless true. This fact is a matter of practical significance, however, in but one respect, the attitude we take toward mathematical precision in both collecting and using cost data. On the one hand, we might say that if cost data are not exact there is little use in collecting them, for their utilization in control or as a measuring device will be inaccurate and lead to unforeseen and undesirable results. There is a real element of truth in such an attitude. Practically, however, it need not be a matter of too great concern.

When the sun sets, it becomes dark. As yet the mind of man has developed no means whereby we can reproduce, during hours of darkness, the general illuminating effects of sunlight. Yet because we cannot reproduce the full illumination of the sun we do not stay at home. We have developed ways of securing a partial illumination of restricted areas, and by such means we move about and continue our activities long past the sunset hour.

In treating of business costs we do the same. Just because we cannot determine production costs with mathematical exactness and precision we need not go out of business, nor need it be the part of wisdom to disregard costs or fail to utilize such cost data as we can readily acquire. A little light is better than no light at all, both when it comes to driving a car on a mountain road and when one is engaged in controlling the costs of manufacture. The wise executive uses all the information he can readily get, and because he understands their limitations he can use such data intelligently and therefore effectively. There are two extremes to be avoided: the one is to say that because cost data are inexact their use is of little value; the other is to assume that cost data are, or can be made, exact and that they can, therefore, replace experience and intelligence in managerial control.

**9. Cost Control as an Outgrowth of Process Control.** The experience of the superintendent of the pin and coat-of-arms department of the Belmont Jewelry Company is a good illustration of the value of a proper attitude toward the collection and use of cost data. A simple, adequate system for controlling the flow of work in the department had been devised and tried out, and had proved its worth in use. The superintendent proposed a limited amplification of this control device as a means of better planning for cost reduction and then measuring the effects of changes made.[4]

**10. Determining Labor Costs.** The process control routine in the pin and coat-of-arms department had been built around a job ticket. The number of hours of labor required for the production of each job, together with the payroll numbers of the men performing that labor, were recorded on the first, or summary, coupon, which was retained in the department superintendent's office. All that was required, therefore, to find the labor cost of producing any job was to apply the hourly pay rates of the men working on the jobs to the hours spent. The payroll clerk in the accounting office furnished the pin and coat-of-arms department clerk with a list of the men working in that department and their hourly rates. From this list and the job ticket summary it was a simple matter to compute the total labor expended on a job, and by dividing that total by the number of good finished pins in the lot the labor cost of each

---

[4] It is of absolute importance that the student have at this time a clear understanding of the production control system in use by this company. This can be readily obtained by a restudy of Chap. XXI.

pin was quickly and easily ascertained.  To facilitate this process two extra columns were added to the summary coupons of the job tickets.  In one of these could be entered each man's hourly rate and in the other could be entered the labor cost of performing each operation on the lot.  Provision was made for totaling this last column.

**11. Compiling Raw Materials Costs.**  An equally simple means was devised for collecting the cost of raw materials used in the production of each lot of pins.  The principal raw materials required were gold wire, gold strips, and small precious stones.  These were all of small bulk and high unit value.  They were stored in charge of one individual in the plant manager's office.  There was practically no variation in the cost of the gold used.  Each lot of precious stones purchased was stored separately, and the purchase price of the lot was marked on the container.  When the pin department superintendent ordered a given job into production, he wrote a requisition on the storeskeeper for all materials required.  This requisition called for quantities by weight or number.  The storeskeeper issued the requisitioned materials and used the requisition as part of the basis of his raw-materials control.  From the requisition and his own records of the raw materials purchase price it was a simple matter for the storeskeeper to make up a brief bill of materials for each lot and send it to the office of the pin department superintendent.  The clerk in that office entered the amount of raw materials and their cost on the back of the summary coupon for the job involved, and by dividing the total by the number of pins turned out in the lot obtained the materials cost of each pin produced.  As a result of entering separately the cost of each material used for a lot, it was easy to get the materials cost for each operation involved if that information should be desired.

**12. Burden Costs.**  When direct labor and raw materials costs were found, there was but one other cost to be obtained, plant burden.  As a usual thing burden cost is the most difficult of all costs to ascertain.  It cannot be determined with absolute accuracy, and particularly is it difficult to collect the many items of which it is composed until long after raw materials and labor costs are known.  In the interest of speed and economy it is customary to use standard rates for the calculation of burden costs by lots. The superintendent of the pin department in cooperation with the company accountant found from a study of the company's past records that burden in the pin and coat-of-arms department normally tended to vary directly in proportion to the amount of direct labor employed. They found that the longer it took to process an order, the greater was the burden cost of its manufacture, and that the number of labor hours required for a job was a satisfactory index of the length of time required for processing. Their investigation further revealed that for each hour of direct labor employed, burden costs of 40 cents were typically incurred. Thus, to ascertain the burden cost of any job, it was only necessary to multiply the 40-cent hourly burden rate by the number of labor hours charged to the lot on the job ticket. After the standard hourly burden rate for the department had been determined, it was a simple matter to make the necessary calculation on the back of the summary coupon of each job ticket to arrive at the total standard burden cost of the job covered by the coupon. Dividing that total by the number of good pins in the lot gave the unit burden cost for each pin in that lot.

**13. Types of Standard Burden Rates.** In their search for a means of ready determination of burden costs, the superintendent and accountant had considered several possibilities. Those upon which they finally centered their attention were a labor-hour rate (the one adopted), a percentage rate to be applied to the labor cost of the job, and a percentage rate to be applied to the prime costs of production, *i.e.*, to the sum of direct labor and raw materials costs. Investigation indicated that the hourly burden rate was the best of the three for that particular department.

The prime cost percentage was discarded because a study of pin design quickly showed that neither the amount nor the cost of raw materials going into a pin was an indication of the length of time required to make the pin. Time required to process seemed to be the best measure of burden involved and, therefore, the value of raw materials used would bear no relationship to burden. Prime cost could not well be used as a burden index.

The choice between labor hours and labor dollars was finally settled along similar lines. In some degree labor cost was a measure of time required to process. However, variation in existing wage rates and possible future fluctuation in wage rates of individual workers and of the group as a whole tended to make labor costs inaccurate as an index. Also occasional overtime in rush periods, which was paid for at 1½ times the regular rates, was a disturbing influence. The amount of labor time applied to each job was already known, and thus there seemed no practical difficulty in using that figure itself as a measure of burden cost. The burden rate of 40 cents per labor hour charged to the job seemed sufficiently accurate for purposes of departmental control and had besides the very necessary quality of ease of determination and calculation.

**14. Suitability of Standard Burden Rates.** The obvious lack of exactness in this procedure was not considered serious. In the first place the burden costs involved were in but very small measure under the control of the department superintendent, who, therefore, could not be held responsible for them. At the same time the superintendent could help to reduce burden costs by seeing to it that work passed through his department with expedition, and his accomplishments along that line would be reflected in the job costs if the labor-hour rate was used for burden purposes.

**15. Unit Product Costs.** By the simple methods here described, the unit cost of labor, raw materials, and burden could be quickly and easily calculated for any job turned out by the pin and coat-of-arms department. Addition of the three items would give the total cost of producing each pin.

**16. Use of the Cost Data.** In practice, the superintendent found it unnecessary to complete the computation for every job passing through his department. Hourly rates of all workers on every job were entered in the proper column provided on the summary coupon of the job ticket. Also raw materials costs were entered on the back of each summary coupon. Burden was applied and unit costs were figured only as called for by the superintendent. In controlling the work of his department, the superintendent found the availability of such data of great benefit. It helped him to judge the relative excellence of his workmen and of his foremen. The results of changes in methods of doing work were now measurable, and study of the cost records suggested many improvements which had hitherto been unsuspected. The designing department found the information helpful because it showed clearly the effect of different types of design on costs of production. The sales manager also found that he could use this cost information to advantage. While the work of the pin and coat-of-arms department was essentially for special order, analysis showed that almost all the jobs which came in either were basically like jobs that had been done in the past or were new combinations of operations with which the company had had experience. The cost data as compiled made it possible to forecast with great accuracy the probable cost of doing any job. For example, the pin described in the production control case [5] differed from one made the year before only in that another color of enamel was used and the engraved numeral was changed. Had the costs of producing the pin the year before been known in as much detail as the cost system here described provides, the cost of producing the new order could have been accurately predetermined. Such information was of great value to the sales manager in quoting prices on new work. If a customer objected to the price asked for a proposed job, the sales manager was in a position to suggest possible changes in materials or design which would bring the price of the pin within the limit which the customer could pay.

It should be realized, however, that, while the sales manager found the cost data valuable in quoting prices, the cost alone could not be made the basis of price setting. Competition of other producers made such a policy impossible. However, knowledge of costs did enable the sales department to quote prices much more intelligently and did make it possible for executives to foreknow within rather close limits what would be the effect on profits of taking business at the prices set.

**17. Summary and Conclusions.** *Experience of the Belmont Jewelry Company.* The president, department superintendent,

[5] See p. 509.

designer, and sales manager of the Belmont Jewelry Company all found information on costs within the pin and coat-of-arms department of great value. The character of the data collected was such as to make them of maximum usefulness. The method of collection made the information quickly available and enabled the executives to correct errors before they had a serious effect on profits. The simplicity of the system made it very inexpensive in operation. The president of the company was very complimentary in his praise, and other department heads were urged to consider the possibility of collecting and using cost data.

*Cost Records as a Management Device.* No attempt is being made in this volume to train the student in methods of cost accounting. The importance of cost data as indicators of what should be done, as a yardstick of accomplishment, and as a means of fixing responsibility for results, cannot be overlooked in any adequate introduction to the problem of managerial control. The student who proposes to make a career for himself in the field of production will, of course, go on to a thorough study of the methods and technique of cost accumulation. It is important, however, that throughout any such study the student retain his management point of view. To be valuable in production control, a cost system should be simple. It should provide useful information and only useful information. This information should be in the form best suited to the particular ends and individuals served. The data which go to the foreman may well differ, as to both content and method of presentation, from the cost data provided the sales department. Consideration of matters such as the foregoing would often do much to transform costly, cumbersome, unusable cost systems, which are all too frequently regarded by production executives as statistical bone yards, into useful devices invaluable to management. In this day and age, business control that is not predicated on knowledge of costs is almost no control at all. On the other hand, an elaborate cost system all too frequently yields nothing except a feeling of self-righteousness on the part of a cost department plus an increase in the cost of production. The student of production management will gain much if he keeps this thought before him as he works his way through the intricacies of the technique required for the essential tying in of cost and financial accounts.

## QUESTIONS

1. What is a balance sheet? How can it be profitably used in business management?

2. How do two balance sheets of a business taken at different times tend to explain each other?

3. What is the profit and loss, or operating, statement? What is its relation to the balance sheets which immediately precede and follow it?

4. Why is the operating statement often found unsatisfactory for the purposes of the production executive?

5. What are the essential characteristics of cost information if such data are to be of maximum usefulness in the controlling of production processes?

6. What three kinds of cost information are collected? What are the items of cost included in each class?

7. How were labor costs by jobs and operations on each job collected in the pin and coat-of-arms department of the Belmont Jewelry Company?

8. How were raw materials costs for each job and operation obtained?

9. Describe the method of figuring burden costs for each job.

10. Why was it desirable to use a "standard rate" in calculating the burden cost?

11. Why was the number of labor hours applied to a job considered the best index of burden costs in this instance?

12. How was the total cost per pin produced computed?

13. Who, within the Belmont Jewelry Company organization, found the use of the cost data valuable?

14. What use could each of these individuals make of the data?

15. If the cost data described were inaccurate, why was their use desirable?

16. How exact should cost data be?

17. What is the relation between a process control routine and a cost collection system?

18. Why did the clerk of the pin department not compute unit costs for every lot or job produced?

19. Why was each order made the basis of cost collection? Why did they not collect the costs of operating the department for a week or a month and then divide the total costs of the period by the number of pins produced during that period?

20. Wherein may failure to use costs in production control make for mistakes in management?

## ABLE BROTHERS, INC.

Able Brothers, Inc., reconditioned spinning rolls for a number of cotton mills located in a large New England textile city. Extensive improvements had been instituted in the standardization of equipment and tools, layout of machinery, routing of materials, introduction of incentive wage systems, and in the design and installation of an effective procedure for the control of production. As a further step the management wished to secure cost information.

In processing cotton, the yarn passes between leather-covered rolls and fluted steel rolls. The covered rolls are approximately

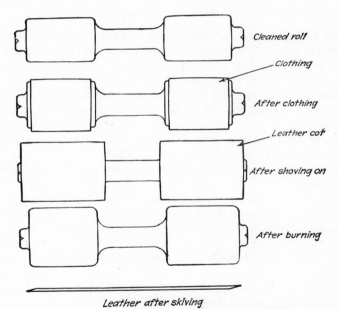

Cleaned roll

Clothing

After clothing

Leather cot

After shoving on

After burning

Leather after skiving

EXHIBIT 1. ABLE BROTHERS, INC. STEPS IN THE PROCESS OF ROLL COVERING.

8 inches long and 1 inch in diameter (see Exhibit 1, above). Continued contact of the rolls ultimately destroys the leather surfacing and requires that the rolls be recovered. An establish-

ment offering such a service to a group of textile mills has an operating condition not unlike that of a laundry in that the property of the customer is brought to the plant at regularly recurring intervals for reconditioning.  For example, at certain of the larger mills serviced by Able Brothers, Inc., rolls were called for on Mondays, Wednesdays, and Fridays, the two-day intervals being sufficient to recover the rolls and to return them when another lot was collected.  In other mills, deliveries and collections occurred once or twice a week.  The mills maintained a small surplus of rolls which allowed them to arrange for recovering without extended stoppage of machinery, since changes of rolls could be made after hours.  Approximately 100,000 rolls were recovered by Able Brothers, Inc., each week.

## DESCRIPTION OF THE PROCESS

The process of reconditioning was as follows:

*Cleaning of Rolls* (6 men).  Rolls which had been collected from mills in mill boxes and delivered by truck to the washroom were placed in perforated steel baskets and dipped in a hot solvent which freed the rolls from felt and leather.  The rolls were washed and removed by hand to a drying screen, after which they were tumbled in sawdust in a tumbling barrel.  They were dumped upon a screen, replaced in mill boxes and sent to the roll-covering department.[6]

*Clothing of Rolls* (10 men).  Rolls were mounted on centers; each "boss" was spun against a glue brush and covered with felt.

*Shoving-on of Rolls* (5 men).  Roll bosses were covered with cylindrical cots of leather.

*Burning of Rolls* (12 men).  Rolls were mounted on high-speed spindle lathes and pressure applied to the overhanging edges of the leather cots, causing them to burn and shrivel under the friction, locking the leather cot tightly to the roll.

*Calendering of Rolls* (2 men).  Rolls were machine-polished between heated plates.

Calendering was the last operation and rolls were then replaced in original mill boxes, invoiced, and delivered to the mills.

[6] When received for the first time each roll was given a distinguishing mark similar to a laundry mark. This symbol was permanently stamped into the metal part of the roll. An office record was kept, showing all symbols and the firms the symbols represented. After a roll had once been recovered, it was unnecessary again to stamp an identification symbol upon it.

## CLOTH PREPARATION

In the preparation of the cloth for assembly with the roll, two operations were necessary:

*Stripping of Cloth* (2 men). Large squares were cut from a roll of felt cloth and piled in layers of four or five thicknesses, after which they were cut into long strips of the required width.

*Squaring of Cloth* (no additional operatives). Strips were cut into pieces of such size that they would exactly surround the circumference of the iron roll.

## LEATHER-COT PREPARATION

In the preparation of the leather for assembly with the clothed roll, several operations were necessary:

*Stripping of Hides* (2 men). Sheepskins were cut into strips of the required width.

*Skiving of Strips* (5 men). Strips were cut into rectangles of proper length to form tightly fitting cots. Strips were cut on a bevel (see Exhibit 1).

*Cementing of Cots* (20 women). Beveled edges were coated with Russian glue and joined under pressure.

*Storage of Cots*. Cots were placed in storage for 48 hours before using in order that the cement might set properly.

A general foreman had charge of all production and each operation was in charge of a working boss who assigned work and supervised operations. As the number of types and sizes of rolls was small and as the customers were rather permanent, cloth squares and cots were made up for stock. Product in process was moved from one operation to another by the operatives, and an inspector approved all work performed after the clothing operation. Final inspection was performed by the calender machine operatives.

Because of the small size of the plant and narrowness of profit margin, it was necessary to install a cost control method which would involve a minimum of expense. The company employed one bookkeeper who also acted as secretary to the owner of the business. A time-study engineer was retained who assisted in such work as the setting of new rates and calculation of payrolls. Maintenance of equipment was cared for by an outside contractor whose shop was in an adjacent building.

Devise a procedure for collecting operation costs for this plant.

Problem 57

## CADILLAC MOTOR CAR COMPANY (B)

The following refers to the department described in the Cadillac Motor Car Company problem, page 328.

Rearrangement of the machines in one section of the connecting-rod department permitted operation of that section with 17 men instead of the 27 used with the old arrangement. The new layout also eliminated several machines, reduced required floor space 40 per cent, and decreased substantially the amount of work in process at any one time. Production of the section, in pieces per hour, was slightly reduced. Individual production of each worker, however, was considerably increased, and this fact caused a material reduction in production costs even though the rate of output was slightly decreased.

Assume that the change in equipment layout in the section here described resulted in a 10 per cent decrease in the total monthly burden costs of the department.[7] Assume that, in the past, burden had been charged to lots of parts going through the section at the rate of 140 per cent of direct labor costs charged to the lot. Assume that as a result of the change in layout the burden rate was increased from 140 to 205 per cent of direct labor costs.

Was such a change in burden rate justified? Explain.

[7] All figures used in this paragraph are purely hypothetical.

## Problem 58

## HUB MOTOR CAR COMPANY

John Bracken wished to buy a used automobile. After shopping around among used-car dealers he found a four-year-old Packard at the Hub Motor Car Company that seemed to be what he wanted. A salesman demonstrated the car for him and said that the car was in first-class mechanical condition except that the overdrive with which it was equipped did not work. The price of the car was $1,050. The salesman said that he would have the overdrive replaced but in that event the price would be $1,095; the additional $45 was the regular standard price for replacing an overdrive unit. Mr. Bracken was not interested in the overdrive. Although the salesman was willing to guarantee that Mr. Bracken would never have any trouble from the defective overdrive if it were left just as it was, Mr. Bracken decided that he did not wish to take that chance. He offered to buy the car for $1,050, provided that the Hub Motor Car Company would remove the overdrive unit completely.

The overdrive could be removed from the car readily. It would take a mechanic five hours to do the work; no new parts or materials would be required. The Hub company had a standard service charge of $3 per hour for all repair work. This covered all costs (except parts which were charged separately) and included a profit for the company. The $3 was based on cost records which the company had built up over a period of time and which the management was convinced were accurate. The Hub company paid its mechanics straight day wages, $10 for an eight-hour day. The men worked on repair jobs as they were assigned to them by the shop foreman.

When Mr. Bracken offered to buy the car, with the overdrive removed, for $1,050, the salesman went to the repair shop. He learned from the shop foreman that the standard charge for removing the unit would be $15. This included $6.25 for labor, $6.25 for burden and general administrative expense, and $2.50 profit. He also was told that the foreman had three good mechanics in the shop who were doing nothing at the time. When work was slack, the foreman did not lay off his men temporarily. Good mechanics were hard to get, and there were times when the shop was so busy that the foreman wished he had several more mechanics than he had. The foreman would be glad to put a mechanic to work removing the overdrive unit at once. He did not like to have his men idle about the shop.

The salesman went to the sales manager and told him that Mr. Bracken would buy the Packard if the company would remove the overdrive. The sales manager refused to do this unless Mr. Bracken would pay an additional $15, the standard charge for the work. He pointed out that considering existing price levels $1,050 was a relatively low price for the car. The Hub Motor Car Company never cut prices on its cars and did not bargain on price with customers. The salesman told the sales manager of the situation in the repair shop but the latter still refused the salesman's request, saying that he was unwilling to take less profit on the car than he would get from the sale of the car for $1,050 in its present condition. The salesman was unable to convince his superior that he should accept Mr. Bracken's offer.

Who was right, the salesman or the sales manager? Explain.

### Problem 59

### SCARRELL COMPANY

The wide variety of miscellaneous metal products manufactured by the Scarrell Company included a small patented part used in automobile assembly. This unit was a very profitable item. Company salesmen had persuaded six large automobile manufacturers and a number of smaller ones to incorporate it in their products. Demand for this part expanded to a point where it was evident to the production executives of the Scarrell Company that promised deliveries could not be made on time unless approximately 25 per cent more crimping capacity was made available. After examining the possibilities in this direction, the engineering department recommended that the ratchet-dial assembly press used in crimping the two sections of this unit together should be fitted with a semiautomatic feed, which would increase its capacity by approximately two-thirds. This fixture could be made in a few days in the company's own machine shop at a total cost of $67.50.

The Scarrell Company sold these patented parts to automobile manufacturers on the basis of annual contracts under which purchasers agreed to buy within a year specified minimum numbers of units to be delivered as called for. The Scarrell Company agreed, on its part, to supply all its customers' requirements during the terms of the contracts. Although the purchasers attempted to give as much advance notice of their needs as possible, they occasionally asked for immediate delivery. Demand was markedly seasonal; as much as one-third of annual deliveries sometimes had been made in a single month.

Under the existing production methods, the operator of the ratchet-dial assembly press fed into the press by hand the two sections which were to be crimped. If the fixture recommended by the engineering department was installed, one part would be fed in automatically from a hopper; the other would still be fed in by hand. This would permit changing the pulley ratio, which would speed up the rotating crimping die, and would result in an increase in the standard hourly output of the press from 2,500 units an hour to 4,167 units an hour. The operator, who was paid on a piece-rate basis, would probably continue to exceed standard output by approximately 30 per cent after he became accustomed to the change in procedure.

The engineering department reported that, if the semiautomatic feed was installed, unit costs of the crimping operation would be reduced 40 per cent as follows:

|  | Cost of Crimping Operation per 1,000 units | |
|---|---|---|
|  | Hand Feed | Semiautomatic Feed |
| Labor........................ | $0.20 | $0.12 |
| Overhead (150% of Labor)....... | 0.30 | 0.18 |
|  | $0.50 | $0.30 |

The cost of the fixture, which could be made up without delay by the permanent staff of the company's machine shop, was estimated as follows:

| | |
|---|---:|
| Labor.................................. | $35.00 |
| Materials.............................. | 15.00 |
| Overhead (50% of Labor)............... | 17.50 |
| | $67.50 |

The ratchet-dial assembly press assigned to the production of this small automobile part was currently being operated on a single-shift basis, although some of the company's equipment was being operated in two or even three shifts. The output of this press could therefore be increased by operating it in two shifts. Moreover, any one of several ratchet-dial assembly presses which were standing idle in the company's plant could be converted to the crimping of this part by expenditure of $60 for dies. If either of these alternative methods was adopted, the semiautomatic feed would not be required to meet deliveries.

Should the recommendation of the engineering department be carried out?

# CHAPTER XXV

## BUDGETARY CONTROL

### GENERAL ELECTRIC COMPANY

**1. An Example of Modern Methods of Budgetary Cost Control.**

The General Electric Company operated 11 plants. These plants were organized into a total of 250 departments, 175 of which served and facilitated the work of the 75 departments that actually made the products sold by the company. Manufacturing expense in this huge organization amounted to half a million dollars a week and obviously called for the most careful control. This necessary control was exercised by executives who relied in large measure upon information furnished them by a budgetary system which emphasized the need of flexibility to meet the requirements of fluctuations in volume.

**2. Nature of Production Costs.** Production costs may be classified for purposes of executive control into three types: raw materials, direct labor, and burden. Burden, in turn, may be subdivided into indirect labor, indirect materials and supplies, and fixed charges. Although burden in total is less affected by changes in volume of production than are raw materials and direct labor costs, different items of burden cost are variously affected by changes in volume. For example, depreciation on equipment ordinarily bears little relation to volume, while wages of hourly paid subforemen often are as variable as direct labor; between these extremes are a wide variety of items, such as wages of production and cost clerks.

**3. Management Control of Costs.** There are two common management attitudes toward control of production costs. First, there are those managers who believe that if production is carried on, costs are inevitable, and therefore careful practice of economy and efficiency during the production period will result in costs as low as possible under the circumstances. Results obtained can be determined only upon the expiration of the operating period, when costs can be compiled and compared with income, and profit or loss results ascertained. In many cases, this is the method and extent of control exercised by management over costs of production.

The other philosophy of cost control emphasizes the assumption that in considerable degree costs will be what management makes them. Study of the nature of production costs shows that various items are affected differently by changes in production load. Study of individual items of production cost reveals that within certain ranges of volume the effect of volume change upon cost items is under managerial control. Case studies of management policy and activity demonstrate that many factors other than change in volume influence costs. Product design, line make-up, scheduling practices, and plant layout are such matters. One must conclude, therefore, that sound management dictates the desirability of accepting the philosophy that costs are what management makes them.

If costs are in considerable degree under the control of management, it becomes incumbent upon executives to preplan costs, to control operations in terms of plans, and to accept responsibility for variations of actual from forecast results. This responsibility has long been recognized, and the procedure adopted to facilitate the discharge of the function is known as budgeting.

**4. Budgeting.** Budgeting control embraces three main activities: planning of results, continuous comparison of actual with estimated figures, and executive action resulting from consideration and comparison of estimated and actual costs. Budgeting is widely applied, as in the following:

Manufacturing operations budgets
Raw materials budgets
Labor budgets
Manufacturing expense or burden budgets
Equipment or plant investment budgets
Sales budgets
Financial budgets

Budgeting procedure usually starts with drawing up a sales budget, which gives the physical output expected. This is followed by a manufacturing budget made up of individual budgets for raw materials, labor, and expense. These may be simple estimates or complex, depending on conditions of operation, size of the business, nature of the business, and other factors.

Such budgets also may be static or variable. The former give a cross section of average expected results, while variable budgets make allowance for adjustment to variable volumes of production. The theory of the variable budget can be applied to any of the elements that go to make up costs.

Following is an example of a static weekly budget as applied to a small shop employing a superintendent, two salaried foremen, three subforemen, one methods man, ten service employees, two maintenance men, nine clerks (five salaried), and three inspectors.

| | | |
|---|---|---|
| Raw Materials (detailed)............................... | | $3,154.00 |
| Direct Labor: | | |
| 25 × 50¢ per hour × 36 hours............... | $ 450.00 | |
| 50 × 60¢ per hour × 36 hours............... | 1,080.00 | |
| 25 × 80¢ per hour × 36 hours............... | 720.00 | |
| Total Direct Labor............................. | | 2,250.00 |
| Indirect Labor: | | |
| 1 Superintendent, 40 hours................. | $ 78.00 | |
| 2 Salaried Foremen, 40 hours each.......... | 100.00 | |
| 3 Subforemen, 36 hours each at 80¢........ | 86.00 | |
| 1 Methods Man, 40 hours.................. | 47.00 | |
| 10 Service Employees at 50¢, 36 hours each... | 180.00 | |
| 2 Maintenance Men at 60¢, 40 hours each... | 48.00 | |
| 9 Clerks (5 salaried), 3 at 80¢, 1 at 40¢...... | 290.00 | |
| 3 Inspectors............................. | 75.00 | |
| Total Indirect Labor........................... | | 904.00 |
| Power, Heat, and Light........................... | | 393.00 |
| Supplies........................................ | | 106.00 |
| Other Expenses.................................. | | 78.00 |
| Fixed Charges, Depreciation, etc.................. | | 735.00 |
| Total Cost to Manufacture........................ | | $7,620.00 |

These figures are set on the basis of expected volume and past experience as to costs, with consideration given to any anticipated changes. A quarterly or annual budget could be built up from the weekly budget.  If seasonal changes or other influences affect the expected rate of operation, it is desirable to adjust items in the weekly budget to take into account such influences.

A static budget of the type illustrated above is satisfactory only as long as the volume manufactured remains in the vicinity of the estimate upon which the budget was calculated.  If volume should increase or decrease materially, this measuring stick would not be adequate.  This shortcoming would be felt as soon as one attempted to prepare a quarterly or annual budget from the weekly figures, since a steady weekly load is uncommon to most departments, shops, or plants.  The reason for inadequacy of the static budget is of course to be found in the nature of cost items and their characteristic reactions to volume changes.

**5. Effect of Volume Change on Cost—the Profitgraph.**[1] From the standpoint of the effect of volume load on costs of manufacture, costs are often classified as fixed, or nonvariable, and variable, but realism necessitates a reclassification into fixed, variable, and partly variable or semivariable costs.

According to this classification, variable costs are those which vary directly and continuously as volume changes.  Semivariable costs, on the other hand, are those which are influenced by changes in the volume of production but do not vary continuously as volume changes.  In a department where piece rates prevail, increase in volume results in proportionate increase in direct labor costs.  These costs go up or down in proportion as volume increases or decreases unless some change is made in piece rates or processing.  Cost of departmental supervision does not fluctuate so automatically with output change.  This item of cost is influenced by volume, however, although not continuously.  If production increases to such a point that the department foreman is overloaded, he may be given an assistant.  Should volume fall to a very low point, the foreman may spend most of his time at some direct labor job within the department, his compensation as foreman being reduced.  It is seen, therefore, that departmental supervision is a cost which varies with changes in rate of operation but does not vary continuously.  Changes in the item

[1] See C. E. Knoeppel, *Profit Engineering*, McGraw-Hill Book Company, Inc., New York, 1933.

will be brought about as a result of management action, the amount of the changes and the time of their becoming effective being under the control of management.

Adding or dropping a shift causes substantial changes in semi-variable costs. The result is illustrated in Exhibit 1. The time when such a change is made will in large degree determine the form of the cost curve in relation to volume of output. Actually a cost curve at varying volumes of production is likely to assume the form shown in Exhibit 1. The sales line is added on the assumption that the volume sold equals the volume produced.

It should be noted in connection with Exhibit 1 that fixed costs

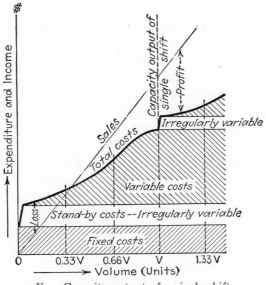

$V$ = Capacity output of a single shift.

EXHIBIT 1. COST CURVE AT VARYING VOLUMES OF PRODUCTION.

are those costs which would still be experienced in the event of complete temporary shutdown. When the department or plant is put into operation, a jump in costs is experienced which bears little relation to initial volume of operation. It represents the difference in costs between shutdown and minimum operation. These costs are characterized as "stand-by costs." They are variable but in an irregular way.

It also should be noted that such sudden jumps in costs may be experienced at other points in the production scale. The jump experienced when volume is increased beyond single-shift capacity represents a new series of stand-by costs resulting from the additional shift. Items such as salaried foremen, found among the initial stand-by costs, are characteristic of the costs incurred when a second shift is added.

The character of the total curve between the points of 33 per cent and 100 per cent of one-shift operation is important. The regularity of increase within that range suggests the practical possibility of assuming that for normal volumes variation in costs is directly proportionate to volume change.

Projection of the sales line graphically displays the important part which volume of operation plays in the making of profits or losses.

Obviously, budgetary estimates should be prepared so as to make possible anticipation of results at varying volumes and judgment of actual results at whatever volume is finally experienced. In other words, the variable budget recognizes the fallibility of sales estimates and makes control possible even though volume varies.

**6. Practice and Experience of the General Electric Company.**[2] The General Electric Company developed a uniform procedure for cost control for its 11 widely separated plants. In these plants were 250 departments, 75 of which made the products the company sold. These products varied from massive apparatus which required months in process to items produced at the rate of thousands daily. Facilitating the work of the 75 production departments were 175 departments which rendered a variety of services.

Costs were controlled for each department separately. The method used was the variable straight-line budget, *i.e.*, one prepared for varying volumes. The assumption was made that costs generally varied directly with volume changes. Departmental expenses, or burden, were budgeted separately from depart-

---

[2] Exhibits 2, 3, 5, and 6, together with certain other material in this case, were adapted by permission from F. V. Gardner, "The Variable Budget," *Factory Management and Maintenance*, February and March, 1934.

mental labor and raw materials costs. As the principles involved in all three types were similar and factory expense was the most difficult of control, methods and practices of burden control only will be discussed here.

Use of departmental budgets fixed responsibility and furnished a basis for rewarding accomplishment. Departmental budgets were periodically consolidated into works budgets for purposes of control by senior executives and for comparing results of the different plants.

Exhibit 2, page 592, is an example of the form of tabulation used as a basis for drawing up the variable departmental expense budgets which are illustrated later.

Detailed direct labor costs are given for three different loads, one for 30 hours of operation and two for 36 hours. Load 1 (30 hours) involves 2,710 hours of direct labor at a cost of $1,690; load 2 (36 hours) involves 3,600 hours of direct labor costing $2,250; and load 3 (36 hours) involves 4,430 hours of direct labor at a cost of $2,800. These direct labor loads correspond, of course, to certain production volumes.

Nonproductive labor, indirect material and other expense, and fixed charges constitute the departmental burden, all items of which are calculated in detail for no load, 30-hour load, and the two 36-hour load bases.

For adequate control of expense in this department it was considered necessary to prepare for loads ranging from a low of approximately $1,700 to a high of $2,800. The three static budgets, marked loads 1, 2, and 3, were set up to cover this range. By relating the low, mean, and high activity points it was possible to develop a control which would measure any range of activity between them. Examination of loads 1 and 3 shows differences between most of the corresponding items. Except for "Superintendent" all items in load 3 are greater than corresponding items in load 1. The spread in load between 1 and 3 is $1,110 ($2,800 − $1,690 = $1,110). For this $1,110 of load spread there is a variation in indirect labor of $291; a variation in total operating expense of $534; and a difference in total burden (manufacturing expense) of $548. For each dollar of load change there is a total burden variation of $0.494.

## EXHIBIT 2
### General Electric Company
Details of Indirect Expenses of Department 861 for Three Conditions of Direct Labor Load

| Function | No Load Basis | | 30-hour Load Basis — Load 1 | | | 36-hour Load Basis — Load 2 | | | Load 3 | | |
|---|---|---|---|---|---|---|---|---|---|---|---|
| | Actual Fixed at Zero | Theoretical or Mathematical Fixed at Zero | No. of Employees | Total Hours | Take-home Pay | No. of Employees | Total Hours | Take-home Pay | No. of Employees | Total Hours | Take-home Pay |
| Total Productive Operatives | 0 | 0 | 90 | 2,710 | $1,690 | 100 | 3,600 | $2,250 | 125 | 4,430 | $2,800 |
| **Nonproductive Expense Labor:** | | | | | | | | | | | |
| Superintendent | $ 50 | $ 78 | 1 | | $ 78 | 1 | | $ 78 | 1 | | $ 78 |
| Salaried Foremen | | 68 | 2 | | 90 | 2 | | 96 | 2 | | 104 |
| Hourly Foremen | | 30 | 3 | | 72 | 3 | | 85 | 3½ | | 99 |
| Methods Men | | | 1 | | 35 | 1 | | 51 | 1½ | | 60 |
| Service Employees | | | | | | | | | | | |
| Helpers | | | 5 | | | 5 | | | 6 | | |
| Stockkeepers | 60 | 60 | 3 | | 166 | 3 | | 202 | 3 | | 237 |
| Others | | | 2 | | | 2 | | | 3 | | |
| Maintenance | 28 | 28 | | | 43 | 2 | | 48 | 2 | | 53 |
| Clerical | | | | | | | | | | | |
| Shop Clerks | | | 3 | | | 3 | | | 3 | | |
| Cost Clerks | 30 | 85 | 2 | | 240 | 2 | | 290 | 2 | | 340 |
| Other Clerks | | | 3 | | | 4 | | | 5 | | |
| Inspectors | | | 3 | | 68 | 3 | | 90 | 3 | | 112 |
| Total Nonproductive Labor | $168 | $ 349 | 28 | | $ 792 | 31 | | $ 940 | 35 | | $1,083 |
| **Materials and Other Expenses** | | | | | | | | | | | |
| Miscellaneous Shop Material | $ 15 | $ 15 | | | $ 85 | | | $ 105 | | | $ 127 |
| Power, Heat, and Light | 47 | 47 | | | 307 | | | 390 | | | 475 |
| Other Operating Expense | | | | | 52 | | | 68 | | | 85 |
| Total Operating Expense | $230 | $ 411 | | | $1,236 | | | $1,503 | | | $1,770 |
| Fixed Charges | $706 | $ 706 | | | $ 728 | | | $ 735 | | | $ 742 |
| Total Manufacturing Expense | $936 | $1,117 | 28 | | $1,964 | 31 | | $2,238 | 35 | | $2,512 |
| Per Cent Nonproductive Labor to Productive Labor | Infinite | Infinite | | | 47 | | | 42 | | | 39 |
| Per Cent Total Manufacturing Expense to Productive Labor | Infinite | Infinite | | | 116 | | | 99 | | | 90 |

A corresponding relationship can be found for each item of expense by comparing the change in the item with the load change. The item "Service Employees" amounts to $166 at $1,690 load and $237 at $2,800 load. The increase, $71, when compared with the load change, $1,110, gives a variable of $0.064 per dollar of load change. If the same calculation is made for each burden item, the sum of the variables computed will be equal to the total, $0.494, previously calculated for total expense.

If on a chart a line passing through the three load points is projected to zero load, it will cut the expense scale at $1,117. That amount ($1,117) is shown in Exhibit 2 as total manufacturing expense in the Theoretical column of the budget based on no load. By similar projections or application of the variations per dollar of load already computed, theoretical no-load figures can be determined for all individual expense items, the total of which will, of course, be equal to the $1,117 figure just calculated for total manufacturing burden. This figure represents the fixed costs plus the stand-by costs shown in the diagram in Exhibit 1, the graphic representation of a flexible budget. In Exhibit 1, the amount representing the sum of fixed and stand-by costs at minimum load was not determined by the projection of the load cost line. It was set by careful estimate of costs at minimum load in the manner described in the following paragraph.

The cost figures in the Theoretical column in Exhibit 2 do not exactly correspond to the figures in the Actual column, since the latter figures were estimated from experience just as were the figures in the Load 1, Load 2, and Load 3 columns. The difference represents certain management actions taken in view of an abnormal situation. It appears that the superintendent's salary was reduced from $78 to $50 a week and that the salaried foreman, the hourly foreman, and two clerks were laid off. The department could still operate if business was available. The exact point between zero load and $1,690 load at which such executive action was taken is not shown. It is important to know that such action was taken at some load level within this area, and it was important to keep that situation before the executives who were responsible for initiation of the changes. The purpose was to ensure definite consideration. In practice, the changes indicated might have taken place all at once, but they were more likely to have been initiated individually as operating conditions and urgency of the times dictated. Such items are the costs heretofore referred to as being irregularly variable.

**7. Summary of Principles Employed by the General Electric Company in Cost Control.** The basis of the cost control system of the General Electric Company was the departmental budget. This budget was broken down to isolate types of costs, of which the expense, or burden, budget was an example. The method adopted was the straight-line variable budget which was based on the assumption that within common load areas variable burden costs varied directly with load as represented by direct labor costs.

For typical direct labor loads, static budgets were drawn up, and individual items were related to the totals of these loads to calculate the amount of change for individual items per dollar of load change and total expenses per dollar of load change. By application of these change rates to individual items a budget for any load within the area could be quickly set up and used for comparison with actual costs at the load experienced. In addition, by use of the change rates theoretical no-load costs could be computed, including both fixed costs at shutdown and stand-by costs. Stand-by costs could be estimated on the same basis as were the original static budget costs at different load levels. Stand-by costs so calculated seldom coincided with theoretical stand-by costs resulting from the application of change rates. The differences, which represented management activity, were used to place before executives the need of considering taking such action. The point at which such action was taken was determined by the executives responsible for the changes.

**8. Typical General Electric Operating Department Expense Control.** In the General Electric Company some $500,000 of weekly burden cost was controlled by means of departmental expense budgets. The exact form of control adopted in each department depended somewhat on conditions in the department. In every instance, however, the principles employed were those just explained and summarized. A typical setup for control in an operating department follows in Exhibit 3.

## EXHIBIT 3
### General Electric Company
### A Typical Operating Department Setup for Control

| Account | Present Full-time Take-home Pay | | | Fixed Indirect Expense | | | | | | | | | Total Expense at $3,000 Direct Labor | | | Variable Portion | |
|---|---|---|---|---|---|---|---|---|---|---|---|---|---|---|---|---|---|
| | | | | From $0 to $750 Direct Labor | | | From $751 to $1,500 Direct Labor | | | From $1,501 to $3,000 Direct Labor | | | | | | | |
| | No. of Persons | Hours per Person | Dollars | No. of Persons | Hours per Person | Dollars | No. of Persons | Hours per Person | Dollars | No. of Persons | Hours per Person | Dollars | No. of Persons | Hours per Person | Dollars | Amount, Dollars | Dollars per Dollar of Direct Labor |
| Foremen—Salaried | 3 | 40 | $131.84 | 2 | 40 | $ 83.66 | 2 | 40 | $ 83.66 | 3 | 40 | $131.84 | 3 | 40 | $ 131.84 | | |
| Foremen—Hourly | 11 | 37½ | 328.95 | | | | | | | | | | 11 | 37½ | 328.95 | $ 328.95 | $0.1096 |
| Inspectors | 2 | 35 | 42.13 | | | | | | | | | | 2 | 35 | 42.13 | 42.13 | 0.0140 |
| Elevator and Crane Operatives | 2 | 35 | 28.70 | | | | | | | | | | 2 | 35 | 28.70 | 28.70 | 0.0096 |
| Stockkeepers and Helpers | 8 | 35 | 138.00 | | | | | | | | | | 8 | 35 | 138.00 | 138.00 | 0.0460 |
| Service Employees | 9 | 35 | 137.50 | | | | | | | | | | 9 | 35 | 137.50 | 137.50 | 0.0458 |
| Production Clerks | | | | | | | | | | | | | | | | | |
|   1 Supervisor | 1 | 40 } | 98.35 | 1 | 36 } | 58.60 | 1 | 40 } | 70.35 | 1 | 40 } | 98.35 | 3 | 40 | 98.35 | | |
|   2 Clerks | 2 | 40 } | | 1 | 32 } | | 1 | 40 } | | 2 | 40 } | | | | | | |
| Cost Clerks | | | | | | | | | | | | | | | | | |
|   Supervisor | 1 | 40 } | 70.86 | 1 | 36 } | 59.02 | 1 | 40 } | 70.86 | 1 | 40 } | 70.86 | 1 | 40 | 70.86 | | |
|   Clerk | 1 | 40 } | | 1 | 32 } | | 1 | 40 } | | 1 | 40 } | | | | | | |
| Shop Stock Clerk | 1 | 40 | 15.00 | | | | | | | | | | 1 | 40 | 15.00 | 15.00 | 0.0050 |
| Shop Clerk | 1 | 40 | 15.00 | | | | | | | | | | 1 | 40 | 15.00 | 15.00 | 0.0050 |
| Production Followers | 1 | 40 | 60.40 | | | | | | | | | | 1 | 40 | 60.40 | 60.40 | 0.0201 |
| Maintenance | 2 | 40 | 40.00 | | | | | | | | | | 2 | 40 | 40.00 | 40.00 | 0.0133 |
| Other Labor | 2 | 35 | 26.00 | | | | | | | | | | 2 | 35 | 26.00 | 26.00 | 0.0087 |
| Indirect Labor | | | $1,132.73 | | | $ 201.28 | | | $ 224.87 | | | $ 301.05 | | | $1,132.73 | $ 831.68 | $0.2771 |
| Shop Supplies | | | 340.00 | | | 50.00 | | | 50.00 | | | 50.00 | | | 340.00 | 290.00 | 0.0967 |
| Maintenance Material | | | 104.00 | | | 40.00 | | | 40.00 | | | 40.00 | | | 104.00 | 64.00 | 0.0213 |
| Other Material | | | 68.00 | | | | | | | | | | | | 68.00 | 68.00 | 0.0027 |
| Total Controllable | | | $1,644.73 | | | $ 291.28 | | | $ 314.87 | | | $ 391.05 | | | $1,644.73 | $1,253.68 | $0.4178 |
| Fixed Expense | | | 1,200.00 | | | 1,200.00 | | | 1,200.00 | | | 1,200.00 | | | 1,200.00 | 1,253.68 | |
| Total Expense | | | $2,844.73 | | | $1,491.28 | | | $1,514.87 | | | $1,591.05 | | | $2,844.73 | $1,253.68 | $0.42 |

In the first column at the left (Account) are listed the items of expense found in that department. In the following column are given figures which represent conditions in the department at the time the weekly budget was made up. These figures include number of people, hours per person, and dollars of cost for each item. Costs other than indirect labor are, of course, given in dollars only.

In the next three columns are detailed all variable items of cost that did not vary constantly and directly with load change. These are given for three load ranges: from $0.00 direct labor to $750 direct labor, from $751 direct labor to $1,500 direct labor, and from $1,501 direct labor to $3,000 direct labor. Items in these columns include costs labeled in Exhibit 1 as stand-by costs as well as other expenses for which variations were controlled as to time and amount through executive action. In this department the points at which such management action was expected are indicated by the figures in the three columns.

In the next column to the right are detailed all expense items at the maximum load shown in the preceding column. In this instance, this load, $3,000 of direct labor, was the load at the time the weekly budget was set up. In the last column to the right is given the variable portion of each item of expense which experience had shown varied constantly and directly with load change. The amount of variation of each item per dollar of load change is also shown.

As the department load changed during succeeding weeks, budgets for the loads experienced could be quickly prepared from this control tabulation. Variable expenses could be calculated by multiplying the cents of expense per dollar of load by the number of dollars of the new load. Costs that did not vary directly with load change could be read from the table. Fixed costs were added, and in that way a detailed standard was prepared. Comparison of actual costs with budget costs at the actual load were thus possible, and afforded a basis for management control of expense items in the department.

Exhibit 4 is a weekly departmental budget for a load of $2,250 direct labor cost compiled from the standard budget for $3,000 direct labor cost.

EXHIBIT 4

General Electric Company

Departmental Budget for Direct Labor Load of $2,250
Computed from Standard Budget for $3,000

| Account | Total Expense | | | Nonvariable Portion | | | Variable Portion | | Total Budgeted Expense at $2,250 Direct Labor Load | Actual Expense at $2,250 Direct Labor Load | Per Cent of Realization |
|---|---|---|---|---|---|---|---|---|---|---|---|
| | No. of Persons | Hrs. per Person | Dollars | No. | Hrs. | Dollars | Dollars | $ per Dollar Direct Labor | | | |
| Foremen—Salaried | 3 | 40 | $131.84 | 3 | 40 | $131.84 | | | $131.84 | $131.84 | 100 |
| Foremen—Hourly | 11 | 37½ | 328.95 | | | | $328.95 | $0.1096 | 246.60 | 278.55* | 89 |
| Inspectors | 2 | 35 | 42.13 | | | | 42.13 | 0.0140 | 31.50 | 32.65 | 96 |
| Elevator and Crane Operatives | 2 | 35 | 28.70 | | | | 28.70 | 0.0096 | 21.60 | 22.10 | 98 |
| Stockkeepers and Helpers | 8 | 35 | 138.00 | | | | 138.00 | 0.0460 | 103.50 | 112.30 | 92 |
| Service Employees | 9 | 35 | 137.50 | | | | 137.50 | 0.0458 | 103.05 | 99.50 | 104 |
| Production Clerks | 3 | 40 | 98.35 | 1⎫ 2⎭ | 40 40 | 98.35 | | | 98.35 | 102.35 | 96 |
|   1 Supervisor | | | | | | | | | | | |
|   2 Clerks | | | | | | | | | | | |
| Cost Clerks | | | | 1⎫ 1⎭ | 40 40 | | | | | | |
|   Supervisor | 1 | 40 | 70.86 | | | 70.86 | | | 70.86 | 75.65 | 94 |
|   Clerk | 1 | 40 | 15.00 | | | | 15.00 | 0.0050 | 11.25 | 11.25 | 100 |
| Shop Stock Clerk | 1 | 40 | 15.00 | | | | 15.00 | 0.0050 | 11.25 | 12.00 | 94 |
| Shop Clerk | 2 | 40 | 60.40 | | | | 60.40 | 0.0201 | 45.23 | 90.80† | 50 |
| Production Followers | 2 | 40 | 40.00 | | | | 40.00 | 0.0133 | 29.93 | 37.14 | 81 |
| Maintenance | 2 | 35 | 26.00 | | | | 26.00 | 0.0087 | 19.58 | 31.50 | 62 |
| Other Labor | | | | | | | | | | | |
| Total Indirect Labor | | | $1,132.73 | | | $301.05 | $831.68 | $0.2771 | $924.52 | $1,037.63 | 89 |
| Shop Supplies | | | 340.00 | | | 50.00 | 290.00 | 0.0967 | 50.00 / 217.57 | 50.30 / 213.20 | 99 / 102 |
| Maintenance Material | | | 104.00 | | | 40.00 | 64.00 | 0.0213 | 40.00 / 47.93 | 41.10 / 49.10 | 97 / 98 |
| Other Material | | | 68.00 | | | | 68.00 | 0.0227 | 51.08 | 47.30 | 108 |
| Total Controllable | | | $1,644.73 | | | $391.05 | $1,253.68 | $0.4178 | $1,331.10 | $1,438.63 | 93 |
| Fixed Expense | | | 1,200.00 | | | 1,200.00 | | | 1,200.00 | 1,207.20 | 99 |
| Total Expense | | | $2,844.73 | | | $1,591.05 | $1,253.68 | $0.42 | $2,536.05 | $2,645.83 | 96 |

* Two additional foremen required on spraying because of complaints of streaks in boxes; will take six or eight weeks.

† Additional expense necessary to install production control system; will require six weeks.

Exhibits 3 and 4 are typical of the control procedures of the 75 separate operating department expense budgets of the General Electric Company. Departmental expense budgets differed somewhat in form, but they were always based on the concepts already explained. In every instance the measure of load was direct labor cost, and the control incorporated a fixed allowance and a variable allowance in cents per dollar of productive load.

Use of common load basis for all departments permitted consolidation into totals, an important part of the plan. Exhibit 5 shows such a consolidation for one plant. Tabulations for all the plants were also summarized periodically. Exhibit 6 is an example.

**9. Summary and Conclusions.** *The Variable Budget as a Cost Control Device.* In considerable degree, costs are subject to managerial control. The extent to which management may currently influence costs depends in large measure on the nature of the cost items. Considered from this point of view, so-called fixed costs can usually be influenced indirectly by operating executives. In general, the extent to which cost economies may be devised, and the company thereby enabled to obtain a greater share of the business potentially available, limits the influence of the production executive over fixed costs. He cannot increase or decrease the costs themselves, but in whatever degree he is responsible for increased or decreased volume he can influence fixed costs per unit of product produced.

The operating executive's control over variable costs is frequently limited to indirect influences much as in the case of fixed costs. When piece rates are paid for labor, the unit labor cost does not change, the total cost practically automatically going up or down as volume increases or decreases. The production supervisor has greater opportunity to influence these costs indirectly than he does in the case of fixed costs. He may devise better methods of doing the work. As volume increases he may be able to schedule the work so as to keep operatives more continuously on one job and thereby be justified in reducing the piece rate. He may improve the workability of the materials with somewhat the same result. If time wages are paid, his opportunities and consequently his responsibility for labor produc-

## EXHIBIT 5

General Electric Company
Consolidated Budget for Indirect Labor for All Departments in One Plant
Compared with Actual Expenses

| Account | Week Ending Dec. 16 | | Week Ending Dec. 23 | | Jan. 1 to Date Accumulated Allowance |
|---|---|---|---|---|---|
| | Variable Budget | Actual Indirect Labor | Variable Budget | Actual Indirect Labor | |
| **Manufacturing** | | | | | |
| Winding.................. | $    57 | $    61 | $    62 | $    59 | $   188 * |
| Fourth Floor............. | 67 | 57 | 73 | 51 | 234 * |
| Fifth Floor.............. | 152 | 160 | 165 | 157 | 307 |
| Third Floor.............. | 275 | 293 | 298 | 307 | 79 * |
| Solenoid................. | 54 | 48 | 59 | 48 | 31 * |
| First Floor.............. | 292 | 298 | 316 | 390 | 463 * |
| Finishing................ | 105 | 127 | 114 | 116 | 107 * |
| Second Floor............. | 239 | 231 | 258 | 238 | 416 |
| Total Manufacturing.... | $1,241 | $1,275 | $1,345 | $1,366 | $   379 * |
| **Service Department** | | | | | |
| Test Inspection........... | $   567 | $   587 | $   614 | $   569 | $    93 |
| Salvage.................. | 54 | 66 | 58 | 58 | 17 * |
| Grounds—Buildings....... | 887 | 982 | 961 | 965 | 1,138 * |
| Power.................... | 144 | 148 | 144 | 157 | 29 * |
| Production............... | 2,198 | 2,219 | 2,381 | 2,234 | 306 * |
| Total Service.......... | $3,850 | $4,002 | $4,158 | $3,983 | $1,397 * |
| **Administrative** | | | | | |
| Warehouse................ | $   782 | $   813 | $   846 | $   822 | $    89 * |
| Personnel................ | 150 | 160 | 163 | 160 | 135 * |
| Payroll.................. | 715 | 755 | 774 | 758 | 319 * |
| Service.................. | 138 | 154 | 150 | 154 | 204 * |
| Wage Rate................ | 313 | 345 | 339 | 346 | 83 * |
| Management............... | 379 | 396 | 379 | 396 | 298 |
| Clerical................. | 717 | 768 | 777 | 779 | 641 * |
| Total Administrative.... | $3,194 | $3,391 | $3,428 | $3,415 | $1,173 * |
| Total for Works........... | $8,285 | $8,668 | $8,931 | $8,764 | $2,949 * |
| Direct Labor.............. | $8,231 | | $9,255 | | |
| Budget Realization.......... | | 95.6% | | 101.9% | |

* Deficit.

## EXHIBIT 6

### General Electric Company
Weekly Summary of Actual Direct and Indirect Labor and Budgeted Indirect Labor
for All Plants

| Works | Actual Week Ending Dec. 30 | | % In-direct to Direct Labor | Indirect Labor Variable Budget Amount | Indirect Labor | | | |
|---|---|---|---|---|---|---|---|---|
| | Direct Labor | In-direct Labor | | | % to Direct Labor | % of Realization | | % Aver-age, No-vem-ber |
| | | | | | | Dec. 30 | Dec. 23 | |
| Works 1... | $ 91.0 | $ 88.0 | 97 | $ 85.3 | 94 | 97 | 96 | 94 |
| Works 2... | 40.9 | 48.1 | 118 | 44.7 | 109 | 93 | 94 | 94 |
| Works 3... | 9.6 | 12.4 | 130 | 12.3 | 128 | 99 | 99 | 98 |
| Works 4... | 17.9 | 22.3 | 125 | 21.9 | 122 | 98 | 97 | 100 |
| Works 5... | 30.9 | 30.1 | 97 | 30.2 | 98 | 100 | 102 | 99 |
| Works 6... | 50.7 | 38.2 | 75 | 37.0 | 73 | 97 | · 95 | 95 |
| Works 7... | 7.8 | 8.4 | 108 | 8.1 | 104 | 96 | 96 | 97 |
| Works 8... | 29.0 | 21.8 | 75 | 22.6 | 78 | 104 | 102 | 102 |
| Works 9... | 10.1 | 13.5 | 134 | 12.9 | 128 | 96 | 94 | 93 |
| Works 10.. | .9 | .8 | 89 | .8 | 89 | 100 | 96 | 98 |
| Works 11.. | 6.8 | 6.2 | 91 | 5.9 | 87 | 95 | 97 | 93 |
| Total, All Works | $295.6 | $289.8 | 98 | $281.7 | 95 | 97 | 96 | 94 |

tivity are even greater than is the case if piece rates are paid. Management control of other variable costs follows lines rather similar to the situation in the case of direct labor.

Semivariable costs probably call for the exercise of even greater judgment than do typically variable or nonvariable costs. Control of semivariable costs must be effected in terms of output volume and volume change. The decision as to when changes in such costs should be brought about often requires far more discernment and judgment than does a decision as to the advisability of adding more direct workers, for example. To realize that a foreman has become overloaded or to judge the time when a foreman should be converted into a working boss requires a fine sense of management values and a perception of the results of change. Volume of output will exert some measure of control over semivariable costs, but not nearly so much as it does in the case of directly variable costs. The measure of good supervision is in great degree the extent to which the supervisor controls the elements of operation which are responsible for these irregularly variable costs.

Budgets can be a great help to the executive who seeks to control these costs for which he is responsible. Such budgets will be valuable to the extent that they are so planned as to conform to actual conditions and are then used as a means of measuring results and taking action. To this end it is obvious that budgetary procedure must reflect the differences in reaction of various costs to changes in rate of operation. The variable budget seems to be the means best suited to this purpose. The variable budget recognizes the fallibility of sales forecasts. It is arranged to provide a yardstick for cost measurement regardless of normal volume variation. It can be made to emphasize the differences in effects of volume on variable, semivariable, and fixed costs. A budget which does these things can be most helpful to an executive who understands the purposes and use of budgets in control of costs.

*Experience of the General Electric Company.* Such has been the experience of the General Electric Company in the development and utilization of expense control. In the words of Mr. F. V. Gardner of that company, "Expense is only the measure of a supervisor's ability in rendering service: in obtaining quantity and quality production and keeping promises. Successful expense control involves three fundamentals: sound conception, simplicity, and reduction of lags." These principles form the basis of the variable budget procedure of the General Electric Company.

*Sound Conception.* In the General Electric Company, expense control costs are always meticulously preplanned, "blueprinted," for every normal circumstance under which these costs will be experienced. The detailed operating department setup given in Exhibit 3 exemplifies this principle.

*Simplicity.* Exhibit 4 shows the clarity and lack of complication of the departmental budget. This table shows details for the department and the character of every item and the amount which it should be under given circumstances. Actual results are set forth simply side by side with the yardstick against which they are measured, and the results of such measurement, the degree of the supervisor's accomplishment, is given. Whenever results depart substantially from the blueprint, reasons must be given for such failure by the executive responsible, the department supervisor. In Exhibit 4, two such instances are explained by footnotes which detail the expense involved, causes for the realization failure, and probable length of time required to bring the item back into line. Throughout the complete control procedure, and particularly at all points of contact with personnel, simplicity in the interest of clarity is the keynote. The use of direct labor hours as a measurement of load is an example of this. There are undoubtedly instances in so huge and diverse an organization in which some other volume index would seem preferable. However, through adherence to the one basis of measurement, simplicity is fostered in at least two ways. Use of direct labor hours as an index of load is universally understandable, and, as has been pointed out, provides a simple basis for consolidating departmental budgets into larger units and makes possible departmental and plant comparisons. Probably no characteristic is more essential to success in expense control than simplicity in conception and form.

*Reduction of Lags.* The necessity of eliminating time lags in securing actual figures is self-evident. The extent to which this has been done in the General Electric Company plan is in large measure responsible for the cost reductions that have been accomplished. First, it is important to note that the departmental budgets are weekly budgets. Then, much attention has been given the problem of making the reports which show degree of realization of the budget promptly available to departmental supervisors. In this way accomplishment and failure are quickly known and brought to the attention of the individual responsible. For example, failures to take action on semivariable costs at the times indicated by load area changes such as are shown in Exhibit 3 for Fixed Indirect Expense items become quickly known and can be rectified before they seriously affect expense totals. Likewise, display of exceptional judgment in the control of such costs instantly shows up in terms of dollars and cents. It has long been recognized that all too frequently cost accounting systems have failed to bring about the expected results because of a time lag between the performance and availability of knowledge of performance. The importance of preventing such time lag is even more essential to successful control of expense by means of the variable budget.

*Effectiveness of the Variable Expense Budget.* Given sound conception, simplicity, and elimination of lag, education of the executive force in cost control will produce highly satisfactory results. These results will evidence themselves in departmental cost figures. Even more graphically are they seen if their effect on the total cost line in Exhibit 1 is studied. It has been the experience of the General Electric Company that expense control has not only lowered this curve throughout its entirety but it has also effected a substantial straightening of the curve. This result is, of course, of great importance, and at first thought might seem surprising. When one considers, however, certain aspects of variable budget control, the inevitableness of such an outcome becomes more apparent. In the first place, the budgeting of costs in advance of their incurrence naturally focuses attention on undesirable highs. Such spotlighting makes possible remedial action. Thus irregularities tend to disappear, total costs rise and fall more uniformly with volume fluctuation, and unit costs become more stable. As the curve straightens, the angle of slope will naturally become the focus of executive attention, particularly in relation to its point of reading on the expenditures scale at minimum operating volume. In this latter matter, General Electric Company executives have found it possible to accomplish much. It is interesting to note that in the manufacture of certain lines of product it has become possible to pass from one-shift to two-shift operation, or vice versa, with almost no jump or drop in the total cost curve at point of change.

In the average business the potentialities of cost control seem hardly to have been tapped. The manufacturing operations of the General Electric Company are carried on in several plants. Some of these are large, some are small, and the products turned out are varied. If a single, uniform procedure for expense control can be worked out to apply to this diverse group, it would seem that in the average, less complicated business, the possibilities of getting somewhat comparable results would be great.

## QUESTIONS

1. Department 112, in common with other departments of the plant, operated under the variable budget system. For several weeks it had been operating with a direct labor load of $3,000 per month. The detailed expense budget of Department 112 at that rate of operation is shown in Exhibit 3 of the case. The department superintendent had been notified that characteristic seasonal dullness would necessitate substantial curtailment of operations in Department 112 and that the direct labor load for the ensuing week would be $1,400.

Using the data shown in Exhibit 3, page 595, prepare an expense budget for Department 112 for a direct labor load of $1,400. Use of the form shown in Exhibit 4, page 597, will be helpful.

2. In the General Electric Company budgetary program, responsibility for getting the results outlined in the budget was placed squarely upon the supervisor in charge of the department. Department 112 had been operating for some time at a load level of $3,000 direct labor cost. In anticipation of seasonal dullness, rate of operation of Department 112 was to be reduced to a direct labor load of $1,400 with the expectation that the department would operate at or around that rate for six to eight weeks, after which activity was expected to increase gradually.

Assume that you are the department supervisor, and that you have been notified to put your department on a $1,400 direct labor load the following week and have been furnished with the department budget for that figure. Using the budget you worked out in question 1, prepare a statement outlining in detail whatever action you believe should be taken to meet the budget requirement of Department 112.

## LARKIN FOUNDRY COMPANY

The Larkin Foundry Company, located about 60 miles from Gadsden, Alabama, produced an extensive line of high-quality ranges, cookstoves, heaters, and parlor furnaces, ranging in price from $2 to $120. These products were sold direct to retailers by the company's own salesmen in 10 Southern states. The company was organized in 1919, and the quality of its products had become favorably known. The line consisted of over 90 models, many of which incorporated patented features. The management of the company planned an operating budget for 1949 on the basis of increased volume and value of output over the two preceding years.

The Larkin Foundry Company was organized and incorporated in 1919 with an authorized capital stock of $50,000. Later the charter was amended to increase capital stock to $100,000. Officers of the company were the president, vice-president, manager and treasurer, and secretary. Active management of the business was in the hands of the manager-treasurer, who also held financial control of the corporation.

The Larkin Foundry Company manufactured for stock. There were three operating departments: foundry and cleaning, nickeling, and mounting. The foundry and cleaning department was equipped with a cupola for melting pig iron and with the necessary molding equipment. The molders were highly skilled. Exceptionally good workers were employed in this department, since otherwise much labor would have been required to grind and machine parts in preparation for mounting. By employing only highly skilled union molders [3] and paying high wages, it was possible to produce castings which required a minimum of drilling and grinding to prepare them for assembly. So successful had been the policy of high-quality output in the foundry that no grinding department was maintained. Whatever fitting was found necessary in assembly was done by the mounters on grind-

[3] There were four other stove manufacturers in the vicinity and 25 in the Southern territory. None of them employed union workers, and none of them paid such high wages as did the Larkin Foundry Company.

EXHIBIT 1

Larkin Foundry Company

Comparative Statement of Income, Profit and Loss, 1943, 1947, and 1948, with Estimates for 1949

| | 1943 Actual | 1943 % of Net Sales | 1947 Actual | 1947 % of Net Sales | 1948 Actual | 1948 % of Net Sales | 1949 Estimated | 1949 % of Net Sales | % of Increase, 1949 Estimated Over 1948 Actual |
|---|---|---|---|---|---|---|---|---|---|
| Gross Sales | | | $92,509.18 | 101.66 | $208,271.12 | 100.69 | $275,308.36 | 100.60 | 32.18 |
| Deduct Discounts and Allowances | | | 1,514.21 | 1.66 | 1,424.56 | 0.69 | 1,650.00 | 0.60 | 15.82 |
| Net Sales | $317,118.16 | 100.00 | $90,994.97 | 100.00 | $206,846.56 | 100.00 | $273,658.36 | 100.00 | 32.29 |
| Cost of Goods Sold: | | | | | | | | | |
| Cost of Finished Goods Manufactured | | | $58,762.90 | 64.79 | $115,832.35 | 56.00 | $163,776.84 | 59.85 | 41.39 |
| Add Decrease in Inventory | | | 14,309.67 | 15.51 | 5,458.48 | 2.64 | 6,985.00 | 2.55 | 27.96 |
| Cost of Goods Sold | $195,779.72 | 61.74 | $73,072.57 | 80.30 | $121,290.83 | 58.64 | $170,761.84 | 62.40 | 40.78 |
| Gross Profit on Sales | $121,338.44 | 38.26 | $17,922.40 | 19.70 | $ 85,555.73 | 41.36 | $102,896.52 | 37.60 | 20.26 |
| Selling Expense: | | | | | | | | | |
| Commissions | $ 24,954.88 | 7.87 | $ 6,718.34 | 7.38 | $ 16,987.52 | 8.21 | $ 20,625.00 | 7.54 | 21.41 |
| Advertising | 9,977.79 | 3.15 | 2,519.89 | 2.77 | 3,033.56 | 1.47 | 4,125.00 | 1.51 | 35.97 |
| Traveling Expense | 700.92 | 0.22 | 1,267.70 | 1.39 | 885.72 | 0.43 | 1,100.00 | 0.40 | 24.19 |
| Dues and Subscriptions | 863.50 | 0.27 | 752.12 | 0.83 | 823.35 | 0.40 | 825.00 | 0.30 | 0.20 |
| Maintenance—Automobile | | | 395.80 | 0.44 | 309.82 | 0.15 | 412.50 | 0.15 | 33.14 |
| Depreciation—Automobile | 523.06 | 0.16 | 236.28 | 0.26 | 236.29 | 0.11 | 275.00 | 0.10 | 16.38 |
| Collection—Fees and Exchange | 935.00 | 0.30 | 277.09 | 0.30 | 468.76 | 0.23 | 550.00 | 0.20 | 17.33 |
| Parcel Post on Repair Parts, etc. | | | | | | | | | |
| Total Selling Expense | $ 37,955.15 | 11.97 | $12,167.22 | 13.37 | $ 22,745.02 | 11.00 | $ 27,912.50 | 10.20 | 22.71 |
| Selling Profit | $ 83,383.29 | 26.29 | $ 5,755.18 | 6.33 | $ 62,810.71 | 30.36 | $ 74,984.02 | 27.40 | 19.38 |

## EXHIBIT 1

### Larkin Foundry Company (Continued)

| | 1943 Actual | 1943 % of Net Sales | 1947 Actual | 1947 % of Net Sales | 1948 Actual | 1948 % of Net Sales | 1949 Estimated | 1949 % of Net Sales | % of Increase, 1949 Estimated Over 1948 Actual |
|---|---|---|---|---|---|---|---|---|---|
| **Administrative and General Expense:** | | | | | | | | | |
| Officers' Salaries............ | $ 9,900.00 | 3.12 | $ 7,300.00 | 8.02 | $ 7,071.04 | 3.42 | $ 10,560.00 | 3.86 | 49.34 |
| Office Salaries............... | 1,991.00 | 0.63 | 1,606.26 | 1.77 | 1,689.13 | 0.82 | 1,858.04 | 0.68 | 9.99 |
| Office Expense............... | | | 1,198.53 | 1.32 | 2,034.65 | 0.98 | 2,543.31 | 0.93 | 24.99 |
| Credit Risk Insurance........ | | | 586.14 | 0.64 | 756.25 | 0.36 | 756.25 | 0.28 | |
| Depreciation................. | 273.71 | 0.09 | 548.67 | 0.60 | 530.20 | 0.26 | 530.20 | 0.19 | |
| Telephone and Telegraph...... | 369.99 | 0.11 | 290.48 | 0.32 | 359.46 | 0.17 | 359.46 | 0.13 | |
| Freight and Drayage.......... | 1,451.86 | 0.46 | | | | | | | |
| Office Supplies.............. | 861.68 | 0.27 | | | | | | | |
| Audit Fee................... | 535.34 | 0.17 | | | | | | | |
| Postage..................... | 225.47 | 0.07 | | | | | | | |
| Legal Expense............... | 165.00 | 0.05 | | | | | | | |
| Premiums on Life-insurance Policy—Manager................. | 611.05 | 0.19 | | | 223.09 | 0.11 | 223.09 | 0.08 | |
| Royalties................... | 20.90 | 0.01 | | | 559.29 | 0.27 | 559.29 | 0.20 | |
| Total Administrative and General Expense | $ 16,405.99 | 5.17 | $11,530.08 | 12.67 | $ 13,223.11 | 6.39 | $ 17,389.64 | 6.35 | 31.50 |
| Net Operating Profit or Loss.... | $ 66,977.30 | 21.12 | $ 5,774.90* | 6.34 | $ 49,587.60 | 23.97 | $ 57,594.38 | 21.05 | 16.14 |
| Other Income Credits......... | 8,330.83 | 2.63 | 8,233.46 | 9.04 | 3,728.15 | 1.80 | 2,715.96 | 0.99 | 27.14† |
| Gross Income................ | $ 75,308.13 | 23.75 | $ 2,458.56 | 2.70 | $ 53,315.75 | 25.77 | $ 60,310.34 | 22.04 | 13.11 |
| Other Income Charges......... | 15,470.66 | 4.88 | 5,890.85 | 6.47 | 7,458.63 | 3.60 | 9,625.00 | 3.52 | 29.04 |
| Net Profit or Loss........... | $ 59,837.47 | 18.87 | $ 3,432.29* | 3.77 | $ 45,857.12 | 22.17 | $ 50,685.34 | 18.52 | 10.52 |

\* Loss.

† Decrease.

EXHIBIT 2

Larkin Foundry Company

Comparative Statement of Cost to Manufacture, 1947 and 1948, with Estimates for 1949

| Cost of Manufacture | 1947 Actual | 1948 Actual | Estimated 1948 if Increased Wages Had Not Affected Last Half of Production Costs | Estimated 1949 Based on Same Volume as 1948 | Increase of Estimated 1949 over Actual 1948 | | Increase of Estimated 1949 over Estimated 1948 | |
|---|---|---|---|---|---|---|---|---|
| | | | | | Dollars | Per Cent | Dollars | Per Cent |
| Foundry and Cleaning Room: | | | | | | | | |
| Pig Iron | $ 6,070.59 | $ 15,840.45 | $ 12,989.17 | $ 18,691.73 | $ 2,851.28 | 18.00 | $ 5,702.56 | 43.90 |
| Sand | 470.07 | 1,076.02 | 968.42 | 1,183.62 | 107.60 | 10.00 | 215.20 | 22.22 |
| Coke | 756.12 | 1,278.95 | 230.22 | 2,327.70 | 1,048.75 | 82.00 | 2,097.48 | 911.08 |
| Supplies | 759.58 | 1,290.18 | 1,161.17 | 1,419.18 | 129.00 | 10.00 | 258.01 | 22.22 |
| Manufacturing Expense * | 3,226.88 | 4,915.55 | 4,915.55 | 4,915.55 | | | | |
| Indirect Labor | 2,873.86 | 6,189.45 | 5,267.83 | 7,111.06 | 921.61 | 14.89 | 1,843.23 | 34.99 |
| Direct Labor—Molding | 12,425.77 | 28,844.73 | 24,570.77 | 33,118.69 | 4,273.96 | 14.82 | 8,547.92 | 34.79 |
| Direct Labor—Molding, Paid on Broken Castings | 341.98 | 1,085.02 | 1,085.02 | 1,085.02 | | | | |
| Total Foundry and Cleaning Room | $26,924.85 | $60,520.35 | $51,188.15 | $69,852.55 | $ 9,332.20 | 15.42 | $18,664.40 | 36.46 |
| Nickeling Room: | | | | | | | | |
| Labor—Indirect | $ 382.96 | $ 1,422.77 | $ 1,219.60 | $ 1,625.94 | $ 203.17 | 14.28 | $ 406.34 | 33.32 |
| Supplies | 155.99 | 399.96 | 359.96 | 439.96 | 40.00 | 10.00 | 80.00 | 22.22 |
| Manufacturing Expense * | 86.05 | 131.08 | 131.08 | 131.08 | | | | |
| Total Nickeling Room | $ 625.00 | $ 1,953.81 | $ 1,710.64 | $ 2,196.98 | $ 243.17 | 12.45 | $ 486.34 | 28.43 |
| Copper | $ 233.26 | $ 938.86 | $ 844.98 | $ 1,032.75 | $ 93.89 | 10.00 | $ 187.77 | 22.22 |
| Steel | 1,491.92 | 3,424.51 | 3,082.07 | 3,766.95 | 342.44 | 10.00 | 684.88 | 22.22 |
| Trimmings | 8,261.81 | 16,772.48 | 15,095.23 | 18,449.73 | 1,677.25 | 10.00 | 3,354.50 | 22.22 |
| Mounting Room: | | | | | | | | |
| Supplies | 249.67 | 947.63 | 852.86 | 1,042.39 | 94.76 | 10.00 | 189.53 | 22.22 |
| Manufacturing Expense * | 645.37 | 983.11 | 983.11 | 983.11 | | | | |
| Indirect Labor | 255.63 | 319.53 | 271.95 | 367.10 | 47.57 | 14.89 | 95.15 | 34.99 |
| Direct Labor | 5,047.52 | 12,313.42 | 10,555.06 | 14,071.78 | 1,758.36 | 14.28 | 3,516.72 | 33.32 |
| Total Mounting Room | $ 6,198.19 | $ 14,563.69 | $ 12,662.98 | $ 16,464.38 | $ 1,900.69 | 13.05 | $ 3,801.40 | 30.02 |

## EXHIBIT 2

### Larkin Foundry Company (Continued)

| Cost of Manufacture | 1947 Actual | 1948 Actual | Estimated 1948 if Increased Wages Had Not Affected Last Half of Production Costs | Estimated 1949 Based on Same Volume as 1948 | Increase of Estimated 1949 over Actual 1948 | | Increase of Estimated 1949 over Estimated 1948 | |
|---|---|---|---|---|---|---|---|---|
| | | | | | Dollars | Per Cent | Dollars | Per Cent |
| Warehouse and Shipping Department: | | | | | | | | |
| Supplies | $ 1,649.68 | $ 2,608.55 | $ 2,086.84 | $ 3,130.26 | $ 521.71 | 20.00 | $ 1,043.42 | 50.00 |
| Manufacturing Expense* | 344.20 | 524.33 | 524.33 | 524.33 | | | | |
| Labor—Indirect | 2,593.52 | 4,125.49 | 3,511.21 | 4,739.78 | 614.29 | 14.89 | 1,228.57 | 34.99 |
| Total Warehouse and Shipping | $ 4,587.40 | $ 7,258.37 | $ 6,122.38 | $ 8,394.37 | $ 1,136.00 | 15.65 | $ 2,271.99 | 37.11 |
| Manufacturing Expense Not Allocated to Departments: | | | | | | | | |
| Depreciation on Buildings | $ 5,562.19 | $ 5,402.24 | $ 5,402.24 | $ 5,402.24 | | | | |
| License and Taxes | 2,722.47 | 2,706.24 | 2,706.24 | 2,706.24 | | | | |
| Fire Insurance | 979.34 | 732.99 | 732.99 | 732.99 | | | | |
| General Factory Expense | 183.05 | 177.10 | 132.83 | 221.38 | $ 44.28 | 25.00 | $ 88.55 | 66.67 |
| Building Repairs | 104.39 | 199.26 | 199.26 | 199.26 | | | | |
| Night Watchman | 889.03 | 1,182.45 | 763.24 | 1,601.65 | 419.20 | 35.45 | 838.41 | 109.85 |
| Total Unallocated Manufacturing Expense | $10,440.47 | $ 10,400.28 | $ 9,936.80 | $ 10,863.76 | $ 463.48 | 44.56 | $ 926.96 | 93.29 |
| Total Cost to Manufacture up to and Including Warehouse | $58,762.90 | $115,832.35 | $100,643.23 | $131,021.47 | $15,189.12 | 13.11 | $30,378.24 | 30.18 |

Increase in Cost Resulting from 25% Increase in Physical Volume................ $ 32,755.37

Estimated Total Cost to Manufacture, 1949................ $163,776.84

* See Exhibit 4.

## EXHIBIT 3

### Larkin Foundry Company

Recapitulation of Cost to Manufacture, 1947 and 1948, with Estimates for 1949

| | 1943 Actual | 1943 % of Total Cost | 1947 Actual | 1947 % of Total Cost | 1948 Actual | 1948 % of Total Cost | 1948 Estimated, if Increased Wages Had Not Affected Last Half of Costs | 1948 % of Total Cost | 1949 Based on 1948 Volume Estimated | 1949 % of Total Cost | % of Increase, 1949 over 1948 Estimated Costs |
|---|---|---|---|---|---|---|---|---|---|---|---|
| **Labor:** | | | | | | | | | | | |
| Foundry and Cleaning Room | $ 62,379.92 | 29.42 | $12,767.75 | 21.73 | $ 29,929.75 | 25.84 | $ 25,655.79 | 25.49 | $ 34,203.71 | 26.11 | 33.32 |
| Mounting Room | 28,887.46 | 13.62 | 5,047.52 | 8.59 | 12,313.42 | 10.63 | 10,555.06 | 10.49 | 14,071.78 | 10.74 | 33.32 |
| Total Labor | $ 91,267.38 | 43.04 | $17,815.27 | 30.32 | $ 42,243.17 | 36.47 | $ 36,210.85 | 35.98 | $ 48,275.49 | 36.85 | 33.32 |
| **Raw Materials and Purchased Parts:** | | | | | | | | | | | |
| Foundry and Cleaning Room | $ 33,602.24 | 15.84 | $ 7,296.78 | 12.42 | $ 18,195.42 | 15.71 | $ 14,187.81 | 14.10 | $ 22,203.05 | 16.95 | 56.49 |
| Copper | 2,248.60 | 1.06 | 233.26 | 0.39 | 938.86 | 0.81 | 844.98 | 0.84 | 1,032.75 | 0.79 | 22.22 |
| Steel | 7,652.36 | 3.61 | 1,491.92 | 2.54 | 3,424.51 | 2.96 | 3,082.07 | 3.06 | 3,766.95 | 2.87 | 22.22 |
| Trimmings | 23,253.05 | 10.97 | 8,261.81 | 14.06 | 16,772.48 | 14.48 | 15,095.23 | 15.00 | 18,449.73 | 14.08 | 22.22 |
| Total Raw Materials and Purchased Parts | $ 66,756.25 | 31.48 | $17,283.77 | 29.41 | $ 39,331.27 | 33.96 | $ 33,210.09 | 33.00 | $ 45,452.48 | 34.69 | 36.86 |
| **Burden** Indirect Labor: | | | | | | | | | | | |
| Foundry and Cleaning Room | | | $ 2,873.86 | 4.89 | $ 6,189.45 | 5.34 | $ 5,267.83 | 5.23 | $ 7,111.06 | 5.43 | 34.99 |
| Nickeling Room | | | 382.96 | 0.65 | 1,422.77 | 1.23 | 1,219.60 | 1.21 | 1,625.94 | 1.24 | 33.32 |
| Mounting Room | | | 255.63 | 0.44 | 319.53 | 0.28 | 271.95 | 0.27 | 367.10 | 0.28 | 34.99 |
| Warehouse and Shipping Department | | | 2,593.52 | 4.41 | 4,125.49 | 3.56 | 3,511.21 | 3.49 | 4,739.78 | 3.62 | 34.99 |
| Total Indirect Labor | $ 23,568.65 | 11.11 | $ 6,105.97 | 10.39 | $ 12,057.24 | 10.41 | $ 10,270.59 | 10.20 | $ 13,843.88 | 10.57 | 34.79 |

## EXHIBIT 3

### Larkin Foundry Company (Continued)

| | 1943 Actual | % of Total Cost | 1947 Actual | % of Total Cost | 1948 Actual | % of Total Cost | 1948 Estimated, if Increased Wages Had Not Affected Last Half of Costs | % of Total Cost | 1949 Based on 1948 Volume Estimated | % of Total Cost | % of Increase, 1949 over 1948 Estimated Costs |
|---|---|---|---|---|---|---|---|---|---|---|---|
| **Supplies:** | | | | | | | | | | | |
| Foundry and Cleaning Room | | | $ 759.58 | 1.29 | $ 1,290.18 | 1.11 | $ 1,161.17 | 1.15 | $ 1,419.18 | 1.08 | 22.22 |
| Nickeling Room | | | 155.99 | 0.27 | 399.96 | 0.35 | 359.96 | 0.36 | 439.96 | 0.34 | 22.22 |
| Mounting Room | | | 249.67 | 0.42 | 947.63 | 0.82 | 852.86 | 0.85 | 1,042.39 | 0.79 | 22.22 |
| Warehouse and Shipping Department | | | 1,649.68 | 2.81 | 2,608.55 | 2.25 | 2,086.84 | 2.07 | 3,130.26 | 2.39 | 50.00 |
| Total Supplies | $ 9,126.12 | 4.30 | $ 2,814.92 | 4.79 | $ 5,246.32 | 4.53 | $ 4,460.83 | 4.43 | $ 6,031.79 | 4.60 | 35.22 |
| **Manufacturing Expense:** | | | | | | | | | | | |
| Foundry and Cleaning Room | | | $ 3,226.88 | 5.49 | $ 4,915.55 | 4.24 | $ 4,915.55 | 4.89 | $ 4,915.55 | 3.75 | |
| Nickeling Room | | | 86.05 | 0.15 | 131.08 | 0.11 | 131.08 | 0.13 | 131.08 | 0.10 | |
| Mounting Room | | | 645.37 | 1.10 | 983.11 | 0.85 | 983.11 | 0.98 | 983.11 | 0.75 | |
| Warehouse and Shipping Department | | | 344.20 | 0.58 | 524.33 | 0.45 | 524.33 | 0.52 | 524.33 | 0.40 | |
| Unallocated | | | 10,440.47 | 17.77 | 10,400.28 | 8.98 | 9,936.80 | 9.87 | 10,363.76 | 8.29 | 9.33 |
| Total Manufacturing Expense | $ 21,345.20 | 10.07 | $ 14,742.97 | 25.09 | $ 16,954.35 | 14.63 | $ 16,490.87 | 16.39 | $ 17,417.83 | 13.29 | 5.62 |
| Total Burden | $ 54,039.98 | 25.48 | $ 23,663.86 | 40.27 | $ 34,257.91 | 29.57 | $ 31,222.29 | 31.02 | $ 37,293.50 | 28.46 | 19.45 |
| Total Labor, Raw Materials, and Burden Cost | $212,063.61 | 100.00 | $58,762.90 | 100.00 | $115,832.35 | 100.00 | $100,643.23 | 100.00 | $131,021.47 | 100.00 | 30.18 |

ing wheels located in the mounting department. At the same time, the number of rejected castings was kept exceptionally low. Castings were cleaned and moved either to storage or directly to the mounting department. Parts to be plated with copper, zinc, and nickel were cut and plated in a special department. Because of the small volume of enameling required, all such work was done outside. Cast, plated, and sheet-metal parts and purchased trimmings were assembled in the mounting department by highly skilled union labor.

The principal raw materials used were pig iron, trimming and plating materials, steel, coke, and sand. In 1943, materials and supplies accounted for approximately 35 per cent of total manufacturing cost; direct and indirect labor, about 55 per cent; and general manufacturing expense, about 10 per cent. In 1947, the approximate percentages were materials and supplies, 35 per cent; labor, 40 per cent; and general manufacturing expense, 25 per cent.

The net sales for the year 1943 were $317,118.16; in 1947 they were only $90,994.97; but in 1948 raw materials again became obtainable and sales increased to $206,846.56.[4] Careful consideration of conditions in the Southern market led the management to believe that sales for 1949 would be materially in excess of the 1948 figure.

On August 1, 1948, executives of the company signed an agreement with a foundry workers' union. As a result, about one-half of the 1948 production was produced with much higher labor costs. Wages of direct and indirect labor were increased 33⅓ per cent and 35 per cent, respectively, on August 1, and many other costs were affected for the balance of the year.

Exhibits 1, 2, 3, and 4 show income, costs, and profit or loss for the years 1943, 1947, and 1948. They also show estimated income, costs, and profits for 1949. In addition, estimates of probable income, costs, and profits for 1948 if costs had not been affected by the union agreement are included.

The volume of gross sales estimated for 1949, $275,000, was arrived at on the basis of expectancy of selling a physical volume increase of 25 per cent. In 1948, the foundry was operated 192 days, and sales amounted to $208,271.12. If the foundry had

[4] See Exhibit 1.

## EXHIBIT 4

Larkin Foundry Company

Allocation of Manufacturing Expense, 1947 and 1948, with Estimates for 1949

| | 1947 | 1948 | Estimated 1949 |
|---|---|---|---|
| **Manufacturing Expense Allocated to Departments:** | | | |
| Superintendence.................... | $1,792.20 | $1,909.08 | $1,909.08 |
| Heat, Light, Power, and Water.......... | 1,570.21 | 2,933.88 | 2,933.88 |
| Freight, Express, and Drayage.......... | 541.96 | 603.20 | 603.20 |
| Machinery Repairs................... | 108.92 | 256.70 | 256.70 |
| Pattern Repairs..................... | 246.11 | 370.28 | 370.28 |
| Compensation Insurance.............. | 43.10 | 480.93 | 480.93 |
| Total...................... | $4,302.50 | $6,554.07 | $6,554.07 |
| **Distribution to Departments:** | | | |
| Foundry and Cleaning Department.. 75% | $3,226.88 | $4,915.55 | $4,915.55 |
| Nickeling Department........... 2% | 86.05 | 131.08 | 131.08 |
| Mounting Department........... 15% | 645.37 | 983.11 | 983.11 |
| Warehouse and Shipping Department 8% | 344.20 | 524.33 | 524.33 |
| Total................. 100% | $4,302.50 | $6,554.07 | $6,554.07 |

been operated 240 days, a comparable increase in sales would have brought that figure to $260,338.89. It was expected that 1949 selling prices would average 5.75 per cent higher than 1948 prices. Such an increase applied to the $260,338.89 sales figure would yield $14,969.47, or a total of $275,308.36. That figure was used in the 1949 budget estimates.

The 1949 budget figures shown in this case were prepared for the manager-treasurer of the company at his request. The probable operating rate for 1949 of 240 foundry days was agreed upon by company executives prior to the preparation of the budget.

### QUESTIONS

1. Should the manager-treasurer of the Larkin Foundry Company have planned 1949 operations on the basis of the budget shown in the Exhibits? Explain your answer.

2. If you do not approve of the budget as presented in the case, prepare one that would be more acceptable to you.

## Problem 61

## UNITED STATES RADIO AND TELEVISION CORPORATION

The United States Radio and Television Corporation made radio and television sets in a variety of models. When operating at normal capacity, it employed about 1,200 workers. Inasmuch as the chief risk of the business was sudden changes in design to include technical improvements or style changes, close control of inventory of parts and finished products was especially important. Shortly before a sharp decline in radio sales in 1946, the company had adopted a plan of sales forecasting and budgetary control based chiefly on the use of standard costs. These forecasts had been so accurate that when the decline came the company had practically cleared its inventory.

According to a policy adopted in 1946, practically all the planning and budgeting work of the United States Radio and Television Corporation was based on the determination and use of standard production costs. In most instances, the company was able to make use of already existing records. The standard costs, divided into direct labor, raw materials, and other costs, were collected for each model produced and for each factory department. Standard direct labor costs were based on engineering time studies of actual operations. Direct laborers were paid on a group bonus plan, their pay depending on the number of completed parts or sets that passed inspection. They were paid an hourly rate plus a bonus of 100 per cent of any saving above the standard time allowance. Group foremen shared in the bonus, but general foremen and inspectors were paid day rates. The direct labor cost for each model remained constant except when a group failed to earn the bonus, which was unusual, or when the rate of hiring employees was changed and resulted in a change in the proficiency of the employees.

Standard materials costs for each model were figured when a model was put into production by pricing necessary quantities including waste allowance at a standard amount.

Standard costs for other departmental expenses were estimated carefully by the factory superintendent and foremen. They took into consideration the number of helpers required and the proper allowance for department supplies, power, and other expenses, including an allocated share of the costs of nonproductive departments. Each foreman signed the expense calculation he accepted as satisfactory and that was taken as the standard for his department. All expenses were divided into two groups: those which were fixed regardless of volume of production and those which were proportional to production and controllable. A summary expense sheet showing the total of the estimates of itemized departmental expenses gave directly the cost of doing any given volume of business. Profits were about the same percentage of price on all models.

After the standards were set up, the next step in budgeting was to make a sales forecast. The sales manager drew up a preliminary estimate of sales by models and prices based on the trend of sales during the previous two years, corrected for changes in business conditions and prices and for stocks in dealers' hands. The sales manager showed the preliminary estimate to the president, comptroller, and factory manager, who reviewed it in the light of their knowledge of market conditions, customers' requirements, and the standard costs. Recognizing the need for firsthand knowledge of current conditions, executives kept informed of the state of the industry and made frequent calls on the company's wholesalers, who numbered more than 100. In addition they received reports of dealers' stocks twice a month. Use of the standard cost data enabled executives to tell whether the estimated sales could be produced profitably for the price assumed by the sales manager and to see the effects of a higher price and smaller volume compared with a larger volume and lower price. Discussion of the advantages of the various alternatives led to a final forecast of sales and production requirements. The company reached such accuracy in determining the standard costs and forecasting sales that actual sales were normally within 2 or 3 per cent of the forecast, and expenses were even nearer.

Using the figures for estimated production and standard costs, executives computed costs of operation and made out both an annual budget as a basis for general plans and commitments and a monthly budget as authorization for detailed manufacturing and purchasing schedules and for borrowing money. The budget for each period was practically an estimated profit and loss statement supported by detailed estimates by departments. From this statement could be computed balance sheets showing the position of each asset and liability account at any time. Additional financial and operating reports were compiled monthly. Estimates of the company's cash position did not vary more than 3 per cent from actual.

For controlling current operations, use of standard costs was very effective. Frequent reports of actual operations compared with the standard costs provided accurate bases for taking prompt remedial measures when actual costs were too high. Daily reports of variations from standard labor costs were made to foremen, and similar reports for all departments were made to the production executives. Daily reports also were made to operating executives showing sales, orders, collections, disbursements, commitments, labor force, and production volume. More comprehensive analyses of profit variations were reported monthly.

The standard costs were used for purposes of cost accounting, and variations of actual from standard were cleared periodically through variation accounts into the profit and loss account. From analyses of the variation accounts, reports were compiled showing the causes of the variations, whether a price change, spoiled work, or something else.

The separation of fixed and controllable expenses also had been of great practical value. The company had been operating two factories, but analysis of expenses by the new method had brought to light an enormous fixed expense that had been concealed in general overhead. As a result, one plant was closed in 1948 and the office and supervisory staffs were consolidated. Fixed expense was reduced by one-half.

Executives also made use of standard costs in determining general policies. Finding the most economical size of inventory of finished sets to carry was an example. Available records showed to what extent telegraph and express charges, unallocated and idle production time, and delays in filling orders would increase expenses as inventory decreased, and how obsolescence, interest charges, and other carrying charges increased as inventory increased. With this information, executives decided on the optimum size of inventory.

Expense analysis was also useful to executives in deciding whether to accept new business. They considered not only the permanence of the new demand, but also the effects on costs of changes in the volume of operations for the plant or the effect of model changes on a departmental budget. They could tell, furthermore, how far they could cut prices without operating at a loss.

The executives were convinced of the value of the budgetary system and had found it very inexpensive to operate. One clerk kept the books and made out the reports. An elaborate supply of forms had not been necessary, and many reports had been run off on duplicating machines. Reports not required for record were destroyed and those not used were discontinued. The plan provided executives with an accurate basis for forming general policies, fitting production to sales, and measuring actual results of operations by focusing their attention on variations from standard. Average inventory turnover after the adoption of the new policy was 11.8 times a year.

## QUESTIONS

1. Is the budgetary procedure here outlined adequate to the needs of the United States Radio and Television Corporation?

2. This company did not make its sales forecasts until after it had worked out cost estimates. When, if at all, is this good procedure?

# CHAPTER XXVI

## ORGANIZATION

### ATCHESON TOOL AND FORGE COMPANY [1]

## 1. A Large Manufacturing Company Adapts Its Executive Organization to Changing Conditions.

For a number of years the Atcheson Tool and Forge Company had operated as a line organization. In 1915, however, when the company became a manufacturer of munitions and more than doubled its work force, a highly centralized functional organization was developed. In 1918, when its contracts for munitions were canceled and the problems of sales and costs became urgent, the functional departments were decentralized, although a staff officer in charge of each function was kept on the staff of the general superintendent. These changes were made to adapt the organization to the different problems of administration resulting from rapid changes in the size and nature of the business.

## 2. What Organization Involves. The need for management organization in a manufacturing business occurs when one individual is unable to discharge all the varied responsibilities of the enterprise. When two or more executives share these responsibilities, the scope of activity of each must be clearly delineated to prevent duplication of effort and to make certain that every problem that arises receives prompt attention. It is the purpose of organization to define the activities of each executive and to coordinate their individual efforts. Thus, we find that organization essentially includes three concepts: division of responsibility for problem solution among the executives of a company; delegation of authority to take such action as is necessary to make decisions effective; coordination of the activities of individual executives in terms of company aims and policies.

---

[1] This case is more than thirty years old. The reasons for its retention in this revision are given at the end of the discussion on p. 633.

The most common basis [2] of division of the management field is in terms of major business functions: production, marketing, and finance. If the volume of business permits, there will be one executive in charge of each of these divisions: a production manager, a sales manager, and a secretary-treasurer. To make sure that the activities of each functional specialist are in harmony with the activities of the others, there must be a correlating force. This is usually embodied in the job of the general manager, who may or may not be the president or one of the functional executives.

When the work of management is subdivided, fixing of responsibility and delegation of authority go hand in hand. In the preceding chapter on budgetary control, it was pointed out that a requisite to successful control of costs is management action based on a comparison of plans and results. A company which utilizes a budget must depend on a number of executives, including departmental supervisors or foremen, to take the requisite action. Each supervisor is held responsible for the costs of his department and for doing things which will keep those costs in line with plans. No foreman can operate successfully under such a system unless three conditions exist. First, he must be charged only with those costs over which he has some control—in terms of organization, the area of his responsibility must be clearly and properly defined. Second, he must have the right to take such action as is necessary to control his costs—again, in terms of organization, his authority to act must be commensurate with his responsibility for results. Third, he must take action that will be compatible with company policy—in terms of organization, he must correlate his acts with those of others functioning in the organization.

Business policy may be defined as that body of understanding generally possessed throughout an organization which makes it possible to predict what type of action any executive within the organization will take under a given set of circumstances. Policy is a practical means employed to obtain coordination of the action of the various individuals that make up a business executive

[2] Many of the advantages and disadvantages of subdividing the work of management among a number of individuals, together with the more usual bases for subdivision, are given in Chap. III.

staff.  It has been pointed out with reference to the budgetary control methods of the General Electric Company, described in the preceding chapter, that department foremen must take only such action as is compatible with company policy.  If the foreman has been informed through budget channels that the operations of his department are to be contracted for a time, it is necessary for him to reduce the number of man-hours worked in his department.  One way to do this would be to lay off some men.  Another would be to retain all workers and reduce the number of hours each works.  In deciding which method to employ, the foreman will be guided by his knowledge of company policy.  His superiors will be certain of the type of action he will take under the circumstances because they will know that he understands company policy in this matter and will act in accordance with it.  Thus, in event of general curtailment of operations, all departmental supervisors will meet the problem in the same way.  Friction and labor trouble will not arise as the result of one foreman's laying off men while others spread the available work among all workers in their departments.

**3. The Dynamic Nature of Organization.**  Organization should be a result, the solution of the problem how to manage, rather than an aim.  Organization should exist solely to serve a business.  When business operation calls for a certain type of executive organization, it should be set up, never before.  No organization should exist merely because it is a "sound form of organization."  The only excuse for any particular form of organization is that it best serves the particular conditions that called it into being.

If organization is the result of a business demand, it follows that, as the need for organization changes, the organization should change.  This is basic.  A fundamental test of good organization is its ability to change, to adapt itself to new conditions.  Many organizations can do this; some cannot.  An organization which finds change difficult is usually an agglomeration of vested interests, bureaucracies.  The business they control exists to serve their individual ends, not they to serve the business as a whole.  The trouble with the inflexible business organization is that it is usually out of step with the profit-making possibilities of the business world as they exist at any one time. The less the need for organization, the better from the standpoint of executive control. The less organization required to meet the need adequately, the better from the standpoint of the exercise of executive control. The following experience is an excellent example of this principle of good organization, namely, suitability to the needs of the moment. The case will be presented and discussed from that viewpoint.

**4. Organization of the Atcheson Tool and Forge Company during the Prewar Period.** In 1914, this company was employing about 1,200 workers in the manufacture of a line of hand tools, such as hammers, axes, chisels, and bits, and machine tools, such as lathes and boring mills. The plant consisted of a foundry, a forge shop, three finishing shops for the hand tools, and a machine shop for making the lathes and boring mills. Most of the buildings were of modern construction, and the company had sufficient land to provide for an indefinite expansion of the plant.

The organization was almost entirely on a line basis [3] with the departments divided by products rather than by processes. At the head was the president, who with the secretary and treasurer constituted the corporate organization. The only functional departments of the administrative organization were the plant-maintenance department, which furnished power and took charge of the general maintenance of the plant and machinery, and the personnel department, which had charge of employing and discharging workers but had at that time no other functions. A chart of this organization is shown in Exhibit 1, page 622.

Each line officer was responsible to his superior for all matters in the department under his charge except power, maintenance, and personnel. The engineering and technical work and the control of stores, planning, scheduling, production, and inspection were carried on in each shop by the foreman in charge assisted by a subforeman and the workmen themselves. In some cases, the superintendent might be consulted, but the routine conduct of all operations in the shop centered in the shop foreman.

Since tools had been produced in practically the same manner for years, everyone, from the general superintendent to the fore-

[3] See Chap. III for definition.

men and workmen, was familiar with the products and processes. Because the development of new products or new styles of old products occurred so seldom and usually required two or three years for completion, the personnel of the shop was able to become familiar with the new processes required. While this condition of uniformity in production continued, the line organiza-

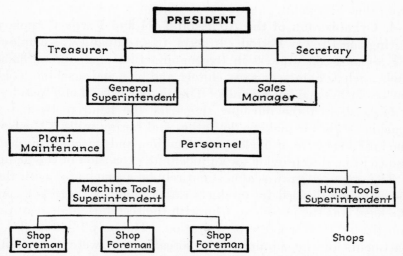

EXHIBIT 1. ATCHESON TOOL AND FORGE COMPANY. CHART TO SHOW PREWAR ORGANIZATION.

tion was highly efficient. The major policies of the company were determined by the president and the heads of the main departments. Although the margin between costs and sales was diminishing on all products as competition became more severe, the firm was successful, and the volume of sales was constantly increasing.

**5. The Early War Period (1915 to 1917).** In 1915 the company received large orders from France and Russia for small shells and fuses. These war orders involved the rapid development of the new products and an enormous increase in productive capacity. The personnel was doubled in a short time. Additions were made to the plant, and the old lines of manufacture were almost forsaken in order to devote the entire productive capacity to this new business. There was a constant increase in the volume of production until at one time about 15,000 persons were employed.

When large contracts were first accepted, an effort was made to have this work handled by the old line organization, but the responsibilities which this situation threw on the line officers were so great that the development of the new products and processes progressed slowly, and production suffered.

The first step in the development of a more suitable organization was the institution of a management committee of five members to confer with the president, who was also the general superintendent, on problems affecting different departments of the business. This was an advisory body consisting of men who were asked to sit on this committee in order to coordinate the work of their departments with that of other departments. The five members were as follows:

    Head of the shell department (machine-tool department)
    Head of the fuse department (hand-tool department)
    Head of the plant-maintenance department
    Treasurer
    Personnel manager

Except for the treasurer, these men were from the plant departments, so that the determination of policies was placed in the hands of men trained, for the most part, in production. Because at this time sales problems were of secondary importance, the sales department was not represented except indirectly through the president.

The manufacturing departments were reorganized by the addition of functional departments which undertook various phases of the work. Engineering departments were organized to take charge of the technical work incident to the design and manufacture of equipment for the new production and the determination of specifications and processes. Planning departments were organized to take charge of the preparation of material and the determination of the quantity and kind of products to be made in each shop. The planning departments had to do only with finished products. The component parts and the subassemblies were controlled by the scheduling departments, which were separate from the planning departments because of the volume of work to be handled.  Inspection departments were also organized to handle the inspection of finished products, the inspection of parts and subassemblies being left in the hands of the manufac-

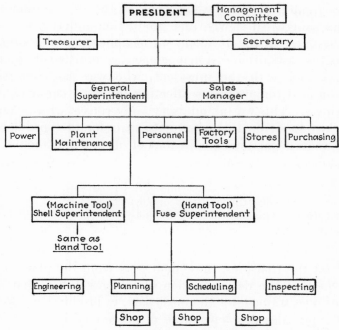

EXHIBIT 2.  ATCHESON TOOL AND FORGE COMPANY.  CHART TO SHOW ORGANIZATION IN THE EARLY WAR PERIOD.

turing departments.  The functional departments were organized in each of the two main manufacturing departments, as illustrated in the organization chart, Exhibit 2.

Because of the increased volume of production, the plant maintenance department was divided into three branches, and the head of each occupied a position on the staff of the general superintendent.  The first of these was the superintendent of power, the second, the superintendent of maintenance of plant and equipment, and the third, the superintendent of the factory tool department.  The latter was in charge of the production of tools, jigs, and fixtures for use in the shops. The head of the plant-maintenance department represented these three branches on the management committee. Similarly, the departments of stores and purchasing were organized to care for the increased work in these functions. Exhibit 2 illustrates the organization in effect in 1916.

These functional departments were organized in order to reduce the load on the manufacturing departments. The change in organization was analogous to a change from the method of operation whereby the worker is required to get his own tools and materials, set up his machine, and produce his goods to the method whereby tools are secured and set up in the machine by a helper and materials brought to the operative, who is required merely to produce the goods on that machine. This was substantially what was done on a large scale in this whole plant. The old operating departments remained as they were, but instead of being required to do all the work incident to the planning and preparation for producing goods, this was done for them so that their attention and energy could be devoted to the actual production of goods in their departments. Coordination was secured by daily interdepartmental meetings of the staff.

**6. Why the Organization Was Changed as It Was.** Changes made in the organization of the Atcheson Tool and Forge Company were simple adaptations of the old organization to meet new conditions. Two fundamental changes in the business had occurred: volume had increased tremendously and with great rapidity, and entirely new and different products were being made. These changes created many new problems which the old organization was inadequate to solve.

The advisory committee was formed to work out an organization to meet the new demands. The old organization did not provide for this function, and therefore a new unit to handle it was provided. The increase in physical facilities overloaded the old plant-maintenance department. To meet the new situation, the old department was subdivided, and control was specialized under three department heads: a power superintendent, a factory tools superintendent, and a maintenance superintendent. Increase in the volume of materials to be purchased and stored, in addition to wartime difficulties of obtaining adequate supplies, made purchasing too difficult and the burden too great for operating department supervisors. Therefore raw materials control was specialized under two executives: a purchasing officer and a stores department superintendent.

If the purchasing of materials to be used for shells had been very different from the purchasing of materials going into fuses, it might have been wise to set up four departments: a shell purchasing department, a fuse purchasing department, a shell stores department, and a fuse stores department. This was not necessary, however, for the raw materials were not great in number, and since they were essentially similar for shells and fuses, the problems of their procurement were not unlike.

The work of materials provision could have been divided differently into a shell purchasing and stores department and a fuse purchasing and stores department. The differences between procurement and stores problems, however, would make such a division of the work inadvisable as compared with having one specialist in charge of all purchasing and another in charge of all stores.

The change to new products and the greatly increased number of workers overloaded both foremen and superintendents. Relief was secured for these men by specializing parts of the work they had done. The tasks most suitable for specialization were engineering, planning, scheduling, and inspection. Four functional departments were provided for each product division to meet these specialized problems. This allowed the foremen to give their entire time to problems of operating control and made it possible for division superintendents to direct more of their attention to other duties.

The entire revision was in the interest of providing for the new needs of the business.

**7. Late War Period (1917 to 1919).** When the United States entered the First World War and the variety of products was further simplified, it was found advantageous from the productive standpoint to combine the functional operations in centralized functional departments, the heads of which were members of the staff of the general superintendent, as illustrated in Exhibit 3. The management committee was discontinued.

The main change was in having the functions of engineering, planning, scheduling, and inspection carried on for the entire plant instead of for only one manufacturing department. The

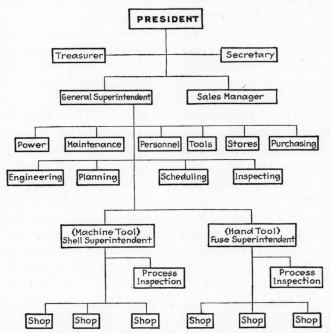

EXHIBIT 3. ATCHESON TOOL AND FORGE COMPANY. CHART TO SHOW ORGANIZATION IN THE LATE WAR PERIOD.

engineering department did the technical work for the entire plant. Its work was related principally to formulating the specifications and processes for new products; it was seldom concerned with repeat orders. The planning and scheduling and inspection departments were involved in every order, their function being to relieve the production departments of the activities preparatory to actual production and of final inspection.

The producing departments were in no way relieved of their responsibility for either quality or quantity of product, and the inspection during production was directly under their supervision. The inspection department protected the quality of the company's products and acted in relation to the production departments in much the same way that the government inspectors would act in relation to the company as a whole. Furthermore, the production department was held entirely responsible for the fulfillment of the plans and assignments of the departments which did preparatory work.

With this high degree of centralization, the company operated successfully in producing an enormous quantity of four or five products only. This form of organization was well adapted to dealing with the problems of volume production. Exhibit 3 represents the relationships existing at that time.

**8. Why These Changes Were Made.** The organization of the later wartime period was essentially similar to that which preceded it. The increased simplification and standardization of products made it possible and desirable to remove the functional departments entirely from the operating divisions and to consolidate duplicate departments into general functional departments. During this period the aims of the management were two: speed in production and quality that would meet government standards. Removing the functional departments from the operating divisions allowed the heads of the latter to concentrate all attention on speed of output of standard quality product. This simplified the tasks of operating division executives and made for increased management efficiency. As most of the problems of readjustment had been solved, the general superintendent was in position to take over direct control of engineering, planning, and scheduling. Having these functional department heads directly responsible to him gave him closer control of the direction of operation and enabled the operating division men to give their entire attention to getting out on time the work assigned to them.

Centralization of final inspection made for better relations with government inspectors. This department acted as a government relations agency. Conditions of the period made this relationship of primary importance to the company. Concentration of the maintenance of government relations in a single department made for greater efficiency in discharge of the function.

The advisory committee had completed its work. It was no

longer necessary, and therefore it was discontinued. Organization changes made at the time were all of the same nature, simplification of control and specialization of functions in terms of the new aims of the business.

**9. The Postwar Period (1919).** At the close of the First World War, the management of this company was faced with the problem of utilizing a plant expanded to more than double its original size. This necessitated products in addition to those manufactured prior to the First World War and involved the rapid development of new lines with a wide variety of styles and sizes. It also involved market analysis and investigation to determine lines that could be distributed through the same channels by the same sales force as the old products of the company, and the establishment of specifications and determination of probable volume for these various new products.

In adapting the organization to the new problems, the functional departments of engineering, planning, scheduling, and inspection were decentralized so that these functions were performed in each department by a group responsible to the head of that department and also responsible to a staff officer who remained on the staff of the general superintendent. Instead of being centralized in the engineering department, the time-study men were divided into groups, one group being sent to the hand tool department. The man in charge of this group was responsible to the superintendent of the hand tool department for the performance of all time-study work in that department. He was also responsible to the head of the engineering department for the methods employed and for the standards obtained in doing the work. An industrial engineer was secured to assist the general superintendent in the development of systematic control.

A similar change was made in the organization of the planning department. The central planning department received manufacturing orders from the sales department and distributed these orders to the proper production departments. It coordinated and controlled the orders for finished products and set the schedule for the delivery of these products. Planning and scheduling of the parts and subassemblies were done by planning and scheduling departments within the main production departments. The

head of the planning department within the hand tool department was responsible to the superintendent of the hand tool
department as a line officer for all planning done within the department, but was also responsible to the head of the central

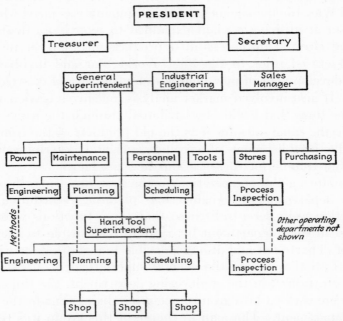

EXHIBIT 4.  ATCHESON TOOL AND FORGE COMPANY.  CHART TO SHOW ORGANIZATION
IN THE POSTWAR PERIOD.

planning department as a staff officer for the method of doing
the work and for coordinating the planning within that department with the schedules set by the central planning department.
This organization is illustrated in Exhibit 4.

These changes made each main product division essentially a
factory in itself, in charge of a division superintendent to whom
functional department heads were responsible.  To coordinate
the work of the functional departments of the various manufacturing divisions, advisory staff officers were retained on the staff
of the general superintendent.

**10. Justification of the New Organization.**  The changes
made in organization following cessation of war were sound.  The

need for speed in getting out volume production was gone. This brought relief to the personnel of operating divisions and enabled them to take over much of the work that they had been unable to do when the pressure for output was great. The shift to different product lines indicated the desirability of breaking up the centralized planning, engineering, scheduling, and inspection departments. The problems connected with the discharge of these functions would differ greatly for different classes of product. Planning, engineering, scheduling, and inspection functions, therefore, were decentralized, and separate departments for each were set up in each operating division. The division superintendents then had the time to direct this work, and, as the problems were peculiar to each operating division, they were the logical executives in the organization to assume the responsibility for proper discharge of these functions.

The retention of the old central department heads on the staff of the general superintendent was advisable, at least for some time. This would ensure against loss of valuable experience gained during the time when the centralized departments were large and highly developed. These staff officers could advise the decentralized department heads on matters of method and the like. However, department heads would be directly responsible for their work to the operating division superintendents. The work of the staff officers would be purely advisory.

This new organization was the answer to new conditions. No attempt was made to make the old organization serve new purposes by minor adaptations. The new need was clearly seen. The most direct and simple organization suited to the new conditions was set up.

**11. An Emergency Organization Development to Meet an Emergency Need.** The company had an opportunity to sell a large amount of the product of the hand tool department through outlets in Canada which up to that time had not been developed. This market required the addition of new styles of tools to meet the peculiar conditions of demand in this field. For instance, a special type of ax was necessary to meet the requirements of consumers in Quebec. None of the axes made by the company was of the exact type required.

Because of a lack of coordination between production and sales, it took so long to develop a new product and place it on the market that much of the business was lost to competitors. The same difficulty had arisen with respect to the domestic market, but it was especially important in preparing products for the new Canadian business. It was evident that there should be some coordinating agency to ensure that this work of developing new designs and getting the goods on the market would be done rapidly and efficiently. After careful consideration of various suggestions for getting the desired results, the president of the company decided to take charge personally of product development work. This arrangement was to be temporary. Just how long the president would retain personal control would depend on the rapidity with which this major problem was solved. The president was in an excellent position to promote development of interdepartmental cooperation in bringing out new products rapidly. However, he should not have expected to direct this work indefinitely. Rather, his aim should have been to get the organization functioning smoothly along the desired lines as quickly as possible. An emergency existed, and the president's decision to take the problem under his personal control was probably wise. His aim should have been to work himself out of this job as quickly as possible.

**12. Summary and Conclusions.** The prewar to postwar experience of the Atcheson Tool and Forge Company affords an excellent opportunity to study organization change. The management of this company looked upon organization purely as a matter of arranging executive duties to fit the needs of the occasion. The management was not interested in any particular form of organization. When jobs were to be done, someone had to do them. When problems arose, someone had to be ready to solve them. Who was best able to do this or that type of work? The answer depended on conditions as they existed at the time. The organization was always flexible. Even the president could change the emphasis of his job, and did so when occasion demanded. In this respect, business organization was no problem; rather it provided the means of solution of many problems. That was as it should be.

The Atcheson Tool and Forge Company case is more than 20 years old. The writer has been greatly tempted to replace it with a "modern" one. Careful appraisal of a number of similar situations that occurred during and following the Second World War revealed an almost identical management approach to the problem. These situations included not only metalworking plants but a large rug manufacturing company, a men's shirt manufacturer that sold more than $35,000,000 worth of men's and boys' shirts in 1947, a molded rubber products producer, and other equally diversified manufacturers. The greatest weakness of case learning is its tendency to neglect time perspective. The Atcheson Tool and Forge Company experience of 1915 to 1917 occurred again with scores of companies in the 1941 to 1947 war and reconversion periods. Here is a management experience that seems to have stood the test of time. It appears that if there be such things as basic principles of organization at work in this situation in 1917, they were at work again 30 years later. And therefore we resist the temptation to replace the old with that which is new. Atcheson Tool and Forge Company retains its place in this volume just as it was in earlier editions in the belief that the experience of this management has gained in validity and therefore in significance as time has gone on.

## QUESTIONS

1. Why is organization usually essential in business management?

2. What is organization designed to accomplish?

3. What characteristics must an organization possess if it is to accomplish its purpose?

4. What is the most common basis of subdivision of executive control? Why is this?

5. What are the basic differences between line, functional, and staff types of management organization?

6. How are organization principles applied in budgetary control?

7. What is business policy? What are its purposes?

8. What is meant by "The Dynamic Nature of Organization"?

9. What is the chief objection to an inflexible business organization?

10. What is the best form of business organization?

11. Describe the prewar organization of the Atcheson Tool and Forge Company.

12. Was that organization well suited to the demands made upon it? Explain.

13. Describe the organization of the company during the early war period, 1915 to 1917.

14. Why were the changes made?

15. Describe the organization of the later war period, 1917 to 1919.

16. Were these changes to the company's advantage? Explain.

17. Describe the postwar organization.

18. What were the reasons for making organization changes at that time? Was the action which was taken sound?

19. Why did the president of the company take over the work of developing new products and getting them into production quickly? Should he have done so?

20. What are the requisites of good organization?

21. Are there any dangers involved in using business policy as a means of control? If there are, how may they be overcome?

## Problem 62

### OLDS ELECTRICAL DEVICES COMPANY

The Olds Electrical Devices Company manufactured fuses, circuit breakers, and other electrical protective devices. In 15 years the company had grown from a small shop to a factory employing from 250 to 400 men, depending on the state of business. The company had preserved the line organization with which it started. It had been suggested that changes be made in this organization.

As the Olds Electrical Devices Company grew in size, the same methods of control were kept in force. The superintendent relied on strict discipline and close personal contact with the foremen to accomplish the necessary work. He did not believe in any kind of organization except the military type, and distrusted any form of divided responsibility.

The eight foremen were directly responsible to the superintendent. Any instructions to the men from the designing engineer, for example, had to be sent through the medium of the superintendent. As far as possible, each foreman was in charge of one type of work, and machines under his authority were grouped in one section of the floor. This arrangement was also followed in the benchwork sections, and there was no conflict of authority.

Normally, a foreman supervised 30 to 35 workmen, but in periods of accelerated production this number might be increased to 60. The superintendent's requirements for a foreman were rigid. He must have a complete knowledge of the operations he was to supervise; he must understand thoroughly his men's abilities and faults; and he must be able to maintain discipline. The superintendent expected a foreman who filled these requirements to be competent to meet most of the situations that arose. This prevented minor matters from coming up to him for decision. He kept in close personal touch with his foremen, however, in order to make sure that they carried out their assignments correctly.

The employees of the Olds Electrical Devices Company had varying degrees of skill. In times of depression, only the most competent men were retained. When production was heavy, however, there was an influx of unskilled men whom the foremen were required to train. The extra effort took much time and energy with a consequent slighting of regular duties. When the pressure on a foreman became too severe, an assistant was assigned to him to supervise the older and more experienced men. This subforeman was chosen from the best of the workers in a group, and his appointment lasted until production declined to normal proportions.

The manufacture of the devices produced by this company demanded technical knowledge. The workmen frequently required advice which their foremen, without technical training, were ill-fitted to give. The foremen had to experiment with various tools and methods, especially when new devices were being made, until they were satisfied that they were producing the required quality at the highest rate possible. Although the quality of the production was not impaired greatly by this trial-and-error method, production costs apparently were so high that the usual profit could not be obtained in competition with similar devices made by other manufacturers. It was suggested, therefore, to the superintendent, that two or three functional experts were needed who could determine the best methods of performing the operations on the machines and who could develop special tools for the production of new apparatus. Also, these men could establish a standard method of training new employees in time of business activity, and thus reduce the burdens of the foremen. The superintendent objected to the suggestion and maintained that the practical experience of the foremen was more valuable than technical training. He prophesied the loss of control of the workmen by the foremen and himself as soon as functional control was installed, and the existence of too many opportunities for the work force to shift responsibility for errors. He was apprehensive of the breakdown of the morale of his work force when his foremen lost part of their authority and became subordinates of the experts brought in from outside the company.

## QUESTIONS

1. Should the superintendent have made any changes in his organization to reduce manufacturing costs?

2. Can discipline be maintained under the functional type of organization?

### Problem 63

## JAMESON MANUFACTURING COMPANY

The Jameson Manufacturing Company had devoted all its production capacity to military equipment during a war period, so that upon the return of peace it was faced with the necessity of building up new products and at the same time keeping expenses at a minimum. The president, while giving his main effort to the development and sale of new products, exerted pressure upon all officers in the direction of expense reduction.

During a wartime emergency period the Jameson Manufacturing Company had shifted all its facilities to the production of items that were badly needed by the armed services. During this period there had been great urgency for volume of output. Cost of production was of secondary moment, and the Jameson Company like many manufacturers deliberately adopted policies which it recognized as thoroughly unsound in times of peace and price competition.

With the cessation of hostilities, the company resumed the production for the civilian market. The management believed that its greatest reconversion problem was to change the thinking and attitude of all its workers from office boy to plant supervisor. A program of waste elimination and cost reduction was planned.

The policy of expense reduction in the Jameson Manufacturing Company was reflected in the appointment of an expense manager, a staff officer acting directly under the authority of the president and having a power of veto upon all new expenses at the time when they were first proposed, as well as the duty of scrutinizing all current expenses. An expense statement was prepared monthly for each department and submitted to the superintendent of the plant, to the comptroller, and to the expense manager.

The expense manager worked for several years with considerable success. He was a tactful and considerate man who sought to avoid any appearance of arbitrary dictation. Whenever question arose as to any item of expense, it was always put to the manager who proposed it in the form, "Would you spend this money in this way if the department were your own business?" It was well understood that, in the event of their failing to agree, recourse might be had to the president, but he would support the expense manager in all reasonable efforts to keep down expense, so that such appeals were in fact extremely rare. Operating managers found in the expense manager a man with whom they could discuss their problems constructively, with a view to getting better results at less cost. In the maintenance department, for example, a saving was effected by employing fewer men but increasing the requirements of skill, and by a redistribution of work among them. Another question arose as to the wages of die-makers and toolmakers. The Jameson Manufacturing Company was the principal employer of this type of worker in the city, having about 50, while few other local manufacturers employed more than 1 or 2. It was a small matter to other manufacturers, therefore, to bid as much as 10 or 12 cents an hour more than the Jameson company paid. Men were sometimes tempted away from the latter by these rates, and the foreman of the department wanted to increase his rates to meet those of other companies. It was known that men preferred to work for the Jameson company because of greater steadiness of employment the year round and better working conditions. When, therefore, this matter came before the expense manager, he suggested that an increase of 3 or 4 cents per hour to the better men would meet the situation, instead of 10 or 12 cents for all. This was done and was found to be sufficient to hold the good men. If occasionally one of the others left, no great loss was suffered. These examples were typical of the general effect and influence which the expense manager exerted throughout the plant. The administration of direct labor was under the factory officers, but certain standards were set for labor costs, and excess costs over the standards set were noted by the expense manager. All manufacturing burden, including repairs and maintenance, all new construction, and all selling and administrative overhead were subject to the direct scrutiny and supervision of the expense manager.

Considerable success was achieved in controlling selling expenses; these amounted to nearly 6 per cent of sales, including as principal items traveling 1 per cent, salaries 1 per cent, commissions 1 per cent, and clerical salaries 0.5 per cent. Salesmen were under the control of 14 district managers, but on the subject of expenses they reported to the expense manager. The district managers discussed routes and the best ways of covering them with their salesmen. No quotas had been set, but a salesman was expected to maintain a certain satisfactory ratio between expenses and sales, due weight being given to the number of towns he covered, their population, trade activity within the territory, and whether or not he was a new salesman. The selling force was divided into direct salesmen and missionary men; the latter were not expected to cover their own expenses immediately, but the territory worked should show returns within a short time. In some cases, several men worked the same territory, which made a direct comparison possible. One fact which developed from the expense scrutiny was that many of the older salesmen did not very readily take up the new lines, with the result that their sales per customer suffered and their expense ratio was poor.

Among the older lines were certain classes of sporting goods. The company had paid the expenses of salesmen to join clubs which used these goods, and had permitted them to devote some of their time to the sports. As these goods became a smaller part of the total sales, the wisdom of these expenditures of time and money became questionable, and under the prompting of the expense manager and of the district sales managers, they were gradually given up. In all these activities care was taken to avoid any show of force or dictation, with respect either to expenses or to sales. A few years earlier the company had employed a high-pressure sales director, who had effected large shipments from the factory to local warehouses, and even to dealers' shelves; but there they stayed, and the subsequent cleanup was attended by considerable loss.

When it came to proposed expenditures on plant or other fixed assets, the expense manager always wished to have a plain statement as to what would be the savings, either by expense reduction or by increased output, attributable to the new equipment.

In the case of clerical and administrative salaries, even the replacement of a man was subject to the veto of the expense manager. Sometimes he would suggest a rearrangement of duties which would permit that position to be dropped, or he would question the necessity of the work itself.

The expense manager devoted about half his time to consideration of manufacturing expenses and about half to selling and administrative expenses. After a certain point he found the process of staff reduction more and more difficult, since he then encountered favoritism and friendships among the staff. While he was willing to consider these factors, he found it difficult to deal with them.

## QUESTIONS

1. Do you consider that the Jameson Company made the best possible approach to its expense problems?

2. What would be the alternative to the appointment of the expense manager, assuming the same necessities?

3. Would you recommend the appointment of an expense manager in every large manufacturing company?

# INDEX

# ALPHABETICAL LIST OF CASES AND PROBLEMS

## Date Due

| ★ MAR 25 1968 | | | |
|---|---|---|---|
| | | | |
| | | | |
| | | | |
| | | | |
| | | | |
| | | | |
| | | | |
| | | | |
| | | | |
| | | | |
| | | | |
| | | | |
| | | | |
| | | | |
| | | | |